CONTENTS

PREFACE

We live in a period in which a thorough knowledge of semiconductor devices in their various forms has become essential for all students majoring in electronic and applied physics. Present day devices, however, are no longer just diodes or transistors but are either large scale integrated circuits or special purpose components whose design and performance are intimately connected with their physics and processing.

There are many books covering semiconductor physics, others that cover fundamental devices, such as diodes and transistors, and others still that handle basic integrated circuits and their processing. There are far fewer books which try to combine those interrelated subjects, and fewer still which succeed in doing so without becoming too cumbersome or falling apart at the junction between the physics and engineering parts.

Most of these books concentrate on one part at the expense of the other, sometimes giving a great deal of background physics which is not applied in the sections on devices, and sometimes going more deeply into properties of materials and technology than is necessary for the systems-oriented student. This textbook, intended for both electronic and applied physics undergraduates who aim to work in or with solid state devices, tries to avoid these pitfalls.

For the future electronic engineer, it is no longer enough to study the terminal electrical characteristics of the semiconductor device while treating the device itself as a 'black box'. Most of the sophistication of modern electronics is hidden in that box, and more and more engineering and scientific effort will be required for work in device development, design, simulation, production and testing in the future. The devices in fact become subsystems, ready for the use of the systems engineer. Even he, the user of the devices, will not be able to get the most out of them or contribute towards design of more advanced ones without a good knowledge of the principles underlying their operation and the technology used in manufacturing them.

This book is intended to provide the fundamental step in the education of young engineering students who intend either to specialize in semiconductor devices or to be mainly a user of them. The former may later specialize in the technology of microelectronics, integrated circuit design or special semiconductor devices. The latter will gain a broad enough knowledge of semiconductors, devices and basic integrated circuit approaches to tackle them with confidence in their future courses on electronic circuits and systems.

In a complementary way, physics students who intend to specialize in semiconductors will gain from this book an understanding of both discrete and integrated circuit devices, the relationship between their physical and electrical properties and the way they function in the electronic system. They will learn to see the subject from the viewpoints of the device designer, tester and user, to complement their future and more extensive courses in solid state physics.

It is the purpose of the 2nd edition to lead the electronics or physics major from basic semiconductor physical concepts into the world of VLSI circuits and of other sophisticated components, a world in which device requirements are no longer stated only in terms of transistor betas or breakdown voltages but also in terms of propagation delays and noise margins.

SI units are used throughout, with the addition of the centimeter and electron-volt to conform with their universal use in the semiconductor industry and market.

The prerequisites for this book are, from the mathematical side: some knowledge of differential and integral calculus and first- and second-order differential equations. On the physical side, some knowledge of modern physics and statistical thermodynamics will be helpful. However, a short summary of the necessary physics is given whenever necessary. The background requirement from electrical engineering is basic electrical network analysis under d.c., a.c. and transient conditions.

Since, in this book the student meets for the first time a host of new terms and ideas which he or she must learn to recognize and use, these terms and ideas are introduced gradually, sometimes in two stages, and physical clarity is preferred to full and rigorous mathematical treatment. The authors experience in teaching this course for several years in the Technion, Israel Institute of Technology has led him to believe that, in a fundamental course such as this, mathematics should be used only to clarify the physical picture and provide tools for the student laboratory work, and should be avoided if it becomes so complicated that most of the student effort is diverted into following it. The place for the more advanced and rigorous treatment is in specialized graduate courses, which may follow this one, when the student has already mastered and understood how and why things work. For the same reason this book is not cluttered with too many references and bibliographies. However, following each important topic covered, the student is referred to one or two books or review papers which can be used for broader coverage of that topic.

The book has essentially four parts:

1. *Semiconductor materials and physics.* Here the student is led towards the electrical properties of semiconductors. This part is composed of Chapters 1–7 and is given on a basic level suitable for the general electrical student, and can be considered only as an introduction for a physicist wanting to specialize in semiconductor physics. It reviews methods for preparation of semiconductor materials, describes crystal structure,

defines the important electrical parameters: mobility, conductance, diffusion constant and life time. Methods for their measurements are then described. The simple valence model is used first because it is easier for the student to grasp intuitively, makes possible quantitative treatment at an early stage and leads the student gradually to the more complex energy-band theory based on quantum mechanics through the Kronig–Penney model. The density of states in the bands is then found and the probability of their occupation by current carriers is calculated. This leads to the concept of Fermi level, and the homogenous intrinsic and extrinsic semiconductor cases. Only that part of solid state physics that is essential for understanding semiconductor device operation is included.

2. *Basic devices.* This part is composed of Chapters 8, 9, and 11 to 15. It starts with PN junction properties (including generation–recombination currents and heterojunctions) and continues to analyze all the important classes of basic devices, such as the various kinds of diodes, MOS, JFET and bipolar transistors. The small and large signal models are developed and deviations of real devices from their idealized models is discussed, together with the dependence of the model parameters on operating point, ambient conditions or frequency. Examples are then given of the use of such models in analyzing elementary circuits. Although electronic circuits as such are outside the scope of this book, the author feels that understanding of such basic ideas as amplification, load line, frequency response or switching times is essential for understanding integrated circuit building blocks. These are covered in Chapter 13, following the first active device family described, the FETs.

3. *Integrated circuit devices and processes.* This part starts with Chapter 16 describing the various major technologies in use today in semiconductor manufacturing. Knowledge of such processes helps in understanding the limitations of devices, the yields and parameter spread expected of various device families and other differences between them. Chapter 17 covers bipolar ICs, including such topics as design philosophy and fundamental building blocks for analog and for digital applications. Chapter 18 is dedicated to MOS ICs (NMOS, CMOS, static and dynamic gates, CCDs and memory cells) together with a discussion of the VLSI era and related problems, such as scaling or large area photolithography.

4. *Special semiconductor devices.* This part is based on parts 1 and 2 and is independent of 3. It includes optoelectronic devices (Chapter 10) introduced early so that student interest is boosted by applying their already accumulated knowledge to a modern, real life field. It continues in Chapters 19 and 20 which deal with power semiconductor devices (thyristors, bipolars, vertical MOST and the static induction transistor) and microwave devices (bipolars, varactors, transferred electron and impatts) respectively. This part ends with Chapter 21 which looks at devices and technologies of the future, subjects that are still in developmental stages or just entering into use.

Four appendices close the book. The first sums up the subject of the various two-part representations and their interrelationships. The method and equations developed are useful for working with equivalent circuits. The second covers the fundamentals of thermionic emission and vacuum tubes. Triodes and their small-signal models, limitations, and short descriptions of the cathode ray tube and photomultiplier are included. The third lists important and useful physical constants and semiconductor material properties and the last gives silicon processing data necessary for working out problems related to diffusions or implantations.

Each chapter is followed by a list of questions to test the reader's grasp of the various ideas outlined in the chapter, and then by a list of problems to train the reader in applying the mathematical approaches and equations. Some of the problems actually supplement and broaden the information previously given.

To cover all the material a two-semester course is necessary in which the chapters composing parts 1 and 2 are covered in the first one and may be looked upon as a basic course, while parts 3 and 4 may be considered a more advanced course and covered in the second one. As already mentioned, parts 3 and 4 are independent of one another and the teacher may elect to cover only selected chapters from them.

A teacher's manual containing the solutions to the problems can be obtained from the publisher.

ACKNOWLEDGEMENTS

The author would like to thank his colleagues in the Technion with whom he worked when developing this course, and his many students, without whose questions many obscure points would have been left in the dark.

Special thanks are due to Dr D. Lubsens, Dr Shacham-Diamand and Mr Kornfield of the Microelectronic Laboratory at the Technion, IIT, who helped in obtaining some of the photographs.

I would also like to thank Motorola Inc. U.S.A., N.V. Philips Gloeilampenfabrieken, The Netherlands and National Semiconductors (Israel), who permitted the use of their published data sheets, characteristics and parameters for various devices used in this book to illustrate the connection between theory and practice.

A. B-L.

SEMICONDUCTORS AND THEIR PREPARATION FOR ENGINEERING USE 1

1.1 Semiconductors

Semiconductor materials are distinguished by having their specific electrical conductivity somewhere between that of good conductors (10^6 $(\Omega cm)^{-1}$) and that of good insulators ($10^{-5}(\Omega cm)^{-1}$); hence the name. Among those materials, by far the most important in engineering use is silicon (Si). Of quite lesser importance is germanium (Ge), which, like silicon, is an element belonging to Group IV of the periodic table (Table 2.2). Becoming more important daily are the compound semiconductors, usually compounded of two elements (but sometimes more) of Groups III and V or II and VI of the periodic table. From those gallium arsenide (GaAs) is the most important. Also in use for specific purposes are indium antimonide (InSb), gallium phosphide (GaP), cadmium sulphide (CdS), lead–tin–telluride (PbSnTe) and others.

We shall mainly concentrate on Si, Ge and GaAs, from which the majority of present-day devices are being made, but the theoretical results apply to all of them.

Electronic devices necessitate use of almost absolutely pure semiconductor materials in which an exactly measured amount, usually extremely small, of a foreign dopant has been included to control its electrical properties. Also, the semiconductor must normally be in the form of a single crystal throughout the device, since, as we shall see, its desired electrical properties depend on the ordered, periodic nature of the crystal structure and any faults would be detrimental.

Let us give a short review of present-day engineering solutions to the purity and single crystal requirements.

1.2 Purification

Silicon, one of the most abundant elements on earth, is always found in a compound form in nature, usually combined with oxygen (sand is mainly SiO_2). It is first purified as far as possible by chemical methods. Reduction with carbon, according to $SiO_2+2C \rightarrow Si+2CO$, yields metallurgical grade silicon of up to 99% purity. By combining it with HC1, it is converted to liquid $SiHC1_3$. This is further purified using fractionation processes similar to those employed in the petroleum industry, and then reduced in hydrogen according to $SiHC1_3+H_2 \rightarrow Si+3HC1$ and vapor deposited on thin silicon rods used as hot substrates. The deposition forms thick, semiconductor grade, polysilicon rods in which the concentration of troublesome impurities is about 1 in 10^9 silicon atoms. In single crystal form such silicon would have a resistivity of about 200 Ωcm which is sufficient for most applications. For special uses very high purity (and consequently resistivity) Si is needed. This is obtained by a method called zone refining, also used for germanium. It is based on the tendency of most impurities to remain in the liquid part when the melted semiconductor gradually solidifies. The ratio of the impurity concentration on the solid side of the liquid–solid interface C_s to that on the liquid side C_l is called the *segregation* (or distribution) coefficient K of that specific impurity and is usually much smaller than one.

Figure 1.1(a) describes such a purification system for Si using a floating zone; a solid Si bar is held vertically inside a fused silica (also called quartz) tube without touching it. (This is important, since melted Si, at 1420°C, is extremely active chemically and combines with or sticks to everything it touches.) Surrounding the tube there is a short copper coil in which a high-frequency current (about 0.5 MHz) passes, generated by an induction heating generator. Strong eddy currents are induced in the section of the Si bar inside the coil and this section melts. If this section is short, the strong surface tension of molten Si, combined with its low density, is sufficient to support the molten zone in its place. The quartz tube, being an insulator, is not affected.

The coil is slowly moved vertically relative to the Si, with the region immediately in front of it melting and that behind it solidifying. Because of the small segregation coefficient, most impurities stay in the melt and are therefore 'swept' along the bar towards one end. This may be repeated several times, the relatively dirty edge sawn off, the remainder recast into a new bar and the whole process repeated. A very high degree of purity results, with the remaining undesired impurity concentrations ten orders of magnitude or more below that of the Si. The zone refining is usually done in a hydrogen atmosphere to reduce the oxygen content. Germanium can be zone refined in horizontal graphite boats as it is much less active at its melting temperature of 937°C.

It can easily be shown (Problem 1.4) that if the original impurity concentration C_0 in the semiconductor is uniform, then, after a single molten zone

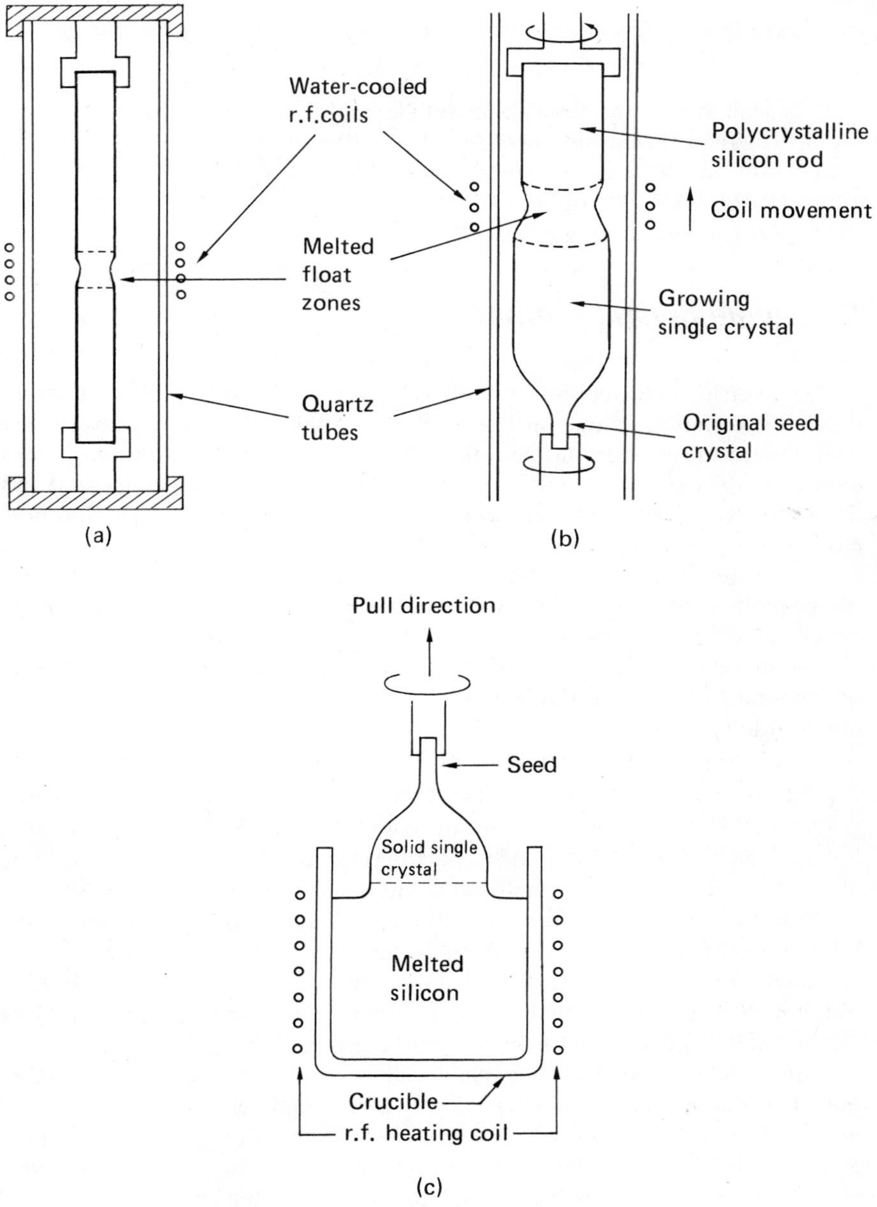

Figure 1.1. (a) Float zone (FZ) purification of Si; (b) single crystal growth by FZ technique; (c) the Czochralski single crystal pulling technique.

pass starting at $x=0$, one gets a new impurity concentration profile of

$$C_s(x)=C_0[1-(1-K)e^{-Kx/L}], \tag{1.1}$$

where L is the length of the molten zone.

This equation is the initial impurity distribution for the second pass. For copper ($K=4\times10^{-4}$) or iron ($K=8\times10^{-6}$), e.g., only a few passes suffice to appreciably reduce the impurity content.

1.3 Single-crystal Formation

Conversion of the polysilicon rods to single crystal may be done by a similar float zone technique shown in Fig. 1.1(b). The polyrod is mounted vertically over a piece of single crystal, Si, called *the seed*, that is pre-cut in the desired crystallographic orientation. RF heating is used to melt the top of the seed and the bottom of the polyrod and form a molten float zone. If the RF coil is now moved very slowly upwards, the bottom of the molten zone would start to solidify on top of the seed, continuing its single crystal structure and orientation. As the molten zone traverses the polyrod, it transforms the rod's polycrystalline structure into a single crystal.

Both rod and seed are slowly rot. ed during growth to preserve uniformity of temperature and composition. Crystals of 10 cm diameter and 50 cm long are grown routinely today.

The most common method for silicon crystal growing in use today is the Czochralski pulling technique. The purified Si is remelted in a quartz-lined graphite crucible, shown schematically in Fig. 1.1(c). The *seed*, attached to a holder, is dipped into the molten Si and then very slowly pulled up again, turning at the same time to preserve uniformity. Molten Si sticking to the seed will start to solidify, if the temperature is properly controlled, and its crystal structure will follow that of the seed. The growth is performed with the growing crystal containing an exactly known amount of some specific impurity previously added to the melt, which, as we shall see, determines the electrical properties. Long crystals of 10 and 12.5 cm diameter can be grown.

Since Si in molten form is chemically very reactive, Czochralski (CZ) pulled crystals are not as pure as FZ grown ones and contain some undesired impurities, like carbon and oxygen, absorbed from the crucible and its lining, and sometimes even minute traces of heavy metals. As we shall learn, this affects the electrical properties of devices built in such a crystal.

Compound semiconductors are much more difficult to grow in single crystal bulk form. The difficulties stem from the usually very different vapor pressures of the compound constituents causing the more volatile one to evaporate away from the melt.

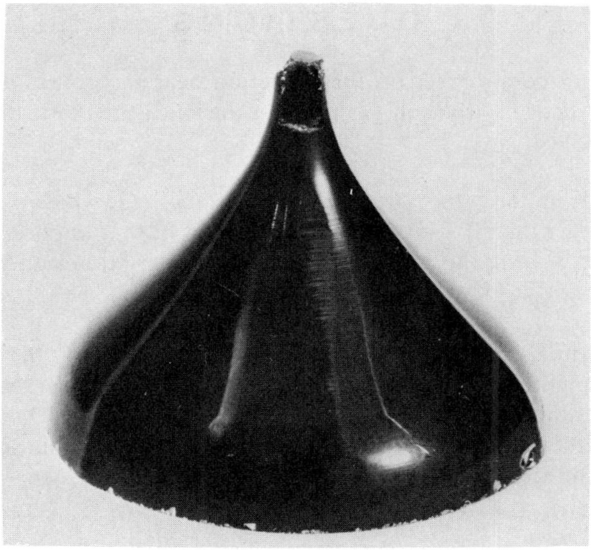

Top section of a pulled silicon single crystal still attached to the seed crystal.

A technique known as Liquid Encapsulated Czochralski (LEC) is often used today to grow such crystals: the melt of the compound constituents is covered on top by a liquid encapsulant, which floats on it, is not missible in it and has a low vapor pressure. $B_2 0_3$ is often used for GaP growth. The encapsulant, coupled with inert gas overpressure in the crucible, prevent the volatile constituent from evaporating away during growth. Another method uses an hermetically sealed tube that can carry the pressure at the growth temperature, with different parts of it maintained at different temperatures. A second problem is that variations from stoichiometry (proper ratio of the constituents) and crystal defects may dominate the electrical properties. Since bulk semiconductor purification and crystal growth is done by special material suppliers and is not an in-house technology in the electronic device industry, we shall not deal with it further, however, integrated circuit and GaAs device technology often require an in-house growth of a thin single crystal layer on a matching single crystal substrate with different electrical properties. This is done by a method called *epitaxy* which will be described in Chapter 16.

Additional information on semiconductor material technology can be found in Reference 1.

QUESTIONS

1.1 Will there be an effect on the induction heating process of Fig. 1.1 if either hydrogen or argon gas flows in the silica tube instead of its being evacuated?

1.2 A specific impurity has a segregation constant in Ge which is smaller than 1 but larger than 0. Can Ge containing a lot of that impurity be purified just by repeating the zone refining process many times on the same Ge bar?

1.3 A sample of single-crystal Si is grown from the melt by the Czochralski pulling method. In order to obtain the desired electrical conductivity a certain amount of the impurity antimony (Sb) with $K \simeq 0.02$, is also melted in the crucible of the liquid Si before the growth is started. Will the content of Sb in the grown crystal be uniform along its length?

PROBLEM

1.4 Assuming an originally uniform impurity distribution C_0 along a Si bar, show that eq. (1.1) results after one zone pass. How will you proceed to obtain the impurity distribution after the second pass? After the next pass?

CRYSTAL STRUCTURE AND VALENCE MODEL OF A PURE AND DOPED SEMICONDUCTOR 2

2.1 A Simplified Picture of a Semiconductor Crystal

We shall now give a very simplified first picture of the situation inside a semiconductor, with and without impurities. Qualitative explanations will be used here and any quantitative results must therefore be considered as rough approximations only. In the next chapters we shall return to the various concepts appearing here for the first time, using a more quantitative (and, unfortunately, more difficult) approach.

Both Si and Ge atoms have 4 valence electrons, i.e. electrons belonging to the outer shell of the atom. Those are the electrons which participate in chemical bonding when the atoms form compounds. Upon solidifying from the liquid phase both Si and Ge crystallize in the diamond structure (the crystalline form of carbon), because for those elements this is the structure which minimizes the free energy. The basic unit cell of the diamond structure is shown in Fig. 2.1.

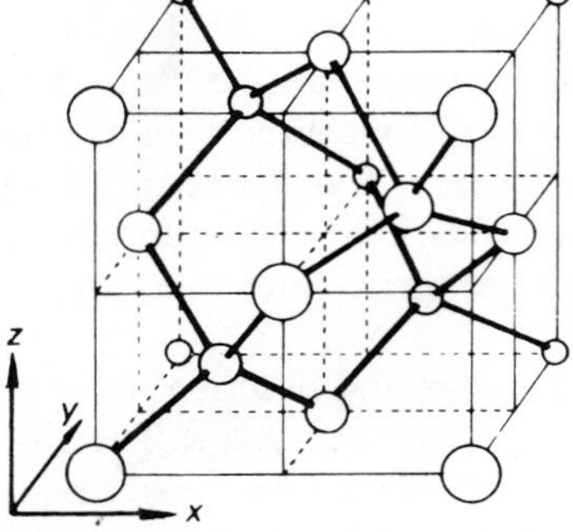

Figure 2.1. The diamond crystal structure. (Atoms are not drawn to scale; they should be envisaged as touching each other.)

Each atom is seen to have 4 nearest neighbors, set in a tetrahedral structure (GaAs and many other compound semiconductors crystallize in the zincblende structure, which is similar to that of diamond, with Ga and As atoms occupying alternating positions).

The basic unit cell length *a* and the distance between two neighboring atoms (which is equal to the atomic diameter *D*) are given in Table 2.1, with several additional properties of Si, Ge and GaAs.

Table 2.1. Some of the properties of the most important semiconductors (m_0= Free electron rest mass)

Property	Si	Ge	GaAs
Atomic No.	14	32	—
Atomic weight	28.08	72.60	144.6
Density (kg m^{-3})	2.33×10^3	5.33×10^3	5.32×10^3
Melting point (°C)	1420	937	1237
Atoms per unit volume (m^{-3})	5×10^{28}	4.42×10^{28}	2.21×10^{28}
$\varepsilon/\varepsilon_0$	11.8	16	12.5
$m_e^\star/m_0$	0.26	0.12	0.07
$m_h^\star/m_0$	0.49	0.28	0.5
Unit cell length *a* (nm)	0.543	0.566	0.565
Atomic diameter (nm)	0.235	0.246	—

For additional information see Appendix 3.

Each of the 4 valence electrons of an atom in the diamond structure can be looked upon as shared between it and one of its four nearest neighbors, belonging to both of them. Each atom has then, in effect, 8 shared electrons in its outer shell in four pairs with opposite spins. This is a very stable low-energy structure. The bonding created by equal numbers of shared electrons is called *covalent* bonding. It does not involve electric charge transfer between different locations in the lattice. In a compound semiconductor like GaAs, however, the internal bonding in the crystal is also partly ionic, since the As atom has higher electronegativity than the Ga and the electron cloud shifts towards it. There is more negative charge then near the As while the vicinity of the Ga is positive. This charge transfer results in the semiconductor being polarized under electric fields. This is important when dealing with the processes that hinder charge carrier movements (scattering mechanisms) in such semiconductors.

Let us now simplify things and describe the semiconductor crystal, say Si, in a two-dimensional form as in Fig. 2.2(a). The little dots represent pairs of electrons with opposing spins, shared by the atom and its nearest neighbor. This is the so-called valence model, which is helpful in obtaining a simple, qualitative explanation of many properties of the semiconductor.

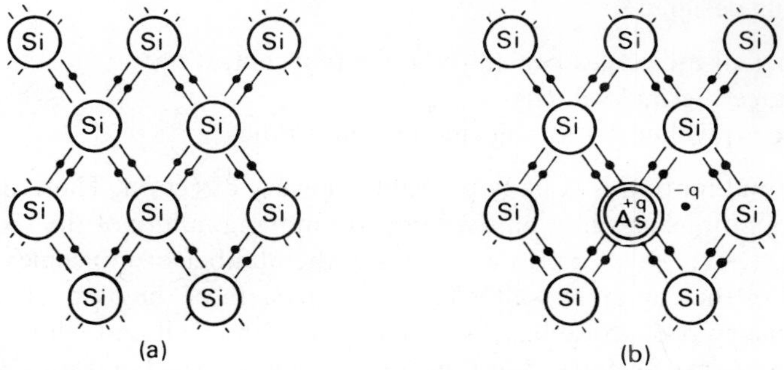

Figure 2.2. A two-dimensional picture of a Si crystal: (a) pure; (b) including some arsenic atoms (a donor impurity, see Section 2.3).

2.2 Free Charge Carriers

First let us consider a completely pure semiconductor and look for availability of charge carriers in it. At very low temperatures one can expect such material to behave like an insulator, since a shared valence electron is bound to its locality and there are no sources from which it can obtain the extra energy necessary to free itself from its bonds and make it available for current-carrying purposes. Electrons in inner shells nearer to the nucleus are even more tightly bound. The extra energy necessary to free a valence electron can be obtained from absorption of light photons arriving from the outside, if such light is available, or from the thermal vibrations of the crystal lattice atoms around their proper positions. These vibrations, called phonons, are a measure of the temperature and are very weak at low temperatures.

An idea of the available thermal energy can be obtained by comparing the vibrating crystal atoms to the molecular motion in an ideal gas inside a hypothetical container, as in Fig. 2.3.

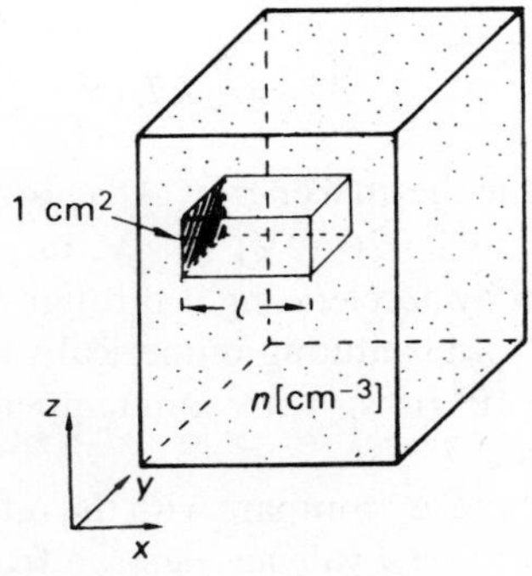

Figure 2.3. An ideal gas container for obtaining the thermal energy associated with molecular motion.

Let us designate:

n—number of molecules per unit volume (concentration)
v_{th}—average thermal velocity
l—distance travelled by a molecule in a unit time.

Thermal motion is equally probable in every direction. Therefore at any moment $\frac{1}{6}n$ molecules in a unit volume are moving in any of the six possible directions ($\pm x$; $\pm y$; $\pm z$). In a unit time, the number of molecules hitting a unit area of the container wall is equal to one-sixth of the number contained in a parallelepiped whose base is a unit area of the wall and whose height is $l = v_{th} \bullet 1 = v_{th}$ (m), as marked in Fig. 2.3. This number is therefore

(2.1)
$$\frac{1}{6} nl \bullet 1 = \frac{nv_{th}}{6} \text{ (molecules).}$$

But from the kinetic theory of gases we know that the pressure on the wall p (force per unit area) is given by

(2.2)
$$p = nkT,$$

where

k = Boltzman constant (1.38×10^{-23} J °K^{-1}), and
T = absolute temperature in °K.

Our $\frac{1}{6}nv_{th}$ molecules impinging on a unit area of the wall in each second exert on it a force equal to the pressure. This force is the total change in molecular momentum per unit time. Assuming a rigid wall and elastic collision, this change, for one molecule, is $2mv_{th}$ (the velocity changes direction). Therefore

$$p = \tfrac{1}{6}nv_{th} \bullet 2mv_{th} \text{ (N m}^{-2}\text{)}.$$

Combining with (2.2) and rearranging, we obtain

(2.3)
$$\frac{mv_{th}^2}{2} = \frac{3}{2} kT.$$

Hence kT is a measure of the thermal energy. At a normal room temperature of 300°K (27°C) it is equal to 0.026 (eV) (1 eV, or one electron-volt, is the energy given to an electron by accelerating it through 1 V potential difference; it is equal to 1.6×10^{-19} J). Substituting numerical values (from Appendix 3) into eq. (2.3), we get $v_{th} \simeq 10^5$ (m s^{-1}) at room temperature, which is approximately the measured value.

How does the thermal energy compare with the internal ionization energy, i.e., the energy necessary to free a valence electron from its bond to a specific locality, so it can become a free charge carrier and contribute to current if external fields are applied? As we shall see in subsequent chapters this energy is about 1.1 eV for Si and 0.67 eV for Ge. At room temperature the average thermal energy, kT, is much lower, and therefore only very few electrons in Ge will manage to break free and even fewer in Si. The reason that few such electrons do exist is that the numbers mentioned are average values. There is a very small probability that an electron may accumulate a much higher thermal energy than the average. Although the probability is small, the number of valence electrons is high (about 10^{23} (cm^{-3})) and therefore the concentration of free carriers won't be completely negligible even at room temperature, and is expected to grow as the temperature increases.

When a valence electron is ionized, two charge carriers are actually created. The second one, called a *hole*, is the charge located in the vicinity vacated by the electron. That vicinity is left with a net positive charge of $+q$. Any one of the other valence electrons moving nearby can step into the vacated state with very little additional energy (less than the thermal energy) thereby shifting the net positive charge, i.e. the hole, to a new location. Both the free electron and the hole can therefore move around in the semiconductor crystal.

When one applies an electric field to the semiconductor, the random movement of the free electrons and holes is immediately affected. Before the field is applied this movement is the result of successive collisions with various scattering centers in the crystal lattice—for instance defects, ionized impurity atoms and thermal vibrations—which cause frequent changes in direction and velocity of the moving charge carriers. This random movement results in zero average current. With an external field the movement is very similar but will have an average component in the direction of the external field. This average velocity depends on the field and is called *drift velocity* and we shall return to it in the next chapter.

The moving carriers, though called 'free', are confined inside the crystal, subject to the potential fields of the atomic nuclei arranged periodically at the lattice sites. The electronic motion depends on both the externally applied field and these internal periodic fields. In Chapter 6 we shall see that the overall effect of the internal fields on the electronic movement can be taken into account by assigning the electron an *effective mass*, $m_e^\star$, different from its mass in vacuum m_0. The effective mass may be dependent on the direction of movement in respect to the crystallographic axes in some crystals (though in Si or Ge this averages out).

The hole too, has an effective mass $m_h^\star$, positive and different from that of the electron. Superficially, this may look surprising: it is easily understood that hole movement is accompanied by positive charge movement as explained. But where does the positive mass come from? In fact, this mass is a mathematical concept resulting from application of quantum-mechanical principles to the crystal structure, as will be shown in Chapter 6. However, some understanding of it may be obtained by remembering that hole movement consists actually of valence electrons moving from one atom to the next. A force (an external field) is necessary to accelerate the hole, and if there is a force and resulting acceleration, directed in the correct way for a positive charge, their ratio can be looked upon as a positive mass. The values of the effective masses for electrons and holes in various semiconductors is given in Table 2.1.

2.3 Impurities in Semiconductors; Carrier Concentrations

It is clear that the number of free electrons, n, in a pure semiconductor is exactly equal to the number of holes, p, in it. Such pure semiconductors are called *intrinsic*, and an index 'i' is appended to n and p in this case:

$$n_i = p_i \tag{2.4}$$

The intrinsic carrier concentrations are very small and depend strongly on temperature. In order to fabricate devices such as diodes or transistors, it is necessary to increase the free electron or hole population by a large amount (henceforth the adjective 'free' applied to the electrons and holes will be omitted, although always implied, since only the free ones are of importance in device behavior). This is done by intentionally *doping* the semiconductor, i.e., adding specific impurities in controlled amounts. Such a doped semiconductor is called *extrinsic*.

The choice of the proper impurity and its effect can be understood by examination of Table 2.2, which is a section of the periodic table of elements, including some of those that belong to Groups III, IV and V (the Roman numeral being equal to the number of valence electrons). The atomic number, representing the total number of electrons for each element, is also included.

Table 2.2. A section of the Periodic Table of Elements

Group II	Group III	Group IV	Group V	Group VI
	5 B (boron)	6 C (carbon—diamond)	7 N (nitrogen)	
	13 Al (aluminum)	14 Si (silicon)	15 P (phosphorus)	16 S (sulfur)
30 Zn (zinc)	31 Ga (gallium)	32 Ge (germanium)	33 As (arsenic)	34 Se (selenium)
48 Cd (cadmium)	49 In (indium)	50 Sn (tin)	51 Sb (antimony)	52 Te (tellurium)

Thus, silicon and germanium have 4 valence electrons in their outer shell while boron and gallium have 3 and phosphorus, arsenic or antimony have 5.

If a Si (or Ge) atom in the crystal lattice is replaced by an impurity atom from Group V of about the same size, say arsenic, four of the valence electrons of the arsenic will take part in the covalent bonding with the neighboring Si atoms while the fifth one will be only weakly attached to the arsenic atom location. Because its orbit is relatively large, encompassing many Si atoms, this electron can be looked upon as moving in a silicon-filled space, with the relative dielectric constant of Si (about 12). This reduces the Coulomb attraction between it and its nucleus twelve-fold. Such an impurity atom is shown schematically in Fig. 2.2(b).

In order to get a quantitative estimate of the additional energy necessary to free this fifth electron altogether, to make it available as a free charge carrier, let us regard the arsenic nucleus, screened by all its electrons but that distant fifth one, as equivalent to a large hydrogen nucleus with a net positive charge of one proton $+q$ and with this single fifth electron moving around it in a space of a relative dielectric constant of 12. This is shown schematically in Fig. 2.4.

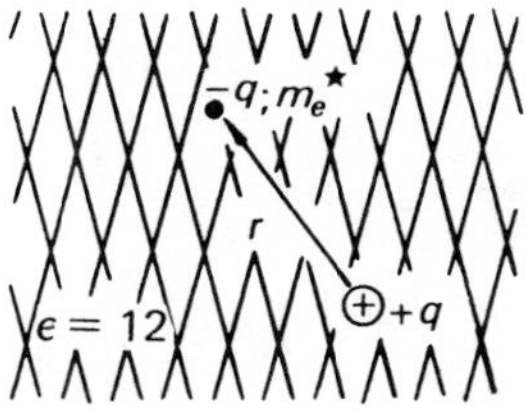

Figure 2.4. A hydrogen-like atom, embedded in a dielectric material with $\varepsilon = 12$ for calculating the ionization energy of the fifth electron (such as an As atom in Si).

Bohr's model of the atom can be used to find the ionization energy of our hydrogen-like atom of Fig. 2.4. By comparing the balanced centripetal and electric attraction forces, we obtain

$$\frac{q^2}{4\pi\varepsilon r^2} = \frac{m_e^\star v^2}{r}. \tag{2.5}$$

According to De Broglie, the electron wavelength λ and its momentum p are related to its orbit radius r and Planck's constant h:

$$2\pi r = \lambda = \frac{h}{p} = \frac{h}{m_e^\star v}. \tag{2.6}$$

On separating v out, this gives

$$v = \frac{h}{2\pi m_e^\star r}. \tag{2.7}$$

Substituting v into eq. (2.5) and separating out r gives

$$r = \frac{h^2\varepsilon}{q^2 m_e^\star \pi} = \frac{h^2\varepsilon_0}{q^2 m_0 \pi}\left(\frac{\varepsilon}{\varepsilon_0}\right)\left(\frac{m_0}{m_e^\star}\right) = r_H\left(\frac{\varepsilon}{\varepsilon_0}\right)\left(\frac{m_0}{m_e^\star}\right), \tag{2.8}$$

where r_H is the radius of the electron orbit in the hydrogen atom and ε_0 the permittivity of empty space. Using the numbers of Table 2.1 one finds that the orbital radius of the fifth electron in our hydrogen-like impurity atom is about 45 and 130 times that of hydrogen in the cases of Si and Ge respectively. Since the size of the impurity atom is only about 2.5 times that of hydrogen, the path is indeed large enough to include many of the host material atoms.

To find the ionization energy of the fifth electron, we remember that this energy E is the algebraic sum of the kinetic and the potential energies, with the latter negative since it is taken as zero for the free electron:

$$E = \frac{m_e^\star v^2}{2} - \frac{q^2}{4\pi\varepsilon r}. \tag{2.9}$$

Substituting $m_e^\star v^2$ and r_H from eqs. (2.5) and (2.8) respectively yields:

$$E = -\frac{q^2}{8\pi\varepsilon_0 r_H}\left(\frac{\varepsilon_0}{\varepsilon}\right)^2\left(\frac{m_e^\star}{m_0}\right) = E_H\left(\frac{\varepsilon_0}{\varepsilon}\right)^2\left(\frac{m_e^\star}{m_0}\right), \tag{2.10}$$

where E_H is the ionization energy of hydrogen and is equal to -13.6 eV. Using this and the values in Table 2.1 one gets $E \simeq 0.025$ eV and 0.01 eV for impurities in Si and Ge respectively.

We have mentioned that the average thermal energy at room temperature is $kT = 0.026$ eV, i.e., about equal to the values we found. Moreover, as we shall later find by more exact analysis, it is enough for the thermal energy to be about one-tenth of the ionization energy to free the extra impurity electron for conduction. Therefore, above 100°K most of the impurity atoms are already ionized and the electrons they contribute are available as current carriers. Silicon doped with As, Sb or P will, therefore, be rich in electrons compared to holes (note: ionization of the fifth, weakly bound electron, does not create a hole, i.e. an empty state into which a valence electron can step without an appreciable increase of its energy, since the valence electrons are much more tightly bound and consequently at a much lower energy state). Such a semiconductor is called *N-type* on account of its numerous negative charge carriers. The corresponding doping impurity is called a *donor*, having 'donated' an electron for conduction. Donor impurities for Si and Ge belong to Group V in Table 2.2.

If Si or Ge are doped with an atom of Group III of Table 2.2, having only 3 valence electrons, then at the location of that impurity one of the covalent bonding electrons is missing. The location is electrically neutral, but with a little additional energy (comparable to the ionization energy of the donor atom) one of the other valence electrons can cross over and complete the missing bond. When this happens—and it does happen, thanks to the available thermal energy—a hole is created at the position vacated by that valence electron. The impurity atom, having accepted an additional electron, is called an *acceptor* and is now ionized with a net negative charge of $-q$. A semiconductor doped with acceptors is rich in holes, i.e., positive charge carriers, and therefore called *P-type*.

Energy levels of valence and conduction electrons, donors and acceptors, are shown in Fig. 2.5. The donor ionization energy is $E_c - E_d$. The acceptor ionization energy is $E_a - E_v$. E_g is called the gap energy. We shall return to this energy picture in Chapter 6.

Donor and acceptor impurities which are useful for Si and Ge doping and their measured ionization energies are listed in Table 2.3.

Table 2.3. Ionization energies of common impurities: (a) in Si and Ge; (b) in GaAs

Impurity (Type)	Ionization energy (eV) Si	Ge
B (P)	0.045	0.0104
Al (P)	0.057	0.0102
Ga(P)	0.065	0.0108
In (P)	0.16	0.0112
P (N)	0.044	0.0120
As (N)	0.049	0.0127
Sb (N)	0.039	0.0096

(a)

Impurity (Type)	Ionization energy (eV)
Zn(P)	0.0307
Cd(P)	0.0347
Si (P)	0.0345
Si (P)	0.00581
S (N)	0.00610
Se (N)	0.00589
Te (N)	0.0058

(b)

A compound semiconductor, like GaAs, is doped N-type by tellurium (Group VI), P-type by cadmium (GroupII) and either P or N by Si (Group IV). (See Question 2.3). One vital point must be emphasized: the addition of impurities does not violate the electrical neutrality of the semiconductor. N-type material would have many mobile electrons but also the same number of ionized, positively charged donor impurity atoms, which are, however, fixed in their lattice positions. The same holds for P-type material with reversed charge signs. Any tendency of the mobile charge cloud to vacate a certain region would immediately lead to net charges forming and the creation of internal fields (by Poisson's equation) to counteract that tendency till neutrality is restored.

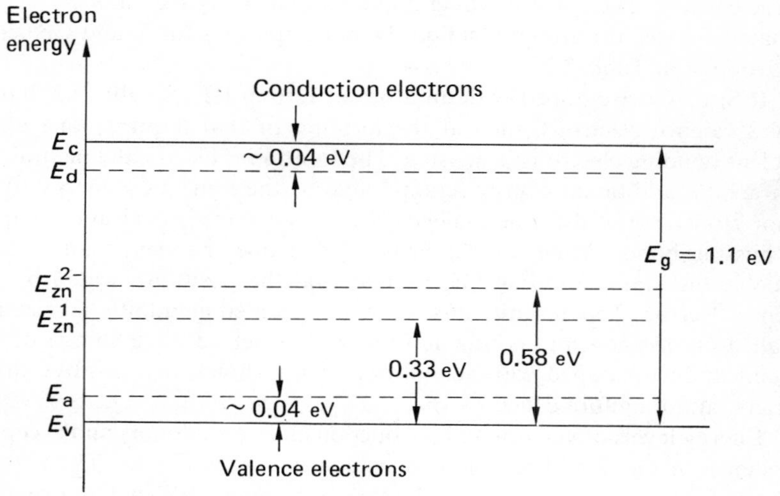

Figure 2.5. Electron energy levels in doped silicon:

E_v	is the highest level of valance electrons bonding the crystal lattice atoms together;
E_a	is the typical level of electrons occupying the empty bonds on acceptor atoms sites;
E_{Zn}^{1-}, E_{Zn}^{2-}	are deep impurity levels created by Zn doping;
E_d	is the typical level of the fifth donor electron when still bound to the donor atom;
E_c	is the lowest level of conduction electron, free to move inside the semiconductor;
$E_g = E_c - E_v$	is the extra energy a valence electron must obtain to become free for conduction. It is much larger than the available thermal energy $kT = 0.026$ eV at room temperature.

Electrons in N-type material and holes in P-type are called *majority carriers*, while holes in N-type and electrons in P-type are called *minority carriers*, for reasons that will now be discussed.

An important relation will now be shown to hold: the product of the concentrations of majority and minority carriers in thermodynamic equilibrium is independent of the doping impurity concentration and is a function only of the temperature and the semiconductor material.

We shall henceforth denote concentrations at thermodynamic equilibrium by a bar above the letter ($\bar{n}$, $\bar{p}$). These concentrations are the average result of two opposing dynamic processes:

(a) Generation rate G of electron–hole pairs per unit volume and time. In equilibrium G is the result of thermal energy only manifested by vibrational waves in the crystal lattice (phonons), which may sometimes be large enough to ionize a semiconductor atom, thereby creating a hole–electron pair. In equilibrium, G depends only on temperature and the intrinsic material properties and not on the impurities, since these are already ionized in the range of useful temperatures. Hence G in doped material is equal to that of an intrinsic material.

(2.11) $$G = G_i(T) \text{ (pairs m}^{-3}\text{ s}^{-1})$$

(b) The recombination rate R of electrons with holes (pairs per unit volume and time). When carriers recombine they disappear, giving off their kinetic energy and momentum by emission of phonons (i.e. heating the crystal) or photons (emission of radiation). Recombination rate must be equally dependent on the concentrations of electrons and holes and of course, must depend on T as well:

$$R = R(\bar{n}, \bar{p}, T)$$

under equilibrium conditions the recombination and generation rates must be equal:

(2.12) $$R(\bar{n}, \bar{p}, T) = G_i(T).$$

By (2.12) the value of R is independent of the impurity content.

Obviously, no recombination is possible if either $\bar{n}$ or $\bar{p}$ are zero. Therefore R must contain some product of $\bar{n}$ and $\bar{p}$. The simplest such function is

(2.13) $$\bar{R}(\bar{n}, \bar{p}, T) = \bar{n}\bar{p}r(T),$$

where $r(T)$ is a function of T only. (2.13) also means that electrons and holes have equal effects on the recombination rate which is reasonable. Assuming (2.13) is correct then by substituting it in eq. (2.12) one gets

(2.14) $$\bar{n}\bar{p} = \frac{G_i(T)}{r(T)}.$$

Since this product is a function of T only and independent of the impurity content we can apply it to intrinsic material, and by virtue of eq. (2.4) get

(2.15) $$\bar{n}\bar{p} = n_i^2.$$

This important relation will be proved in a more rigorous way in Chapter 7 to find its functional dependence on the material parameters and temperature. The numerical values obtained at 300°K are

$$n_i \text{ (Si)} = 1.4 \times 10^{10} (\text{cm}^{-3})$$
$$n_i \text{ (Ge)} = 2.4 \times 10^{13} (\text{cm}^{-3})$$
$$n_i \text{ (GaAs)} \simeq 1.7 \times 10^{6} (\text{cm}^{-3}).$$

Relative to the number of atoms in the crystal (about 5×10^{22} atoms per cm^3), these numbers are indeed very small. Adding impurities with concentrations typical of semiconductor devices will usually make n_i negligible in comparison to the majority carrier concentration, especially in GaAs and Si.

Thus, if Si is made P-type by adding $N_A=10^{16}$ cm^{-3} boron (acceptor) atoms, the available number of majority holes around room temperature will be essentially equal to N_A, since the intrinsic hole concentration is six orders of magnitude lower and negligible. The electron (minority) concentration in this material will be given by eq. (2.15).

$$\bar{n}=\frac{n_i^2}{\bar{p}}\simeq\frac{n_i^2}{N_A}=1.9\times10^4 \text{ cm}^{-3}.$$

We see that the minority concentration is drastically reduced from the intrinsic state by the addition of impurities. This can be intuitively understood considering that the probability that an electron will meet and combine with a hole is very much increased by the addition of acceptor impurity, since the number of holes has increased tremendously and the few intrinsic electrons find themselves in a sea of holes with which to recombine. This makes no measurable change in the number of holes but has a very noticeable effect on the minority concentration, which is the concentration of electrons in this case.

2.4 Compensation and Deep Impurities

A semiconductor doped by equal concentrations of donor and acceptor impurities is said to be fully *compensated*. The free electrons donated by the donors are 'grabbed' by the acceptors since a free electron comes down in energy when it occupies an acceptor state, as can be seen in Fig. 2.5, and each system tends in equilibrium towards its lowest possible energy.

In a fully compensated semiconductor, therefore, all the donated electrons have been caught by acceptor states and none is available for conduction. All the valence electrons stay in the valence levels since no acceptor state is left unoccupied, so there are no holes either. The number of available charge carriers will be very low, like in an intrinsic, undoped, semiconductor. Contrary to intrinsic material, however, a compensated semiconductor has a lot of positively and negatively charged ions (the donors and acceptors) embedded in it and though macroscopically it is electrically neutral, these charges would affect its conductivity as we shall see in Chapter 3.

If an atom from Group II, like Zn, is used to dope a Group IV semiconductor like Si, two bonds in the lattice will be missing in the vicinity of the Zn atom. This atom can therefore accept either a single electron from the valence band and become singly ionized, or accept two and become doubly ionized. The energy levels that these valence electrons must attain to be 'accepted', however, are much higher than for a Group III acceptor like boron (E_a in Fig. 2.5) and are shown in the figure too. Such levels are called *deep*. Thermal energy is not sufficient to excite valence electrons into them but they can catch (trap) free electrons from the conduction level. As we shall learn, this enhances the recombination of such trapped electrons with holes that may come by. Thermal energy is not sufficient to liberate an electron trapped in a deep impurity. One therefore finds that deep impurities drastically reduce the number of electrons free for conduction and an N-type material so doped behaves like an insulator. Deep levels may be created in semiconductors by crystalline defects and by many heavy metal atoms. Especially useful are gold (Au), which in minute quantities is used in Si to enhance recombination and increase the operating speed of switching devices (Chapter 11), and chromium (Cr), used to dope p-type GaAs, create deep donor levels that cause compensation and turn it into a practical insulator called *semi-insulating GaAs*. Such GaAs has resistivities of up to $10^9 \Omega$cm and is used as a single crystal substrate on which digital circuits or microwave devices of GaAs are made. As we shall see, such circuits benefit greatly from the insulating property of the substrate. Another method by which semi-insulating GaAs may be obtained is by growing it undoped which gives it a very high specific resistivity to begin with. This can be further increased in selected regions by bombarding them with high energy protons in vacuum. The protons (hydrogen nuclei) wreck the crystalline structure, create many deep levels, and make the bombarded region amorphous and highly resistive.

Other regions of such a substrate can be doped to a lower resistivity by ion implantation (to be described in Chapter 16) so that transistors can be built there. Undoped GaAs substrates pose fewer processing problems than chromium-doped ones and their use is increasing.

2.5 High Doping Densities and Degenerate Semiconductors

In all our treatment up to now and in the theories that are developed in the next chapters there is one implicit assumption and that is that the impurity atoms are few and far between in the semiconductor crystal. If their concentration is made large enough for the orbits of the fifth distant electrons of neighboring donor atoms to start to overlap, then they begin to be influenced by each other and then the semiconductor properties, such as the behavior of its conductivity with temperature, will change. Such a material is called *degenerate*, i.e., one can no longer consider the allowed orbits of the electrons (and the energies associated with them) independently. They unite into a single system in which the Pauli exclusion principle, forbidding electrons to have the same allowed state, holds. We shall return in Section 7.3 to this principle and to its consequences on the allowed energy states of those extra impurity electrons. We can, however, obtain an estimate of the impurity concentration, N, above which energy levels of impurity atoms become affected by the nearness of other impurity atoms in their neighborhood, as follows:

The average distance between neighboring impurity atoms is $N^{-1/3}$ if N is their concentration. If this distance becomes comparable to the diameter of the fifth electron orbit as given by eq. (2.8), degeneracy sets in. This leads to a value of approximately 10^{19}cm^{-3} as the limiting concentration (about three orders of magnitude less than the semiconductor atom concentration). The technological limit to impurity inclusion is usually higher and is called the *solid solubility* limit. This is a property of the semiconductor, the impurity and the temperature at which the impurity is introduced. Attempts to increase the impurity concentration further will fail because the excess impurity will segregate, form inclusions in the crystal and will not be electrically active, i.e., will not contribute carriers. High doping densities also introduce mechanical stresses in the crystal because of accumulated differences in atomic sizes and increase the number of crystal faults.

QUESTIONS

2.1 When electrons in a semiconductor accumulate high energies, e.g., when the semiconductor is heated, some of them may be energetic enough to be emitted out of the material. Can this also happen to holes?

2.2 What will happen to a semiconductor doped by equal amounts of donors and acceptors?

2.3 Why are donors appropriate to Si and Ge chosen from the elements in Group V of the periodic table? What role do you think a Si atom has in a GaAs crystal if it replaces an As atom? A Ga atom? (Such dopants are called *amphoteric*).

2.4 Will a good or a bad match between the sizes of an impurity and the host semiconductor atom have any effect? Will it affect the solid solubility?

2.5 How do you think the number of majority and minority carriers will change in Si doped by Sb when the temperature is changed from 0°K to near melting temperature? Do you expect exactly the same behavior if the Sb is replaced with As? (*Hint*: Make use of data in Table 2.3.)

2.6 Can the electron's effective mass be measured by applying magnetic or electric fields to an electron while it moves in vacuum?

PROBLEMS

2.7 Using Fig. 2.1, calculate the following properties of Si:

(a) The atomic diameter (unit cell size for Si crystal is 0.543 nm).

(b) The number of atoms in 1 cm^3.

(c) The number of atoms per unit area in the crystal planes (111), (110), (100). These are Miller indices, which are used to indicate specific planes in the crystal.) These three planes are the ones most frequently encountered in semiconductor technology and are shown in Fig. 2.6.

(d) The specific weight (atomic weight of Si is 28). Compare your results with those found in Table 2.1.

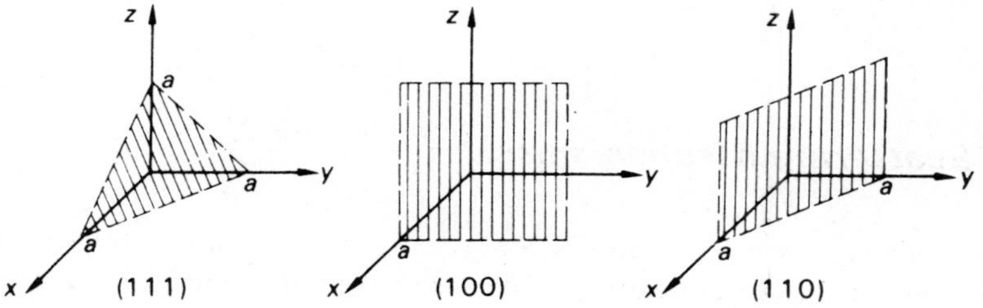

Figure 2.6. The most commonly encountered crystal planes.

2.8 Find the electric field strength E necessary to accelerate an electron from rest to the thermal limiting velocity of 10^5 m s^{-1} within a distance equal to the unit cell dimension in Si.

2.9 How many electron-volts are there (a) in 1 kg m, and (b) in 1 J?

2.10 What are the equilibrium concentrations of holes and electrons at 300°K in

(a) Si doped with $N_D = 3 \times 10^{14} cm^{-3}$ donors;

(b) Ge doped with the same density of acceptors as in (a)?

(c) State your conclusions regarding (i) acceptable engineering assumptions in each case, and (ii) the relative importance of the thermally generated carriers compared to those contributed by the impurities.

MOBILITY AND ELECTRICAL CONDUCTIVITY 3

3.1 Scattering Mechanisms

If a constant voltage source is connected to the two sides of a semiconductor chip, an electrical field **E** (V cm^{-1}) is created in it. This field acts upon the free charge carriers and causes them to drift in the direction of the force it applies, thereby creating a current called *drift current*.

When a charge carrier, say an electron, is acted upon by a constant electrical field in a vacuum, its ensuing acceleration, **a**, is (Newton's law):

$$\mathbf{a} = \frac{q\mathbf{E}}{m_e}, \tag{3.1}$$

and its velocity **v** at time t, if it started from rest:

$$\mathbf{v} = \int_0^t \mathbf{a}\, dt = \frac{q\mathbf{E}t}{m_e}, \tag{3.2}$$

i.e., velocity increases linearly with time.

Inside a semiconductor, on the other hand, the movement of the charge carrier is not smooth but is perturbed by various obstacles, causing what is known as *scattering*. There are two main types of scattering mechanism (there are more but we shall neglect the less important):

(a) *Lattice scattering* is caused by collisions of the moving carrier with disturbances in the periodic internal potential inside the semiconductor crystal. These disturbances are due to the vibrations of the crystal lattice atoms around their 'proper' place in the lattice because of their thermal energy. The effect of the internal periodic potential itself, which exists in any crystal, can be taken into consideration by assigning an effective mass $m^\star$ to the moving electron or hole, as we shall see in Chapter 6. These masses are different from the mass m_0 of the electron outside the crystal. Therefore it is only the disruptions in the periodic potential, caused by the thermal vibrations of the atoms, that scatters the drifting free carriers: at a certain moment an electron can bump into a region where the crystal atoms are more densely packed than usual, yet a moment later it may find itself in a sparsely packed region. The dense and sparse regions form pressure waves existing inside the crystal.

These thermally-caused, lattice pressure waves have also corpuscular or particulate properties, just as photons do. Their energy distribution also follows the same statistical law obeyed by photons, as we shall learn in Chapter 6.

These vibrational wave–particle entities are called *phonons*. They can exist only inside the lattice and have wavelength and velocity like any other wave, or energy and momentum like any other particle. The energy and momentum, however, are not independent. They are related by the so-called dispersion equation, which is obtained when one considers the movement of atoms in lattice under the elastic forces existing between each atom and its near neighbors, like a number of point masses tied together with springs.

The wave or particle nature that phonons exhibit depends on the type of experiment performed. Their interaction with current carriers inside the semiconductor results from the local disturbances introduced by the existence of phonons in the otherwise periodic lattice potential. The interaction can also be looked upon as collisions between the current carriers and phonons. In these collisions, the total energy and momentum are conserved, but become redistributed, changing magnitude and direction of carrier velocity, i.e., they cause the carrier to be scattered. The carrier thus loses the kinetic energy it has accumulated through being accelerated by the external field since the previous scattering event.

Following the collision the carrier is again accelerated in the direction of the field and, inevitably, scattered again, and this repeats all the time. It is obvious that lattice scattering will grow more severe with increasing temperature.

(b) *Impurity scattering* is caused by the presence of ionized impurity atoms in various positions in the crystal lattice. Due to their net charge, they exert a force on the free carrier passing nearby, causing it to change its direction (like a comet entering the gravity field of a star). This type of scattering is less severe if the free carrier is moving faster (i.e. at higher temperatures), and spends less time in the vicinity of the ionized impurity atom.

3.2 Average Drift Velocity; Mobility

Our purpose now is to find an expression for the average velocity of a charge carrier under the effect of a field **E**, when there is a scattering mechanism such that if we start with n_0 carriers at time $t=0$, measured for each carrier from the moment of its last collision, then a time t later there are still $n(t)$ that have not suffered a second scattering collision and that are still accelerating in the direction of the field. Between t and $t+\mathrm{d}t$ an additional $\mathrm{d}n$ carriers will suffer a second collision and lose their momentum in the field direction. The number of still accelerating carriers will therefore be reduced by $\mathrm{d}n$ which, to a first approximation, is proportional to the number of still uncollided carriers n and to the time increment $\mathrm{d}t$ but not to the moving carriers' energy. Let us call the proportionality constant $1/\tau$; then

$$-\mathrm{d}n=\frac{1}{\tau}\,n\,\mathrm{d}t. \tag{3.3}$$

The solution of this equation, by separation of variables, is

$$n=n_0\exp\left(-\frac{t}{\tau}\right), \tag{3.4}$$

where τ has the dimensions of time. Actually it is the average free time between collisions. To see this, let us find the probability for a collision during the period $\mathrm{d}t$, which is $\mathrm{d}n/n_0$. From (3.3), (3.4) we get

$$-\frac{\mathrm{d}n}{n_0}=\frac{1}{\tau}\exp\left(-\frac{t}{\tau}\right)\mathrm{d}t. \tag{3.5}$$

The right-hand side of (3.5) gives the distribution of the time t that a carrier moves till it collides (a Poissonian distribution). We see, for instance, that a relatively large fraction of the starting n_0 carriers will collide again near $t=0$, at the beginning of their movement, because at $t=0$ the right-side of (3.5) is maximum. But there will be some, on the other hand, whose time t to the next collision will be very long because $\exp(-t/\tau)$ never quite reaches zero in a finite time. Therefore some electrons or holes will be accelerated to very high velocities, while most will reach only a low velocity before colliding and being scattered again. To find an average velocity, or an average time between collisions, we must sum the times to the second collision for the various carriers, assigning a proper weight to each time t depending on the relative number of carriers colliding at that time. This weighting function is $|\mathrm{d}n/n_0|$, given by eq. (3.5). Let us also assume that the carrier's velocity $\mathbf{v}_0$ (magnitude and direction) immediately after a collision is completely random (that is a good assumption).

Let **r** be the radius vector. Then, at time t, accelerated by the influence of an electric field **E**, the carrier will be at:

$$\mathbf{r}=\mathbf{r}_0+\mathbf{v}_0 t+\frac{q\mathbf{E}}{m^\star}\frac{t^2}{2}$$

where $\mathbf{r}_0$ is its original position and $q\mathbf{E}/m^\star$ is its acceleration.

The average distance travelled by a carrier during t is therefore:

$$<\mathbf{r}-\mathbf{r}_0> = <\mathbf{v}_0 t> + \frac{q\mathbf{E}}{2m^\star}<t^2>.$$

Since the starting random velocity $\mathbf{v}_0$ and the time t to the next collision are unrelated, the average of their product is equal to the product of their averages, and since the average of the random quantity $\mathbf{v}_0$ is zero, the first term on the right-hand side of the last equation is zero. The average velocity, i.e., the carrier drift velocity $\mathbf{v}_d$, will be given by

(3.6)
$$\mathbf{v}_d=\frac{<\mathbf{r}-\mathbf{r}_0>}{<t>}=\frac{q\mathbf{E}}{2m^\star}\frac{<t^2>}{<t>}$$

The averages of t^2 and t can be calculated using their proper weighting function $\left|\mathrm{d}n/n_0\right|$, as already explained:

$$<t> = \int_0^{n_0} t\left|\frac{\mathrm{d}n}{n_0}\right| = \int_0^{\infty} t\,\frac{e^{-t/\tau}}{\tau}\,\mathrm{d}t=\tau$$

$$<t^2> = \int_0^{n_0} t^2\left|\frac{\mathrm{d}n}{n_0}\right| = \int_0^{\infty} t^2\,\frac{e^{-t/\tau}}{\tau}\,\mathrm{d}t=2\tau^2.$$

(The integrals are easily solved using integration by parts.) We see that indeed τ is the average or mean free time between collisions.

Substitution of those values into eq. (3.6) of $\mathbf{v}_d$ will give

(3.7)
$$\mathbf{v}_d=\frac{q\tau}{m^\star}\mathbf{E}.$$

We obtained a velocity that is proportional to the field and is constant in a constant field. The proportionality factor is called *mobility* and is usually assigned the letter μ:

(3.8)
$$\mu_{e,h}=\frac{q\tau}{m^\star_{e,h}}; \qquad \mathbf{v}_d=\mu\mathbf{E}.$$

The index e or h indicates whether one is referring to an electron or hole, respectively. In most semiconductors the electron's mobility is higher.

Sometimes, as in GaAs or InSb, it is higher by one or more orders of magnitude. Typical values are given in Table 3.1.

Actually the proportionality between v_d and E (the magnitudes of $\mathbf{v}$ and $\mathbf{E}$) is gradually lost at higher and higher fields. When a charge carrier accumulates a very high kinetic energy (as it will do in a high field), it may fall prey to additional scattering processes, previously ignored, which depend on its energy. As a result v_d will gradually saturate to a value equal to the average thermal velocity of about 10^7 cm s^{-1} at fields of some several tens of kilovolts per centimeter. The concept of mobility is therefore meaningful, and it can be considered a constant only at relatively low fields where v_d is still proportional to E. As already mentioned, the mobility is a result of both lattice and impurity scattering, and both depend on temperature but in opposing manners. At temperature T the carriers rush around in the semiconductor with an average thermal velocity v_{th} given by (2.3) and proportional to $T^{1/2}$. The lattice vibrations, due to temperature, increase their amplitude with T, which makes the mean free path of a carrier between lattice scattering events l_L become proportional to T^{-1}. Substituting $\tau = l_L/v_{th}$ in (3.8) makes μ_L, the mobility due to lattice scattering alone:

(3.9) $$\mu_I \propto T^{-3/2}.$$

Impurity scattering becomes severe if the thermal energy kT, of a carrier moving a distance r from a charged impurity, becomes comparable to the potential the charge creates there which is proportional to r^{-1}. The distance r for effective impurity scattering, therefore, is proportional to T^{-1}. Each impurity atom thus presents a scattering area (called a scattering cross section) of πr^2 to the moving carrier. The mean free path between impurity scattering events l_I, is inversely proportional to that area and therefore proportional to T^2. Substituting $\tau = l_I/v_{th}$ in (3.8) give μ_I, the mobility due to impurity scattering alone:

(3.10) $$\mu_I \propto T^{3/2}.$$

When both scattering mechanisms are present, as in any doped semiconductor operating at a temperature above abolute zero, the group of carriers dn colliding between t and $t + dt$ will be composed of two subgroups, completely independent of each other and therefore summable. Equation (3.3) should be written in this case in the form:

$$-dn = -(dn_1 + dn_2) = \frac{n}{\tau_1}\, dt + \frac{n}{\tau_2}\, dt = \left(\frac{1}{\tau_1} + \frac{1}{\tau_2}\right) n\, dt,$$

where τ_1 is the average time between collisions of the first kind (lattice), and τ_2 between collisions of the second kind (impurity). Comparing to (3.3), we see that we can repeat the whole calculation with

$$\frac{1}{\tau'} = \frac{1}{\tau_1} + \frac{1}{\tau_2}$$

substituted for $1/\tau$. The resulting mobility will then be

$$\frac{1}{\mu}=\frac{1}{\mu_L}+\frac{1}{\mu_I}\,. \tag{3.11}$$

The dependence of μ on the temperature will therefore be determined by μ_I at low temperatures (when μ_I is the smaller of the two), and by μ_L at high temperatures (when μ_L is smaller). The higher the doping level the lower μ_I becomes, and consequently the lower μ becomes. In fact it may become so small that even at room temperature and above μ_I would still determine the total mobility.

For real semiconductors these are only rough approximations since additional scattering mechanisms might exist. Thus in a partially ionic material like GaAs the electrons of the gallium atom are drawn nearer to the arsenic nucleus which renders the gallium locations in the lattice slightly positive while the arsenic locations become slightly negative with an electric field in between. We call such material *polarized.* A free electron moving in the crystal will interact with the polar field and may lose energy and momentum to it (i.e., be scattered). In practice, therefore, the exponent of T usually differs from 3/2.

In compensated semiconductors, there are a lot of charged ions in the crystal lattice. This increases impurity scattering and reduces the total mobility compared to uncompensated material with the same density of free carriers.

Table 3.1 gives numerical data for μ in various, almost pure semiconductor materials, around room temperature.

Table 3.1. Mobilities of electrons and holes in various intrinsic semiconductors at 300°K

Material	$\mu_e(cm^2\,V^{-1}\,s^{-1})$	$\mu_h(cm^2\,V^{-1}\,s^{-1})$
Ge	3900	1900
Si	1350	480
GaAs	8500	480
GaP	450	20
InSb	80,000	200
InAs	23,000	100

3.3 Conductivity

Having found the charge carriers' drift velocities in a semiconductor containing electrons and holes under the influence of a field **E**, we can calculate the ensuing drift current densities:

$$\mathbf{J}_e\ (\text{drift}) = -qn(\mathbf{v}_d)_e = +qn\mu_e\mathbf{E},$$

$$\mathbf{J}_h\ (\text{drift}) = +qp(\mathbf{v}_d)_h = +qp\mu_h\mathbf{E},$$

and the total drift current density will be their sum, since even though electrons and holes have charges of opposite sign, their velocity in the field **E** has opposite direction also and therefore

$$\mathbf{J}\ (\text{drift}) = \mathbf{J}_e + \mathbf{J}_h = q(n\mu_e + p\mu_h)\mathbf{E}. \tag{3.12}$$

(We have been repeating the word 'drift' because, as will be seen in the next chapter, the current may have an additional component caused by diffusion of the carriers.)

The *specific conductance* σ of the semiconductor is defined as the ratio of the magnitudes of J and E.

$$\sigma \triangleq \frac{J}{E} = q(n\mu_e + p\mu_h)\ [\Omega\text{cm}]^{-1}. \tag{3.13}$$

In the case of intentionally doped extrinsic material, one of the terms in the brackets of (3.13) is usually negligible compared to the other. In the case of an intrinsic material, where the number of electrons equals the number of holes,

$$\sigma_i = qn_i(\mu_e + \mu_h). \tag{3.14}$$

The specific conductivity varies with temperature for two main reasons. One is the dependence of the free charge carriers concentration on temperature which will be felt either at very low temperatures (when not all the impurity atoms are ionized) or at very high temperatures (when the rate of generation of thermally-created free carriers becomes very high). The second reason is the dependence of mobility on temperature already mentioned, which has less effect and determines the conductivity in the intermediate range. Figure 3.1 gives the general shape of this dependence on temperature for an

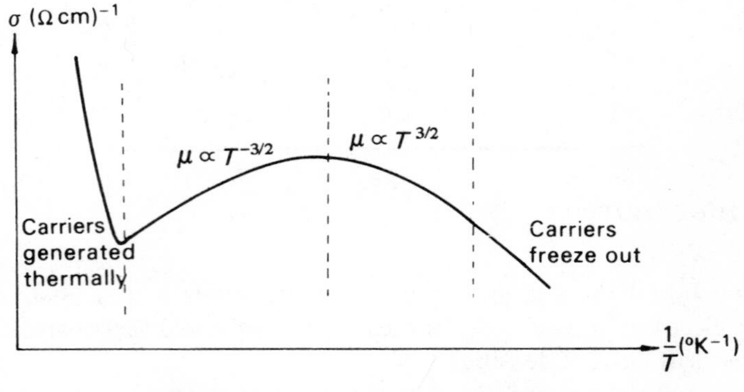

Figure 3.1. The general dependence of specific conductivity on temperature for a semiconductor with an average (10^{15}–10^{16} cm^{-3}) doping.

extrinsic semiconductor with medium doping. It should be mentioned that if the doping is high and the material degenerate, the conductivity becomes more or less constant with temperature in the low and intermediate ranges. At low temperatures this results from the ability of the extra electron or hole associated with the dopant atom to hop from one impurity atom to its very near neighbor without the necessity for thermal energy to ionize it.

The mobility obtained from conductivity measurements is called *conductivity mobility* and refers to majority carrier movement, i.e. electrons in N-type material and holes in P-type. The mobility of the minority species is usually termed *drift mobility*, and is approximately equal to the conductivity mobility for the same doping. As we shall see in Chapter 5, mobility can also be measured by a special effect, called the Hall effect, and one gets then slightly different values. Mobility so measured is termed *Hall mobility*.

QUESTIONS

3.1 A potential difference is applied between two parallel metal plates held in vacuum. An electron is put into the electric field region and starts to move. Can its mobility be calculated?

3.2 The bonding between atoms in a GaAs crystal is partially ionic. Does this introduce an additional scattering factor? If so, why?

3.3 Imagine a semiconductor in which the electron's effective mass is reduced when the applied external field is increased (and this really happens in GaAs or InP). How will this affect the resistivity of such a semiconductor?

3.4 A *compensated semiconductor* is one doped with both donors and acceptor atoms in the same concentration. In such a material $\bar{n}=\bar{p}=n_i$, as in an intrinsic material. Does its resistivity also equal that of an intrinsic undoped material? If not, why not?

PROBLEMS

3.5 Using Table 3.1, calculate the resistance at room temperature (300°K) between the contacts of the silicon chip shown in Fig. 3.2, for the following cases:

(a) the silicon is intrinsic;

(b) it is doped with donors, with $N_D = 10^{16}$ cm^{-3};

(c) it is doped with acceptors, with $N_A = 10^{16}$ cm^{-3}.

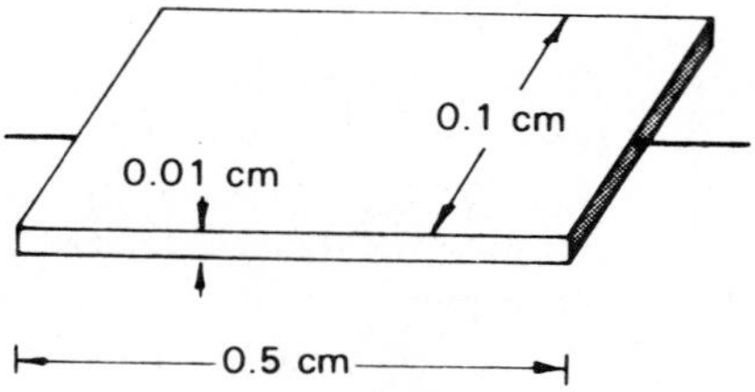

Figure 3.2.

3.6 Show that the specific conductivity will be minimized (or resistivity maximized) in a semiconductor doped slightly P-type, if $\mu_e/\mu_h = b > 1$. Find the dopant concentration N_A needed to obtain this conductivity in terms of b and recalculate the resistance of the silicon in Fig. 3.2 under these conditions.

3.7 A square silicon chip of $0.04\,\text{cm}^2$ area is made of two layers of different resistivities. The bottom layer, $150\,\mu\text{m}$ thick, is doped with 10^{18} cm^{-3} donors and the top layer, $10\,\mu\text{m}$ thick, is doped with 10^{15} cm^{-3} donors. Calculate:

(a) the resistivity, in ohm-centimeter, of each layer,
(b) the total resistance between a top and a bottom contact.

Which layer dominates the total resistance?

Hint: Use the mobility–impurity density relation given in Appendix 4.

3.8 An N-type germanium chip has a specific resistivity of 0.1 Ω cm and a thickness of 10^{-2} cm. There are contacts on the two opposite sides of the chip between which a voltage of 1 V is applied. Find

(a) The current density in the chip.
(b) The time it would take a carrier to cross the chip.
(c) Evaluate the contribution of the hole current component to the total drift current, and give your opinion as to the necessity of considering both drift current components in such cases in the future.

3.9 Assuming the average time between collision is $\tau = 10^{-12}$ s, calculate the electric field intensity which will give a free carrier top kinetic energy of 1 eV between collisions, for

(a) an electron in Si,
(b) a hole in Ge.

3.10 τ in (3.3) is also called the scattering relaxation time. Consider the change in momentum of an accelerating electron within one such relaxation time to obtain eq. (3.7) directly.

3.11 The conductivity of a certain extrinsic N-type semiconductor was measured and found to be 0.183 $(\Omega\text{cm})^{-1}$ at 300°K and 0.1 $(\Omega\text{cm})^{-1}$ at 435°K. n_i can be assumed negligible in this temperature range.

(a) What scattering mechanism dominates the mobility in this temperature range?

(b) What is the exponent of T in the mobility expression here?

(c) What conductivity do you expect to have at 400°K?

EXCESS CARRIERS, LIFETIME, DIFFUSION AND TRANSPORT PHENOMENA 4

4.1 Excess Carriers and Lifetime

The densities of carriers in the semiconductors dealt with previously were determined under thermal equilibrium conditions, i.e. with temperature uniform and equal to the surrounding ambient temperature, and with no external carrier-injecting mechanisms, such as irradiation by photons, or forces, such as electric fields, applied. We also dealt only with homogeneously doped semiconductors. Under such conditions, only the temperature, dopant density and the semiconductor material determine the carrier concentrations, which are uniform (statistically) in time and position, since there is no reason for them to vary. Equilibrium, however, can be disturbed: carrier concentrations can be increased well above the values appropriate to the temperature. When this happens we say that the semiconductor contains *excess carriers*.

Let a bar above the letter denote the equilibrium value and a circumflex the excess value. The total carrier concentrations are then

$$n = \bar{n} + \hat{n}, \qquad p = \bar{p} + \hat{p}. \tag{4.1}$$

A common method to generate excess carriers is to irradiate the semiconductor by photons with a wavelength short enough (i.e. energy high enough) to ionize the valence electrons, thereby generating electron–hole pairs. In such a case $\hat{n} = \hat{p}$. However, if the semiconductor is doped, say type N, it has many more electrons than holes, so that the relative importance of the additional excess electrons is much smaller than that of the excess minority holes. The number of these may be increased by several orders of magnitude. One can therefore expect that in any such experiment on extrinsic material the most striking effect will be the increase in minority carrier density. The total generation is the sum of the ever-present thermal generation G_{th} and the photon generation G_{ph}. In thermal equilibrium, G_{th} is balanced by the equilibrium recombination rate as given by (2.13), i.e.,

(4.2) $$\bar{R}(T) = r(T)\bar{n}\bar{p} = G_{th}(T).$$

When the semiconductor is not in equilibrium because of the light irradiation and this irradiation is suddenly stopped, some time will pass before the excess carriers recombine and the semiconductor returns to equilibrium. During that time the recombination rate, being proportional to the increased n and p, is higher than thermal generation, which is unchanged because the temperature is kept constant. The excess carriers will therefore gradually disappear.

During this period the excess of recombination over generation is

(4.3) $$\hat{R} = R - \bar{R}(T) = R - G_{th} = rnp - r\bar{n}\bar{p}.$$

Substituting n, p from (4.1), we obtain

(4.4) $$\hat{R} = r(\bar{p}\hat{n} + \hat{p}\bar{n} + \hat{p}\hat{n}).$$

For N-type extrinsic material, where $\bar{n} \simeq N_D$; $\hat{n} = \hat{p} \ll \bar{n}$, the only significant term in eq. (4.4) is the one containing $\bar{n}$:

(4.5) $$\hat{R} \simeq r\bar{n}\hat{p}.$$

(In P-type material the roles of n and p are simply reversed.) This equation shows that excess recombination is proportional to excess minority concentration.

If the light, after generating carriers for some time, is turned off at $t=0$, then the decay of excess minority carriers (here holes) during the time segment dt, t seconds later, will be

$$d\hat{p}(t) = -\hat{R}(t)\, dt = -r\bar{n}\hat{p}(t)dt.$$

Defining τ_h (with dimensions of time) as

$$\tau_h \triangleq \frac{\hat{p}(t)}{\hat{R}(t)} = \frac{1}{r\bar{n}} = \text{const.},$$

one gets

(4.6) $$\frac{d\hat{p}}{dt} = -\frac{\hat{p}}{\tau_h}.$$

The parameter τ_h is called the *excess holes lifetime*. It is very important, and controls the electronic behavior of devices such as transistors and diodes at high frequencies and during switching.

In a P-type material the same approach leads to a definition of *excess electron lifetime*, denoted τ_e. The idea of lifetime can be applied to all semiconductors, although the actual mechanism of recombination may be different in each. One can divide the semiconductors into two groups. In one, called direct band-gap semiconductors (Chapter 6 will clarify the concept) of which GaAs is one, both electron and hole have relatively low crystal momentum and they recombine radiatively, i.e., by giving off the excess energy through photon emission. In such semiconductors the lifetimes are relatively short, 10^{-9}s or less. In the second group, called indirect band-gap semiconductors and including Si and Ge, the electron has high momentum but the permitted state representing the hole has low momentum. Since momentum must be conserved upon recombination and photons carry practically no momentum, recombination occurs mainly by the electron first being trapped (i.e. becoming localized) in a recombination center, which may be a crystal defect or some special impurity such as Au or Si, and then recombining with a hole, losing its excess energy and momentum to phonons, i.e., heating the crystal. In this case the lifetime depends on the density of traps and their trapping ability (i.e. *cross section*) rather than on the number of majority carriers as in our definition. Minority lifetime, in good quality Ge, may be several milliseconds, while in Si it may reach 100 μs or more.

The solution of eq. (4.6.) is immediate:

$$\hat{p}(t)=\hat{p}(0)\exp\left(-\frac{t}{\tau_h}\right), \tag{4.7}$$

where $\hat{p}(0)$ is the excess concentration at the moment at which the light is turned off.

4.2 Diffusion of Carriers; Einstein's Relations

Electric field and drift are not the only mechanisms by which a net carrier flow in some direction can arise in a semiconductor. To understand how else this can happen let us examine a situation where only a part of the semiconductor is exposed to light, as shown in Fig. 4.1, and direct our attention to the minority carriers' behavior.

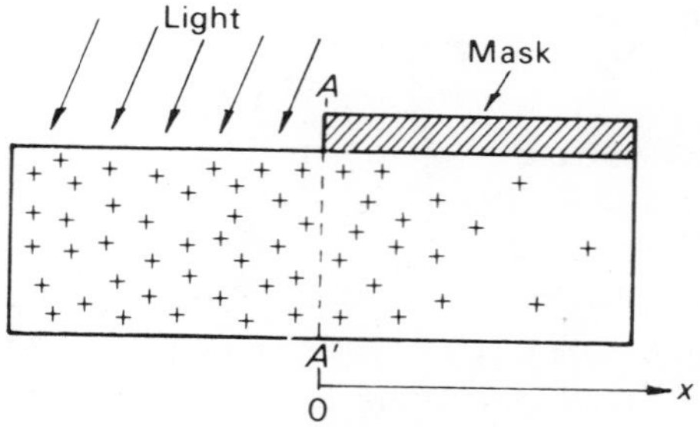

Figure 4.1. Type N semiconductor, partially exposed to light. Electrons (the majority) are not marked. Holes (the minority) are marked with +.

Left of plane AA' there are a lot of holes due to the photon generation, assumed uniform in depth. To the right of it there is no generation and their number is much smaller. The holes are moving around randomly all the time, colliding with phonons, changing direction, sometimes recombining. Referring to the x component of their movement, at each point x there are equally many holes (statistically) moving in the $+x$ and the $-x$ directions. We shall therefore have many more holes crossing the boundary plane AA' in the $+x$ direction than going the opposite way, for the simple reason that their number is much higher on the left. In other words: there is a net flow of holes crossing the boundary plane in the $+x$ direction. This flow must grow with the difference in concentrations (the gradient) on both sides. Such a flow, arising from the random thermal movement of the particles in question (holes in this case) and depending on the concentration gradient, is called *diffusion*. This is a universal phenomenon and not limited to semiconductor charge carriers.

To obtain an expression for the particle flow resulting from diffusion, let us consider a piece of semiconductor of unit cross section, in which (for the sake of simplicity) there is a concentration gradient in the x direction only, as in Fig. 4.2.

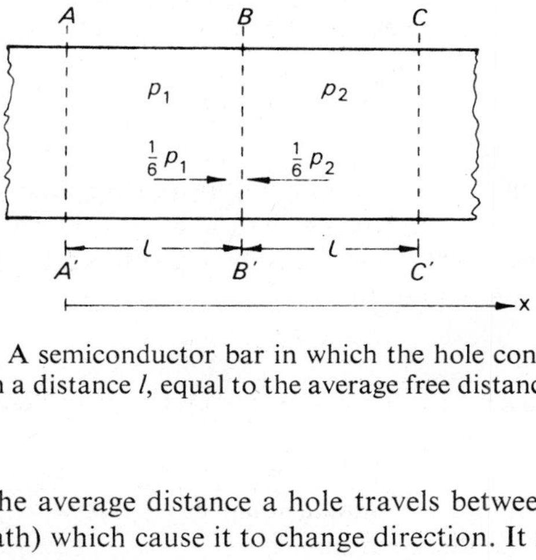

Figure 4.2. A semiconductor bar in which the hole concentration varies within a distance l, equal to the average free distance between collisions.

Let l denote the average distance a hole travels between two successive collisions (mean path) which cause it to change direction. It may therefore be assumed that the hole concentration is constant within a distance l. Let p_1 be the hole concentration between planes A and B, a distance l apart, and p_2 that between planes C and B. The number of holes in the left region moving at any time towards the right is $\frac{1}{6}p_1l$ (remember that random thermal motion is equally probable in any of the six possible directions). The number moving towards the left from the right region is similarly $\frac{1}{6}p_2l$. The average distance the hole moves is from the center of one region to the center of the second, i.e. l. Assuming an average thermal velocity v_{th}, of eq. (2.3), the net flow of holes through plane B (the number crossing per unit time) in the $+x$-direction is

$$\phi=\frac{(l/6)\,(p_1-p_2)}{l/v_{\text{th}}}=-\frac{lv_{\text{th}}}{6}\frac{p_2-p_1}{l}.$$

$(p_2-p_1)/l$ represents the concentration gradient in the x-direction and can be replaced by $\mathrm{d}p(x)/\mathrm{d}x$ while $\frac{1}{6}lv_{\text{th}}$ is called the *diffusion constant* (dimensions: $\text{cm}^2\ \text{s}^{-1}$), usually denoted by D_{h} (where the index h denotes holes). Thus

(4.8) $$\phi=-D_{\text{h}}\frac{\mathrm{d}p(x)}{\mathrm{d}x}.$$

Use of (3.8) for the mobility expression, which also involves carrier motion with free distance between collisions of $l=\tau v_{\text{th}}$ (τ, the relaxation, or mean time between collisons, is about 10^{-13} s and not to be confused with the lifetimes) yields

(4.9) $$\frac{D}{\mu}=\frac{lv_{\text{th}}/6}{q\tau/m^\star}=\frac{m^\star v_{\text{th}}^2}{6q}.$$

Actually, our use of various average values all along is not accurate. Statistical mechanics should have been applied to the statistical distribution of hole velocities. If this is done, another factor of 2 appears in the numerator. Then substituting the ratio (2.3) between kinetic energy and kT into (4.9) yields the important *Einstein's relations*:

(4.10) $$\frac{D_{\text{e,h}}}{\mu_{\text{e,h}}}=\frac{kT}{q}.$$

These relations enable one to find the diffusion constant from mobility data and vice versa for both electrons of holes.

In the more general three-dimensional case the gradient, a vector, should replace the derivative in eq. (4.8)

(4.11) $$\boldsymbol{\phi}=-D_{\text{h}}\,\nabla p.$$

The hole flow caused by diffusion results in a current density of

(4.12) $$\mathbf{J}_{\text{h}}(\text{diff})=q\boldsymbol{\phi}_{\text{h}}=-qD_{\text{h}}\,\nabla p.$$

In our more common, one-dimensional case, but with p possibly being a function of time too, this corresponds to

(4.13) $$J_{\text{h}}(\text{diff})=-qD_{\text{h}}\frac{\partial p(x,t)}{\partial x}.$$

In the similar case of electron concentration gradient, one must remember that electrical current there flows in the opposite direction to carrier flow, to yield

(4.14) $$J_{\text{e}}(\text{diff})=-q\phi_{\text{e}}=+qD_{\text{e}}\frac{\partial n(x,t)}{\partial x}.$$

4.3 The Transport and Continuity Equations; Diffusion Length

In the general case where both concentration gradients and electrical fields are present the current carried by each type of charge carrier has two components: diffusion due to concentration gradients and drift due to electric field. From (3.12), (4.13) and (4.14) these current densities are

$$J_h = q\mu_h pE - qD_h \frac{\partial p}{\partial x}, \tag{4.15}$$

$$J_e = q\mu_e nE + qD_e \frac{\partial n}{\partial x}, \tag{4.16}$$

and the total conduction current will be the sum $J = J_h + J_e$.

These current-transport equations form a starting point for semiconductor device analysis.

Returning to our diffusion case of Fig. 4.1, a question arises as to how deep the excess carriers can penetrate the covered region in Fig. 4.1 before their number is reduced back to equilibrium due to recombination.

To solve this, the continuity equation for the charge carriers must first be developed. Referring to Fig. 4.3, we examine a narrow, differential section of our unit-area semiconductor bar, between planes x and $x+dx$ in the covered region.

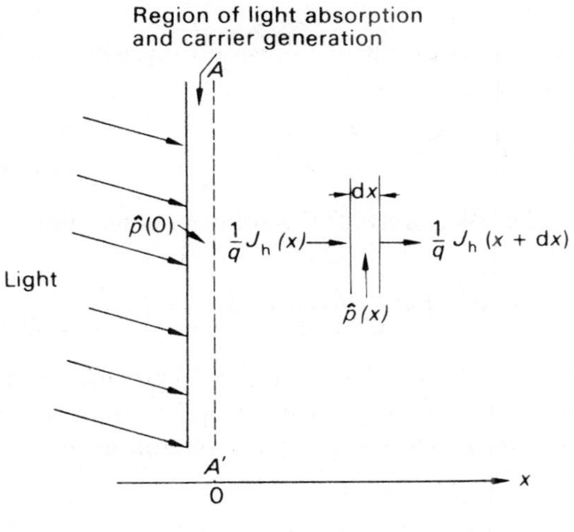

Figure 4.3. Hole flows in and out of an infinitesimal region to demonstrate the continuity equation.

Equating the time change in hole concentration there to the difference in hole flows into and out of this section, adding the thermally generated new holes and subtracting those recombining, all per unit time, will get us the continuity equation:

$$\frac{\partial p}{\partial t} \bullet 1 \bullet \mathrm{d}x = 1 \bullet \left[\frac{1}{q} J_{\mathrm{h}}(x,t) - \frac{1}{q} J_{\mathrm{h}}(x+\mathrm{d}x,t)\right] + 1 \bullet \mathrm{d}x\left(G_{\mathrm{th}} - \frac{p}{\tau_{\mathrm{h}}}\right)$$

(For a unit area, $1 \bullet \mathrm{d}x$ is the volume of our section).

From equilibrium we know that $G_{\mathrm{th}} = \bar{p}/\tau_{\mathrm{h}}$, where $\bar{p}$ is the time-independent equilibrium hole concentration. Substituting this and $p = \hat{p} + \bar{p}$ into our equation and dividing throughout by $\mathrm{d}x$ yields

(4.17)
$$\frac{\partial \hat{p}(x,t)}{\partial t} = -\frac{1}{q}\frac{\partial J_{\mathrm{h}}(x,t)}{\partial x} - \frac{\hat{p}(x,t)}{\tau_{\mathrm{h}}}.$$

Similarly for electrons:

(4.18)
$$\frac{\partial \hat{n}(x,t)}{\partial t} = +\frac{1}{q}\frac{\partial J_{\mathrm{e}}(x,t)}{\partial x} - \frac{\hat{n}(x,t)}{\tau_{\mathrm{e}}}.$$

If there is any additional carrier generating mechanism (besides thermal) in our infinitesimal section, it should also be added on the right-hand side of our continuity equations.

Let us now restrict our attention to the static, time-independent, field-free situation of Fig. 4.1. The concentration in the covered region at a depth x will be governed by eq. (4.17), which is then reduced to

(4.19)
$$-\frac{1}{q}\frac{\mathrm{d}J_{\mathrm{h}}}{\mathrm{d}x} - \frac{\hat{p}}{\tau_{\mathrm{h}}} = 0.$$

Current in our case is the result of diffusion only, since no electric field is applied. Substituting J_{h} from (4.13):

(4.20)
$$\frac{\mathrm{d}^2\hat{p}}{\mathrm{d}x^2} - \frac{\hat{p}}{\tau_{\mathrm{h}} D_{\mathrm{h}}} = 0.$$

This equation can be easily solved, the solution containing two integration constants:

(4.21)
$$\hat{p}(x) = c_1 \exp\left(-\frac{x}{\sqrt{(\tau_{\mathrm{h}} D_{\mathrm{h}})}}\right) + c_2 \exp\left(+\frac{x}{\sqrt{(\tau_{\mathrm{h}} D_{\mathrm{h}})}}\right).$$

The first boundary condition is that at large x, $\hat{p}(x)$ must become zero due to recombination. This makes $c_2 = 0$. The second is that at $x = 0$ the excess concentration is $c_1 = \hat{p}(0)$, determined by the photon generation in the irradiated region. Therefore:

(4.22)
$$\hat{p}(x) = \hat{p}(0) \exp\left(-\frac{x}{\sqrt{(\tau_{\mathrm{h}} D_{\mathrm{h}})}}\right).$$

The quantity $\sqrt{(\tau_h D_h)}$ has the dimensions of distance and is called the *diffusion length* for holes:

(4.23) $$L_h \triangleq \sqrt{(\tau_h D_h)}.$$

The excess hole concentration drops to e^{-1} times its initial value at a distance of L_h and is practically back to equilibrium after three or four diffusion lengths. A diffusion length for electrons, L_e, is similarly defined.

4.4 Internal Field in a Semiconductor with a Nonuniform Doping

So far we have considered only semiconductors whose impurity doping density is uniform everywhere. Let us now examine a case where there is a concentration gradient of the dopant along the x axis.

If the outside current circuit is left open, then we must have

(4.24) $$J = J_e + J_h = 0.$$

If the semiconductor is also in thermodynamic equilibrium, then also the current of each individual carrier type must be zero (the law of detailed balance):

(4.25) $$J_e = J_h = 0.$$

Substituting (4.15) and (4.16) into (4.25), we then find that in the case of a nonuniform semiconductor at equilibrium, an internal 'built-in' electric field must exist:

$$E = \frac{D_h}{\mu_h} \frac{1}{\bar{p}} \frac{d\bar{p}}{dx} = -\frac{D_e}{\mu_e} \frac{1}{\bar{n}} \frac{d\bar{n}}{dx}.$$

One should note that it is the same field, irrespective of whether $\bar{n}$ or $\bar{p}$ is used to find it.

Using Einstein's relations (4.10),

(4.26) $$E = \frac{kT}{q} \frac{1}{\bar{p}} \frac{d\bar{p}}{dx} = -\frac{kT}{q} \frac{1}{\bar{n}} \frac{d\bar{n}}{dx}.$$

The physical reasons for this internal field, dependent on carrier gradients, are as follows. Assume the dopant concentration, say that of donors, decreases with x. The free electrons contributed by the donors tend to diffuse towards the lower concentration, i.e. in the $+x$ direction. The donors, which are positively ionized, cannot move from their lattice positions. Consequently, a net positive charge will be created on the left, equal to $q[N_D(x) - \bar{n}(x)]$, while on the right, there are now more electrons than donors and the net charge will be negative, so that a field will arise. The diffusion and the field cause two opposing currents and equilibrium is reached when the two effects just balance each other.

For actual calculations based on (4.26) one can assume $\bar{n} \simeq N_D(x)$ (or $\bar{p} \simeq N_A(x)$), because the disturbance in charge neutrality needed to support the field is slight. Exact calculations entail the solution of (4.26) and Poisson's equation simultaneously by numerical means. As we shall learn, such built-in fields are intentionally incorporated in modern transistors in order to increase their frequency range.

QUESTIONS

4.1 A piece of semiconductor is irradiated by light pulses. How does its resistivity change if the time between pulses is short compared to the carrier lifetime? If it is long compared to it?

4.2 Will the light effects on resistivity be intensified or reduced if the temperature is increased?

4.3 Suggest experiments for showing diffusion phenomena (a) in gases, and (b) in liquids.

4.4 Can you explain qualitatively why the ratio D/μ increases with temperature?

4.5 What is the form of the continuity equation for atoms of one substance diffusing through another material?

4.6 Add y and z axes in Fig. 4.1. Is there diffusion in these directions under our assumption of uniform generation caused by photons, independent of depth left of plane AA'?

PROBLEMS

4.7 A piece of Ge with a donor concentration of 10^{17}cm^{-3} is irradiated continuously by photons, of sufficient energy to ionize it. The Ge is kept at room temperature. Given that the generation due to photons is uniform at

10^{12} cm^{-3} s^{-1}, find the excess carrier concentrations and the relative change in each type caused by the light, for $\tau_e = \tau_h = 2$ ms.

4.8 The energy necessary to ionize and free a valence electron in Si is 1.1 eV. What is the maximum wavelength of light that can generate carriers in it? What is it for InSb for which the necessary energy is 0.23 eV?

4.9 The light in Problem 4.7 is turned off at $t = t_0$. Plot the change in hole concentration in the Ge as a function of time for $t > t_0$. When will this concentration reduce to 5% of its initial value?

4.10 Given that the lifetime of electrons in some P-type Si is 10 μs and their mobility is 1000 cm^2 V^{-1} s^{-1}, find the diffusion constant and the diffusion length at room temperature, and verify that the dimensions of J_e in eq. (4.14) are indeed those of current density.

4.11 Given $N_A(x)$ in a piece of semiconductor, write down an exact single differential equation for obtaining $\bar{p}(x)$, $\bar{n}(x)$ at thermodynamic equilibrium.

4.12 In a given piece of P-type Si at room temperature, the acceptor concentration depends exponentially on x according to

$$N_A(x) = N_0 \exp(-x/x_0),$$

where $x_0 = 0.5$ μm. Assuming that $\bar{p}(x) = N_A(x)$,

(a) find an expression for the built-in field. Is it dependent on position in this case?

(b) calculate E and the two hole–current density components if

$D_h = 10$ cm^2 s^{-1} and $\mu_h = 400$ cm^2 V^{-1} s^{-1}.

MEASURING THE ELECTRICAL PARAMETERS OF A SEMICONDUCTOR 5

The basic electrical semiconductor parameters of main interest are as follows:

(a) the conductivity σ (or resistivity $\rho = 1/\sigma$)
(b) the majority carrier concentration
(c) the type (N or P)
(d) the mobility
(e) the diffusion constant
(f) the lifetime.

In this chapter several laboratory techniques for measuring those parameters will be described.

5.1 The Resistivity

This measurement is the simplest to understand, though not necessarily to perform. It can be done by making four metal contacts to the semiconductor, as shown in principle in Fig. 5.1(a).

The two outside contacts are used to pass a known current I (supplied by a current source) while the two inner ones are used to measure the ensuing voltage V, using a voltmeter with a high input impedance compared to the measured value. In this way the metal–semiconductor contact resistance, which may be high, nonlinear and dependent on current direction, does not affect the results: The contact resistances at points A, B of Fig. 5.1(a) are immaterial, since they do not control the constant current forced through them, while the voltage developed across them is not measured anyway. The contact resistance at C and D is also unimportant because the high input impedance voltmeter draws negligible current. From the figure,

$$V=\rho \frac{L}{Wd} I;$$

therefore

$$\rho=\frac{Wd}{L}\frac{V}{I}. \tag{5.1}$$

The voltage-measuring contacts should be as narrow as possible in the current direction since they short out the semiconductor region over which they lie. The current contacts on the two sides should be uniform to insure uniform current density.

A more practical, simpler way of getting the same results is by using a commercially obtainable probe, which has a head with four springy metal points, arranged in a line, usually less than 1 mm apart, as in Fig. 5.1(b). When the probe is lowered onto the semiconductor surface, the two outside points are used for passing the constant current while the two inner ones are used for the voltage measurement. The current density in this case is not uniform but if the proper current-flow field problem is solved, one finds that for a semiconductor wafer with thickness d much bigger than the distance s between points, and for a measurement performed far enough from the edge of the wafer, the resistivity is given by

$$\rho=2\pi s \frac{V}{I} \quad (\Omega\text{cm}), \qquad (s \ll d).$$

If the thickness d of the wafer or of the measured semiconductor layer is much less than s, then:

$$\rho=\frac{\pi}{\ln 2}\frac{V}{I} d=4.53 \frac{V}{I} d \quad (\Omega\text{cm}), \qquad (s \gg d).$$

In between these two extremes a correction factor is needed.

This method is especially useful for very thin semiconductor layers, such as are obtained when dopant atoms of one type of impurity are allowed to diffuse from the surrounding ambient into a semiconductor already doped with the opposite type of impurity (a basic process in modern transistor technology). After about an hour of diffusion at high temperature, a thin layer on the semiconductor surface changes type because the density of the new impurity there exceeds that of the original. The diffused impurity density, however, is not uniform in depth. Instead of average resistivity we then prefer

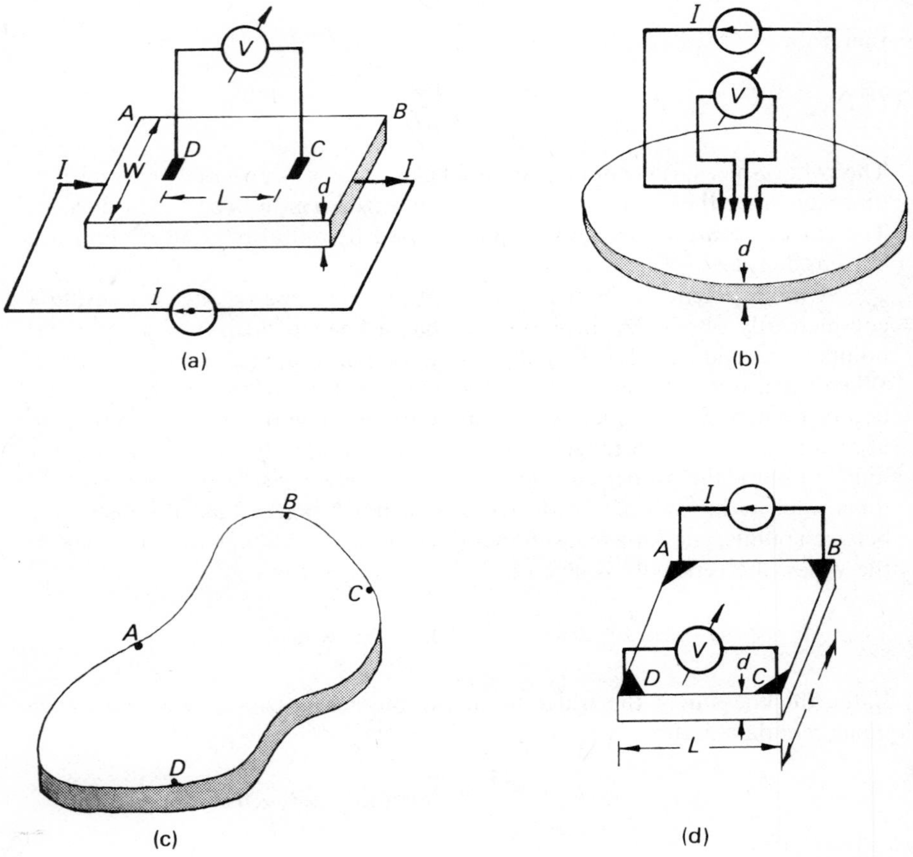

Figure 5.1. Methods for measuring resistivity: (a) the four-contact method; (b) the four-points probe; (c) the Van der Pauw method; (d) a symmetrical sample for Van der Pauw's method.

to speak of the layer *sheet resistivity* R_S, measured in 'ohms per square', defined as the resistance of an arbitrary size square of that layer:

(5.2) $$R_S = \frac{\rho}{d} = 4.53 \frac{V}{I} \quad (\Omega/\square).$$

Such diffused layers are used to form resistors in integrated circuits. If a resistor of R (Ω) is required, one gives the diffused layer the surface geometry of a rectangle, of length L and width W, so chosen that

$$R = R_S \frac{L}{W} \ (\Omega).$$

A second method, known as Van der Pauw's method, enables one to measure ρ of a semiconductor wafer of thickness d, and an arbitrary shape, like in Fig. 5.1(c). Four small contacts, A, B, C, D arranged along the periphery, are used to pass current and measure voltage as before.

If by $R_{AB,CD}$ one denotes the ratio of the voltage V_{CD} measured between contacts C and D, to the current I_{AB} flowing between A and B, then Van der Pauw has shown that

$$\exp\left(-\frac{\pi d}{\rho} R_{AB,CD}\right) + \exp\left(-\frac{\pi d}{\rho} R_{BC,DA}\right) = 1. \tag{5.3}$$

If the contacted wafer is completely symmetrical, like a circle or the square in Fig. 5.1(d), this equation yields ρ explicitly:

$$\rho = \frac{\pi d}{\ln 2} \frac{V_{CD}}{I_{AB}}. \tag{5.4}$$

5.2 Majority Carrier Concentration, Type and Mobility by the Hall Effect

The Hall effect, discovered in 1874 by E. H. Hall, is an often used experimental tool to measure the mobile carrier density, together with the sign of their charge. If the conductivity is known, one can also calculate the mobility.

The Hall effect results from the force **F**, with which a magnetic field **B** (W m^{-2}) acts on a current density **J**, according to the vector product:

$$\mathbf{F} = \mathbf{J} \times \mathbf{B} \tag{5.5}$$

If **J** and **B** are perpendicular, as in Fig. 5.2, then **F**, **J**, **B** form a right-handed Cartesian coordinate system and the direction of the force is as marked in the figure.

This force acts on the charge carriers, which happen to be electrons here, moving at a drift velocity **v**, opposite to the conventional current direction. Equation (5.5) shows, however, that the force depends on the current **J** and *not* on the type of carriers, so it will remain in the same direction, pushing the carriers towards the back, even if the N-type semiconductor is replaced by a

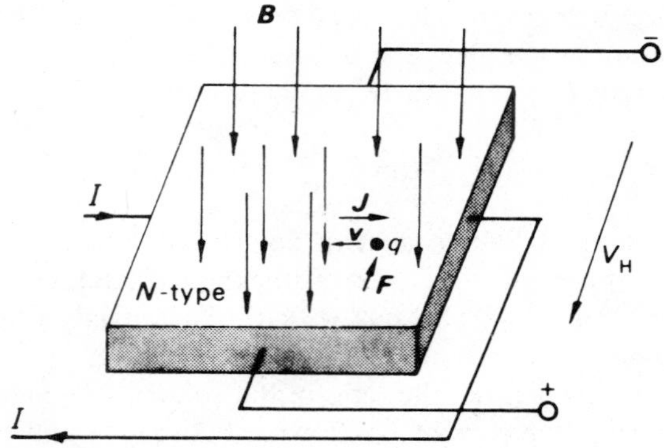

Figure 5.2. The Hall effect. An N-type semiconductor with current density **J** in a normal magnetic field **B**. A force **F** acts on an electron q carrying the current.

P-type, with hole carriers moving in the same direction as the current. When the mobile carriers are pushed towards the back, the front becomes depleted and the semiconductor loses its local neutrality. There is now an excess of the mobile type of charge at the back and an excess of the opposite ionized impurity charge at the front. In the case of Fig. 5.2, the electrons, pushed to the back, will make the back contact negative with respect to the front contact, which will be made positive. This gives rise to a measurable voltage V_H, called the *Hall voltage*. For a P-type semiconductor the polarity of V_H is in the reverse direction. This method also provides an experimental demonstration of the existence of holes.

The value of the Hall voltage will be determined by the balance that must be reached between the forces that the transverse electric field E_H, related to V_H, and the magnetic field **B** exert on the carriers. They exactly oppose each other and their vector sum must be zero.

For **J** normal to **B** one can dispense with the vector product sign and consider magnitudes only:

$$F\,(\text{magnetic}) + F\,(\text{electric}) = 0,$$

or

$$JB + nqE_H = 0$$

(5.6)
$$E_H = -\frac{1}{nq}JB.$$

The Hall coefficient, R_H, is defined as

(5.7)
$$R_H \triangleq \frac{E_H}{JB}.$$

Therefore for electrons

$$R_H = -\frac{1}{nq}. \tag{5.8}$$

While for holes, where the electrical force F(electric) is in the opposite direction,

$$R_H = +\frac{1}{pq}. \tag{5.9}$$

Actually, the drift velocity of the carriers, responsible for the magnetic force, is not a constant but a statistical average as seen in Chapter 3. Also there are sometimes nonlinear effects dependent on the value of $|\mathbf{B}|$. Consequently, a correction factor r_H (usually between 1 and 1.5, sometimes as small as 0.5), called the *Hall coefficient factor* should be added to the magnetic force equation making

$$R_H = -\frac{r_H}{nq} \quad \text{or} \quad R_H = +\frac{r_H}{pq}. \tag{5.10}$$

For our purposes r_H can be assumed to be about 1.

Measurement of R_H, the Hall coefficient, gives us the carrier concentration directly. It can be measured at any desired temperature and, if that is low enough for some of the impurities not to be ionized, it tells us the fraction that is (by comparison with its value at higher temperatures when all impurities are ionized). Also, in defective crystals full of dislocations, a sizable fraction of the impurities may not be ionized because they are located at grain boundaries or dislocations and not at proper lattice sites. Then R_H yields the active fraction only. Hall measurements can be made highly sensitive, enough to sense concentrations as low as $10^{12}(\text{cm}^{-3})$.

For semiconductor materials that contain both electrons and holes at about the same concentrations, i.e. approximately intrinsic, the Hall voltage caused by one is cancelled by the other; the net result is a function of both concentrations and mobilities and may even be zero.

From the definition of the conductivity of an extrinsic semiconductor,

$$\mu_h = \frac{\sigma}{q\bar{p}} \quad \text{or} \quad \mu_e = \frac{\sigma}{q\bar{n}}. \tag{5.11}$$

Comparing with (5.8) and (5.9) we see that mobilities can be found from the Hall coefficient and conductivity:

$$\mu_{e,h} = \sigma \, |R_H|_{e,h}. \tag{5.12}$$

Mobility measured in this way is called *Hall mobility*, while that found directly from σ, $\bar{n}$ or $\bar{p}$ or from the Haynes–Shockley experiment, to be described in Section 5.4, is called *conductivity mobility*. The ratio of the two is the Hall coefficient factor r_H of eq. (5.10) which, as mentioned, may be slightly different from 1.

To make a Hall measurement, the sample is prepared in a bridge form as in Fig. 5.3(a). The d.c. current is fed via contacts A and B and the Hall voltage is measured between C and D, or E and F (or both with an average taken). The same sample may be used for conductivity measurement too.

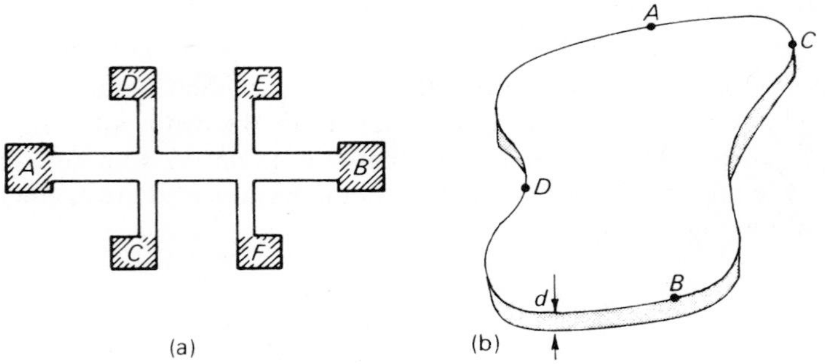

Figure 5.3. Semiconductor samples for Hall and conductivity measurements: (a) using a bridge form; (b) using an arbitrary form by Van der Pauw's method.

A sample of an arbitrary form may also be used. Van der Pauw has shown that application of a perpendicular magnetic field would result in a change in $R_{AB,CD}$, defined as in (5.3), compared to its zero magnetic field value and

$$\mu_H = \frac{\sigma d}{B} \Delta R_{AB,CD}. \tag{5.13}$$

Note (Fig. 5.3(b)) that here current is applied and voltage measured at diagonally opposite pairs of contacts.

The Hall effect has many uses today, besides measurement of semiconductor parameters. The vector product property, for example, may be utilized for angular position sensing; the ability to sense *static* magnetic fields by a tiny device is exploited in mapping magnetic fields in cramped spaces.

Hall devices for such uses are usually made from N-type InSb which, as Table 3.1 tells us, has a very high electronic mobility, and therefore high R_H and high sensitivity.

5.3 Carrier Type by the Hot Probe Method

This is a simple, frequently used method, unencumbered by the necessity for the preparation of a special sample.

One simply touches the unknown semiconductor surface by two identical metal probes, between which a galvanometer is connected as in Fig. 5.4(a). One of the probes is heated while the other is at room temperature. The hot probe heats the semiconductor immediately under it, with a consequent rise in the kinetic energy of the free carriers there. These then move with higher thermal velocities than their cooler neighbors. The carriers therefore diffuse out of the hot region faster than their slower neighors can diffuse back into it from the vicinity. This results in the hot region becoming slightly depleted of majority carriers and acquiring the potential of the ionized impurities there, while the vicinity of the cold probe remains neutral. Current will therefore flow in the galvanometer, the direction of which depends on the sign of the charge of the ionized impurity. Thus, on an N-type semiconductor, the hot probe is the more positive one, while on a P-type it is the more negative. The cold probe polarity therefore indicates the type.

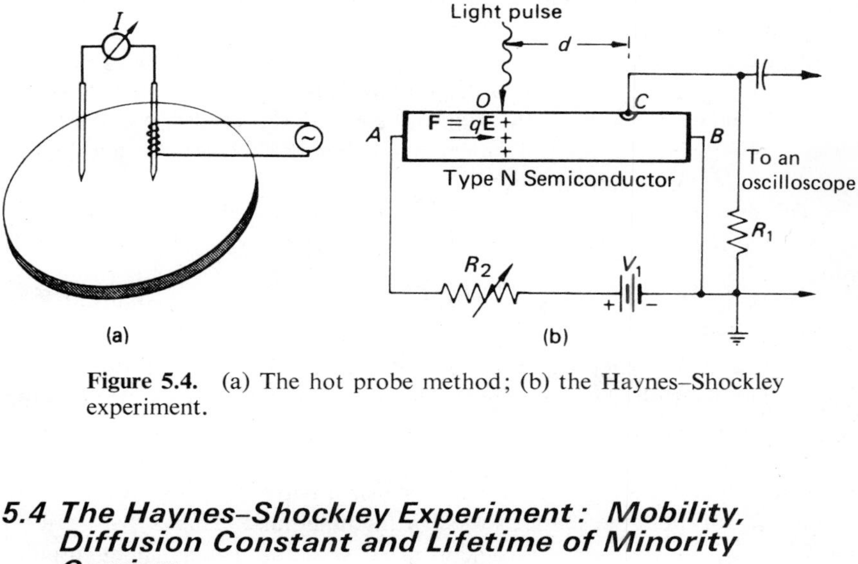

Figure 5.4. (a) The hot probe method; (b) the Haynes–Shockley experiment.

5.4 The Haynes–Shockley Experiment: Mobility, Diffusion Constant and Lifetime of Minority Carriers

The mobility of the minority carriers, the diffusion constant and the lifetime were measured together in a classical experiment, performed in 1949 by Haynes and Shockley. The experiment is very illuminating. The set-up is as in Fig. 5.4(b): A semiconductor bar of a constant cross section (Haynes and Shockley used N-type Ge) with three contacts, is mounted on a holder. Contacts A and B are ohmic, i.e. they have low contact resistance that is independent of current polarity and magnitude and the equilibrium near them is not disturbed. Those contacts are used for passing current and creating a known electric field E in the semiconductor. The field may be controlled by varying R_2. Contact C is not ohmic. It is made by converting a small spot of the semiconductor there to the opposite type, i.e. to P-type in our case, and making a metal contact to it. The boundary between the N- and P-regions is called a *PN junction* and we shall deal with it in detail in Chapters 8 and 9. For the purpose of this experiment it suffices to know only one property of the PN junction: when the P region is biased negative with respect to the N region, (called reverse bias), then majority carriers on both sides cannot cross it. However, minority carriers that happen to move near the junction are swept across. Since their number is normally very small, the current through C and R_1 is negligible and C is practically at ground potential (the N region just under the junction is biased positive by the main current between A and B so the junction is indeed reverse biased). But if additional minority carriers, say a bunch of holes, pass under C, many of them will be collected by it, with a resulting jump in the current through C and R_1, across which a voltage pulse will form. This pulse is measurable by the oscilloscope.

If now a strong and narrow light impulse hits the semiconductor surface at point O, it generates there a corresponding impulse of excess electrons and holes. The relative change in the majority electron density is very small and the bar resistance is practically unchanged, but the relative change in the minority hole population is very large.

This pulse of excess holes is marked in the figure. The holes do not stay at O because the field E in the semiconductor pushes them with a force F towards contact B.

The holes drift at a velocity determined by E and their mobility. While the hole impulse moves to the right its shape changes. From being sharp and narrow it becomes progressively lower and wider, as the holes diffuse to both sides (where their number is smaller). The total number of excess holes in the pulse is also decreasing because of recombination. When the remaining holes drift under the collecting junction C, those which are nearest are swept across (because they are minority carriers) and cause a corresponding current pulse through R_1, of the same shape as the drifting hole pulse. This is then seen on the scope, whose time scale is synchronized with the original light impulse and so measures the drift time of the hole pulse from point O to point C. This time is a direct measure of the hole mobility. The widened pulse shape is a measure of the diffusion constant and the pulse area or height measure the number of remaining excess holes. By controlling E and so the drift time, this number is changed, and the lifetime can be computed from this change.

The light impulses can be applied periodically, with a period longer than the drift time from O to C, and by synchronizing them with the scope x-deflection one obtains wave forms which look like Figs. 5.5(b) and (c), each taken for a different drift field E. In Fig. 5.5(a) the newly created hole impulse is shown. This cannot be seen on the scope unless points O and C coincide.

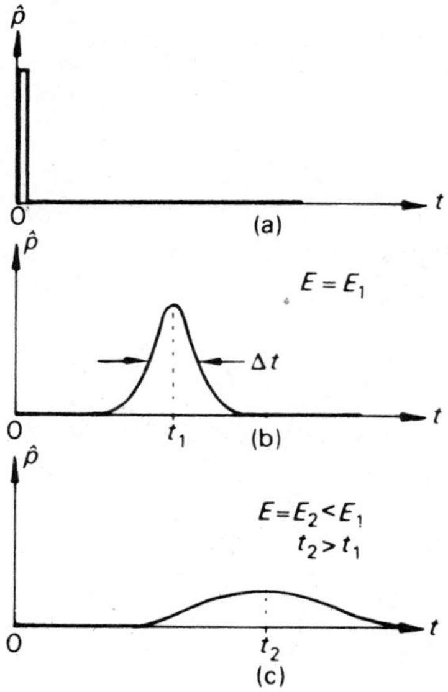

Figure 5.5. The excess holes current pulse as seen on an oscilloscope: (a) as created, with points O and C coinciding; (b) at its collection at C a distance d away and an average drift time t_1 later; (c) at its collection at C, an average drift time $t_2>t_1$ later.

Having understood the ideas behind the experiment, we can proceed with the quantitative interpretation of the measurements. To obtain the hole pulse shape we must solve the hole continuity equation (4.17) substituting J_h in it from the hole transport equation (4.15). Let us do it by stages starting from a simplified situation.

First, consider the expected shape of the hole pulse with zero field, $E=0$, in the semiconductor. The pulse then stays at O, its center unmoving but its shape widening because of diffusion. J_h is then reduced to $J_h=-qD_h\,\partial p(x,t)/\partial x$, the result of diffusion only. Next, let us assume for the moment that there is no recombination (i.e. $\tau_h=\infty$) which simplifies the form of (4.17). Substituting J_h in it, yields (x is measured from the pulse center at O):

$$\frac{\partial \hat{p}(x,t)}{\partial t}=D_h\frac{\partial^2\hat{p}(x,t)}{\partial x^2}, \tag{5.14}$$

This partial differential equation, known as the diffusion equation, must be solved together with the boundary condition which states that the total number of holes is constant (remember: no recombination):

$$\int_{-\infty}^{\infty}\hat{p}(x,t)\,\mathrm{d}x=\hat{p}_0.$$

$\hat{p}(x,t)$ is symmetric, since diffusion does not depend on direction. This condition can, therefore, be written as:

(5.15) $$\int_0^\infty \hat{p}(x,t)dx = \frac{\hat{p}_0}{2}.$$

Applying the Laplace transform to (5.14) turns it into an ordinary differential equation for the transform $P(x,s)$, i.e., $sP = D_h d^2P/dx^2$. The general solution is

$$P(x,s) = C_1 \exp(-\sqrt{\frac{s}{D_h}}x) + C_2 \exp(+\sqrt{\frac{s}{D_h}}x).$$

However, $C_2 = 0$ because P must go to zero for $x \to \infty$.

Transforming the boundary condition (5.15) and substituting our solution in it yields:

$$\frac{p_0}{2s} = \int_0^\infty P(x,s)dx = C_1\sqrt{\frac{D_h}{s}} \text{ or } C_1 = \frac{p_0}{2\sqrt{D_h s}}$$

Our solution is therefore

$$P(x,s) = \frac{p_0}{2\sqrt{D_h s}} \exp(-\sqrt{\frac{s}{D_h}}x).$$

Using transform tables, the inverse transform of $P(x,s)$ in the time domain is found to be

(5.16) $$\hat{p}(x,t) = \frac{\hat{p}_0}{2\sqrt{(\pi D_h t)}} \exp\left(-\frac{x^2}{4D_h t}\right).$$

This is the Gaussian curve, shown schematically in Fig. 5.6 for a constant t and variable x.

When recombination is taken into account, the total number of excess holes should decrease in time as $\exp(-t/\tau_h)$, according to (4.7). From (5.15) we see that this would be the case if $\hat{p}(x,t)$ were multiplied by this factor. The solution with recombination is therefore

(5.17) $$\hat{p}(x,t) = \frac{\hat{p}_0}{2\sqrt{(\pi D_h t)}} \exp\left(-\frac{x^2}{4D_h t} - \frac{t}{\tau_h}\right).$$

This is the solution with no field in the semiconductor. When there is a field E the hole pulse travels towards the negative contact B with a drift velocity $v = \mu_h E$, passing on its way under the collector C, a distance d away, and causing a current pulse in R_1. The drift time is equal to the delay t_1 between the light impulse striking at O and the arrival of the pulse maximum at C, as measured on the scope wave form of Fig. 5.5(b):

$$t_1 = \frac{d}{v} = \frac{d}{\mu_h E},$$

from which the mobility is immediately obtainable:

$$\mu_h = \frac{d}{t_1 E}. \tag{5.18}$$

The hole pulse shape, with the drift included, should be written as

$$\hat{p}(x,t) = \frac{\hat{p}_0}{2\sqrt{(\pi D_h t)}} \exp\left(-\frac{(x-vt)^2}{4D_h t} - \frac{t}{\tau_h}\right),$$

but it takes only a very short time for the complete pulse to drift past the collector C and during this time its shape changes only a little, especially if this time is short compared to t_1. Therefore, with no great error, one can assume the pulse shape is fixed while passing under C in the form given by $\hat{p}(x,t_1)$.

For the diffusion constant measurement, only the shape of the pulse, and not the fact that the pulse is drifting, is important. Substituting $x' = x - vt$ and $t = t_1$ in the last equation gives us a new coordinate x' with its origin always located at the pulse center. The pulse is now given by

$$\hat{p}(x', t_1) = \frac{\hat{p}_0}{2\sqrt{(\pi D_h t_1)}} \exp\left(-\frac{x'^2}{4D_h t_1} - \frac{t_1}{\tau_h}\right). \tag{5.19}$$

The scope time scale can be used to measure the width Δt between two points on the pulse at which its height is half the maximum (Fig. 5.5(b)). This width then measures the time it takes for the central portion of the pulse, between points $x' = \pm\delta$ in Fig. 5.6, to drift past C.

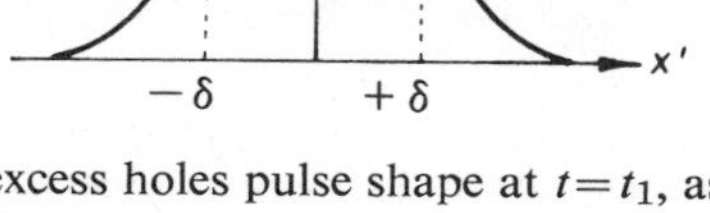

Figure 5.6. The excess holes pulse shape at $t = t_1$, as a function of $x' = x - vt_1$.

δ is obtained by equating the only term in (5.19) which is dependent on x' to $\frac{1}{2}$ at $x' = \pm\delta$:

$$\exp\left(-\frac{\delta^2}{4D_h t_1}\right) = \frac{1}{2}$$

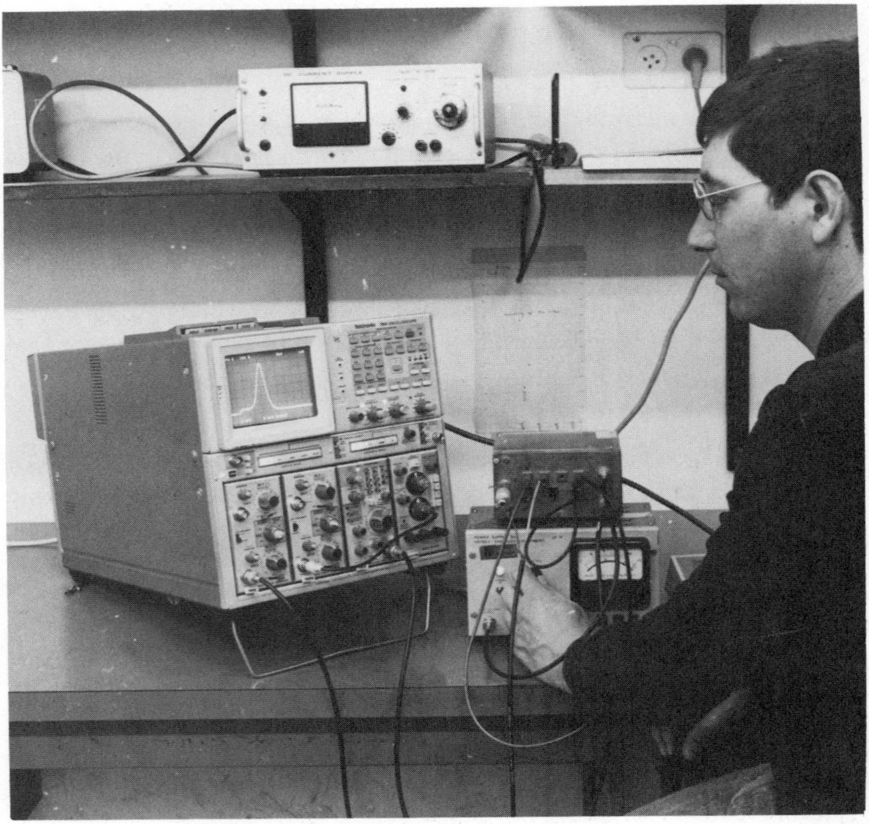

Performing the Haynes–Shockley experiment on a silicon sample. The Microelectronics Laboratory, Technion IIT, Haifa, Israel.

or

$$\delta^2 = 4 D_h t_1 \ln 2. \tag{5.20}$$

The measured Δt is related to δ by

$$\Delta t = \frac{2\delta}{v}. \tag{5.21}$$

Substituting for δ from this, using $v = \mu_h E = d/t_1$ and separating D_h out, we obtain

$$D_h = \frac{(d\ \Delta t)^2}{(16 \ln 2) t_1^3} = \frac{(d\ \Delta t)^2}{11.1 t_1^3}. \tag{5.22}$$

With d measured by a micrometer, E found from the voltage across the semiconductor bar and its length (or from current density and resistivity), t_1 and Δt measured on the scope, one can calculate both μ_h and D_h. Einstein's relation (4.10) can be demonstrated by this experiment.

The lifetime τ_h can be found from the change in the pulse area (proportional to the number of remaining excess holes at $t \simeq t_1$) when t_1 is changed (by changing E or d).

This is easily seen since the area S is the integral of $\hat{p}(x', t)$, given by (5.19), on x':

$$S = \frac{\hat{p}_0}{2\sqrt{(\pi D_h t_1)}} \exp\left(-\frac{t_1}{\tau_h}\right) \int_{-\infty}^{\infty} \exp\left(-\frac{x'^2}{4 D_h t_1}\right) dx' = \hat{p}_0 \exp\left(-\frac{t_1}{\tau_h}\right), \tag{5.23}$$

or

$$\ln S = \ln \hat{p}_0 - \frac{t_1}{\tau_h}. \tag{5.24}$$

A graph of ln S against t_1 on a semilogarithmic scale has a slope of $-1/\tau_h$, independent of any proportionality constant relating S and p_0. This method is also usable when the pulse shape is distorted because of trapping. Some crystals include traps which are characterized by their ability to trap, i.e. localize, free carriers, some of which then recombine, and others are released again with the help of thermal energy. Those carriers first subtract from the front of the pulse and then add to its tail, thereby distorting its shape. If there is no trapping and the pulse shape is indeed Gaussian, one can get τ_h just by comparing two pulse heights H_1, H_2 for two corresponding drift times t_1 and t_2. It can be easily shown (Problem 5.12) that

$$\tau_h = \frac{t_2 - t_1}{\ln (H_1/H_2) - \frac{1}{2} \ln (t_2/t_1)}. \tag{5.25}$$

More extensive and detailed information about modern semiconductor measuring techniques can be found in Reference 4.

QUESTIONS

5.1 Can one rely on the four-point probe resistivity method when the semiconductor layer under test lies on top of a metal substrate? of an insulator substrate?

5.2 What do you expect to get from a hot probe test if the semiconductor under test is intrinsic or nearly so?

5.3 A Haynes–Shockley experiment was set up exactly as in Fig. 5.4(b) but with a P-type semiconductor. However, no minority carrier pulse appeared on the scope. Why? What changes should be made in the set-up to obtain it?

5.4 In a Haynes–Shockley experiment, the semiconductor under test has a limited density of minority carrier traps characterized by an average trapping time, after which most of the trapped carriers are released again.

Draw the expected pulse shape on the scope for two cases:

(a) The trapping time is long compared to the drift time t_1,

(b) The trapping time is about half the drift time t_1. Assume the total number of traps is lower than the number of excess carriers and that only one carrier can be in a trap at the same time.

5.5 Is it important that only ratios and not absolute values of pulse heights or areas are needed to interpret the Haynes–Shockley experiment?

5.6 A Hall measurement is done on a bridge sample like the one shown in Fig. 5.3(a). However, a small voltage reading might be obtained between contacts C and D even without a magnetic field. Suggest an experimental procedure that overcomes this possible source of error.

PROBLEMS

5.7 A Ge sample, doped to 10^{17}cm^{-3} and of 0.1×0.2cm cross section, is used in a Hall experiment. Find the Hall voltage that would be measured between the two side contacts (0.2 cm apart) if a current of 0.6 A flows in the long direction and a normal magnetic field of 5000 gauss is applied (1 G$=10^{-4}$ W m^{-2}).

5.8 A Hall measurement was done on the Si sample shown in Fig. 5.7. The following data were obtained:

$l=1.0$ cm	$I=5$ mA	$V=0.245$ V
$d=0.1$ cm	$B=1$ W m^{-2}	$V_H=2.0$ mV
$b=0.2$ cm		

The Hall coefficient factor is known and equal to 1.18. Find:
(a) the conductivity type,
(b) the majority concentration,
(c) the Hall mobility,
(d) the conductivity mobility,
(e) the diffusion constant.

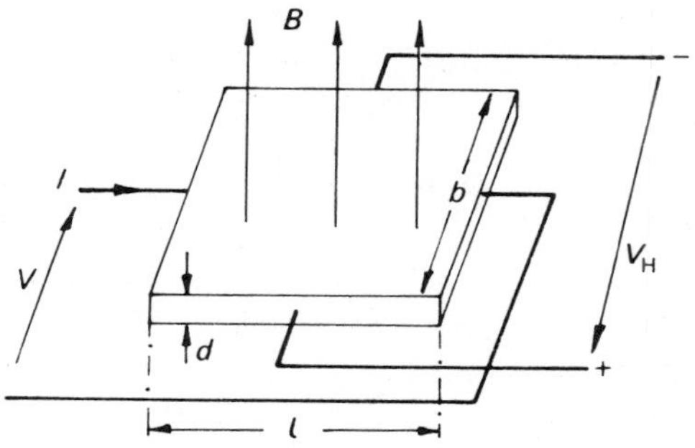

Figure 5.7. The Si sample for Problem 5.8.

5.9 What sheet resistance should one use in order to make a thin film, 6 kΩ resistor by evaporating the resistive material in vacuum, in a surface geometry of 25×1200 μm. What is the resistivity of the thin film layer if its thickness is 40 nm?

5.10 Check solution (5.16) by substituting it into (5.14) and (5.15).

5.11 Plot against x the function $\hat{p}(x,t)/\hat{p}_0$ that would be obtained in a Haynes–Shockley experiment, if recombination were neglected, for the two values $t=5$ μs and 20 μs. Assume $\mu_h=577$ cm^2 V^{-1} s^{-1}, $T=300$°K, $d=2.0$ mm (distance between points O and C in Fig. 5.4(b)). Compare the areas of the two curves.

5.12 Prove eq. (5.25) for a semiconductor with negligible trapping.

5.13 The temperature dependence of the specific conductivity σ and the Hall constant R_H of a certain semiconductor was measured and is shown in Fig. 5.8.

(a) Explain the behaviour of σ and R_H at high temperatures.
(b) Calculate $\bar{n}$ at $T<600°K$.
(c) Calculate the mobility at 300°K, how does it depend on temperature?

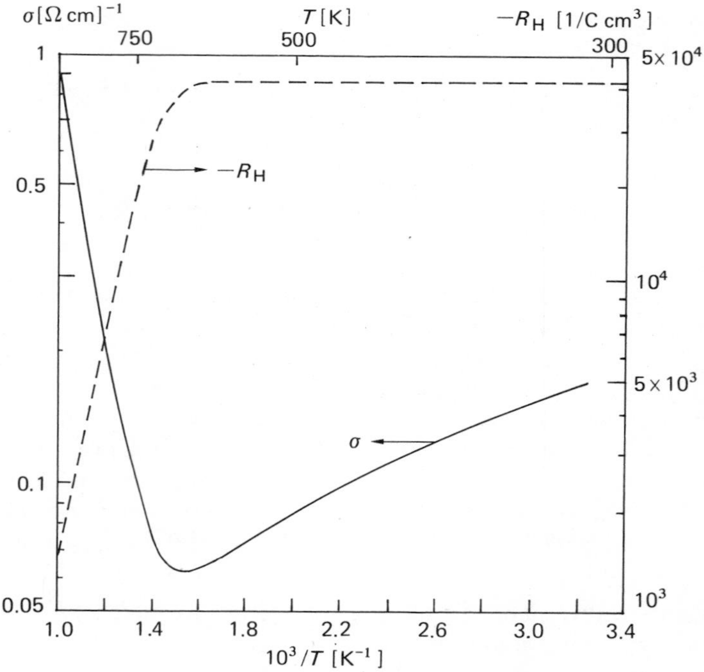

Figure 5.8. Measured data for Problem 5.13.

ENERGY BANDS IN SOLIDS 6

The qualitative description of the behavior of charge carriers in semiconductors as presented in the previous chapters gives only a limited view, with no quantitative details on many important points, such as the necessary energy for releasing a valence electron for conduction, the concentration of free carriers at any given temperature, the relation of effective mass to crystal structure and many others. Even a simplified treatment of these problems necessitates use of quantum-mechanical principles that lead to allowed energy states in a periodic crystal lattice structure and of statistical mechanics that give us the probability of occupation of those states. Our purpose in this chapter is not to go deeply into solid-state physics or statistics but to review the relevant results of these important fields so as to gain a deeper insight and understanding of the operation of semiconductor devices.

6.1 Quantum States of a Single Atom

Let us first compare the allowed energy states of the electron in a single atom and in an atom that is a part of a periodic crystal.

In the simplest case of the hydrogen atom each permitted state is characterized by four quantum numbers:

n —the principal quantum number defining the total energy. It is a positive integer, $n = 1, 2, \ldots$.

l —the azimuthal quantum number, a positive integer related to the magnitude of angular momentum, $l = 0, 1, 2, \ldots, n-1$.

m —the magnetic orbital number, a real integer associated with quantization of the momentum vector orientation with respect to a special reference axis in space. $m=0, \pm 1, \pm 2, \ldots, \pm l$;

s —the electron's own angular momentum, its spin, which can have one of two directions.

These quantum numbers, resulting from the solution of the generalized Schrödinger wave equation, determine the allowed states of the electron. For a single hydrogen atom these states are shown in Fig. 6.1(a). The reference energy is that of a free electron which is taken as zero. The lowest energy of a bound electron, $-E_1$, corresponds to $n=1$. This energy E_1 is therefore the energy necessary to ionize the hydrogen atom. Each value of n represents a shell of several allowed states, each depending on the values of the other quantum numbers, l, m, and s. The azimuthal quantum number l, which the theory shows to be a positive integer smaller than n, represents a subgroup of states inside the shell, or a subshell. By common practice, originating in spectroscopy, these subshells are called by special names. Those with $l=0$ are called 's states', those with $l=1$ 'p states', $l=2$ 'd states' and $l=3$ 'f states'. The arrows in Fig. 6.1(a) indicate the two possible spin directions.

The energy possessed by the electron cannot be intermediate between the allowed values. Any change in its energy must be in definite 'chunks' of energy, or *quanta*, equal to the energy difference between its former and new states. Figure 6.1(a) shows many states with the same energy because we are dealing with an atom having a single electron. In a multielectron atom the states in each shell will split into a range of energies because of inter-electronic influences. State 2s (shell $n=2$, subshell $l=0$), for example, will now have different energy from state 2p ($n=2$, $l=1$). No two electrons in the same system can have the same four quantum numbers (Pauli's exclusion principle). In equilibrium, each additional electron to the atom occupies the lowest energy level that is still free.

Energy splitting in multielectron atoms can lower the energy of an upper-shell state, say 4s, below one belonging to a lower shell such as 3d.

In the most common semiconductors, Si and Ge, the electron distribution in the various quantum states is described by the following notation:

(6.1a) $1s^2 2s^2 2p^6 3s^2 3p^2$ for Si (14 electrons)

(6.1b) $1s^2 2s^2 2p^6 3s^2 3p^6 3d^{10} 4s^2 4p^2$ for Ge (32 electrons)

Taking Si as an example, the meaning is that in shell $n=1$ the s state ($l=0$) contains 2 electrons (with opposing spins). This is written $1s^2$. In the second shell $n=2$ the s state contains 2 electrons ($2s^2$) and the p state ($l=1$) contains 6 electrons ($2p^6$) and so on.

Equation (6.1) tells us that the top populated shell in Si is $n=3$ and it

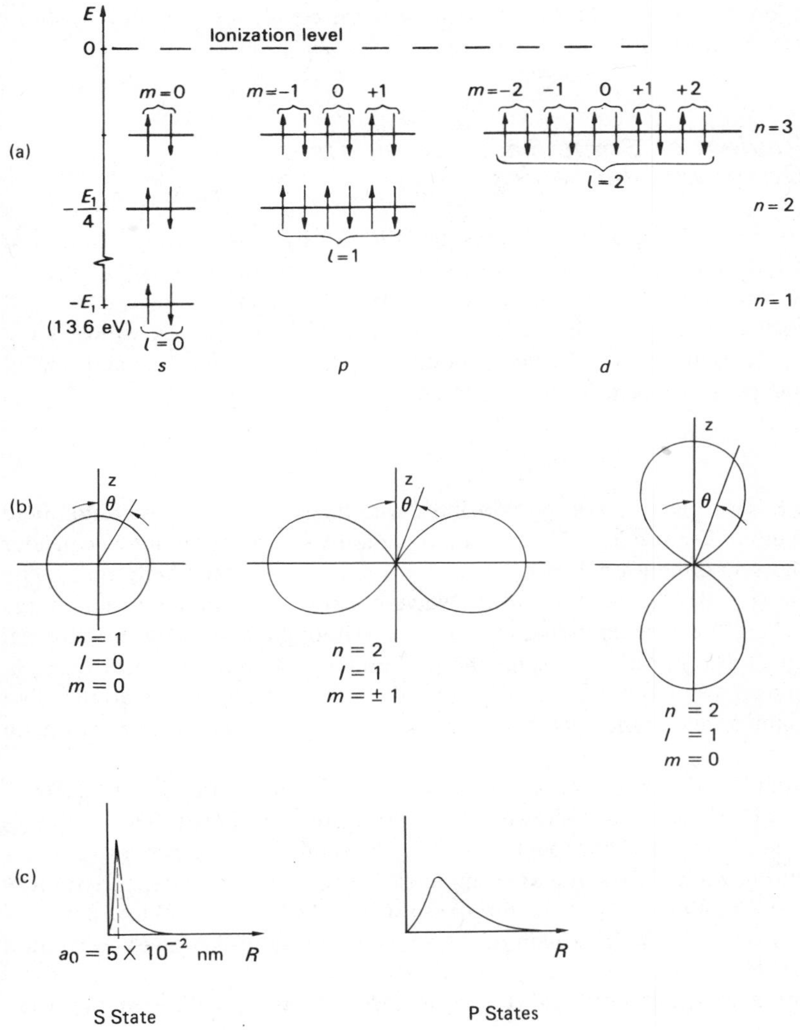

Figure 6.1. (a) Allowed states for an electron in the hydrogen atom; (b) angular dependence of wave functions; (c) radial probability density for *s* and *p* states.

contains 4 electrons: 2 in *s* states and 2 in *p* states. There remain 4 vacant *p* states in this shell with somewhat higher energies. The situation is not much different in Ge but with 32 electrons to account for the top partially occupied shell is $n = 4$ in which there are also two *s* and two *p* electrons. In crystal formation these outer electrons participate in the covalent bonds and constitute the valence electrons.

6.2 Review of Some Basic Concepts in Quantum Mechanics

To see how the allowed states are affected by neighboring atoms in a periodic structure we shall review without proof some fundamental quantum-mechanical concepts which are necessary for our purpose.

Each allowed state can be described by a state function ψ, which is the solution to Schrödinger's wave equation. We shall need only the stationary, time-independent form of that equation:

$$\nabla^2\psi+\frac{2m}{\hbar^2}(E-V)\psi=0 \tag{6.2}$$

where E is the electron energy associated with the state, V is the potential field in which the electron is and $\hbar=h/2\pi$. To simplify the notation, let us consider only the one-dimensional case where both ψ and V depend only on x. The solution ψ is an eigenfunction of the wave equation and the allocated energy levels E are the corresponding eigenvalues. Although ψ itself has no physical meaning, $|\psi(x_0)|^2\,dx$ represents the probability of finding the electron at x_0. Schrödinger's equation can be solved exactly only for the hydrogen atom where the potential field of the nucleus and the force it exerts on the single electron are known.

Some of the solutions for $n=1$, $l=m=0$ (s state) and for $n=2$, $l=1$, $m=0, \pm 1$ (p states) are shown schematically in Fig. 6.1(b). The s state is spherically symmetric (ψ depends on R but not on θ or ϕ) and has zero angular momentum while the p states are symmetric about the z axis (ψ depends on R, θ but not on ϕ), and have angular momentum. a_0 is the most probable distance of the electron from the hydrogen nucleus when it occupies its lowest permitted state as shown in Fig. 6.1(c).

For a constant potential $V=V_0$ and $E>V_0$ the solution of the wave equation is

$$\psi(x)=A\exp(jkx)+B\exp(-jkx) \tag{6.3}$$

where

$$k^2=\frac{2m}{\hbar^2}(E-V_0)\,. \tag{6.4}$$

This is a constant amplitude wave and k, which is real, is called propagation vector, or *wave vector*, in the general, 3-dimensional case. It is related to the wavelength λ by $k=2\pi/\lambda$, as can be seen from (6.3). If the electron is free, $V_0=0$

and E in (6.4) represents the kinetic energy only. E is related to the wave vector k and momentum p by

$$E=\frac{\hbar^2k^2}{2m}=\frac{p^2}{2m}, \tag{6.5}$$

i.e., $\hbar k$ is the momentum in this case.

A real particle cannot be described by a single wave like (6.3). For that we need a *wave packet*, which is an infinite sum of single waves with varying amplitude and wave vectors, which interfere destructively everywhere but within a certain volume of space where the probability of locating the particle is high.

The wave packet is represented mathematically by the Fourier integral

$$\psi(x,t)=\frac{1}{\sqrt{(2\pi)}}\int_{-\infty}^{\infty} A(k)\exp\,[j(kx-\omega t)]\,dk, \tag{6.6}$$

where $\exp(-j\omega t)$ represents time dependence.

The amplitude function is obtained from the inverse transform:

$$A(k)=\frac{1}{\sqrt{(2\pi)}}\int_{-\infty}^{\infty}\psi(x,0)\exp\,(-jkx)\,dx. \tag{6.7}$$

A state function which is a wave packet looks like Fig. 6.2. The envelope (dashed line) represents the magnitude of $\psi(x)$ and therefore the probability of finding the particle at that x. It can be seen that the particle is most probably at x_0 but there is a finite though smaller probability that it is somewhere else in the range Δx. The narrower Δx is, i.e. the more accurate the position is known, the wider is the spectral range in k space, obtained from (6.7), which is contained in the wave packet. As can be inferred from (6.5), this means that the momentum of the particle, $p=\hbar k$, is less defined and can have a wider range.

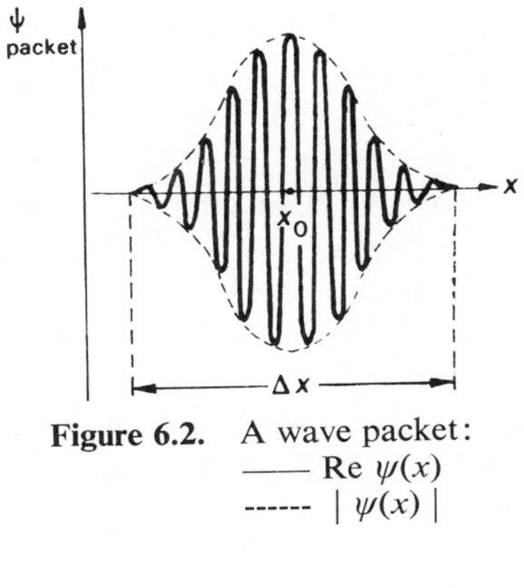

Figure 6.2. A wave packet:
—— Re $\psi(x)$
------ $|\psi(x)|$

This is an expression of Heisenberg's *uncertainty principle*

(6.8) $$\Delta x \, \Delta p \geqslant h.$$

The velocity of the real particle is the phase velocity of the wave packet *envelope*. It is called the *group velocity* and its relation to energy and momentum can be inferred from (6.5):

(6.9) $$v_g = \frac{\partial E}{\partial p} = \frac{1}{\hbar} \frac{\partial E}{\partial k}.$$

Another form for v_g can be obtained from the relation of the energy E to the angular frequency ω, contained in the time-dependent part of ψ (i.e. $\exp(-j\omega t)$), which is $E = \hbar\omega$:

(6.10) $$v_g = \frac{\partial \omega}{\partial k}.$$

A good discussion of quantum mechanics can be found in Ref. [22].

6.3 The Effect of the Lattice Periodicity on the Allowed States

Returning to the atom, let us now see what happens to the allowed energy states in a system of atoms, arranged periodically as in a crystal lattice. The outer electrons of each atom in the crystal are now affected by the outer electrons of neighboring atoms. The whole crystal becomes a single system in which Pauli exclusion principle holds: no two electrons in the same system can have the same quantum state. The discrete energy states of the solitary atom therefore split in the crystal to form a virtual band of permitted energy states; Fig. 6.3 compares the solution of Schrödinger's equation for the potential field of a solitary atom that yields discrete energy levels, which are permitted states, with the solution of the same equation for the potential field of a hypothetical 'crystal' of four similar atoms. In Fig. 6.3(a) the three lowest states of a hypothetical single atom are shown. They are obtained from the wave equation solution to the potential field $V(x)$ of that atom only. If, instead of a single atom, we consider a 'crystal' of four atoms in a line, as shown in Fig. 6.3(b), the resulting potential field is the sum of the contributions of all four and this must now be used in the wave equation.

The new solutions for the allowed states $n=1$ and $n=2$ are essentially unchanged, since the form of $V(x)$ in their vicinity, very near the nucleus, is not affected by the neighbors. But the third state, $n=3$, has an orbit far enough from the nucleus for $V(x)$ to be strongly influenced by the potential fields of the neighbors. This state can no longer be thought of as belonging to that specific atom only but it now belongs to the whole crystal. By Pauli's exclusion principle this level must split up into four sublevels, or four states, so that the four electrons in them, all belonging to the same system, will have different quantum numbers.

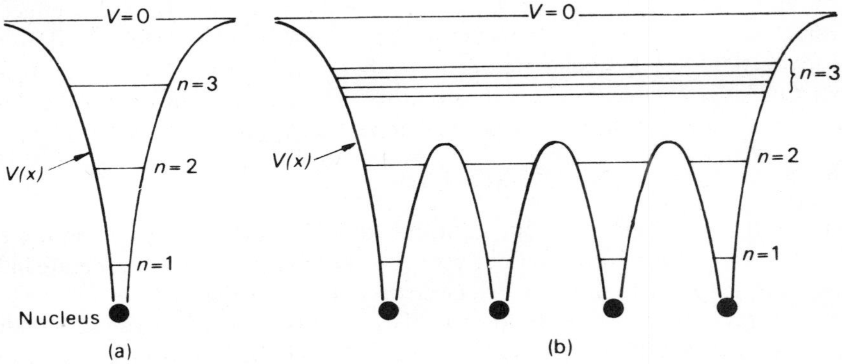

Figure 6.3. Hypothetical allowed energy states, obtained by solving Schrödinger's wave equation: (a) for the potential field $V(x)$ of a single atom; (b) for the potential field $V(x)$ of a 'crystal' of four atoms.

In a real crystal, containing many more atoms, that third level would have split up into a practically continuous band of allowed sublevels, and the electrons in them belong to the whole crystal and not to this or that atom. Those states are said to be *unlocalized.*

In order to obtain a more quantitative insight, we shall make use of a much simplified potential model, known as the *Kronig–Penney model*, for a one-dimensional crystal as shown in Fig. 6.4.

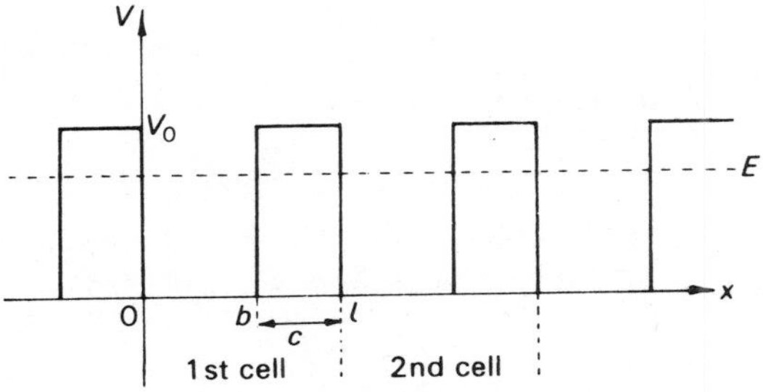

Figure 6.4. The Kronig–Penney periodic potential model (E= the energy of the electron).

E, representing the energy of the electron, is an eigenvalue of the solution of the wave equation. $V(x)$ is the potential to be used for that solution. Its periodicity is that of a lattice with a period l representing the unit cell length.

Therefore,

(6.11) $$V(x+nl)=V(x), \qquad n=1,2,\ldots.$$

In order to obtain a simple solution we must get rid of the end effects, where periodicity breaks down. Let us therefore assume that our one-dimensional crystal has a circular ring form or that it has crystals identical to it on both its sides. Stated mathematically, this means that if there are N atoms altogether in our crystal, then ψ must repeat itself after a distance of Nl:

(6.12) $$\psi(x+Nl)=\psi(x).$$

This restricts the validity of our solutions to the bulk of the crystal and not to its surface. We also know that our wanted solution for ψ must degenerate into the form given by (6.3) for a free electron if $V_0 \to 0$ in Fig. 6.4.

A theorem known as Floquet's theorem may be used to show that the most general solution satisfying (6.11) and (6.12) has the form known as a Bloch wave:

(6.13) $$\psi(x)=U(x)\exp(\alpha x),$$

where $U(x)$ is periodic with a period of l and may be complex. We know from (6.3) that as $V_0 \to 0$ $U(x)$ must become a constant and α is imaginary. The periodicity condition (6.12) requires

$$U(x+Nl)\exp[\alpha(x+Nl)]=U(x)\exp(\alpha x).$$

Since $U(x)$ itself is periodic in l we must also have $\exp(\alpha Nl)=1$ or

$$\alpha=\frac{2n\pi j}{Nl}.$$

Let us define

(6.14) $$k \triangleq \frac{2n\pi}{Nl};$$

our solution (6.13) will then become

(6.15) $$\psi(x)=U(x)\exp(jkx).$$

The wave equation itself will have a simpler form if the relationship between the electron energy E and its momentum $p_1=\hbar k_1$ is used (k_1 is not k):

(6.16) $$E=\frac{p_1^2}{2m}=\frac{\hbar^2 k_1^2}{2m}.$$

Let us also define a new quantity K_2 which measures the difference between the potential maximum V_0 and our electron energy E in Fig. 6.4:

(6.17) $$V_0-E=\frac{\hbar^2 K_2^2}{2m}.$$

Using k, k_1 and K_2 the wave equation for the left-hand part of the first cell in Fig. 6.4 is reduced to

$$\frac{d^2\psi}{dx^2}+k_1\psi=0, \qquad 0\leqslant x\leqslant b, \tag{6.18}$$

while for the right-hand part of that cell it is

$$\frac{d^2\psi}{dx^2}-K_2\psi=0, \qquad b\leqslant x\leqslant l. \tag{6.19}$$

The solutions to such equations are well known. They are respectively

$$\psi(x)=A\exp(jk_1x)+B\exp(-jk_1x), \qquad 0\leqslant x\leqslant b \tag{6.20}$$

$$\psi(x)=C\exp(-K_2x)+D\exp(K_2x), \qquad b\leqslant x\leqslant l. \tag{6.21}$$

In the left-hand part of the second cell, where $l\leqslant x\leqslant l+b$, the solution must be the same as for the left-hand part of the first cell as far as the x dependency is concerned. It can be obtained from (6.20) if x is replaced by $x-l$ for that region. Also, it must fulfill the periodicity condition of (6.15):

$$\psi(x+l)=U(x+l)\exp[j(x+l)]=U(x)\exp(jkx)\exp(jkl)$$

i.e. it must contain a phase shift of $\exp(jkl)$. Therefore the solution for that region of the second cell is

$$\psi(x)=\{A\exp[jk_1(x-l)]+B\exp[-jk_1(x-l)]\}\exp(jkl), \qquad l\leqslant x\leqslant l+b. \tag{6.22}$$

A relation between the constants A, B, C, D, can now be found if one remembers that both ψ and $d\psi/dx$ must be continuous wherever finite discontinuities in potential occur, such as at $x=b$:

$$A\exp(jk_1b)+B\exp(-jk_1b)=C\exp(-K_2b)+D\exp(K_2b),$$

$$jk_1[A\exp(jk_1b)-B\exp(-jk_1b)]=K_2[-C\exp(-K_2b)+D\exp(K_2b)]$$

and at $x=l$

$$C\exp(-K_2l)+D\exp(K_2l)=(A+B)\exp(jkl)$$

$$K_2[-C\exp(-K_2l)+D\exp(K_2l)]=jk_1(A-B)\exp(jkl).$$

These four equations for the unknowns A, B, C, D are homogeneous and therefore have a nonzero solution only when the determinant of coefficients is equal to zero. Reducing this four by four determinant is a long and tedious job which finally results in

$$\cos k_1b\cosh K_2c-\frac{k_1^2-K_2^2}{2k_1K_2}\sin k_1b\sinh K_2c-\cos kl=0 \tag{6.23}$$

where $c=l-b$.

Using (6.14), the definition of k, this can be written

$$\cos k_1 b \cosh K_2 c - \frac{k_1^2 - K_2^2}{2k_1 K_2} \sin k_1 b \sinh K_2 c = \cos kl \tag{6.24}$$

$$= \cos \frac{2n\pi}{N}, \qquad E < V_0;$$

This is an implicit equation for the allowed energy E which is determined by the values of k_1 and K_2. The right-hand side of (6.24) is periodic when n (or k) varies. The cosine term on that side goes through a full cycle as n changes by N (or $k = 2\pi/l$). Both n and k vary discontinuously in very small, discrete steps, and there are N such steps in one period. One can get an idea of the size of the step in k-space when one remembers that the interatomic distance, l, in our model, is about 0.2 nm. Taking a crystal 1 cm long, this means that $N = 5 \times 10^7$, which is the number of steps that k makes while it varies through one period $-\pi/l \leqslant k \leqslant \pi/l$. Since this is a very large number, k can be regarded as a continuous variable with the limitation that it can have only N (the number of atoms in the crystal) different values.

The magnitude of the cosine on the right-hand side of (6.24) is bounded by unity, which means that not every arbitrary value of E (i.e., k_1 and K_2) can satisfy that equation for a given V_0. For some ranges of E, the magnitude of the left-hand side of (6.24) is larger than unity, and therefore the electron cannot have these energies. These ranges are called the *forbidden energy bands*.

In order to see the whole picture of allowed and forbidden energy bands we notice that (6.24) remains essentially the same for $E > V_0$, but K_2, defined by (6.17), then becomes purely imaginary. Let us replace it, therefore, by jk_2, so that (6.24) becomes

$$\cos k_1 b \cos k_2 c - \frac{k_1^2 + k_2^2}{2k_1 k_2} \sin k_1 b \sin k_2 c = \cos kl, \qquad E > V_0. \tag{6.25}$$

In this energy range too there are forbidden and allowed bands. To make the band picture clearer let us sketch the left-hand sides of (6.24) and (6.25) as functions of E/V_0 as shown schematically in Fig. 6.5. The band boundaries occur at points where $\cos kl = \pm 1$, or

$$k = \pm \frac{n\pi}{l}, \qquad n = 1, 2, \ldots$$

Taking the lowest allowed energy band, one can find for each value of E a corresponding value of k by using (6.24) and so plot the graph of Fig. 6.6(a), which is also called the *dispersion curve*. The first band, which covers the range $-\pi/l < k < \pi/l$, is called the first *Brillouin zone*; the second, covering the ranges $\pi/l < k < 2\pi/l$ and $-2\pi/l < k < -\pi/l$, is called the second Brillouin zone, and so forth.

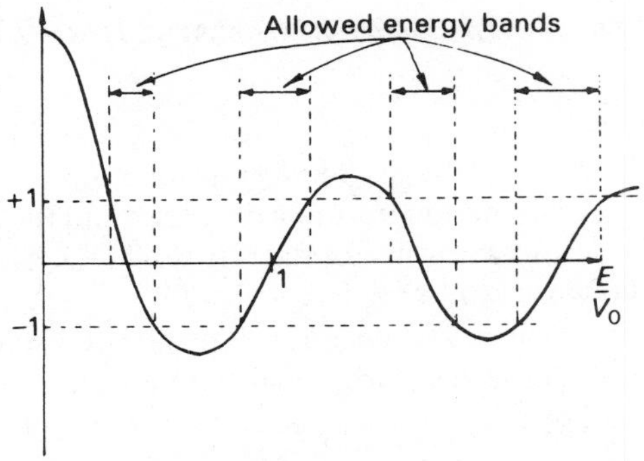

Figure 6.5. The allowed and forbidden energy bands obtained from the graphical form of the left-hand side of (6.24) for $E/V_0 < 1$ and (6.25) for $E/V_0 > 1$.

Since the left-hand side of (6.24) and (6.25) is unchanged when kl changes by $\pm 2n\pi$, it is customary and convenient to shift the curve sections belonging to the second and upper Brillouin zones into the first, along the k-axis, by multiples of $2\pi/l$. This yields Fig. 6.6(b) which is called the *reduced-zone representation* in k-space. Thus, the curve sections marked a and b in Fig. 6.6(a) are shifted by $-2\pi/l$ and $+2\pi/l$ respectively to appear as a' and b' in Fig. 6.6(b).

In each of the Brillouin zones, k has N distinct values, each corresponding to a different allowed energy state. Since each energy state can be populated by two electrons with opposing spins, each zone may contain up to $2N$ electrons.

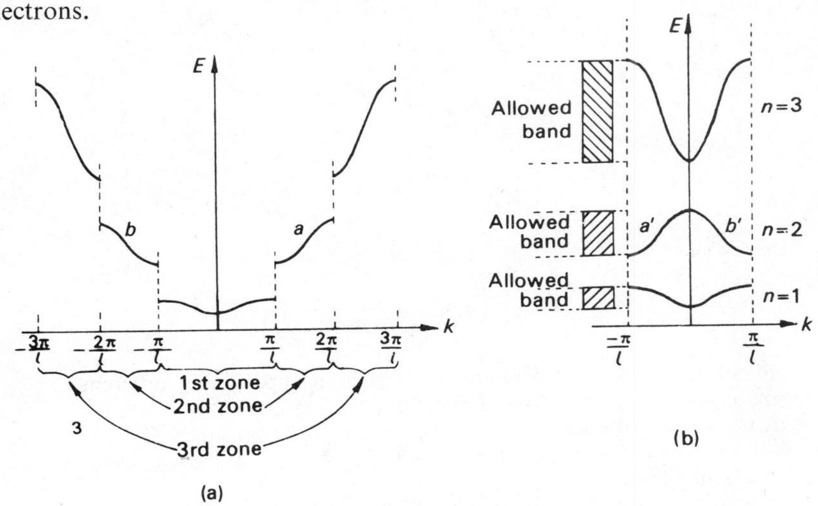

Figure 6.6. (a) The E–k dependence for the Kronig–Penney model; (b) the E–k dependence reduced to the first Brillouin zone.

6.4 Conductors, Semiconductors and Insulators

In a real three-dimensional crystal, the E–k relation is much more complicated and depends on the orientation of the momentum vector **k** with respect to the lattice axes, since interatomic distances and the internal potential field shape depend on direction inside the lattice. The basic effect of energy bands formation, however, still remains.

The electrons in a real crystal occupy all the allowed states, starting from the lowest energy, till all the electrons are accommodated. Above the highest occupied level there are more allowed states which are usually empty.

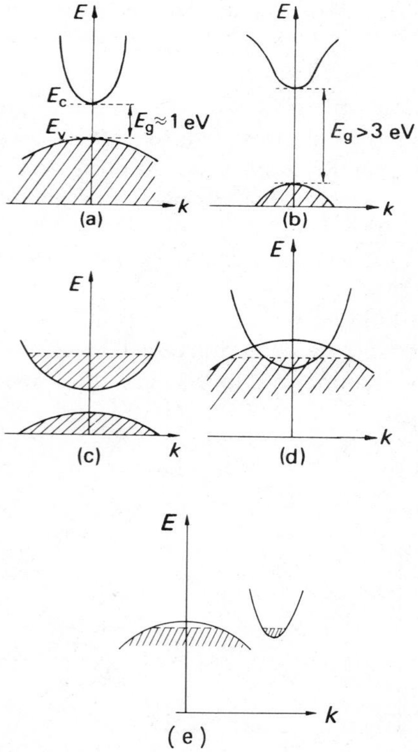

Figure 6.7. The energy bands and their occupation in different materials (hatched regions: levels filled with electrons):
(a) a semiconductor. E_V—the top of the valence band, E_C—the bottom of the conduction band, $E_g = E_C - E_V$ is the forbidden band gap;
(b) an insulator, E_g is large;
(c) a metal conductor; the top band is only partially filled;
(d) and (e) conductors with band overlap.

An intrinsic semiconductor crystal, i.e. a crystal containing no impurities, has the very special property that the upper occupied band, called the *valence band*, is completely full. Above this band comes a relatively narrow (about 1 eV) forbidden energy band called the *band gap*, and above this comes another allowed but normally empty band called the *conduction band*. This band picture is shown in Fig. 6.7(a). The band-gap width is usually denoted by E_g.

Applying an electric field to such a semiconductor, when held at low temperature, does not result in any current, since the field must accelerate the electrons, i.e., increase their kinetic energy, which means that they have to transfer to slightly higher, empty energy levels. No such levels are available. E_g is much too wide a gap for an electron to jump across by virtue of field acceleration. Therefore, no current flows. If the temperature is raised a few of the valence electrons (electrons populating the valence band) will gain sufficient thermal energy to overcome E_g and appear in the conduction band. The electron in the conduction band and the hole left in the valence band can now be accelerated and so carry current. The conductivity, however, is small, and hence the name 'semiconductor'. In an insulating material, such as diamond or silicon dioxide, the band gap is several times wider and even near melting temperatures the thermal energy is not sufficient to transfer an appreciable number of electrons to the conduction band. Its resistivity, therefore, is extremely high. The energy bands in an insulator are as shown in Fig. 6.7(b).

In a metallic conductor, on the other hand, the top occupied band is only partially filled, as in Fig. 6.7(c). Electrons can increase their energy continuously even at low temperatures, and this results in very high conductivity.

Other possible conduction mechanisms are shown in Fig. 6.7(d) and (e). Here the two top bands overlap to some extent, resulting in somewhat different conduction properties. Band overlap occurs in divalent metals, transition metals and semimetals.

6.5 The Effective Mass and the Concept of a Hole

Let us now examine the relation between the electric field strength F and the resulting acceleration of an electron occupying an energy level E near the bottom of an almost empty conduction band. From (6.10) the velocity of the electron is

$$v_g = \frac{1}{\hbar}\frac{\partial E}{\partial k},$$

i.e., it is determined by the shape of the E–k curve. The power supplied by the field, which is the electric field force qF times the velocity v_g, must equal the increase in the energy of the electron per unit time:

$$\frac{\mathrm{d}E}{\mathrm{d}t}=qFv_g=\frac{qF}{\hbar}\frac{\partial E}{\partial k}.$$

But

$$\frac{\mathrm{d}E}{\mathrm{d}t}=\frac{\partial E}{\partial k}\frac{\mathrm{d}k}{\mathrm{d}t};$$

therefore

$$\frac{\mathrm{d}(\hbar k)}{\mathrm{d}t}=qF. \tag{6.26}$$

We find that the time derivative of $\hbar k$ gives the applied external force, as if $\hbar k$ were a momentum. This is an interesting result, since qF is not the whole force, only its external part, while the effects of the internal potential fields are already included in the E–k curve. The quantity $\hbar k$ is therefore called *crystal momentum*, since it plays the same role as momentum does in its relation to *external* forces. It is not, however, the total momentum, and the effects of internal forces are included in the dispersion curve and through it in the $\partial E/\partial k$ term. Henceforth, whenever the momentum of an electron or hole is mentioned, this will mean the crystal momentum.

The acceleration caused by the field is

$$a=\frac{\mathrm{d}v_g}{\mathrm{d}t}=\frac{\partial v_g}{\partial k}\frac{\mathrm{d}k}{\mathrm{d}t}=\frac{qF}{\hbar}\frac{\partial v_g}{\partial k}=\frac{qF}{\hbar^2}\frac{\partial^2 E}{\partial k^2}.$$

Comparing this to Newton's law relating acceleration and force, we can define an *effective mass* $m_e^\star$ for the electron

$$m_e^\star=\hbar^2\left(\frac{\partial^2 E}{\partial k^2}\right)^{-1}. \tag{6.27}$$

The effective mass is therefore determined by the radius of curvature of the E–k curve at the given energy level and already includes all the internal potential field effects. In general, $m_e^\star$ varies with k. In fact, (6.27) predicts that whenever the E–k curve is concave, as at the bottom of the top band of Fig. 6.8 (which is the conduction band), $m_e^\star$ is positive, but when it is convex, as near the top of the lower band in that figure (the valence band) $m_e^\star$ is negative. This means that a particle in that state will be accelerated by the field F in the reverse direction expected for a negatively charged electron, i.e., it will behave as if it had a positive charge and mass. This is the concept of *the hole*.

To clarify this concept let us consider the current carried by an almost full valence band.

As can be seen from (6.24), cos kl is an even function, which makes E an even function of k and therefcre symmetric in respect to $k=0$. The derivative $\partial E/\partial k$ will therefore be an odd, antisymmetric function and from (6.10)

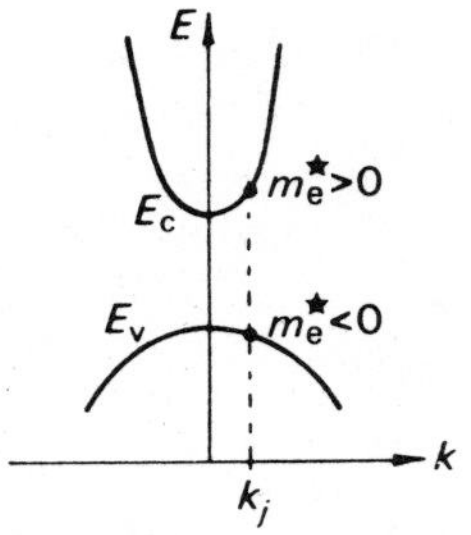

Figure 6.8. The effective mass in the conduction and the valence bands.

this means that

(6.28) $$v_g(-k_0) = -v_g(+k_0) = -\frac{1}{\hbar}\frac{\partial E}{\partial k}\bigg|_{k=k_0}.$$

The total current density carried by n electrons in the valence band is

(6.29) $$J = \frac{1}{V}\sum_{i=1}^{n}(-q)v_{gi}$$

where V is the volume and v_{gi} is the velocity of the ith electron. If the band is completely full, i.e., if $n=2N$, then for each electron in state $+k_0$ there corresponds another in $-k_0$, whose momentum and velocity (by 6.28)) have the opposite direction. The contributions of these two electrons to the current cancel each other. We have arrived at what we already knew: in a full band the total current must be zero.

(6.30) $$J = -\frac{q}{V}\sum_{i=1}^{2N} v_{gi} = 0.$$

If the band is not completely full but contains only $n=2N-p$ electrons, there are p states near the top of the band that are empty. For a positive field direction all the empty states have positive k values (the field pushes the electrons in the negative k-direction and so they fill all the available states with negative k by acquiring momentum in that direction).

The total current density can then be written

(6.31) $$J = -\frac{q}{V}\sum_{i=1}^{2N-p} v_{gi} = -\frac{q}{V}\left[\sum_{i=1}^{2N} v_{gi} - \sum_{j=2N-p}^{2N} v_{gj}\right]$$

$$= -\frac{q}{V}\left[0 - \sum_{j=2N-p}^{2N} v_{gj}\right] = +\frac{q}{V}\sum_{j=2N-p}^{2N} v_{gj}.$$

Since all the p empty states have positive velocities associated with them, J is a positive quantity, as if it were carried by p positive charge carriers of charge $+q$, i.e. by p holes.

Had there been an electron in one of those empty states, it would have been accelerated by the field with

$$a = -\frac{qF}{m_e^\star(k_j)}.$$

But, we have seen that $m_e^\star(k_j) < 0$ for k_j near the convex top of the valence band in Fig. 6.8. So, if we assign our hole a positive charge $+q$ and a positive effective mass given by

$$m_h^\star(k_j) = -m_e^\star(k_j), \tag{6.32}$$

it would have exactly the proper acceleration.

The concept of a hole is very convenient to describe the electrical behavior of an almost full band. Since the valence band in a semiconductor is just that, we always prefer to consider the behavior of those few empty states, the holes, rather than add the contributions of all the electrons in that almost full band.

As already mentioned, the effective masses, as defined by (6.27), are not necessarily constant. They are constant only if the relationship between E and k is parabolic, i.e. $E = ck^2$. Since our interest is in semiconductors, with either an almost empty conduction band (N-type) or an almost full valence band (P-type), only the shapes of the bottom of the conduction band or the top of the valence band need be considered and these can be approximated by parabolas such as

$$E \simeq E_c + \frac{\hbar^2 k^2}{2m_e^\star}, \tag{6.33a}$$

$$E \simeq E_v - \frac{\hbar^2 k^2}{2m_h^\star} \tag{6.33b}$$

which, by applying (6.27), give the proper constant effective masses. These approximations are shown in Fig. 6.13(a).

6.6 Band Shapes of Real Semiconductors

Real semiconductors are usually doped to N- or P-types. The addition of donors actually adds allowed energy states in a level E_d in the forbidden gap, slightly below the bottom of the conduction band, E_c, as shown in Fig. 6.9(a). The abscissa in that figure has no physical meaning and is used for convenience only, while the ordinate is the electron energy. This is a common, simplified way of showing the important levels without sketching the whole $E(k)$ curve. At very low temperatures the extra donor electrons are still attached to their atoms and occupy the E_d levels. Since the impurity atoms are relatively far apart, they do not affect each other and the E_d states are localized and therefore marked on the figure by a broken line. Around 100°K the thermal energy already enables the extra impurity electron to shift

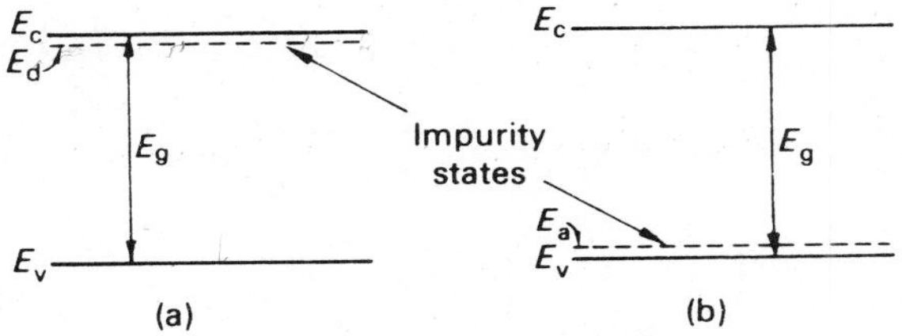

Figure 6.9. A simplified energy band picture with allowed states created by impurity atoms: (a) in N-type semiconductor; (b) in P-type semiconductor.

into one of the many empty states of the nearby conduction band, where it has an effective mass m_e^* and mobility μ_e and can carry current. Addition of acceptor impurities means the addition of allowed but empty (at very low temperatures) states slightly above the valence band at E_a in Fig. 6.9(b). Again at increased temperatures around 100°K valence electrons, from the originally full valence band, will transfer into those states, leaving holes behind.

In real semiconductors the E–k relation is much more complicated than our simplified model. Figure 6.10 shows the valence and conduction bands of three important semiconductors. The curves are not symmetrical since different k-directions are used for each side, so as to show more than one crystal orientation and also the various minima in the conduction bands.

It is only in GaAs that the lowest conduction band minimum occurs at $k=0$, but in this material too there is another local minimum, 0.36 eV higher and situated near the edge of the Brillouin zone, in the $<100>$ direction. In both Si and Ge the lowest conduction-band minimum occurs near the zone edges. The valence band maximum is always at $k=0$. The band gap E_g is the energy difference between the minimum of E_c and the maximum of E_v and only in GaAs they occur at the same k-value. GaAs is therefore called a *direct band gap* semiconductor, as are also InSb, InP, CdS and others. Here an electron transferring from the top of the valence band to the bottom of the conduction band or vice versa changes only its energy and not its momentum $\hbar k$. In Si, Ge and also GaP, AlSb and others both energy and momentum

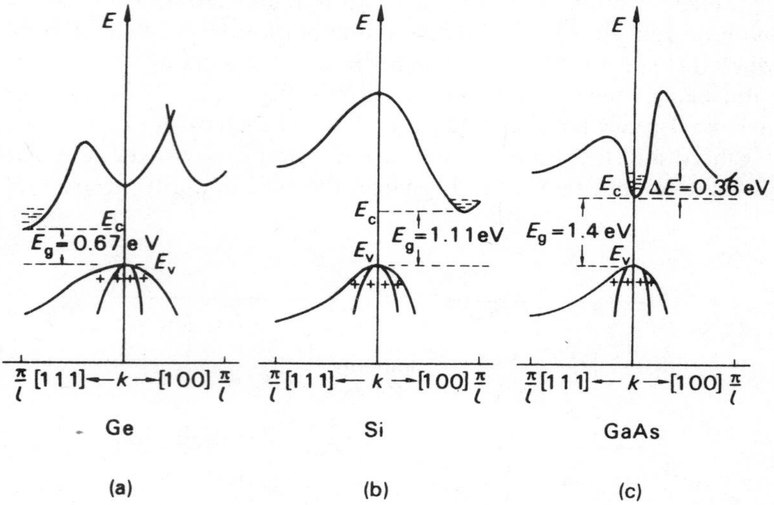

Figure 6.10. The energy bands in momentum space for the important semiconductors, at 300°K: (a) Ge; (b) Si; (c) GaAs.

must be simultaneously changed so they are called *indirect band gap* semiconductors. The type of band gap is very important from the utilization point of view, since both energy and momentum conservation laws must hold during carrier generation or recombination.

When, for example, the generation is by a photon of energy $E_{ph}=hf$, we must have $E_{ph}>E_g$ (the extra energy appears as the kinetic energies of the generated hole and electron) but the momentum must also be conserved. Now, the momentum of the photon is only

$$p_{ph}=mc=\frac{mc^2}{c}=\frac{E_{ph}}{c}=\frac{hf}{c}=\frac{h}{\lambda}=\hbar k_{ph}.$$

Therefore

$$k_{ph}=\frac{E_{ph}}{\hbar c}, \tag{6.34}$$

where c is the velocity of light.

In an indirect semiconductor such as Ge, the change in k involved in a transfer across E_g is approximately from $k=0$ to $k=\pi/l$. For $l\simeq 0.2$ nm this means $\Delta k\simeq 1.5\times 10^{10}$ m^{-1}. When compared with (6.34) for $E_{ph}\simeq 1$ eV we get a value about three orders of magnitude too low. The photon cannot account for the necessary momentum change in either generation or recombination. This means that other quantum particles, such as phonons, must participate and either remove or contribute the necessary excess momentum. This makes radiative recombination (i.e. direct electron–hole recombination with photon emission) an unlikely process in indirect semiconductors. It is, however, a very likely process in direct band gap semiconductors such as GaAs, and it is therefore from such materials that lasing and other light emitting devices are being made, as we shall see in Chapter 10.

The phonons, i.e., the vibrational modes of the lattice mentioned in Section 3.1, propagate in the crystal with the acoustic velocity v_{ac}, which is about 10^5cm s^{-1}. The energy of the phonon is of the order of kT, i.e. about 0.026 eV at room temperature. Using (6.34) to compare the momenta of the photon and the phonon, we find for Ge ($E_g = 0.67$ eV).

$$\frac{k_{phon}}{k_{phot}} \simeq \frac{E_{phon}/\hbar v_{ac}}{E_{phot}/\hbar c} \simeq \frac{kT/v_{ac}}{E_g/c} \simeq 12{,}000.$$

A phonon has therefore a relatively high momentum but relatively low energy. In an indirect semiconductor the most likely recombination process involves transfer of excess energy and momentum to several phonons, i.e., heating the lattice. The carrier is usually first trapped in a trapping center, such as a crystal defect, i.e., it becomes localized, gradually losing its energy and momentum to phonons until it finally recombines with an opposite carrier that passes by. Excess carrier lifetime in such materials is therefore long, and they are used for transistor production where this property is important. Sometimes recombination involves both phonon and photon, as in GaP, which is indirect. There the emitted phonon takes most of the momentum and the emitted photon takes most of the energy and is in the visible red-light range. GaP is therefore extensively used for devices emitting visible light.

Careful examination of Fig. 6.10 reveals another interesting point: the valence band consists actually of two overlapping bands with a common maximum at $k=0$ but with different curvatures (and therefore different effective masses). Consequently, there are two types of holes, called *light and heavy*. In Si the mass of a light hole is $0.16m_0$ and that of a heavy hole is $0.5m_0$. There are many more available states in the heavy band, so most holes are heavy.

From Fig. 6.10(b) we learn that conduction electrons in Si are actually distributed among six equivalent minimums (valleys) of the conduction band (since there are six <100> directions in the crystal). Collisions will scatter the electrons from one valley to another. Due to the large number of available states an external field will not be able to increase the electrons energy by much, they will just scatter into approximately equal vacant energy states; losing their excess momentum and energy to phonons.

This is not the case in the N type GaAs of Fig. 6.10(c) and an even more interesting effect can be foreseen. There are two local minima in the conduction band. The lowest is at $k=0$ and has low effective mass. The other, 0.36 eV higher, is again a six-fold minimum and has a high effective mass and low mobility (eq. (3.8)). In equilibrium, at room temperature, practically all the conduction electrons will occupy states in the lower, central, minimum and will therefore have low mass and high mobility. By applying an electrical field to the GaAs those electrons will be accelerated and their energy increased.

At about 3.2 kV cm^{-1}, their energy will be high enough to transfer into upper minima states which are much more numerous. Given sufficient energy, most conduction electrons will transfer, thereby suddenly reducing the mobility. This manifests itself in the behavior of the average current, or carrier velocity, which first increases linearly with the field (with a slope corresponding to the high mobility) and then starts to drop as more and more electrons transfer into the low mobility, higher energy minima. The resulting velocity–field characteristic is shown in Fig. 6.11.

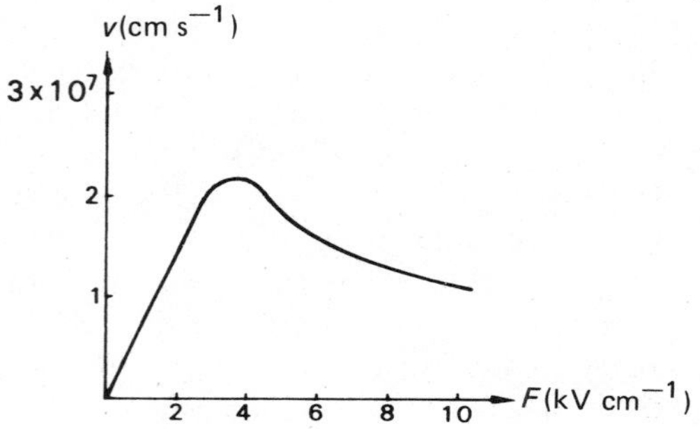

Figure 6.11. The relation between electron drift velocity and applied electric field in GaAs.

The drop in velocity with increasing field means a negative differential resistance effect which was suggested by Ridley and Watkins in 1961 and discovered by J. B. Gunn in 1963, after whom the effect is named. Gunn effect is utilized for microwave frequency generation as we shall see in Chapter 20.

6.7 The Density of States in the Energy Band

Up to now we have dealt only with the shape of the energy bands in k space. But two additional things must be known before the density of carriers in those bands and the resulting conductivity can be found. These are:

(a) the density of states in the band as a function of the energy E;
(b) the probability of those states being populated by charge carriers.

The product of those two functions of E will give us the density of carriers at any given energy level.

To obtain the density of states we assume the parabolic approximations (6.33) to the bands. Taking a rectangular box-shaped crystal with dimensions L_x, L_y, L_z and with interatomic distances l_x, l_y, l_z in the three respective axis directions, then the Kronig–Penney model says that the number of different values of k in each direction equals the number of atoms in the crystal in that direction. There are, therefore,

$$n_x = \frac{L_x}{l_x}, \qquad n_y = \frac{L_y}{l_y}, \qquad n_z = \frac{L_z}{l_z}$$

different values of k_x, k_y and k_z respectively.

The Brillouin zone width in the k_x direction is $2\pi/l_x$, as can be seen from Fig. 6.6(b), and similarly in the other directions. A single level, therefore, requires a section of the zone in the k_x (or k_y or k_z) direction of a width

$$\Delta k_x = \frac{2\pi/l_x}{n_x} = \frac{2\pi}{L_x}$$

and the volume in k space taken by a single level is $\Delta k_x\, \Delta k_y\, \Delta k_z$. Since two states with opposing spins can have the same energy level, a single state requires only half this volume:

$$\tfrac{1}{2}\Delta k_x \Delta k_y \Delta k_z = \frac{(2\pi)^3}{2L_xL_yL_z}. \tag{6.35}$$

Referring to Fig. 6.12, we look for the number of allowed states, dN', in k space in a spherical shell of a radius k and thickness dk. dN' is found by dividing the volume of the shell by the volume taken by a single state:

$$dN' = \frac{4\pi k^2\, dk}{(2\pi)^3/2L_xL_yL_z} = \left(\frac{k}{\pi}\right)^2 L_xL_yL_z\, dk.$$

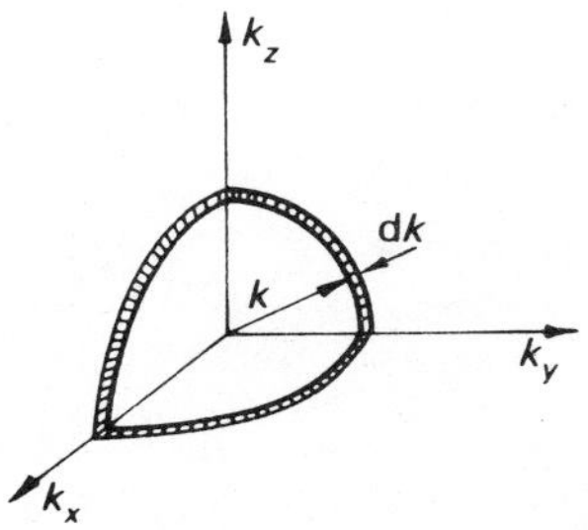

Figure 6.12. A section of a spherical shell in k space for calculating the density of states.

But $L_xL_yL_z$ is the crystal physical volume. Therefore, the density of states dN per unit crystal volume is

$$\mathrm{d}N = \frac{\mathrm{d}N'}{L_xL_yL_z} = \left(\frac{k}{\pi}\right)^2 \mathrm{d}k. \tag{6.36}$$

Replacing k and dk by E and dE with the help of (6.33a), and remembering that $\hbar = h/2\pi$, we get

$$\mathrm{d}N = \frac{4\pi}{h^3}(2m^{\star}_{e})^{3/2}(E-E_c)^{1/2}\,\mathrm{d}E = N_c(E)\,\mathrm{d}E. \tag{6.37}$$

$N_c(E)$ is called the *density of states in the conduction band* in the energy range E to $E+\mathrm{d}E$. This density is zero at $E=E_c$ at the bottom of the band and increases with the square root of the energy as shown in Fig. 6.13(b); the parabolic approximation to the bands is given in Fig. 6.13(a).

The density of allowed states in the valence band can be found in an exactly analogous way by utilizing (6.33b). It is also shown in Fig. 6.13(b). Since the kinetic energy of a hole is higher the lower it is in the valence band (remember, dE/dk is the state velocity which is zero at the top) we have only

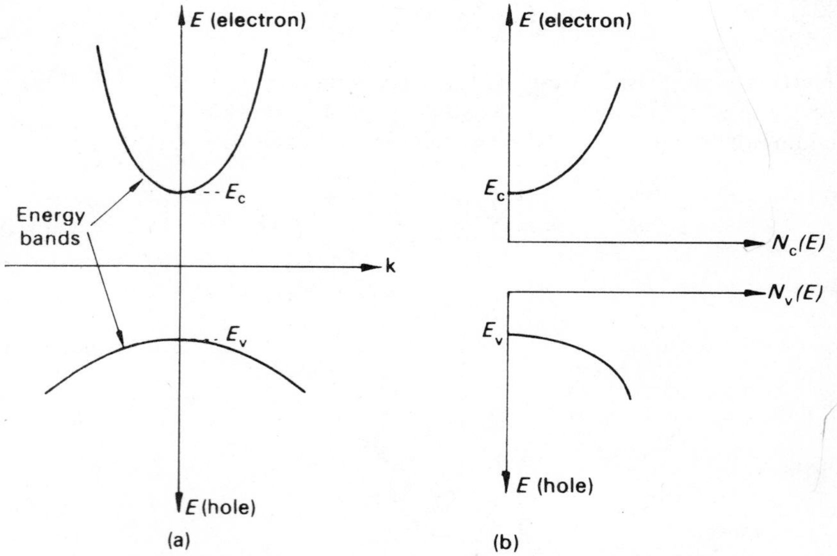

Figure 6.13. (a) The parabolic approximation to the bottom of the conduction band and top of the valence band. (b) The dependence of the density of allowed states on energy. Top for electrons in the conduction band. Bottom for holes in the valence band.

to reverse the direction of the energy axis for holes. The difference in band curvature is taken care of by assigning a different effective mass for the hole, $m_h^\star$, which is larger in this case than $m_e^\star$:

$$\text{(6.38)} \qquad dN(\text{valence}) = \frac{4\pi}{h^3}\,(2m_h^\star)^{3/2}(E-E_v)^{1/2}\,dE = N_v(E)\,dE.$$

6.8 The Probability of Occupation of Allowed States — the Distribution Function

As already mentioned, it is not enough to know the density of allowed states. We must also know the likelihood of a state being populated (for electrons) or unpopulated (for holes). We are facing a problem in statistical mechanics: how does the probability of occupation of a given state at energy E depend on that energy when the semiconductor is at thermodynamic equilibrium at a temperature T. This is not directly related to the former problem of whether or not there are allowed states at E. We look for a distribution function for our particles which, given the number of the particles and their total energy, will tell us the probability of finding particles at any energy.

The solution of this problem depends on the physical laws governing the particle behavior. Different distribution functions result from assuming different sets of physical laws.

The important distributions are the following:

(a) Classical physics assumes that the particles are distinguishable, i.e. can be named by numbering them 1 to n, and that each state can hold an unlimited number of particles. These assumptions yield the *Maxwell–Boltzmann distribution function* which will be denoted by $f_{MB}(E)$.

(b) Quantum physics laws for particles such as photons or phonons, which have symmetric wave functions, state that they are undistinguishable and an unlimited number of them can be accommodated in an allowed state. This results in the *Bose–Einstein distribution function*, denoted by $f_{BE}(E)$. Such particles are called bosons.

(c) Quantum physics laws for particles with antisymmetric wave functions, like electrons, state that they are both undistinguishable and obey Pauli's exclusion principle of accommodating only two electrons with opposing spins in the same energy level. This results in the *Fermi–Dirac distribution function*, denoted by $f_{FD}(E)$. Such particles are called fermions.

We are particularly interested in cases (a) and (c). The detailed methods for obtaining the distribution functions are given in Reference 5. Their general lines are as follows: each level is assumed to be a cell into which one or more particles can be put, depending on the basic physical laws governing them. Then the number of different ways in which the n available particles can be arranged in the cells is calculated, assuming that their total energy is fixed. The number of *different* ways depends of course on whether the particles are assumed to be distinguishable or not. The proper distribution function is the one that maximizes the number W of such different arrangements (for each set of basic laws) since the higher W is, the higher also is the state of disorder of the system measured by its entropy S($S = k \ln W$, where k is Boltzmann's constant). The equilibrium state is the state of highest entropy (or lowest free energy $F = E - TS$).

The obtained Maxwell–Boltzmann distribution for classical particles is:

$$f_{\mathrm{MB}}(E) = \exp\left(-\frac{E}{kT}\right), \tag{6.39}$$

where T = absolute temperature in °K.

The shape of this function is shown in Fig. 6.14(a). The Fermi–Dirac distribution function, which applies to electrons, is found to be

$$f_{\mathrm{FD}}(E) = \frac{1}{1 + \exp\left(\dfrac{E - E_{\mathrm{F}}}{kT}\right)}. \tag{6.40}$$

The energy E_{F} is called the Fermi energy level or *Fermi level*. It is the maximum energy the electrons have at 0°K. At higher temperatures the probability of occupation, or distribution function, has exactly the value $\frac{1}{2}$ at the Fermi level, as can be seen from (6.40). The Fermi level in each material depends on the number of available states and the number of electrons that must be accommodated in them.

This distribution is shown in Fig. 6.14(b) for three different temperatures:

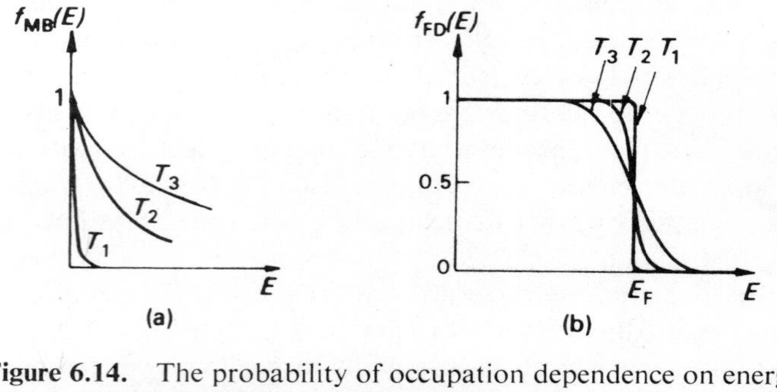

Figure 6.14. The probability of occupation dependence on energy: (a) the Maxwell–Boltzmann distribution; (b) the Fermi–Dirac distribution for three temperatures $T_3 > T_2 > T_1 = 0$°K.

We learn from (6.40) that f_{FD} becomes almost zero for $E-E_F \geq 4kT$. Near room temperature, where $kT \simeq 0.026$ eV, this happens at energies about 0.1 eV above E_F. In metals the Fermi level is somewhere in the middle of the top occupied valence band, with the valence electrons being accommodated in the states up to about E_F. The Fermi level can then be looked upon as the average energy of the most energetic electrons in the metal: almost all levels below it are occupied, and those above it are empty.

The case of a semiconductor will be dealt with in the next chapter.

Before we end this discussion, it is profitable to compare the Fermi–Dirac distribution to that of Maxwell–Boltzmann. We note from (6.40) that if $E-E_F \gg kT$, f_{FD} is approximately given by

$$f_{FD}(E) \simeq \exp\left(-\frac{E-E_F}{kT}\right). \tag{6.41}$$

The ratio of occupation of two states E_1 and E_2, both higher by at least a few kT than E_F, is

$$\frac{f_{FD}(E_2)}{f_{FD}(E_1)} \simeq \exp\left(-\frac{E_2-E_1}{kT}\right). \tag{6.42}$$

The same result is obtained if f_{MB} from (6.39) is used. The physical meaning of this is that a few kT above E_F there are already so many empty states that for the few remaining electrons still to be accommodated Pauli's exclusion principle is no longer important and classical physics, i.e. f_{MB}, can be used. Use of f_{MB} instead of f_{FD} will enable us, in the next chapter, to find analytic solutions to problems that otherwise can only be solved numerically.

QUESTIONS

6.1 Referring to the electronic levels given in eqs. (6.1), which electrons do you expect to belong to the valence band? to lower energy bands? (when the atoms form a crystal).

6.2 What is the difference between phase velocity and group velocity?

6.3 What will be the effect on the energy band if the crystal is put under hydrostatic pressure (which squeezes the atoms slightly nearer each other)?

6.4 Why do we find any electrons at all (even though only a few) in the conduction band of Si (and holes in the valence band) at room temperature, considering that $E_g = 1.1$ eV while $kT = 0.026$ eV only.

6.5 What is the kinetic energy of an electron at the bottom of the conduction band?

6.6 Draw schematically the effective mass as a function of k in the first Brillouin zone.

6.7 For a system with 5 particles and 6 energy levels, draw two possible arrangements of the particles in those levels for each of the three cases: Maxwell–Boltzmann, Bose–Einstein and Fermi–Dirac. Assume the levels are E_0, $2E_0$, $3E_0$, . . . and the total available particle energy is $15E_0$.

6.8 In considering the conductivity of metals only electron movement is of importance. Why are holes not considered?

6.9 An impurity level in a doped semiconductor is a localized level, i.e., the state function is localized in the vicinity of the impurity atom. Does this have a bearing on the k value associated with this state and on light absorption by raising an electron from such a state to the conduction band in an indirect band gap semiconductor?

PROBLEMS

6.10 The forbidden band gap in Ge (32 electrons) is 0.67 eV. In Si (14 electrons) it is 1.1 eV. In diamond, which is a crystal form of carbon (6 electrons) it is 7.0 eV. Discuss possible reasons for a relationship between the number of electrons in an atom to the band gap in its crystal form.

Given that the number of intrinsic carriers depends on E_g according to

$$n_i = c \exp\left(-\frac{E_g}{2kT}\right) \qquad (c=\text{const.})$$

and in Si at room temperature $n_i \simeq 10^{10}$ cm^{-3}, find n_i for Ge and diamond.

6.11 Show that for a group of two waves, one with ω, k the other with $\omega + \Delta\omega$, $k + \Delta k$, the group velocity is indeed given by (6.10).

6.12 Find the maximum wavelength of photons that can generate carriers by being absorbed in the following semiconductors (respective band gap is given in parentheses): Ge (0.67 eV); Si (1.1 eV); GaAs (1.4 eV); CdS (2.45 eV).

6.13 Find the height of the Fermi level above the bottom of the valence band for a monovalent metal with N atoms to the unit volume, at 0°K. Assume a parabolic band.

6.14 Apply the result of the previous problem to copper (density 8.92 g cm^{-3}, atomic weight 63.54) and compare with the known value of $E_F = 7.1$ eV.

6.15 Show that ψ, the solution to Schrödinger's wave equation, and its first space derivative must both be continuous at points where finite potential discontinuities occur.

6.16 Calculate the probabilities of finding electrons at the energy levels of $E_F + 0.1$ eV and $E_F - 0.1$ eV at the following temperatures: 0°K; 150°K; 300°K; 1000°K.

6.17 Assuming that f_{MB} is used from (6.41) with E measured from E_F, instead of f_{FD} from (6.40), calculate the percentage error and draw it as a function of $(E - E_F)/kT$.

6.18 Given N_0 ideal gas molecules in a container, the fraction with velocities between v and $v + dv$ is given by the Maxwell–Boltzmann distribution function for velocities and is

$$dn = 4\pi v^2 N_0 \left(\frac{m}{2\pi kT}\right)^{3/2} \exp\left(-\frac{mv^2}{2kT}\right) dv.$$

Calculate the average velocity $\bar{v}$ and the root mean square velocity (r.m.s. velocity $\sqrt{(\overline{v^2})}$. Show that $\frac{1}{2}mv_{rms}^2 = \frac{3}{2}kT$.

HOMOGENEOUS SEMICONDUCTOR IN THERMODYNAMIC EQUILIBRIUM 7

We shall now proceed to use the results of the preceding chapter to express the concentration of charge carriers, and hence the resistivity of semiconductors, as functions of the temperature and the material parameters such as $m^\star$ and E. The effect on the Fermi level of adding impurities will then be discussed.

7.1 Fermi Level and Resistivity in the Intrinsic Case

First, let us deal with an intrinsic semiconductor, with no impurities, which is kept in thermodynamic equilibrium, i.e. its temperature is uniform and equal to its surroundings, and no external forces (such as an electric field or radiation) are applied to it. The movement of the free carriers will then be due solely to their thermal energy, and their concentration everywhere will be a function of temperature and constant in time.

Let the density of electrons in the conduction band with energies between E and $E+\mathrm{d}E$ be $\mathrm{d}n(E)$. This must be equal to the product of the density of available states at this energy (eq. (6.37)) and the probability for their occupation, f_{FD}, given by (6.40):

$$(7.1)\quad \mathrm{d}n(E)=N_{\mathrm{c}}(E)f_{\mathrm{FD}}(E)\,\mathrm{d}E=\frac{4\pi}{h^3}(2m_{\mathrm{e}}^\star)^{3/2}(E-E_{\mathrm{c}})^{1/2}\left(1+\exp\frac{E-E_{\mathrm{F}}}{kT}\right)^{-1}\mathrm{d}E.$$

The density of electrons in the whole conduction band, which begins at $E=E_{\mathrm{c}}$ and ends at $E=E_{\mathrm{c}}+\Delta E$ is

$$n_{\mathrm{i}}=\int_{E_{\mathrm{c}}}^{E_{\mathrm{c}}+\Delta E}\mathrm{d}n(E)$$

From physical reasoning we can deduce beforehand that E_F is somewhere around the middle of the band gap: the number of occupied states, i.e. electrons, in the conduction band is equal to the number of empty states, i.e. holes, in the valence band in intrinsic semiconductors. For densities of states in the two bands that are not too different, this means that E_F must be about equidistant from E_c and E_v. Accepting that E_F is located at least a few kT below E_c, we are able to make two important approximations which will enable us to compute our integral analytically.

(a) We can replace f_{FD} from (6.40) by F_{MB} of (6.41), since $(E-E_F)/kT \gg 1$ throughout our integration range.

(b) We can raise the top limit of our integral to infinity without materially changing the result since the integrand approaches zero exponentially with E.

The density of electrons in an intrinsic semiconductor will therefore be

$$n_i = \frac{4\pi(2m_e^\star)^{3/2}}{h^3}\int_{E_c}^{\infty}(E-E_c)^{1/2}\exp\left(-\frac{E-E_F}{kT}\right)\,dE.$$

Substituting $x=(E-E_c)/kT$ yields

$$n_i = \frac{4\pi(2m_e^\star kT)^{3/2}}{h^3}\exp\left(-\frac{E-E_F}{kT}\right)\int_0^{\infty}x^{1/2}\exp(-x)\,dx. \tag{7.2}$$

The definite integral in (7.2) is found from tables to be equal to $\sqrt{\pi}/2$, giving

$$n_i = \frac{2}{h^3}(2\pi m_e^\star kT)^{3/2}\exp\left(-\frac{E_c-E_F}{kT}\right) = N_c\exp\left(-\frac{E_c-E_F}{kT}\right), \tag{7.3}$$

where N_c (m^{-3}) is a shortened notation for the coefficient. It is called the *effective density of states* in the conduction band. The upper part of Fig. 7.1 shows the steps leading to n_i. Figure 7.1(a) shows E_F and E_c on the electron's energy axis. Figure 7.1(b) gives the density of states in the conduction band, while Fig. 7.1(c) gives the probability, f_{MB}, of the occupation of those states, assuming E_F is at least a few kT below E_c. Figure 7.1(d) gives the product of Figs. 7.1(b) and (c), i.e., the quantity given in eq. (7.1). The result of integration, n_i, is shown by the hatched area.

It is obvious that our results depend on the position of the energy level E_F, which we still don't know exactly. This can be found from the condition of charge neutrality which, in the intrinsic case, is simply $n_i = p_i$.

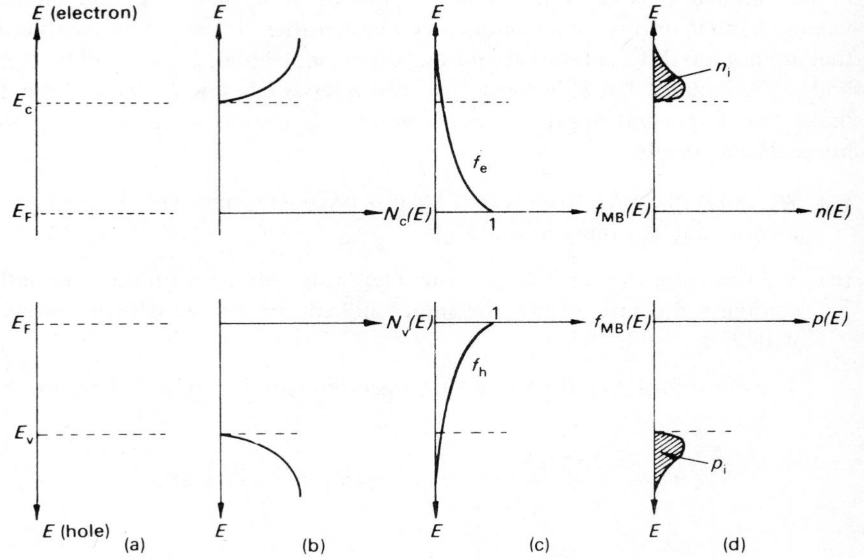

Figure 7.1. Density of carriers in intrinsic semiconductor: (a) energy levels in intrinsic semiconductor; (b) the densities of allowed states in the conduction and valence bands which are assumed parabolic; (c) the probabilities of occupation $f_{MB}(E)$ from (6.41); (d) the product of the density of states and probability. n_i and p_i are shown by hatched areas.

The determination of p_i is completely analogous to that of n_i, except that (6.38), for the density of states in the valence band, is used. As for the probability, $f_h(E)$, of holes occupying these states, it is equal to the probability of not finding an electron there:

$$(7.4) \quad f_h(E) = 1 - f_e(E) = 1 - \left(1 + \exp\frac{E - E_F}{kT}\right)^{-1} = \left(1 + \exp\frac{E_F - E}{kT}\right)^{-1}.$$

$f_h(E)$ is very similar to $f_e(E)$ and both give the same numerical result if $E > E_F$ in $f_e(E)$ and $E < E_F$ in $f_h(E)$ with $|E - E_F|$ the same in either case. But E is the electron's energy and is measured upwards, whereas for holes the positive direction of the energy axis is downward. So if E in (7.4) is taken as the hole energy, $f_h(E)$ is exactly equal to $f_e(E)$ for the same carrier energy E with respect to E_F. Proceeding as for n_i, we therefore obtain

$$p_i = \int_{E_v}^{E_v - \Delta E} N_v(E) f_h(E)\, dE \simeq \int_{E_v}^{} N_v(E) f_h(E)\, dE$$

$$= \frac{4\pi(2m_h^\star)^{3/2}}{h^3} \int_{E_v}^{-\infty} (E_v - E)^{1/2} \exp\left(-\frac{E_F - E}{kT}\right) dE.$$

And with the same substitution as before

$$p_i = \frac{2}{h^3}(2\pi m_h^\star kT)^{3/2} \exp\left(-\frac{E_F - E_v}{kT}\right) = N_v \exp\left(-\frac{E_F - E_v}{kT}\right), \tag{7.5}$$

where the coefficient N_v is now called the *effective density of states in the valence band*. The process leading to p_i is shown in the bottom part of Fig. 7.1.

Equating n_i to p_i according to the neutrality condition and separating E_F out gives:

$$E_F = \frac{E_c + E_v}{2} + \frac{kT}{2} \ln \frac{N_v}{N_c} = \frac{E_c + E_v}{2} + \tfrac{3}{4} kT \ln \frac{m_h^\star}{m_e^\star}. \tag{7.6}$$

In both Ge and Si the effective masses of the holes and electrons are of the same order of magnitude, and therefore E_F is practically midway between E_c and E_v, as was anticipated in our approximation and in the drawing of Fig. 7.1.

The product of n_i and p_i yields n_i^2:

$$n_i^2 = N_c N_v \exp\left(-\frac{E_c - E_v}{kT}\right) = AT^3 \exp\left(-\frac{E_g}{kT}\right), \tag{7.7}$$

where E_g is the forbidden gap and A is a constant.

It is clear that n_i is a very sensitive function of T and E_g (which is also slightly dependent on T). In Ge, n_i is about three orders of magnitude larger than in Si of the same temperature, because of the about 0.4 eV difference in their respective band gaps. Intrinsic GaAs with 1.4 eV band gap is almost an insulator while InSb, with $E_g = 0.18$ eV, is a relatively good conductor at room temperature.

The resistivity of intrinsic semiconductor, given by (3.14), is

$$\rho_i = \frac{1}{\sigma_i} = \frac{1}{q n_i (\mu_e + \mu_h)}$$

which, at room temperature, yields:

$$\rho_i(\text{Ge}) = 47\ \Omega\,\text{cm}$$
$$\rho_i(\text{Si}) = 230\ \text{k}\Omega\,\text{cm}$$
$$\rho_i(\text{GaAs}) \simeq 10\ \text{M}\Omega\,\text{cm}.$$

The temperature dependence of n_i arises mostly from the exponential term. From the expression for ρ_i we see that if the relatively weak temperature dependence of N_v, N_c, μ_e, μ_h and E_g is neglected in comparison to $\exp E_g/kT$, the graph of $\ln \rho_i$ against $(kT)^{-1}$ is a straight line with a slope of E_g (this is one way of measuring E_g).

7.2 Fermi Level and Resistivity in the Extrinsic Case

Introducing impurities into the semiconductor does not change the basic approach and the results found for n and p in the intrinsic case. The only thing that changes is the form of the neutrality condition, which means that E_F is shifted. In the extrinsic case $\bar{n} \neq \bar{p}$ (a bar signifies equilibrium conditions) and eqs. (7.3) and (7.5) then give

$$\bar{n} = N_c \exp\left(-\frac{E_c - E_F}{kT}\right) \tag{7.8}$$

$$\bar{p} = N_v \exp\left(-\frac{E_F - E_v}{kT}\right). \tag{7.9}$$

On calculating the product $\bar{n}\bar{p}$, the Fermi level E_F disappears:

$$\bar{n}\bar{p} = N_c N_v \exp\left(-\frac{E_g}{kT}\right) = n_i^2. \tag{7.10}$$

This has already been deduced in Chapter 2, eq. (2.15), but now we have a detailed expression for n_i^2. The neutrality condition for finding E_F is

$$\bar{p} + N_D^+ = \bar{n} + N_A^-, \tag{7.11}$$

where N_D^+ and N_A^- are the ionized donor and acceptor impurities, respectively.

Simultaneous use of (7.10) and (7.11) yields $\bar{n}$ and $\bar{p}$ separately for a given doping density.

To express E_F we divide (7.8) by (7.9), take the logarithm and separate E_F out:

$$E_F = \frac{E_c + E_v}{2} + \frac{kT}{2} \ln \frac{N_v}{N_c} + \frac{kT}{2} \ln \frac{\bar{n}}{\bar{p}} = E_{F_i} + \frac{kT}{2} \ln \frac{\bar{n}}{\bar{p}}, \tag{7.12}$$

where E_{F_i} is the Fermi level in the intrinsic semiconductor. This equation shows that the increase in the proportion of electrons to holes, caused by introducing donor impurities into the semiconductor, shifts the Fermi level from the intrinsic, i.e. the middle of the gap, up towards the conduction band. The probability of finding electrons in both conduction and valence band states will grow, which means that there are more electrons and less holes. The reverse happens when acceptor impurities, N_A, are added; E_F is then shifted downwards. Both cases are shown schematically in Fig. 7.2.

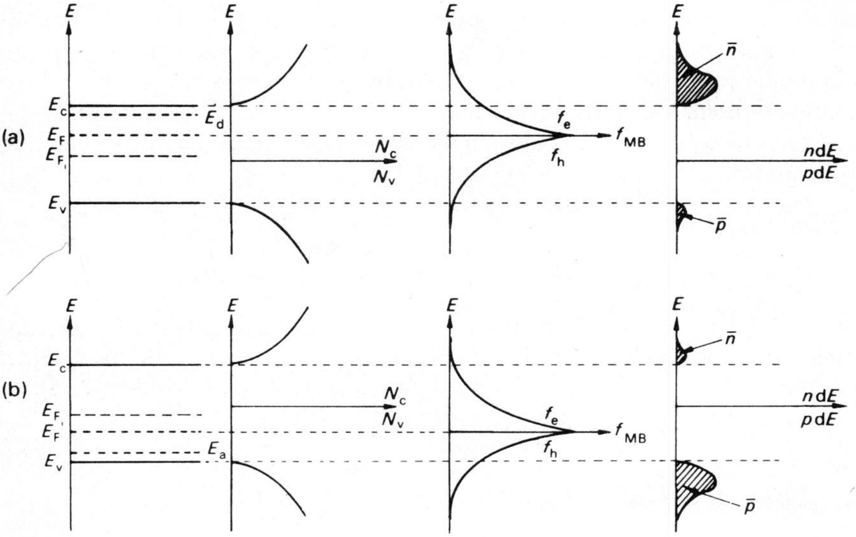

Figure 7.2. Energy levels, occupation probability and carrier concentration in: (a) N-type semiconductor; (b) P-type semiconductor; *E*—the energy of the electron.

At normal operating temperatures practically all the impurities are ionized. In N-type semiconductor, where $N_A=0$, $\bar{n} \gg \bar{p}$ and one can neglect $\bar{p}$ and N_A in (7.11) to yield $\bar{n} \simeq N_D$. The hole concentration is given by (7.10):

$$\bar{p}=\frac{n_i^2}{\bar{n}}=\frac{n_i^2}{N_D}.$$

Substituting into (7.12) yields E_F for N-type semiconductor:

$$E_F=E_{F_i}+kT\ln\frac{N_D}{n_i}. \tag{7.13}$$

Similarly, for P-type

$$E_F=E_{F_i}-kT\ln\frac{N_A}{n_i}. \tag{7.14}$$

As already mentioned in Chapter 6, the addition of impurities adds impurity levels E_d and E_a shown in Fig. 7.2. In the donor case the fifth electron occupies the E_d level at very low temperatures. E_F must then be somewhere between E_d

and E_c for the occupation probability of E_d to be 1 and of E_c to be 0. At slightly higher temperatures, this electron can transfer into the conduction band, which has many available empty states, and the donors become ionized. Similarly, in the acceptor case, E_F is between E_a and E_v at 0°K and the acceptor states at E_a are empty. At higher temperature the change in occupation probability enables valence electrons to occupy those states, thus creating holes in the valence band.

The energy differences between the impurity levels and the band edges for common impurities are given in Table 2.3.

The occupation probability of E_d has the form

$$f(E_d)=\left(1+\frac{1}{2}\exp\frac{E_d-E_F}{kT}\right)^{-1}. \tag{7.15}$$

The factor $\frac{1}{2}$ is a result of the two possible spin directions that the electron can assume in the extra impurity state. Equation (7.15) can be used to evaluate the fraction of ionized impurities at low temperatures (see Problem 7.12).

7.3 Low and High Doping Cases

In practice, it is sometimes necessary to use very low doping concentrations. N-type is then called N^- or ν-type while P is called P^- or π-type. In such cases one cannot ignore thermally generated carrier pairs in comparison to the impurity contribution. In the case of ν material, with $N_A=0$, we get from (7.11) that

$$\bar{n}=N_D+\bar{p}=N_D+\frac{n_i^2}{\bar{n}},$$

which is a quadratic equation for $\bar{n}$.

Another case of practical importance is that of very highly doped semiconductors. In Section 2.5 it was mentioned that highly doped semiconductors are called *degenerate*. They are denoted by N^+ or P^+ depending on the impurity type. 'Degenerate' here means that Maxwell–Boltzmann statistics no longer apply to the energy distribution of the contributed carriers in their respective bands, and Fermi–Dirac statistics must be used. If we take N-type material, for example, (7.13) shows that continuous increase of N_D will finally bring E_F into the conduction band. Our previous assumptions based on $(E-E_F) \gg kT$ no longer hold and f_{FD} in (7.1) cannot be replaced by f_{MB}. This means that the Pauli exclusion principle can no longer be ignored, since there are now so many electrons in the bottom of the conduction band that they occupy most of the allowed states there, up to the Fermi level, E_F. This level is now inside the band, as in a metal. An external field can accelerate only those electrons whose energy is around E_F, since only they have empty states nearby. This situation, where many electrons have about the same energy E_F, is what gives the highly doped material the name 'degenerate', which usually refers to different quantum states that have the same energy.

Equation (7.13) gives for Si a concentration of $N_D \simeq 10^{19}$ cm^{-3} as the value above which E_F is inside the conduction band and the material becomes degenerate. This corresponds well with the value of N_D estimated in Chapter 2 from fifth electron orbit overlap of neighboring impurity atoms. When those orbits overlap, the impurity states become part of a single system, and the exclusion principle then demands that they split and form an impurity band over a range of energies, instead of remaining a discrete single level as in the nondegenerate case. This impurity band extends into the nearby conduction band, forming a continuous allowed band. This is what gives a degenerate semiconductor a conductivity that is almost constant with temperature in a wide range.

Since f_{FD} must now be used in (7.1), the integration giving $\bar{n}$ can only be done numerically.

We shall always deal here with nondegenerate semiconductors unless otherwise stated.

7.4 The Maximum Useful Temperature for a Semiconductor Device

When the working temperature of an extrinsic semiconductor is increased the number of thermally generated carrier pairs (contributed by the semiconductor atoms) increases to the point where they equal or exceed those contributed by the impurities (whose number is fixed). The semiconductor then loses its extrinsic nature and becomes intrinsic, since the concentrations of electrons and holes become about equal. Semiconductor-device operation is always based on its being N- or P-type or N in some regions and P in others. The intrinsic temperature, marked T_{max}, is therefore the absolute maximum for any semiconductor device and in fact one should stay well below it. Taking N-type, for example, we get T_{max} from the condition $n_i \simeq N_D$. Using (7.10), this condition gives

$$n_i = (N_c N_v)^{1/2} \exp\left(-\frac{E_g}{2kT_{max}}\right) = N_D \tag{7.16}$$

$$T_{max} = \frac{E_g}{2k \ln [(N_c N_v)^{1/2}/N_D]}. \tag{7.17}$$

For Si $N_c = 2.8 \times 10^{19}$ cm^{-3}, $N_v = 10^{19}$ cm^{-3} around room temperature. At a doping level of $N_D = 5 \times 10^{14}$ cm^{-3}, this gives

$$T_{max} \simeq 550°\text{K} = 277°\text{C}.$$

For Ge, with smaller E_g, T_{max} is about 100°C. These numbers are reduced for lower doping. A practical maximum working temperature for Ge devices is around 90°C and for Si it is around 200°C, but it may be limited by the manufacturer to even lower values because contacts or sealing problems may make this necessary.

It is obvious from (7.17) that the higher E_g is, the better the semiconductor is for high-power (and therefore high-temperature) operation. This is one of the main reasons for silicon replacing germanium and for the interest in developing GaAs devices with still higher E_g.

QUESTIONS

7.1 What is the position of the Fermi level in extrinsic P-type semiconductor at 0°K? where will E_F be at T_{max} given by (7.17)?

7.2 Is the conductivity of AlSb ($E_g = 1.6$ eV) expected to be higher or lower than that of (a) Si and (b) GaAs?

7.3 Given N-type semiconductor bar in which the donor content is about zero at one edge and at degenerate level near the other edge, sketch the energy levels E_c, E_v and E_F along the bar in equilibrium.

7.4 Iron impurities introduce two donor states in Si, one 0.55 eV and the other 0.7 eV below E_c. Why is iron not used to make N-type Si?

7.5 Where is the Fermi level located in an insulator?

7.6 Why should the impurity level E_d (or (E_a) spread into a band in degenerate semiconductors?

7.7 Based on what you have learned about energy levels and allowed states in semiconductors, explain why a semiconductor doped with both donor and acceptor impurities but with $N_A > N_D$ should behave like P-type. What is the effective doping? Where would the Fermi level be?

PROBLEMS

7.8 (a) Use the measured data of Fig. 5.8 to determine E_g for that particular semiconductor at intrinsic temperature. Check Appendix 3 to determine which material it is. (Neglect μ-dependence on T compared to n_i dependence).

(b) Estimate n_i at 300°K. *Hint*: compare n_i at an intrinsic temperature, like 1000°K, to n_i at 300°K.

(c) Assuming $\mu_e >> \mu_h$, obtain an expression for $\mu_e(T)$ in terms of $\mu_e(300°K)$ for the useful range $300 \leq T \leq 500°K$.

7.9 Assuming Maxwell–Boltzmann statistics, calculate the limiting values of N_A and N_D that would make P- or N-type silicon respectively degenerate. Use effective mass values from Table 2.1. What is the average distance between impurity atoms at these concentrations?

7.10 Calculate the Fermi level in Ge containing $N_A = 10^{15}$ cm^{-3} acceptor impurities at $T = 0$, 100, 300, 400°K, and draw conclusions. Assume that 50% of the impurities are ionized at 100°K and 100% at higher temperatures.

7.11 Express E_F in a P$^-$-type semiconductor where thermal generation cannot be neglected in comparison to N_A.

7.12 The occupation probability of the donor energy level E_d is given by (7.15). This level will be full when it contains N_D electrons (per unit volume). Based on this and eq. (7.8), show that the fraction of ionized impurities depend on temperature according to

$$\frac{\bar{n}}{N_D} = \frac{\left\{ -\frac{N_c}{N_D} + \left[\left(\frac{N_c}{N_D} \right)^2 + 8 \frac{N_c}{N_D} \exp \frac{E_c - E_d}{kT} \right]^{1/2} \right\}}{\left(4 \exp \frac{E_c - E_d}{kT} \right)}.$$

Draw $\bar{n}/N_D$ as a function of $kT/(E_c - E_d)$ for $N_c/N_D = 10^3$ (i.e. $N_D = 2.8 \times 10^{16}$ cm^{-3}). Calculate the fraction of ionized phosphorus impurities in silicon ($E_c - E_d = 0.044$ eV) at 50°K and at 300°K. At what temperature are 95% of the impurity atoms ionized?

7.13 The effective densities of states and E_g dependence on temperature for Ge around room temperature are given by

$$N_c = 1.04 \times 10^{19} \text{ cm}^{-3}$$
$$N_v = 6 \times 10^{18} \text{ cm}^{-3}$$
$$E_g = 0.67 - 3.7 \times 10^{-4}(T - 300) \text{ eV}.$$

Calculate the maximum possible temperature of operation for doping levels of $N_A = 10^{14}$ cm^3 and 10^{18} cm^{-3}.

THE PN JUNCTION 8

The PN junction, i.e. that specific location in the semiconductor where impurity type changes from P to N while the lattice structure continues undisturbed, is the most important region in any semiconductor device. Many of its electrical properties depend on the method by which it is made. In this chapter we shall first describe some processes for making junctions and then develop the electrical characteristics of the junctions under static conditions. Finally, we shall examine the important problem of contacting the semiconductor.

8.1 Methods of Making Junctions

A PN junction is *not* the interface between two pieces of semiconductor of opposite types pressed together. It is a single piece of crystal lattice which contains an excess of donor impurities on one side and of acceptor impurities on the other.

The important current methods of making junctions are diffusion, epitaxy, and ion implantation. A fourth method, alloying, was very important in the Ge era. It is still in use in power transistor processing and in metal to semiconductor contact formation. We shall give here only a short description of each method. Diffusion, epitaxy and implantation will be described in more detail in Chapter 16.

(a) Alloy Junction

On a desired region of the surface of a semiconductor wafer, say N-type, a small amount of impurity of the opposite type (such as Al on Si or In on Ge) is deposited. The wafer is then put into a furnace in an inert atmosphere and the temperature raised towards the eutectic point. A thin film of melt then forms at the interface. On gradual cooling, the melt solidifies in a single crystal form, continuing the lattice structure of the underlying crystal and containing an excess of the new impurity, its concentration depending on the solid solubility of that impurity in the semiconductor. The recrystallized region is therefore of the opposite type to the original wafer, and an alloy junction forms between them. This is one of the oldest methods for making junctions, mostly used in Ge diodes and transistor production. Figure 8.1 shows such an alloy junction between an N-type Ge wafer and an In metal dot. An alloy junction has a characteristic very steep doping profile slope near the plane of the junction, as shown in Fig. 8.1(b). Away from the junction the doping is constant. Such junctions are therefore called *step junctions*.

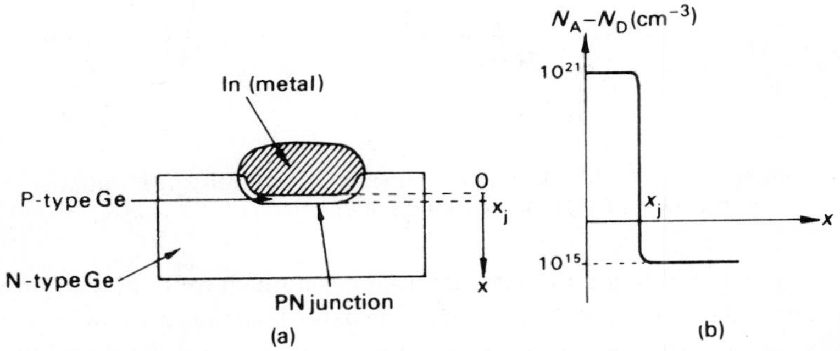

Figure 8.1. N-Ge to In alloy junction: (a) cross section (x_j is junction depth below metal–semiconductor interface); (b) impurity profile of the resulting step junction.

(b) Diffused Junction

Diffusion is the most common way of making junctions today. A semiconductor wafer, called a substrate, which e.g. may be P-type silicon wafer originally doped with boron atoms to a concentration of N_A, is put into a diffusion furnace kept at high temperature, usually above 1000°C. A carrier gas such as nitrogen or argon is introduced into the furnace, carrying with it molecules (in vapor form) of some compound of the opposite impurity type, such as phosphorus in $POCl_3$. At this high temperature the compound breaks down and phosphorus atoms, deposited on the substrate surface, slowly diffuse into the semiconductor. Since a prerequisite for diffusion is a concentration gradient, it is obvious that the maximum concentration of the diffusing impurity will occur on the surface, gradually falling off towards the inside. The depth at which the diffusing impurity concentration is down to the substrate background concentration is the junction depth. By strict control of time and temperature (to better than ±0.25°C) very accurate junction depth, usually a few microns or less, can be achieved. By limiting the diffusion to specific regions on the substrate surface only, through use of a silicon dioxide (SiO_2) diffusion-blocking mask (created beforehand on the substrate by photolithographic techniques to be described in Chapter 16) one can make many junctions of small area on the same wafer. A cross section and typical impurity profile of a diffused junction are shown in Fig. 8.2.

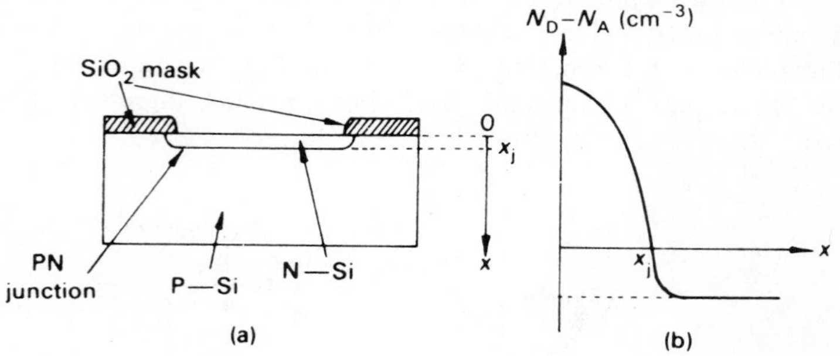

Figure 8.2. Diffused junction: (a) cross section; (b) impurity concentration profile (logarithmic scale).

It should be noted that a diffused junction has a much more graded impurity profile near the vicinity of the junction. The oxide layer has a second important role beside preventing diffusion into unwanted regions. Because diffusion proceeds laterally as well as downwards, the edge of the junction emerges to the surface under the oxide protection, which is important in preventing surface leakage effects. Such junctions are said to be *passivated*. Details of diffusion systems and the impurity profiles resulting from diffusion can be found in References 1 and 12.

(c) Epitaxy

Epitaxial crystal growth is a commonly used step in Si and GaAs device production. It means growing a thin, single crystal layer, doped N or P to the required resistivity, on a single crystal substrate that might be doped differently or with an opposite type dopant. The layer continues the crystallographic structure of the substrate and it is even possible to grow one semiconductor on another provided their lattice constants match (heterostructure). In epitaxy one has more flexibility in controlling the impurity profile, though very sudden changes in concentration are difficult to obtain.

(d) Ion Implantation

This is a new method, finding more and more use today. Ions of the desired impurity are first accelerated in vacuo to high energies and then shot at the semiconductor substrate. The ions penetrate the lattice, usually to a depth of a fraction of a micron. The crystal structure is disturbed by implantation and must later be annealed at elevated temperature, a step which may serve also for further diffusion of the implanted atoms. During annealing they move to substitutional lattice positions where they are electrically active as impurities. Excellent control of the implanted dose, uniformity across the surface and repeatability in production can be achieved.

8.2 The Junction in Equilibrium

First, let us get a physical picture of the junctions in equilibrium. Figure 8.3(a) shows the impurity atoms on both sides of the junction, together with the contributed carriers (the semiconductor atoms are omitted for clarity) as though complete neutrality existed everywhere. At any point the ionized impurities charge is balanced by the opposite charge of the free carriers:

$$N_D + \bar{p} = N_A + \bar{n}. \tag{8.1}$$

Such a situation cannot really exist. The electrons, which are abundant on the N side, diffuse into the P side, where there are very few of them. Holes diffuse in the opposite direction. A momentary diffusion current flow arises, as marked by the dashed line in Fig. 8.3(b). But this flow causes an immediate loss of neutrality: the N side, losing electrons, is charged positive because of the net donor charge left behind, the P side similarly becomes negatively charged. A potential barrier build up across the junction which blocks any further majority carrier diffusion and makes the current zero, as it would be in equilibrium. One can consider that the electric potential difference that forms causes drift currents which exactly balance the diffusion currents set up by the concentration gradients. These drift currents are shown by the solid lines in Fig. 8.3(b). For each carrier type there must, therefore, be two current components, diffusion and drift, which balance each other to zero at thermodynamic equilibrium (the principle of detailed balance).

A region must therefore exist, on both sides of the metallurgical junction, in which there is a built-in field in equilibrium and in which there is a depletion of mobile carriers, since the field sweeps them away. This region is called the *depletion layer*. It is a space-charge region because of the net ionized impurity charge in it. It is shown in Fig. 8.3(c).

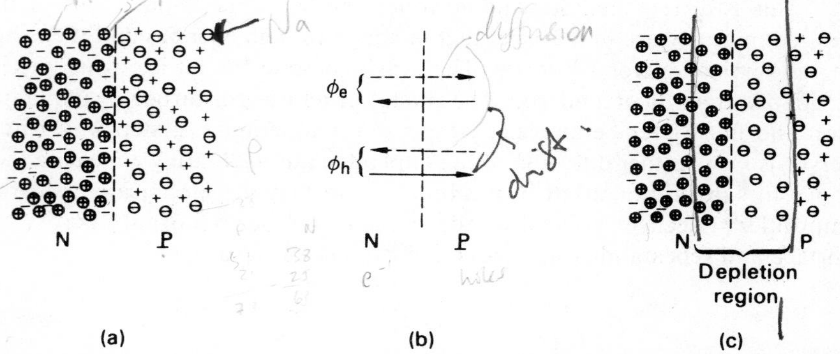

Figure 8.3. The step junction: (a) the junction vicinity as it would look if the carriers did not diffuse: ⊕ionized donors; ⊖ionized acceptors; +holes; −electrons; (b) electron and hole flows: ------ diffusion flow; —— drift flow; (c) distribution of ionized impurities and free carriers in equilibrium.

To obtain quantitative expressions for the built-in field and the width of the depletion layer, we need the transport equations (4.15), (4.16) which are repeated here for convenience

$$J_h = q\mu_h \bar{p} E - qD_h \frac{d\bar{p}}{dx}$$

$$J_e = q\mu_e \bar{n} E + qD_e \frac{d\bar{n}}{dx}$$

and Poisson's equation (in one dimension) which relates the rate of change of the electric field E to the net charge density ρ and dielectric constant $\varepsilon\varepsilon_0$

$$\frac{dE}{dx} = -\frac{d^2V}{dx^2} = \frac{\rho}{\varepsilon\varepsilon_0}$$

where V is the potential. From the preceding discussion we must have $J_h = J_e = 0$ in equilibrium. From $J_h = 0$ we get

$$E\,dx = \frac{D_h}{\mu_h}\frac{1}{\bar{p}}\,d\bar{p}.$$

Integrating E from the P to the N side, between points far enough from the junction for its influence to be negligible and for neutrality to hold, where $\bar{p}_P = N_A$ on the P side and $\bar{p}_n = n_i^2/N_D$ on the N side, one gets the *built-in voltage* denoted by V_B (also known as the *diffusion voltage*):

$$V_B = -\int_P^N E\,dx = -\frac{D_h}{\mu_h}\int_P^N \frac{1}{\bar{p}}\,d\bar{p} = \frac{D_h}{\mu_h}\ln\frac{\bar{p}_p}{\bar{p}_n} = \frac{D_h}{\mu_h}\ln\frac{N_A N_D}{n_i^2}. \tag{8.2}$$

Were we to start from the $J_e=0$ equation, we would have obtained in a similar manner

$$V_B = -\int_P^N E\,dx = \frac{D_e}{\mu_e}\int_P^N \frac{1}{\bar{n}}\,d\bar{n} = \frac{D_e}{\mu_e}\ln\frac{N_A N_D}{n_i^2}. \tag{8.3}$$

Since it is the same V_B irrespective of whether (8.2) or (8.3) is used, we must have:

$$\frac{D_h}{\mu_h} = \frac{D_e}{\mu_e}, \tag{8.4}$$

which can be recognized as part of Einstein's relation (4.10).

It is worthwhile to obtain V_B by using another starting point: the position of the Fermi level. In any type of device, in equilibrium, composed of alternating N and P regions or even of different materials in contact with each other, the Fermi level must be the same throughout. This can be shown as follows: The probability of finding an electron at energy E must be the same throughout, or else the electrons would flow to those regions of higher probability but of the same energy. However, no constant flow is possible in equilibrium. By (6.40) or (6.41) the probability is determined by $E - E_F$; therefore E_F must be constant everywhere. Applied to the PN junction, we know from (7.13) and (7.14), together with Fig. 7.2, that E_F is shifted towards E_c in an N-type semiconductor, and towards E_v in a P-type. If E_F is constant, the conduction and the valence bands have to bend in the vicinity of the junction. This is shown in Fig. 8.4. The energy level E_{F_i} is the position of E_F in an intrinsic semiconductor (approximately in the middle of the gap), qV_n and qV_p are the energy shifts of E_F on the two sides of the junction with respect to E_{F_i}. This bending means that an electric potential difference forms across the junction in equilibrium. This is our built-in voltage V_B. One can consider the junction as a contact between two regions of different chemical potentials, determined by the concentrations of the mobile carriers. The gradient in chemical potential causes diffusion which, because of the charge associated with the carriers, creates an electrical potential difference. This serves to stop further diffusion. In thermodynamic equilibrium, it is the *electrochemical potential* that must be constant throughout, and this is another name for the Fermi level.

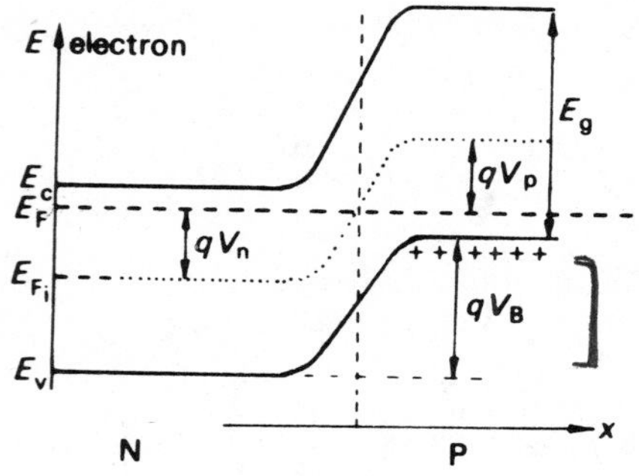

Figure 8.4. Energy levels near a PN junction in equilibrium.

When two different materials, such as a metal and a semiconductor, are brought into contact, the two Fermi levels align themselves, and thus create a contact potential difference. We shall discuss such contacts in Section 8.5.

Returning to Fig. 8.4, we see that

$$V_B = V_n - V_p. \tag{8.5}$$

By using (7.13) and (7.14), we obtain

$$qV_n = kT \ln \frac{N_D}{n_i}, \quad qV_p = -kT \ln \frac{N_A}{n_i}.$$

Substituting into (8.5), we get

$$V_B = \frac{kT}{q} \ln \frac{N_A N_D}{n_i^2}. \tag{8.6}$$

Comparing this with (8.3), we get Einstein's relation of (4.10) again, this time in its full form:

$$\frac{D_e}{\mu_e} = \frac{D_h}{\mu_h} = \frac{kT}{q}.$$

The built-in voltage V_B depends on the concentrations of majority carriers on both sides of the junction. Because of n_i^2 in (8.6), V_B in Si is much larger than in Ge, and it is even larger in GaAs (with all at the same temperature).

8.3 The Depletion Region in Equilibrium and Under Reverse Bias

In order to find how the potential, electric field and charge depend on x, the distance from the junction plane, Poisson's equation must be used because of the net impurity charge in the depletion region. Let us obtain this equation. Use of (7.12) yields for the N side of the junction:

$$qV_n = E_F - E_{F_i} = \frac{kT}{2} \ln \frac{\bar{n}_n}{\bar{p}_n}, \tag{8.7}$$

where V_n depends on x (see Fig. 8.4). Use of $\bar{n}\bar{p} = n_i^2$ gives

$$qV_n = kT \ln \frac{\bar{n}_n}{n_i} \tag{8.8}$$

or

$$\bar{n}_n = n_i \exp\left(\frac{qV_n}{kT}\right). \tag{8.9}$$

Similarly, for the P side

$$\bar{p}_p = n_i \exp\left(-\frac{qV_p}{kT}\right). \tag{8.10}$$

The last two equations are called the *Boltzmann relations*. Using them we can express the carrier concentrations as functions of the potentials V_n and V_p. The two separate potentials can be combined into one by taking the intrinsic Fermi level E_{F_i} at the junction plane $x=0$ as the common reference level of zero potential. This combined potential $V(x)$ would then revert to $V_n(x)$ for $x<0$ and to $V_p(x)$ for $x>0$.

The total charge density in the depletion region is therefore

$$Q = q(N_D + \bar{p} - N_A - \bar{n}) = q\left[N_D - N_A - 2n_i \sinh \frac{qV(x)}{kT}\right], \tag{8.11}$$

where (8.9) and (8.10) have been used.

Poisson's equation can now be written for our one-dimensional junction

$$\frac{d^2V(x)}{dx^2} = -\frac{dE}{dx} = -\frac{q}{\varepsilon\varepsilon_0}\left[N_D - N_A - 2n_i \sinh \frac{qV(x)}{kT}\right]. \tag{8.12}$$

This is a second-order, nonlinear differential equation for $V(x)$. To solve it we must know the impurity profiles $N_A(x)$ and $N_D(x)$. Analytic solutions can be obtained only for very simple cases such as the ideal step junction, where

$N_D = \text{constant}$	$N_A = 0$	for $x < 0$
$N_D = 0$	$N_A = \text{constant}$	for $x > 0$

or a linearly graded junction, where $N_A = gx$ $(x>0)$ and $N_D = -gx$ $(x<0)$. g (m^{-4}) is a positive constant.

In real junctions where N_A, N_D are complex functions of x, numerical methods must be used.

We shall confine our treatment to step junctions and look upon the results as the limiting case of real junctions. Our treatment includes one additional approximation, which simplifies the resulting expressions considerably. We assume that the mobile carriers are completely swept out of the depletion region because of the built-in field there. This assumption, born out by exact calculations, enables us to neglect the hyperbolic term in (8.12).

The depletion region extends from the junction to as yet unknown distances d_n and d_p into the N and P sides respectively. Beyond it neutrality reigns again with zero field. The change from full depletion to neutrality is assumed to occur in a step form, as in Fig. 8.5. This is shown by exact calculations to be a good approximation.

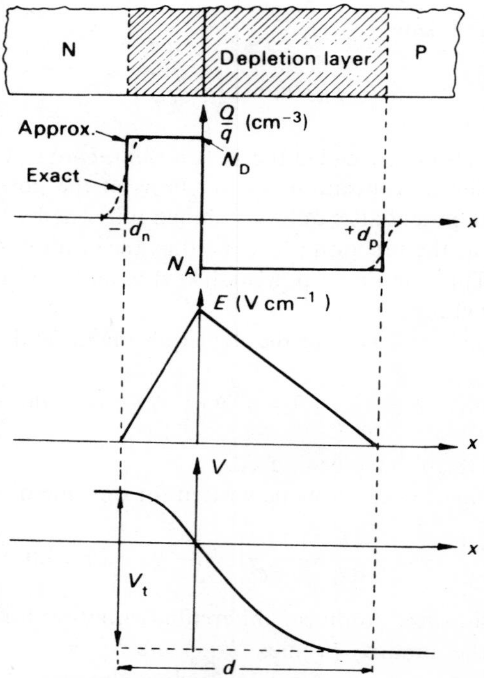

Figure 8.5. The charge, field intensity and potential in the depletion region of a step junction.

The boundary condition for (8.12) is that the total voltage across the junction V_t from $x=-d_n$ on the N side to $x=+d_p$ on the P side, is the sum of the external voltage V_A and the internal built-in voltage V_B given by (8.6). In equilibrium $V_A=0$. If an external voltage V_A is applied it changes V_t and with it d_n and d_p. If V_A has the *same* polarity as V_B (+to N side, −to P side), it is called a *reverse bias* and is then a negative number. Therefore $V_t = V_B - V_A$. If V_A is connected − to N and + to P it is called a *forward bias* and is a positive number. We shall deal with the two cases separately but first let us solve Poisson's equation for any V_t.

Because of the full depletion assumption, (8.12) has the following form on the N side ($n \simeq p \simeq 0$; $N_A = 0$; $N_D = \text{constant}$):

(8.13a) $$\frac{d^2V}{dx^2} = -\frac{qN_D}{\varepsilon\varepsilon_0}, \qquad -d_n \leqslant x \leqslant 0,$$

and on the P side ($n \simeq p \simeq 0$; $N_A = \text{constant}$; $N_D = 0$)

(8.13b) $$\frac{d^2V}{dx^2} = \frac{qN_A}{\varepsilon\varepsilon_0}, \qquad 0 \leqslant x \leqslant d_p,$$

which, after one integration, yield respectively

(8.14a) $$\frac{dV}{dx} = -\frac{qN_D}{\varepsilon\varepsilon_0} x + c_1, \qquad -d_n \leqslant x \leqslant 0,$$

(18.14b) $$\frac{dV}{dx} = \frac{qN_A}{\varepsilon\varepsilon_0} x + c_2, \qquad 0 \leqslant x \leqslant d_p.$$

The integration constants c_1 and c_2 may be replaced by expressions involving d_n and d_p on remembering that the field $E = -dV/dx$ becomes zero at the depletion edges $x = -d_n$ and $x = +d_p$. Therefore

$$c_1 = -\frac{qN_D}{\varepsilon\varepsilon_0} d_n, \qquad c_2 = -\frac{qN_A}{\varepsilon\varepsilon_0} d_p,$$

(8.15a) $$E = -\frac{dV}{dx} = \frac{qN_D}{\varepsilon\varepsilon_0}(d_n + x), \qquad -d_n \leqslant x \leqslant 0,$$

(8.15b) $$E = -\frac{dV}{dx} = -\frac{qN_A}{\varepsilon\varepsilon_0}(x - d_p), \qquad 0 \leqslant x \leqslant \mathrm{d_p}.$$

The field E is shown in Fig. 8.5.

A second integration yields

(8.16a) $$V = -\frac{qN_D}{\varepsilon\varepsilon_0}\left(d_n x + \frac{x^2}{2}\right) + D_1, \qquad -d_n \leqslant x \leqslant 0$$

(18.16b) $$V = \frac{qN_A}{\varepsilon\varepsilon_0}\left(\frac{x^2}{2} - d_p x\right) + D_2, \qquad 0 \leqslant x \leqslant d_p.$$

At $x = 0$ the two equations yield the same potential. Therefore $D_1 = D_2$. Since we took $x = 0$ as the reference plane for zero potential we also have $D_1 = D_2 = 0$. The potential $V(x)$ is also shown in Fig. 8.5.

The potential difference V_t is given by that from $x=-d_n$ to $x=+d_p$, since it is only in this region that there is a field:

$$V_t = V(-d_n) - V(+d_p) = \frac{q}{2\varepsilon\varepsilon_0}(N_D d_n^2 + N_A d_p^2). \tag{8.17}$$

An additional relation is still needed to determine d_n and d_p separately. This can be obtained from the condition that the net positive charge on the N side equals the net negative charge on the P side, or that the field at $x=0$, obtained from (8.15a), is the same as that obtained from (8.15b) (which by Gauss's law amounts to the same thing):

$$\frac{Q}{A} = qN_D d_n = qN_A d_p \tag{8.18}$$

where A is the junction area. The charge Q is also shown in Fig. 8.5. From (8.17) and (8.18) one can obtain d_n and d_p:

$$d_n = \left(\frac{2\varepsilon\varepsilon_0 V_t}{q} \frac{N_A}{N_D(N_A+N_D)}\right)^{1/2} \tag{8.19a}$$

$$d_p = \left(\frac{2\varepsilon\varepsilon_0 V_t}{q} \frac{N_D}{N_A(N_A+N_D)}\right)^{1/2} \tag{8.19b}$$

And the total length of the depletion layer is

$$d = d_n + d_p = \left(\frac{2\varepsilon\varepsilon_0 V_t}{q(N_A+N_D)}\right)^{1/2}\left[\left(\frac{N_A}{N_D}\right)^{1/2} + \left(\frac{N_D}{N_A}\right)^{1/2}\right]. \tag{8.20}$$

It should be noted that d_n and d_p are proportional to $V_t^{1/2}$, which is characteristic of the step junction. Were we to analyze the linear graded junction (Problem 8.14) we would have found $V_t^{1/3}$ dependency.

The maximum field occurs at the metallurgical junction, at $x=0$, as can be seen from (8.15) and (8.19):

$$E_{max} = \frac{qN_D d_n}{\varepsilon\varepsilon_0} = \frac{qN_A d_p}{\varepsilon\varepsilon_0} = \left(\frac{2qV_t}{\varepsilon\varepsilon_0} \frac{N_A N_D}{N_A+N_D}\right)^{1/2}. \tag{8.21}$$

To get an estimate of the numbers involved, let us calculate V_B, d_n and d_p for a step junction in Si with the following parameters:

$$N_A = 10^{18}\ \text{cm}^{-3}, \qquad \frac{kT}{q} = 26\ \text{mV},$$

$$N_D = 10^{15}\ \text{cm}^{-3}, \qquad T = 300°\text{K},$$

$$n_i^2 = 2\times 10^{20}\ \text{cm}^{-6}, \qquad \varepsilon = 12.$$

From (8.6),

$$V_B = 26\times 10^{-3} \ln \frac{10^{18}\times 10^{15}}{2\times 10^{20}} = 0.76\ \text{V}.$$

Using (8.19) for the equilibrium case ($V_t = V_B$),

$$d_n = \left[\frac{2\times 12\times 8.85\times 10^{-14}\times 0.76}{1.6\times 10^{-19}}\ \frac{10^{18}}{10^{15}(10^{18}+10^{15})}\right]^{1/2} = 10^{-4}\ \text{cm} = 1\ \mu\text{m},$$

$$d_p = \left[\frac{2\times 12\times 8.85\times 10^{-14}\times 0.76}{1.6\times 10^{-19}}\ \frac{10^{15}}{10^{18}(10^{18}+10^{15})}\right]^{1/2} = 10^{-7}\ \text{cm} = 1\ \text{nm}.$$

From (8.21),

$$E_{max} = \left[\frac{2\times 1.6\times 10^{-19}\times 0.76}{12\times 8.85\times 10^{-14}}\ \frac{10^{18}\times 10^{15}}{10^{18}+10^{15}}\right]^{1/2} = 15\ \text{kV cm}^{-1} = 1.5\ \text{V}\ \mu\text{m}^{-1}.$$

If a reverse bias of $V_A = -50$ V is applied to this junction, the total voltage across it will be $V_t = V_B - V_A = 0.76 + 50 \simeq 50$ V. The depletion layer widths and maximum field will go up in proportion to the square root of the voltage ratio, i.e. by

$$\left(\frac{V_t}{V_B}\right)^{1/2} \simeq \left(\frac{50}{0.76}\right)^{1/2} \simeq 8.$$

Therefore

$$\begin{aligned} d_n &= 8\ \mu\text{m} \\ d_p &= 8\ \text{nm} \\ E_{max} &= 12\ \text{V}\ \mu\text{m}^{-1}. \end{aligned}$$

This example brings to light the important practical result that if the doping on one side of the junction is two or more orders of magnitude higher than on the other side, the depletion layer extends mostly into the lower doped side and E_{max} is determined by this alone. If one side is degenerate the depletion layer is practically zero in it. Such a junction is called a *one-sided junction* and is of high enough practical importance to warrant writing (8.19) and (8.21) in an approximate form, appropriate for $N_A \gg N_D$ (or vice versa)

(8.22a) $$d_n \simeq \left(\frac{2\varepsilon\varepsilon_0 V_t}{qN_D}\right)^{1/2}$$

(8.22b) $$d_p \simeq 0$$

(8.23) $$E_{max} \simeq \left(\frac{2qN_D V_t}{\varepsilon\varepsilon_0}\right)^{1/2}.$$

It is obvious that only the lower doped side determines these values.

Application of reverse bias causes separation of the Fermi levels on the two junction sides so as to increase the bending of the energy bands, which now appear as shown in Fig. 8.6. Our equations and example show that the width of the depletion layer and the maximum field at the junction grow with reverse bias. This is true for all types of junctions.

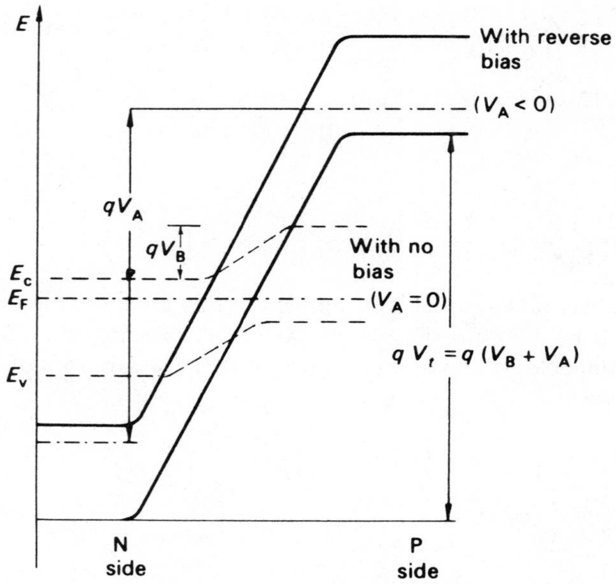

Figure 8.6. Energy levels in a reverse-biased junction.

Since it is the reverse field that blocks diffusion of majority carriers, we can expect the diffusion components in the current expressions (4.22) and (4.23) to become zero. The drift components, due to drift of minority carriers in the opposite direction, are expected to remain unaffected because at the high junction fields, encountered even in equilibrium, the drift velocity is already almost equal to the saturation velocity (about 10^5 m s^{-1}) and cannot grow higher (at fields above about 2 V μm^{-1} new scattering mechanisms start to predominate and the drift velocity saturates).

The two components in the J_e and J_h equations no longer balance to zero as in equilibrium, but in each equation only the drift component, proportional to the small minority density, remains. We therefore expect small net current through the reverse-biased junction, called *leakage current*, which is proportional to the concentrations of the minority carriers. With no minority carriers, the reverse-biased junction current would be exactly zero.

We can understand now why a reverse-biased junction is used for the detection of minority carriers in the Haynes–Schockley experiment (Fig. 5.3): the light-generated minority carriers drift in the semiconductor under the influence of the field until they pass near the junction at C. At that moment they enter the depletion layer and are swept across. The leakage current, being proportional to the minorities, gives us the shape of the minority pulse on the oscilloscope. Detailed expressions for the leakage current will be developed in the next chapter.

8.4 The Junction Under Forward Bias

If two ohmic contacts are attached to the opposite sides of the P and N regions and an external positive voltage V_A applied (+ to P, − to N), the total potential barrier at the junction is reduced to

$$V_t = V_B - V_A. \tag{8.24}$$

(As we shall learn later, V_A is always smaller than V_B.) This is forward-bias connection and it reduces the energy-bands bending as shown in Fig. 8.7.

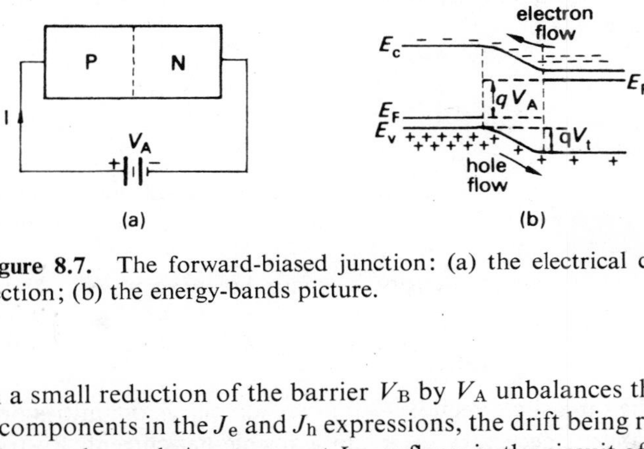

Figure 8.7. The forward-biased junction: (a) the electrical connection; (b) the energy-bands picture.

Even a small reduction of the barrier V_B by V_A unbalances the drift and diffusion components in the J_e and J_h expressions, the drift being reduced and the diffusion unchanged. A net current I now flows in the circuit of Fig. 8.7(a) because of diffusion of majority carriers. It has the opposite direction to the previously discussed leakage-current case. Let us examine the changes in minority carrier concentrations at the boundaries of the depletion layer, these changes being brought about by the diffusion of majority carriers towards that side where they are the minority. First note that the now unbalanced components in the current equations (4.15) and (4.16) are two very large quantities. Taking (4.15), for example, they are $q\mu_h pE$ and $qD_h\, dp/dx$. Using the numerical example of the last section, the carrier concentrations in equilibrium are as shown in Fig. 8.8(a), with very few carriers in the depletion region because of the field there.

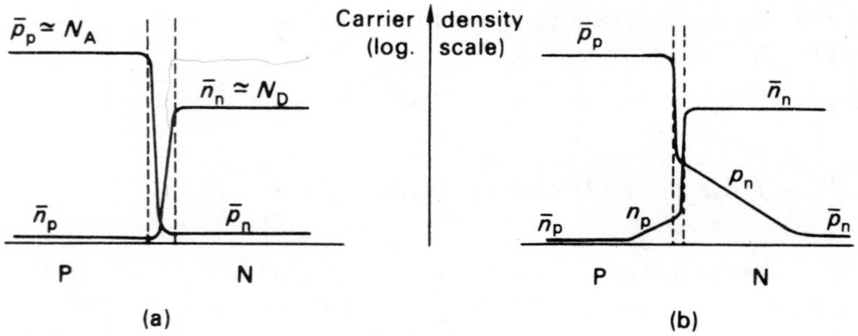

Figure 8.8. Majority and minority carrier concentrations: (a) near a junction in equilibrium; (b) near a junction under forward bias.

One can approximate $\mathrm{d}p/\mathrm{d}x$ by $(\bar{p}_n - \bar{p}_p)/\Delta x$, where Δx is the width of the depletion layer,

$$J_h(\text{diff.}) \simeq -qD_h \frac{\bar{p}_n - \bar{p}_p}{\Delta x} \simeq +qD_h \frac{N_A}{\Delta x},$$

since $\bar{p}_p \simeq N_A$ and $\bar{p}_n = n_i^2/N_D \ll N_A$. From our example, in equilibrium: $N_A = 10^{18}$ cm^{-3}, $\Delta x = 10^{-4}$ cm, and assuming $D_h = 15$ cm^2 s^{-1} in Si we get $J_h(\text{diff.}) = 24\,000$ A cm^{-2}.

This very high current density is exactly balanced by

$$J_h(\text{drift}) = q\mu_h E\bar{p}$$

flowing in the opposite direction. With two such large quantities only a very small unbalance is necessary to obtain a sizable net current. Restricting our attention to such small unbalances it is safe to assume that the functional relationship between E and p or n remains the same in forward bias as it was in equilibrium when $J_e = J_h = 0$. Equations (4.15) and (4.16) then yield respectively

$$E = \frac{D_h}{\mu_h} \frac{1}{p} \frac{\mathrm{d}p}{\mathrm{d}x} = \frac{kT}{q} \frac{1}{p} \frac{\mathrm{d}p}{\mathrm{d}x}$$

$$E = -\frac{D_e}{\mu_e} \frac{1}{n} \frac{\mathrm{d}n}{\mathrm{d}x} = -\frac{kT}{q} \frac{1}{n} \frac{\mathrm{d}n}{\mathrm{d}x}.$$

JACK

Integrating from the P side to the N side boundary of the depletion layer will yield the total voltage V_t as before. Doing this for both expressions of E, we obtain

(8.25a) $$V_t = V_B - V_A = -\int_P^N E\,dx = -\frac{kT}{q}\int_P^N \frac{1}{p}\,dp = \frac{kT}{q}\ln\frac{p_p}{p_n},$$

(8.25b) $$V_t = V_B - V_A = -\int_P^N E\,dx = \frac{kT}{q}\int_P^N \frac{1}{n}\,dn = \frac{kT}{q}\ln\frac{n_n}{n_p}.$$

But n_n and p_p are the majority concentrations at the depletion boundaries, and provided the forward bias is not too high (the exact meaning of which will be explained later), they are not affected by the flow and retain their equilibrium values, namely: $n_n \simeq N_D$ and $p_p \simeq N_A$. Equations (8.25) can then be used to obtain the enhanced minority concentrations at the depletion boundaries:

(8.26a) $$p_n = p_p \exp\left(-\frac{qV_t}{kT}\right) = N_A \exp\left(-\frac{qV_B}{kT}\right)\exp\frac{qV_A}{kT},$$

(8.26b) $$n_p = n_n \exp\left(-\frac{qV_t}{kT}\right) = N_D \exp\left(-\frac{qV_B}{kT}\right)\exp\frac{qV_A}{kT}.$$

The first exponential times N_A or N_D is none other than $\bar{p}_n$ or $\bar{n}_p$ in equilibrium, when $V_A = 0$. To be doubly sure we can compare with (8.6), which tells us that

$$\exp\left(-\frac{qV_B}{kT}\right) = \frac{n_i^2}{N_A N_D} = \frac{\bar{n}_p}{N_D} = \frac{\bar{p}_n}{N_A}.$$

Substituting it into (8.26) we get

(8.27a) $$p_n = \bar{p}_n \exp\frac{qV_A}{kT}$$

(8.27b) $$n_p = \bar{n}_p \exp\frac{qV_A}{kT}.$$

The excess minority concentration, under forward bias, relative to the equilibrium values, are denoted by a circumflex (ˆ) over the letter:

(8.28a) $$\hat{p}_n = p_n - \bar{p}_n = \bar{p}_n\left(\exp\frac{qV_A}{kT} - 1\right),$$

(8.28b) $$\hat{n}_p = n_p - \bar{n}_p = \bar{n}_p\left(\exp\frac{qV_A}{kT} - 1\right).$$

For positive V_A the minority concentrations are therefore increased. In other words, majority diffusion, now unchecked by the reduced drift, increases the same carrier concentration on the other side of the junction, where it plays the minority role. This is called *carrier injection.* The injection grows exponentially with V_A according to (8.28). The situation for a typical forward bias is shown in Fig. 8.8(b). Inside the depletion layer (which is narrowed by the forward bias since V_t is now smaller) there remains a reduced reverse field (since V_A is smaller than V_B) which prevents flooding of it with carriers. The ordinate scale in Fig. 8.8 must be logarithmic to permit inclusion of vastly different concentration values.

The excess minority concentrations near the depletion boundary must gradually decrease as distance from the junction increases, because they recombine with the majorities. The detailed forms of $\hat{n}_p(x)$ and $\hat{p}_n(x)$ depend on the diode structure and will be developed in the next chapter. Equations (8.28) give $\hat{n}_p(0)$ and $\hat{p}_n(0)$ only, where $x=0$ is taken as the respective depletion-layer boundary.

The *injection* is called *low* as long as the increased minority concentration remains at least an order of magnitude lower than the majority on that side, e.g. $p_n < \bar{n}_n/10$. We shall consider this case only, since it is the common one encountered in low-power devices. Under low injection the majority concentrations are practically unchanged from their equilibrium values. In reality, there is a very small change, since the increased minority population starts to violate the electrical neutrality in the bulk semiconductor, outside the depletion region, and as a result a field starts to build up there. This field is immediately felt by the majority carriers and their concentration also grows in the same regions, restoring the neutrality. The relative change, however, in the majority population is negligible under low injection.

The situation is different in the case of *high injection,* i.e. when the forward voltage V_A is high enough to increase the excess minority on at least one side of the junction to the same order of magnitude as the majority on that side. In this case an appreciable field will build up in the bulk semiconductor (outside the depletion layer) on that side, taking up part of the externally applied voltage V_A so that the junction voltage is no longer $V_B - V_A$. In other words, the voltage drop on the bulk N or P regions starts to dominate the device behavior and our equations no longer apply.

Let us clarify this with a numerical example of a step junction in silicon. Let

$$N_A = 10^{19}\ \text{cm}^{-3}, \quad N_D = 10^{16}\ \text{cm}^{-3}, \quad V_A = 10\,\frac{kT}{q} = 0.26\ \text{V}.$$

In equilibrium, therefore, we have outside the depletion region:

$$\bar{n}_n = N_D = 10^{16}\ \text{cm}^{-3}, \qquad \bar{p}_n = \frac{\bar{n}_i^2}{\bar{n}_n} = 2\times 10^4\ \text{cm}^{-3}$$

$$\bar{p}_p = N_A = 10^{19}\ \text{cm}^{-3}, \qquad \bar{n}_p = \frac{\bar{n}_i^2}{\bar{p}_p} = 20\ \text{cm}^{-3}.$$

The increased minority concentrations due to the forward V_A and injection are, by (8.27),

$$p_n(0) \simeq 4.4 \times 10^8 \text{ cm}^{-3}, \qquad \hat{p}_n(0) = p_n(0) - \bar{p}_n \simeq p_n(0)$$

$$n_p(0) \simeq 4.4 \times 10^5 \text{ cm}^{-3}, \qquad \hat{n}_p(0) = n_p(0) - \bar{n}_p \simeq n_p(0).$$

If the majorities are increased by the same amounts, they are left practically unchanged:

$$n_n = \bar{n}_n + \hat{p}_n = 10^{16} + 4.4 \times 10^8 \simeq 10^{16} \text{ cm}^{-3},$$

$$p_p = \bar{p}_p + \hat{n}_p = 10^{19} + 4.4 \times 10^5 \simeq 10^{19} \text{ cm}^{-3}.$$

This is, therefore, a low-injection case.

If the forward voltage V_A is increased to about 30 kT/q, we get

$$\hat{p}_n(0) = 2.1 \times 10^{17} \text{ cm}^{-3}, \qquad \hat{n}_p(0) = 2.1 \times 10^{14} \text{ cm}^{-3},$$

and we see that the excess hole concentration on the lower doped N side is so high as to cause a marked change in the majority population there. We are well into the high-injection region. The two cases are shown in Fig. 8.9.

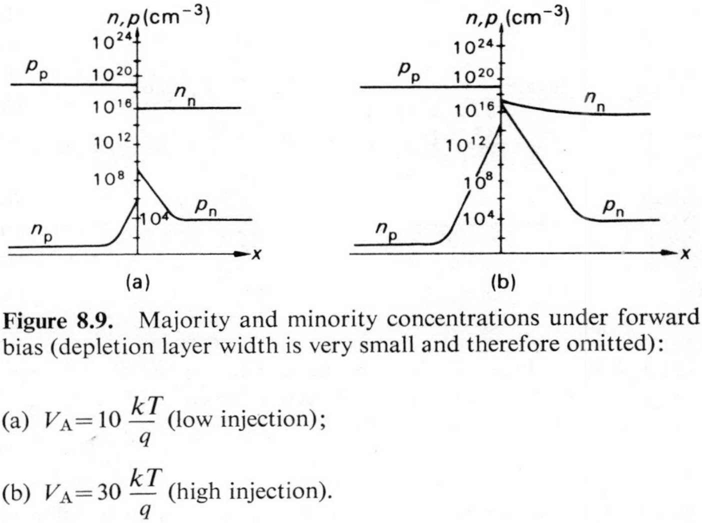

Figure 8.9. Majority and minority concentrations under forward bias (depletion layer width is very small and therefore omitted):

(a) $V_A = 10 \dfrac{kT}{q}$ (low injection);

(b) $V_A = 30 \dfrac{kT}{q}$ (high injection).

8.5 Metal–Semiconductor Contacts

Any practical device involves making metal–semiconductor contacts for outside connections. This is not a trivial problem since such a contact is actually a special type of junction whose conduction properties determine its field of usefulness. These properties can be arrived at from energy-level considerations. We have already mentioned that when two materials are brought into contact the Fermi levels on both sides align themselves after some charge movement.

The Fermi level in metal falls inside the conduction band. Because of the Fermi–Dirac distribution form (6.40), relatively few electrons in the band have higher energies than E_F at room temperature. One can look on E_F as the average energy of the most energetic electrons in the metal. In order for such an energetic electron to be completely emitted from the metal to the outside, one must add to it a certain minimum energy, $E_W(M)$, called the *work function* of the specific metal, above the E_F which it already possesses.

In a semiconductor too, one must add some minimum energy to get electronic emission, but since E_F there is located in the forbidden gap, where there are no electrons, a more meaningful quantity, called *affinity* and denoted by χ, is preferred. This is the additional energy, typical to the semiconductor, that an electron at the bottom of the conduction band, E_c, must have to be emitted. The energy of such an emitted free electron can be taken as a common reference level of zero energy for comparing electron energies in the metal and semiconductor, as is done in Fig. 8.10(a).

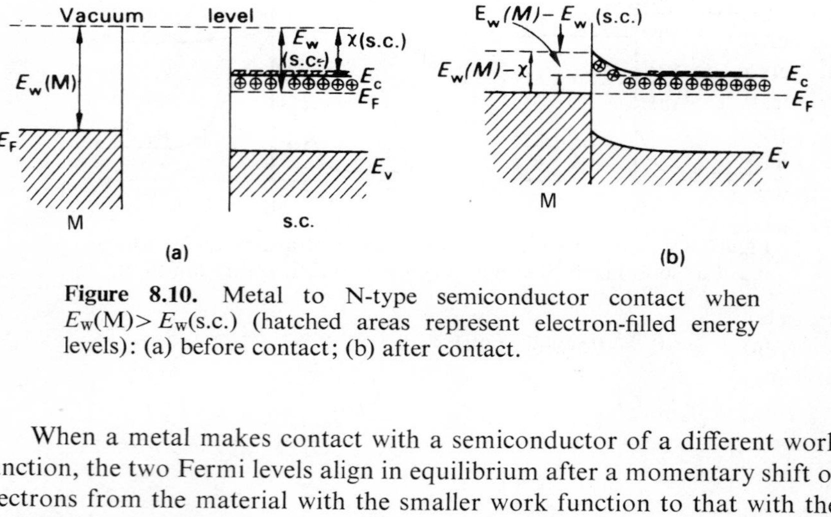

Figure 8.10. Metal to N-type semiconductor contact when $E_W(M) > E_W(s.c.)$ (hatched areas represent electron-filled energy levels): (a) before contact; (b) after contact.

When a metal makes contact with a semiconductor of a different work function, the two Fermi levels align in equilibrium after a momentary shift of electrons from the material with the smaller work function to that with the higher, thus reducing free energy. Fermi-level alignment is reached when an electric potential difference has built up at the interface between the two materials equal to the difference between their work functions. The situation after contact is shown in Fig. 8.10(b), in which an N-type semiconductor is contacted by a metal of a higher work function.

In this case electrons pass from the semiconductor into the metal, which becomes negatively charged, while the loss of electrons creates a positively charged depletion region in the semiconductor near the interface. From the point of view of energy bands, the distance from E_c to E_F in the semiconductor must grow (eq. 7.8) and the bands bend up as shown. The potential barrier that forms opposes further charge shift.

The depletion region extends into the semiconductor for a depth which depends on the doping density. This density is always very much lower than the allowed states and electron densities in the metal around E_F (remember: E_F is near the middle of the conduction band there). The shift of E_F in the metal will therefore be negligible while the shift and band bending in the semiconductor will take up practically all the potential difference given by $E_w(\text{M}) - E_w(\text{s.c.})$. The situation is very similar to the step-junction case, in which one side is very highly doped compared with the other.

Once that potential difference has grown to $(1/q)[E_w(\text{M}) - E_w(\text{s.c.})]$ equilibrium is reached, the depletion region is stabilized and no further net charge will cross the junction.

This difference in work function now forms a barrier which the electrons in the semiconductor must overcome to pass into the metal. The many more numerous electrons in the metal must overcome a higher barrier of

$$\phi_B = E_w(\text{M}) - E_w(\text{s.c.}) + [E_c - E_F(\text{s.c.})] = E_w(\text{M}) - \chi(\text{s.c.})$$

to enter the semiconductor. Use of Boltzmann statistics then shows that the numbers of electrons that have high enough energies to be able to pass one way or the other are equal, and consequently there is zero current and equilibrium.

One should note that holes, the minority carriers, whose energy is higher the lower they are in Fig. 8.10, also have a barrier to overcome to move from the metal, where their energy is above E_F (empty states) into the semiconductor. However, there is no barrier at all – on the contrary there is even an assisting field – to minority hole movement from the semiconductor into the metal. Application of a reverse bias $-V_A$ (N-type semiconductor more positive) lowers the semiconductor bands even further with respect to the metal and increases the barrier which an electron at E_c must overcome to get into the metal. No more electrons will therefore pass that way.

An electron in the metal at E_F, on the other hand, still faces the same barrier ϕ_B as before. Consequently, a small net leakage current will flow, which depends on ϕ_B but not on $-V_A$, as in a reverse-bias PN junction. This situation is shown in Fig. 8.11(b).

Application of a forward bias $+V_A$ (N-type semiconductor negative) lowers the barrier on the semiconductor side, enabling many more majority carriers, i.e. electrons, to cross while the barrier ϕ_B, blocking the metal electrons from crossing back, remains the same. A net large current will now flow. The energy-band picture under this condition is shown in Fig. 8.11(a). The resulting *I–V* characteristic is given in Fig. 8.11(c); the leakage current, however, is too small to be shown. Such a contact is called a *rectifying contact*, which is characterized by widely different resistances in each direction. A device based on such a contact is called a *Schottky-barrier* or a *metal–semiconductor* diode.

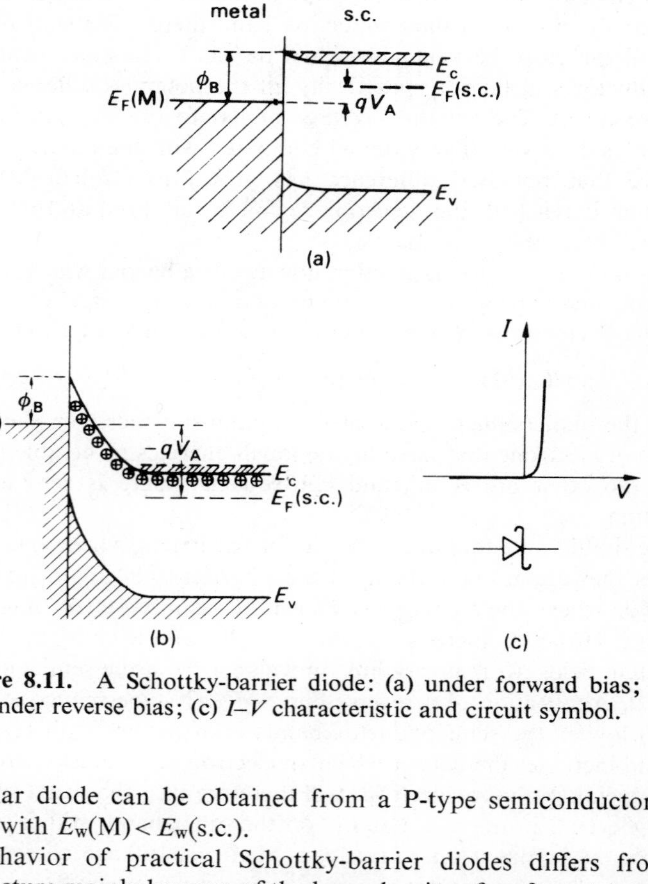

Figure 8.11. A Schottky-barrier diode: (a) under forward bias; (b) under reverse bias; (c) *I–V* characteristic and circuit symbol.

A similar diode can be obtained from a P-type semiconductor–metal contact but with $E_w(M) < E_w(s.c.)$.

The behavior of practical Schottky-barrier diodes differs from our simplified picture mainly because of the large density of surface states, always found at the crystal discontinuity of the surface. These are allowed states with energies inside the band gap. Measurements show surface states to be extra dense around the middle of the gap. The charges contributed by those states force E_F to pass near the center of E_g at the surface, i.e. they cause band bending even without a metal on top. The band picture with no metal looks like Fig. 8.12(a): states below E_F contain electrons, those above it are empty. When the metal is brought into contact with the semiconductor the extra band bending associated with the adjustment of the Fermi levels is slight, since it now requires only a small shift of E_F in the semiconductor to materially change the charge at the surface, namely the charge of those states that moved to the other side of E_F. The band picture with the metal looks, therefore, like Fig. 8.12(b).

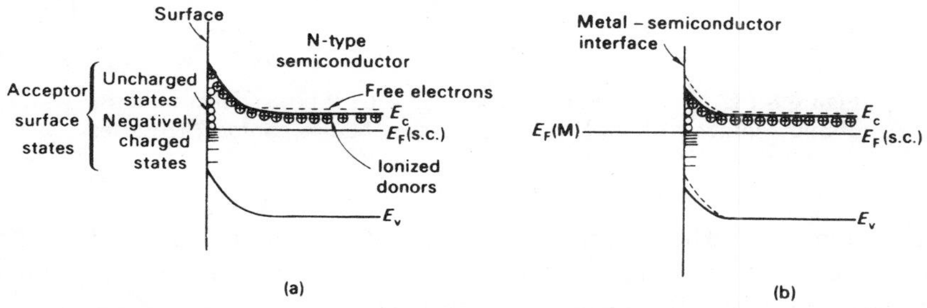

Figure 8.12. The effect of surface states on the metal–semiconductor barrier: (a) bare semiconductor surface with surface states; (b) the effect of the metal on the band bending.

Apparently the surface states reduce the effect of a particular metal work function on the band bending. The type and density of surface states depend on the semiconductor surface treatment. They usually pin E_F at the interface at about $\frac{1}{3}$ E_g above the valence band. Barriers measured on N type semiconductors are therefore about $\frac{2}{3}$ E_g high.

The static characteristics of Schottky-barrier diodes will be discussed in the next chapter and their dynamic behavior in Chapter 11.

For contacting devices, a rectifying contact is undesirable and should be avoided. This can be achieved in two ways.

The first is to choose a metal with a higher work function for a P-type semiconductor (or lower for an N-type). In this case, as shown in Fig. 8.13, the P-type semiconductor is gaining holes in equilibrium, becoming even stronger P-type. From the figure we see that there is no barrier for the holes to surmount, with a consequent very low resistance for current flow in both directions. This is called an *ohmic contact*, whose *V–I* characteristic is given in Fig. 8.13(c). Al is the metal usually used for P-type Si.

For N-type Si, because of the surface states effect mentioned earlier, the contacting problem is more severe. We then use a second approach for obtaining an ohmic contact. This is to increase the semiconductor doping near the interface to the level of degeneracy. The surface states then become completely saturated and the donor impurities keep the Fermi level inside the

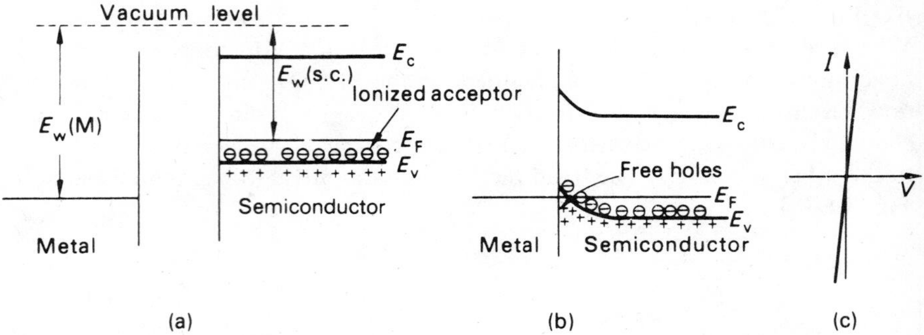

Figure 8.13. Energy bands near a metal to P-type semiconductor ohmic contact with $E_W(M) > E_W(s.c.)$: (a) before contact; (b) after contact; (c) V–I characteristic.

conduction band. The potential barrier and depletion layer formed by the Al contact are then so narrow (a few angströms) that carriers can tunnel through in both directions with very little resistance.

An important property of ohmic contacts is that minority carriers, diffusing in the semiconductor to the vicinity of the contact, readily recombine there because of the large supply of majority carriers. An ohmic contact therefore acts as a virtual sink for minority carriers.

8.6 The Heterojunction

When a layer of a single crystal semiconductor is epitaxially grown on a different semiconductor (which can sometimes be done provided the lattice constants match) then a heterojunction results. It may be an isotype junction if the two have the same type doping (like n–N) or an anisotype if not (like n–P). By convention a lower case letter indicates the smaller band gap semiconductor type and the capital indicates the one with the larger E_g. If the lattice constants of the two materials do not fit, the layer will grow polycrystalline.

Heterojunctions are very attractive since a whole new group of exciting devices (see Chapter 21) become potentially possible once a high quality junction between semiconductors with different band gaps can be made.

The energy band diagram of a heterojunction is much more complicated than that of a homojunction and one must rely heavily on experiment to construct it accurately. To understand the difficulties let us construct that diagram for the two materials (e.g., Ge and GaAs which have lattice fit) shown separated in Fig. 8.14(a) with the vacuum level serving as a common reference point.

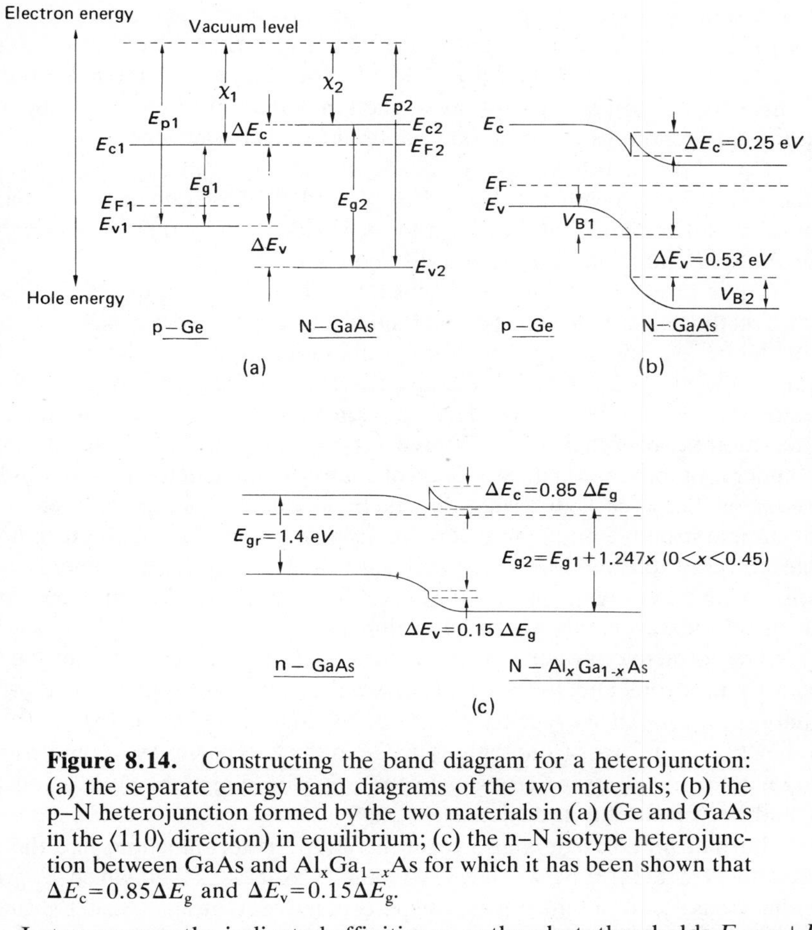

Figure 8.14. Constructing the band diagram for a heterojunction: (a) the separate energy band diagrams of the two materials; (b) the p–N heterojunction formed by the two materials in (a) (Ge and GaAs in the ⟨110⟩ direction) in equilibrium; (c) the n–N isotype heterojunction between GaAs and $Al_xGa_{1-x}As$ for which it has been shown that $\Delta E_c = 0.85\Delta E_g$ and $\Delta E_v = 0.15\Delta E_g$.

Let us assume the indicated affinities χ, or the photothresholds $E_p = \chi + E_g$ (the minimum energy, hf_{min}, that a photon must have if its absorption by the semiconductor may cause a valence band electron to be ejected outside the material) are known. To move an electron from the conduction band E_{c1} of material 1 to E_{c2} of material 2 a net additional energy $\Delta E_c = \chi_1 - \chi_2$ must be added to it. Similarly, to move a hole from E_{v1} to E_{v2} a net additional energy of $\Delta E_v = E_{p2} - E_{p1} = \chi_2 - \chi_1 + (E_{g2} - E_{g1})$ is necessary. Therefore

$$\Delta E_c + \Delta E_v = \Delta E_g. \tag{8.29}$$

Note that for non-degenerate doping levels χ or E_p do not depend on the doping density therefore neither do ΔE_c and ΔE_v.

When a junction is formed, the Fermi levels E_{F1} and E_{F2} (that do depend on the dopings) align themselves by charge movement that results in space charge and band bending on both sides of the interface (like in any junction formation), as shown in Fig. 8.14(b). ΔE_c and ΔE_v at the interface remain unchanged, since one still must invest the same amount of energy to move an electron or a hole from inside one material to inside the other.

Part of the built-in voltage V_B drops on material 1 (marked V_{B1}) and part on material 2 (V_{B2}) with $V_B = V_{B1} + V_{B2}$. V_B and the depletion distances may be found by solving Poisson's equation for each side of the junction, as was done for the homojunction, but using a different ε for each side.

There is, however, a major practical flaw in this procedure. Affinities are not directly measurable and the obtained values depend very much on surface orientation, treatment, regularity, any contamination and the dipole layer that can be shown to form on a free surface. The resulting affinities, which are relatively large numbers (several eV), are known therefore only approximately. One cannot expect their small difference, which gives ΔE_c, to have any useful meaning. A more reasonable theoretical approach pursued today is to construct the energy bands at the interface directly by solving Schrödinger's equation for the atomic structure and potential there, using the same calculation techniques that are used to obtain band structure in a single material. For energy band construction, however, one must still rely on obtaining ΔE_c and ΔE_v from electrical measurements of the heterojunction.

The attractive property of the heterojunction is in the different barriers seen by electrons and holes when a forward voltage is applied. This would enable only one carrier type to be injected. Note that in Fig. 8.14(b) the barrier to holes trying to cross from the p-type Ge to the N-type GaAs would be much larger than for electrons crossing in the opposite direction. Such a junction would be very useful in devices.

Furthermore, barriers also form in isotype heterojunction, like the one shown in Fig. 8.14(c) between n GaAs and N $Al_xGa_{1-x}As$ in which E_g grows with increased Al content (x gives the percentage of Al atoms). Such a structure is very useful in optoelectronics with $0 < x < 0.45$. The ΔE_c and ΔE_v can block carrier diffusion from the GaAs to the $Al_xGa_{1-x}As$ and confine them to the GaAs, which is very important for lasers as we shall learn in Chapter 10.

QUESTIONS

8.1 Can a PN junction in which the impurity concentration drops as one moves away from the junction be obtained by diffusion? By epitaxial growth? (This is called a hyper-abrupt junction).

8.2 Sketch E_c, E_v and E_F along a P-type semiconductor bar in which the doping gradually increases with the distance from one edge.

8.3 Is the junction area obtained by diffusion through a window in a SiO_2 mask the same as the window area? For a rectangular window with sides a and b and a junction depth of x_j, estimate the ratio of junction to window areas.

8.4 How is the junction depth obtained by diffusion into a uniformly doped substrate affected by
(a) increased diffusion temperature,
(b) increased diffusion duration,
(c) the same diffusion performed into a lower resistivity substrate?

8.5 Can one measure separately the drift and diffusion components of J_e and J_h in a junction at equilibrium?

8.6 Is the electric field in the junction increased or reduced by applying a forward bias to it? By using a higher doped semiconductor?

8.7 Towards which side of the junction does the depletion layer extend more in a step junction with unequal doping levels on the two sides? Sketch the depletion layer widths in a junction obtained by diffusion into a uniformly doped substrate when under reverse bias.

8.8 How is the maximum electric field in a junction under a given reverse voltage $-V_A$ affected by increasing the doping of the higher doped side even higher? by increasing the doping of the lower doped side?

8.9 Sketch the energy bands across a metal to P-type semiconductor if $E_w(M) < E_w(s.c.)$.

PROBLEMS

8.10 Compare the built-in voltage V_B in junctions made in Si and in Ge with the same doping concentrations of $N_D = 10^{14}\ cm^{-3}$, $N_A = 10^{17}\ cm^{-3}$.

8.11 Calculate the maximum field and depletion layer widths in the junctions of Problem 8.10.

8.12 The PN junction of Problem 8.10, in Si, is reverse biased by $V_A = -10$V. Make a scaled drawing of the dependence of space charge, field and potential on the distance from the junction.

8.13 Obtain a general expression for the ratio of depletion-layer widths on the two sides of a step junction.

If a junction is made by diffusion into a uniformly doped substrate, the impurity profile in the immediate junction vicinity can be assumed linear as in Fig. 8.15, with g being the concentration slope (dimensions: m^{-4}).

Such a junction is called a linear graded junction. Show that if $d(-V)$ is the total width of the depletion layer under a bias of $-V$, and V_B is the built in (or diffusion) voltage, then

$$V_B = \frac{2kT}{q} \ln \frac{gd(0)}{n_i}, \tag{8.30}$$

$$d(-V) = \left[\frac{12\varepsilon\varepsilon_0 V_B}{gq}\left(1 + \frac{V}{V_B}\right)\right]^{1/3}. \tag{8.31}$$

[*Hint*: solve Poisson's equation assuming that the field is negligibly small at $x = \pm d(0)/2$.]

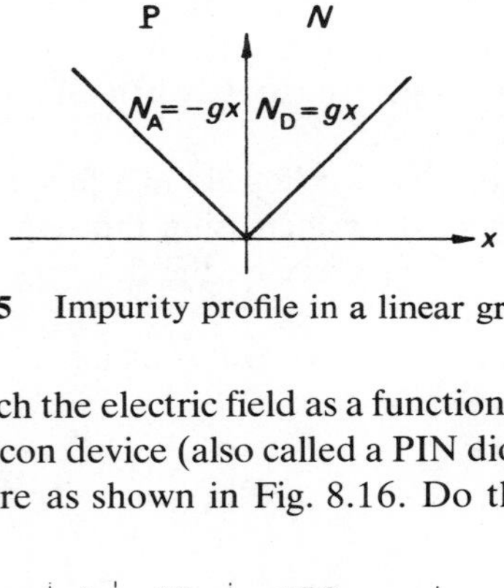

Figure 8.15 Impurity profile in a linear graded junction.

8.15 Calculate and sketch the electric field as a function of distance in a $P^+\nu N^+$ structure of the silicon device (also called a PIN diode) whose dimensions and connections are as shown in Fig. 8.16. Do this for $V_A = -10$V and -100V.

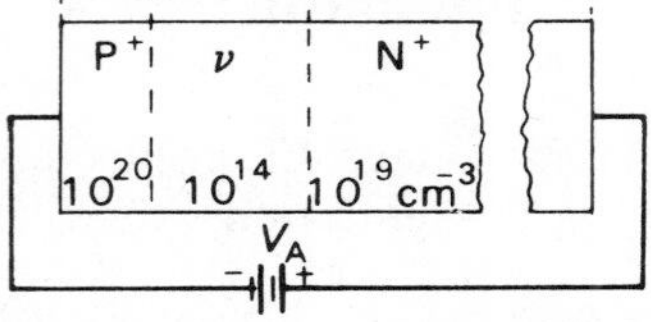

Figure 8.16 A PIN silicon diode for Problem 8.15 (concentrations in cm^{-3}; dimensions in μm).

8.16 Make a schematic drawing of the energy levels near a junction between two P-type regions of different resistivities (also called a *high–low junction*). Given that the doping levels are N_{A_1} and N_{A_2} find the diffusion (built in) voltage of such a junction in equilibrium. Apply an external bias to your energy-band picture and decide whether this junction would behave like an ohmic or a rectifying junction.

8.17 A step junction is made by a short phosphorus diffusion into a boron doped silicon substrate with a doping concentration of 10^{15} cm^{-3}. Assuming the phosphorus concentration is 10^{20} cm^{-3}, estimate the forward voltage at which high injection effects will appear. Show from the carrier distribution that under high injection part of the applied voltage must drop on the bulk of the lower doped side of the junction.

8.18 When gold is deposited on N-type silicon a Schottky-barrier diode of $\phi_B = 0.79$ eV is formed. Obtain an expression for the fraction of the available electrons in the metal that have high enough energy to surmount that barrier and can spill over into the silicon?

Assuming the Si doping is 10^{15} cm^{-3}, what is the barrier height presented to the semiconductor electrons (neglect surface states)?

8.19 Assuming the barrier height in Problem 8.18 is unchanged when the Si doping is increased, calculate the doping concentration necessary to reduce the depletion-layer width in the semiconductor to less than 10 nm in equilibrium (electrons can pass such narrow barriers by tunnelling through them, giving such a junction an ohmic characteristic).

8.20 Show that the capacitance per unit area of a PN heterojunction between material 1 $(N_A, \varepsilon_1\varepsilon_0)$ and material 2 $(N_D, \varepsilon_2\varepsilon_0)$ at a reverse voltage $V_t = V_B + V_A$ is given by

$$\frac{C}{A} = \left[\frac{qN_A N_D \varepsilon_1 \varepsilon_2}{2V_t(\varepsilon_1 N_A + \varepsilon_2 N_D)}\right]^{1/2} \tag{8.32}$$

Start from the depletion approximation and Poisson's equation like for the homojunction.

8.21 What are the expected changes in carrier distribution when an isotype heterojunction between N-type Ge and N-type GaAs is formed? Draw a sketch of the expected energy bands in equilibrium.

JUNCTION DIODES AND THEIR STATIC CHARACTERISTICS 9

The first semiconductor device that we shall analyze is the diode. It is based on the PN junction, but to characterize it completely we must also consider the rest of its structure: area, impurity profile, dimensions and properties of the bulk regions on both sides of the junctions. In this chapter, only the d.c. static characteristics will be covered. The high-frequency and switching properties are described in Chapter 11.

9.1 The Wide-diode Characteristic

By a wide diode we mean a device in which the bulk P and N regions on both sides of the junction are wide compared with the minority diffusion length in them.

We learned in the last chapter that forward biasing a junction causes majority carrier injection from one side to the other, creating excess minority concentrations at the depletion layer edges whose ratio, by (8.28), is

$$\frac{\hat{p}_n(0)}{\hat{n}_p(0)}=\frac{\bar{p}_n}{\bar{n}_p}\simeq\frac{n_i^2/N_D}{n_i^2/N_A}=\frac{N_A}{N_D}. \tag{9.1}$$

In most practical cases one junction side has much higher doping than the other. If, e.g., $N_A \gg N_D$, we see that electron injection to the P side can be neglected compared to hole injection to the N side. We shall first consider such a case.

Figure 9.1 shows what happens to the injected holes: they start diffusing into the depth of the N region, their number gradually falling off because of recombination with the majority electrons. After a distance of a few diffusion lengths, L_h, the excess hole concentration will disappear and we shall be back at equilibrium concentrations.

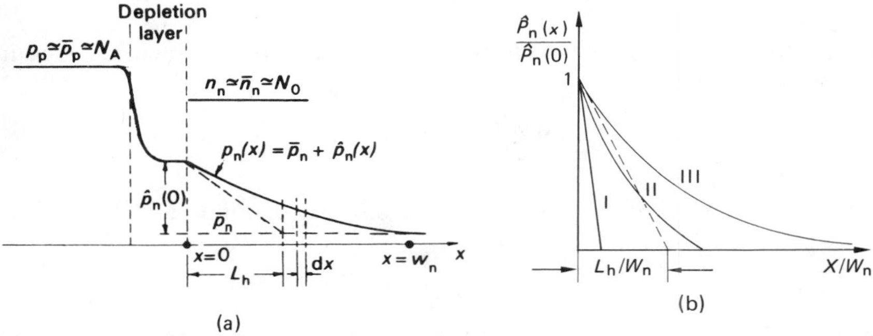

Figure 9.1. Hole concentrations on both sides of a forward–biased junction: (a) definitions for calculating the wide diode case; (b) injected hole concentrations for narrow (I), medium (II) and wide (III) diodes.

In a wide diode, W_n, the width of the N region, is much larger than L_h. In order to find $\hat{p}_n(x)$, where x is the distance from the depletion edge, at a constant V_A, we use the hole continuity eq. (4.19) for the differential volume $A\,dx$ (A = area):

$$0 = -\frac{dI_h}{dx} - qA\frac{\hat{p}_n(x)}{\tau_h}, \tag{9.2}$$

i.e., the hole current change dI_h in the x direction is equal to the charge of the holes recombining in that volume per unit time. The hole current gradually dies away with x ($dI_h < 0$), but Kirchhoff's current law still holds, since as each hole recombines an electron disappears too, so new electrons must flow from the contact at $x = W_n$ to supply the recombining electrons. The current, therefore, gradually changes from being carried by holes to being carried by electrons. Another very small component of the electron current is the one that is injected into the P region (which we neglected in this case of $N_A >> N_D$).

The total current, $I = I_h + I_e$, on the N side is therefore in the positive x direction and is constant at any cross section. To obtain it, it is enough to find $I_h(0)$, since at $x = 0$, before any holes recombine, the whole current is still carried by holes only (i.e., neglecting the injected electrons):

$$I = I_h(0) = I_h(x) + I_e(x). \tag{9.3}$$

The minority hole current is caused by diffusion, since there is a concentration gradient in the x direction. The drift component in the minority current can be neglected, since the field E in the bulk N region is insignificant (though enough to account for the majority electron current $qn_n\mu_e E$ because $n_n \simeq N_D \gg p_n$). The diffusion current, as we already know, is given by

$$I_h(x) = -qAD_h \frac{d\hat{p}_n(x)}{dx}. \tag{9.4}$$

Substituting I_h in (9.2) gives us the diffusion equation, which we met in Chapter 4:

$$\frac{d^2\hat{p}_n(x)}{dx^2} - \frac{\hat{p}_n(x)}{D_h\tau_h} = 0. \tag{9.5}$$

Using the definition of diffusion length, $L_h^2 = D_h\tau_h$, the solution is

$$\hat{p}_n(x) = c_1 \exp\left(-\frac{x}{L_h}\right) + c_2 \exp\left(+\frac{x}{L_h}\right). \tag{9.6}$$

Because of recombination, $\hat{p}_n(x)$ must approach zero for $x \gg L_h$; therefore $c_2 = 0$. At $x = 0$, use of (8.28a) yields $c_1 = \hat{p}_n(0)$, so that our solution becomes

$$\hat{p}_n(x) = \hat{p}_n(0) \exp\left(-\frac{x}{L_h}\right). \tag{9.7}$$

$I_h(0)$ is now found by (9.4):

$$I = I_h(0) = qAD_h \frac{\hat{p}_n(0)}{L_h} \exp\left(-\frac{x}{L_h}\right)\Bigg|_{x=0} = qA\bar{p}_n \sqrt{\left(\frac{D_h}{\tau_h}\right)} \left(\exp\frac{qV_A}{kT} - 1\right), \tag{9.8}$$

where (8.28a) and the definition of L_h have been used.

Let us now make our solution more general by removing the limitation $N_A \gg N_D$, i.e. by including the injected electron current I_e in I. This current adds to those electrons flowing from the contact at $x = W_n$ to recombine with the holes and do not reach the junction (superposition is permitted since all our equations are linear). I_e is found in exactly the same way as I_h was, but with reference to the P side of the junction. The result is analogous to (9.8):

$$I_e = qA\bar{n}_p \sqrt{\left(\frac{D_e}{\tau_e}\right)} \left(\exp\frac{qV_A}{kT} - 1\right). \tag{9.9}$$

Adding I_h and I_e and remembering that $\bar{n}_p \simeq n_i^2/N_A$ and $\bar{p}_n \simeq n_i^2/N_D$ are the known equilibrium values, we get the total current I in the wide diode

$$\begin{aligned} I = I_h + I_e &= qAn_i^2 \left(\frac{1}{N_D}\sqrt{\frac{D_h}{\tau_h}} + \frac{1}{N_A}\sqrt{\frac{D_e}{\tau_e}}\right) \left(\exp\frac{qV_A}{kT} - 1\right) \\ &= I_0\left(\exp\frac{qV_A}{kT} - 1\right), \end{aligned} \tag{9.10}$$

where I_0 includes all the coefficients.

The wide-diode I–V characteristic (9.10) describes its behavior for both positive (forward) and negative (reverse) applied voltage V_A. When $V_A < 0$, the exponent can be neglected compared with the unity and $I \simeq -I_0$. Figure 9.2 shows this characteristic. The diode is obviously a nonlinear device of the *rectifying* type, with high conduction in the forward direction and almost no conduction (I_0 is very small) in the reverse direction.

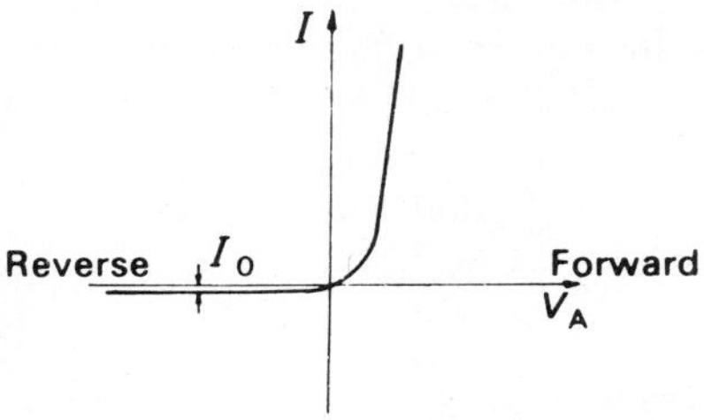

Figure 9.2. The junction-diode characteristic.

To clarify the subject further and to get some idea of the currents involved in forward (but still classified as low) injection let us refer to the diode in Fig. 9.3, in which $N_A \gg N_D$. The total current is denoted by I. At the junction it consists of the injected holes component I_{h_1} plus the injected electrons component I_{e_1} (which is negligible in comparison since $N_A \gg N_D$). These two components decay exponentially with distance from the junction because of recombination, and they disappear after a few diffusion lengths, the current-carrying job being taken over by the majority carriers on each side, which flow in from the contacts to supply the needs for recombination. If I_{e_2} represents this component on the N side, then the total electron current on this side is $I_e(x) = I_{e_1} + I_{e_2}$, and the total current on this side (and everywhere else at any cross section) is $I = I_{h_1} + I_e$. Similarly, on the P side $I = I_{e_1} + I_h$.

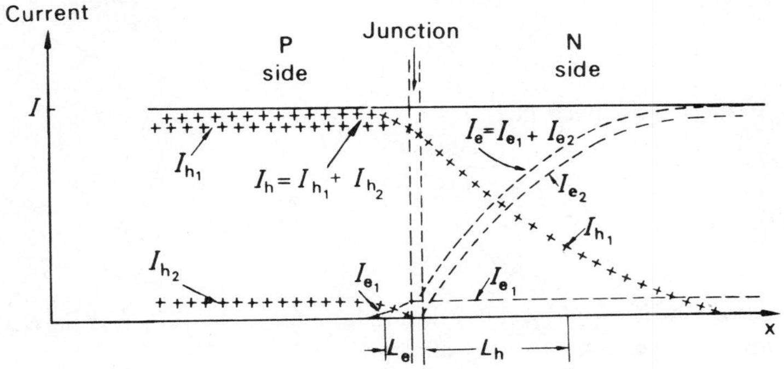

Figure 9.3. The current components in a wide diode with $N_A \gg N_D$ under forward bias: – – – – currents carried by electrons; + + currents carried by holes; —— total current.

Minority flow on each side is due to diffusion: injection + recombination creates gradients in the minority concentrations. Majority flow is due to drift (each injected hole at the junction causes an electron to enter into the N side from the contact to maintain neutrality, and these electrons drift towards the holes to recombine with them) but the drift field is very small because of the relatively high majority concentration. Therefore, practically all the applied voltage V_A appears across the junction (making its total voltage $V_t = V_B - V_A$), only a negligible part of it (a few millivolts) being lost in the main parts of the N and P regions between contacts and junction. This is no longer true in the case of high injection, which we shall discuss later.

9.2 The Narrow Diode

In many devices, including transistors, at least one side of the diode is narrow compared to the minority diffusion length in it. The minority distribution then looks like line I of Fig. 9.1(b).

In order to analyze this case, we assume that $W_n \ll L_h$ and $W_p \ll L_e$, so that the injected minority carriers have no chance to recombine before they reach the ohmic contact at the far end of each region. From Section 8.5, we know that an ohmic contact serves as a sink for excess minority carriers. If they are electrons, they are drawn into the metal contact to continue on their way, carrying the current in the external circuit. If they are holes, they recombine at the contact interface with electrons which carry the external current.

An ohmic contact thus creates equilibrium conditions around itself, and therefore a minority concentration gradient and diffusion current must exist between it and the junction.

Neglecting recombination in the narrow bulk is the same as assuming infinite minority lifetimes. Examining I_h first, this changes (9.2) into

$$\frac{dI_h}{dx} = 0, \tag{9.11}$$

and (9.5), with $\tau_h \to \infty$, becomes

$$\frac{d^2\hat{p}_n(x)}{dx^2} = 0. \tag{9.12}$$

The solution is

$$\hat{p}_n(x) = c_1 x + c_2. \tag{9.13}$$

The boundary condition at $x = 0$ is still (8.28a) while at $x = W_n$ it is $\hat{p}_n(W_n) = 0$ (equilibrium), from which c_1 and c_2 can be found to give

$$\hat{p}_n(x) = \bar{p}_n\left(1 - \frac{x}{W_n}\right)\left(\exp\frac{qV_A}{kT} - 1\right). \tag{9.14}$$

Hole current is again obtained from (9.4):

$$I_h = \frac{qAD_h}{W_n}\bar{p}_n\left(\exp\frac{qV_A}{kT}-1\right). \tag{9.15}$$

This is now independent of x, since we neglected recombination. The electron current injected into the P region gives I_e in an analogous form:

$$I_e = \frac{qAD_e}{W_p}\bar{n}_p\left(\exp\frac{qV_A}{kT}-1\right), \tag{9.16}$$

and substituting $\bar{n}_p$ and $\bar{p}_n$ in terms of N_A, N_D and n_i^2, we get the narrow-diode characteristic

$$I = I_h + I_e = qAn_i^2\left(\frac{D_h}{N_D W_n}+\frac{D_e}{N_A W_p}\right)\exp\left(\frac{qV_A}{kT}-1\right) = I_0\left(\exp\frac{qV_A}{kT}-1\right). \tag{9.17}$$

This has the same form as (9.10) for the wide diode, but with a slightly different expression for I_0, which now depends on the widths of the bulk regions instead of on the diffusion lengths. The dependence on n_i^2 (and hence on temperature) is unchanged. Carrier concentrations and current components in a narrow diode are shown in Fig. 9.4.

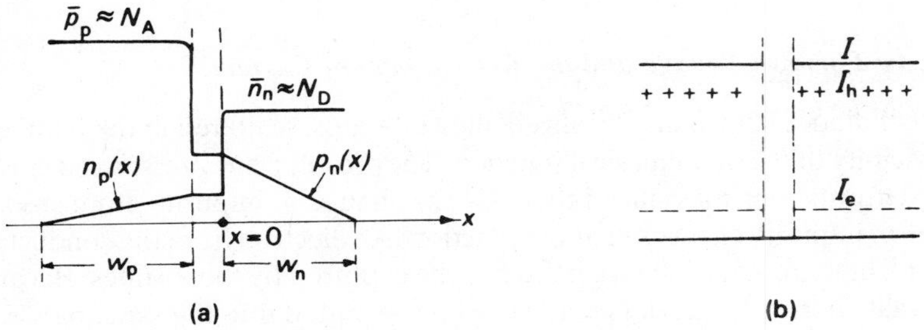

Figure 9.4. The narrow diode: (a) dependence of carrier concentrations on distance from depletion edge; (b) the various current components.

9.3 Diode Characteristic in the General Case

For a diode that is neither wide nor narrow, both recombination and ohmic contact effects are too large to be neglected.

Referring again to the injected holes first, the diffusion equation (9.5) and its general solution (9.6) are the same as in the wide-diode case. The boundary condition of (8.28a) at $x=0$ is also unchanged. The other boundary condition, however, now becomes $\hat{p}_n(W_n)=0$ at $x=W_n$, because of the ohmic contact there. The final solution is then

$$\hat{p}_n(x)=\hat{p}_n(0)\left(\sinh\frac{W_n-x}{L_h}\right)\Big/\sinh\left(\frac{W_n}{L_h}\right). \tag{9.18}$$

The diffusion current $I_h(x)$ is again given by use of (9.4). Taking the value of this at $x=0$ and adding the contribution of the injected electrons gives

$$\begin{aligned} I &= I_h(0)+I_e(0) \\ &= qAn_i^2\left(\frac{D_h}{N_D L_h}\coth\frac{W_n}{L_h}+\frac{D_e}{N_A L_e}\coth\frac{W_p}{L_e}\right)\left(\exp\frac{qV_A}{kT}-1\right) \\ &= I_0\left(\exp\frac{qV_A}{kT}-1\right). \end{aligned} \tag{9.19}$$

which is of the same general form as before. Equation (9.19) reverts to the wide-diode case for $W_n \gg L_h$ and $W_p \gg L_e$,

9.4 The Real Diode: Deviations from the Ideal Picture

(a) Low Forward Voltage and the Recombination Current

Real diodes have many localized allowed states, scattered in the band gap in the vicinity of the metallurgical junction. They result from stresses and crystal lattice deformations introduced there by the change in impurity atom sizes as the type of impurity changes near the junction. An electron from the conduction band or a hole from the valence band may be captured by those states. Because of thermal energy the carriers may later be re-emitted into the same bands, in which case the states are called *traps*, or a state already occupied by an electron (hole) may later capture a hole (electron) and both are annihilated. In this case the state is called a *recombination center.* (Experiment shows that recombination centers density in Si goes up and lifetime goes down with increased device processing temperature. Furnace temperature of 800°C may leave the original wafer lifetime (of about 100μs) almost unaffected. Processing temperature of 1100°C may reduce it to around 10μs and 1200°C to 0.1μs. Heavy metal atoms that diffuse inward from surface contaminations and crystal defects that move and propagate at the high temperature are thought to be the cause.)

Some of the electrons and holes, injected into the depletion region under forward bias, recombine there via the recombination centers, adding a recombination current I_{GR} to the junction diffusion current, given by (9.19), that is carried by the rest of the carriers. Those manage to cross the depletion region without being trapped and then diffuse away in the neutral regions. To obtain I_{GR} let us assume localized states density N_t (cm^{-3}) at an energy level E_t in the gap and look for the capture rate of electrons and holes by those centers in equilibrium.

The number of such states that are occupied by electrons is $N_t f_{FD}(E_t)$, where $f_{FD}(E_t)$ is the Fermi–Dirac distribution (6.40). The number of vacant states is therefore $N_t[1-f_{FD}(E_t)]$.

A vacant state will capture an electron which passes within an area σ_e called the electron *capture cross section* of the state. To visualize the capturing process let us look at the electrons, that move randomly with an average thermal velocity v_{th}, as stationary and make the localized states perform the random movements at the same average velocity v_{th}. This leaves the relative movements unchanged. Each vacant state sweeps a volume $\sigma_e v_{th}$ each second in which there are $n\sigma_e v_{th}$ electrons to be captured (n=electron concentration). The total electron capture rate per unit volume is therefore

(9.20a) $$r_e(\text{capt}) = N_t[1-f_{FD}(E_t)]\sigma_e v_{th} n.$$

If P_e is the probability for electron re-emission from occupied states, then the rate of electron re-emission is

(9.20b) $$r_e(\text{emis}) = N_t f_{FD}(E_t) P_e.$$

States occupied by electrons can also capture a hole from the valence band with a hole capture cross section σ_h with a rate (p=hole concentration)

(9.21a) $$r_h(\text{capt}) = N_t f_{FD}(E_t)\sigma_h v_{th} p$$

A vacant state may re-emit a hole to the valence band (i.e. capture a valence electron) with an emission probability P_h. Therefore

(9.21b) $$r_h(\text{emis}) = N_t[1-f_{FD}(E_t)]P_h.$$

In equilibrium the capture and emission states for each species must balance:

(9.22) $$r_e(\text{capt}) = r_e(\text{emis});\; r_h(\text{capt}) = r_h(\text{emis}).$$

Equations (8.9) and (8.10), which apply also in the junction space change-vicinity, allow us to express $\bar{n}$ and $\bar{p}$ as

$$\bar{n} = n_i \exp \frac{E_F - E_{F_i}}{kT}; \quad \bar{p} = n_i \exp - \frac{E_F - E_{F_i}}{kT}.$$

Substituting into (9.22) together with (6.40) for $f_{FD}(E_t)$ gives us the emission probabilities:

$$P_e = n_i v_{th} \sigma_e \exp \frac{E_t - E_{F_i}}{kT}; \quad P_h = n_i v_{th} \sigma_h \exp\left(-\frac{E_t - E_{F_i}}{kT}\right) \tag{9.23}$$

The net reduction in the free electron and hole population is:

$$-\frac{dn}{dt} = r_e(\text{capt}) - r_e(\text{emis}); \qquad -\frac{dp}{dt} = r_h(\text{capt}) - r_h(\text{emis}). \tag{9.24}$$

Since electrons are got rid of by recombination with holes

$$\frac{dn}{dt} = \frac{dp}{dt}. \tag{9.25}$$

When injection is low the equilibrium is but slightly disturbed, since only the minority population is significantly changed. Assuming that the same rate equations hold with n, p replacing $\bar{n}$, $\bar{p}$, we can substitute (9.20), (9.21) and (9.23) in (9.25) to eliminate $f_{FD}(E_t)$ and obtain:

$$R_t = -\frac{dn}{dt} = -\frac{dp}{dt} = \frac{np - n_i^2}{\tau_{e0}\left[p + n_i \exp\left(-\frac{E_t - E_{F_i}}{kT}\right)\right] + \tau_{h0}\left[n + n_i \exp\left(\frac{E_t - E_{F_i}}{kT}\right)\right]} \tag{9.26}$$

where $\tau_{e0} \triangleq (N_t v_{th} \sigma_e)^{-1}$; $\tau_{h0} \triangleq (N_t v_{th} \sigma_h)^{-1}$.

This is known as the Shockley, Read, Hall (SRH) expression for recombination rate via localized states.

We have net recombination ($R_t > 0$) if $np > n_i^2$ and net generation ($R_t < 0$) if $np < n_i^2$.

To relate this expression to the lifetime defined by (4.6), let us consider an N-type material with $\bar{n} >> \bar{p}$, $\hat{n}$, $\hat{p}$ and for simplicity put the recombination center energy at the middle of the gap, i.e., $E_t = E_{F_i}$. Equation (9.26) then simplifies to (4.6) with $\tau_h \equiv \tau_{h0}$. Similarly τ_e can be identified with τ_{e0} in a P-type material.

Since τ_{e0} is not very different from τ_{h0}, we can simplify further treatment by assuming $\tau_{h0} = \tau_{e0} = \tau$ (this does not change the general results – see Problem 9.26).

(9.27)
$$R_t = \frac{np - n_i^2}{\tau\left[(n+p) + 2n_i \cosh \dfrac{E_t - E_{F_i}}{kT}\right]}$$

States at the center of the gap with $E_t = E_{F_i}$, contribute the most to R_t. We can therefore consider them only:

(9.28a)
$$R_t = \frac{np - n_i^2}{\tau[(n+p) + 2n_i]}\,.$$

n_i can be neglected at forward voltage since injection increases n and p much above n_i throughout the depletion region

(9.28b)
$$R_t \simeq \frac{np}{\tau(n+p)}.$$

At both edges of the depletion region that extends from $x = 0$ (N side) to $x = w$ (P side) we have, from (8.27),

(9.29)
$$n_n(0)p_n(0) = n_p(\mathrm{w})P_p(\mathrm{w}) = n_i^2 \exp \frac{qV_A}{kT}.$$

Anywhere in between $n(x) < n_n(0)$ but $p(x) > p_n(0)$ and it can be shown that $n(x)p(x)$ for any x between 0 and w is given by (9.29). Therefore substituting (9.29) for np in (9.28b):

(9.30)
$$R_t = \frac{n_i^2 \exp \dfrac{qV_A}{kT}.}{\tau(n+p)}$$

For a given V_A, R_t will maximize for $n = p$. By (9.29) we then have $n = p = n_i \exp qV_A/2kT$. This maximum value of R_t is

(9.31)
$$R_t = \frac{n_i}{2\tau} \exp \frac{qV_A}{2kT}.$$

To obtain the recombination current we approximate and take this value as constant throughout the depletion region whose area is A and width W_{dep}

(9.32)
$$I_{GR} = qAW_{dep}R_t = \frac{qn_iAW_{dep}}{2\tau} \exp \frac{qV_A}{2kT} = I_{GR_0} \exp \frac{qV_A}{2kT}.$$

I_{GR} adds to the diffusion current of the ideal diode given by (9.19).

The total diode current at forward voltage V_A is

$$I \simeq I_0 \exp\frac{qV_A}{kT} + I_{GR0} \exp\frac{qV_A}{2kT}. \tag{9.33}$$

Let us compare the two contributions for a wide Si diode with low V_A

$$N_A = N_D = N = 5 \times 10^{15}\ \text{cm}^{-3},\ \tau_e = \tau_h = \tau = 1\,\mu\text{s},\ D_e \simeq D_h = 20\frac{\text{cm}^2}{\text{vs}},\ V_A = 5\frac{kT}{q}.$$

Using (9.10) for I_0, (9.32) for I_{GR0}, (8.6) for V_B and (8.20) for W_{dep}.

$$\frac{I_{GR0}}{I_0} = \frac{NW_{dep}}{4n_i\,(D\tau)^{\frac{1}{2}}} \simeq 10^3. \tag{9.34}$$

This numerical result is typical for Si and shows that I_{GR0} contribution is much larger than that of the diffusion component I_0 at low V_A. This always happens in semiconductors with $E_g \geq 1$eV like Si or GaAs since n_i, given by (7.7), is so small then. With increased V_A, however, the different exponentials in (9.33) cause the diffusion term to increase much faster and it starts to dominate at $V_A \simeq 13\,kT/q$ in our example. Equation (9.33) is usually approximated by the simpler form

$$I = I_s\left\{\exp\frac{qV_A}{\eta kT} - 1\right\} \tag{9.35}$$

where η (called the junction ideality factor) is a coefficient with a value between 1 and 2 and with I_s (called the saturation current) reduced to I_{GR0} at low V_A and to I_0 at higher values. Figure 9.5 shows the diode characteristic I vs. qV_A/kT for $V_A > 0$ for a real diode, drawn on a semilogarithmic scale and with -1 neglected for $V_A > 0$. Region I corresponds to low V_A and has a slope of 1/2 on this scale ($\eta = 2$). In region II the diffusion term in (9.33) dominates and the effective η drops to about 1.2 ÷ 1.3 in Si. Then

$$I = I_0 \exp\frac{qV_A}{\eta kT}. \tag{9.36}$$

This yields a straight line on our semilogarithmic plot. η can be obtained from the slope of region II and I_0 from the intersection with the current axis.

(b) The High Injection Range

Our ideal diode characteristic (9.19) is also not applicable at high injection levels since no ohmic voltage drops across the bulk N and P regions have been

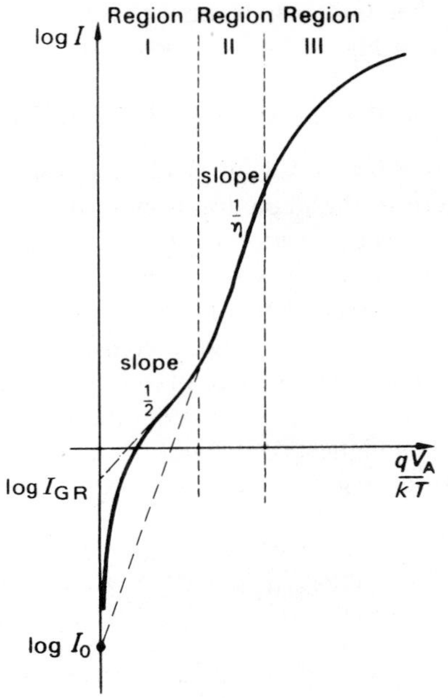

Figure 9.5. The I–V characteristics of a real diode and their use for measuring I_0.

included. These voltage drops grow and eventually become the dominant part of the applied voltage V_A when this voltage is high enough to bring the diode into a high-injection condition. High injection starts when the injected excess minorities on the lower doped junction side become a sizable fraction of the majority concentration there.

Assuming the lower doped side is N, high injection is reached when

$$\hat{p}_n(0) = \bar{p}_n\left(\exp\frac{qV_A}{kT} - 1\right) = \frac{n_i^2}{N_D}\left(\exp\frac{qV_A}{kT} - 1\right) \simeq \frac{N_D}{10}.$$

For large V_A the unity can be neglected, which sets an upper limit on V_A:

$$V_A \leqslant \frac{kT}{q} \ln \frac{N_D^2}{10n_i^2}.$$

At high injection the neutrality condition forces an appreciable increase in the majority concentration on the lower doped side. This is associated with an additional voltage drop on the bulk of that side. The total junction voltage is then $V_t = V_B - V'_A$ with $V'_A < V_A$. For a Si diode with, say, $N_D = 10^{16}$ cm^{-3}, we get $V_A \leqslant 0.64$ V. (High injection effects always occur before V_A equals V_B, the built-in voltage, so that the total junction voltage $V_t = V_B - V'_A$ always retains the reverse polarity of V_B.) The diode current will stop growing exponentially with

V_A and will gradually become proportional to it as those ohmic drops become dominant. Region III in Fig. 9.5 shows those effects.

(c) The Pre-breakdown Reverse Voltage Characteristic

From (9.27) it is clear that when a reverse voltage is applied and n, p become practically zero in the depletion region, then R_t changes its sign. The localized states now act as *generation centers*. Their presence in the band gap creates a sort of stepping stones by which valence electrons, agitated by thermal energy, can reach the conduction band. The reverse junction field then separates the generated hole–electron pairs, increasing the ideal leakage current $-I_0$ of (9.19). (*Remember*: The source of $-I_0$ are minority carriers diffusing back from neutral regions.) This added generation current can be found from (9.27) with $n \simeq p \simeq 0$. The highest contribution comes from states at $E_t = E_{F_i}$ and if we consider only those we get $R_t = -n_i/2\tau$. The total generated current, given by (9.32), is now:

$$I_{GR} = qAW_{dep}\, R_t = -\frac{qAW_{dep}n_i}{2\tau} = -I_{GR_0}. \tag{9.37}$$

This is the same I_{GR0} defined in (9.32). Obviously I_{GR} represents generation current under reverse bias and recombination current under forward bias. That is why I_{GR} is called a *generation–recomination current*.

(d) Temperature effects

Let us now find the temperature effects on the diode characteristics in its useful range where (9.36) holds.

The temperature dependence is due to I_0 and to the exponent $qV_A/\eta kT$. As can be seen from (9.19), I_0 depends on Tthrough n_i^2. Equation (7.10) tells us that

$$n_i^2 = AT^3 \exp\left(-\frac{E_g}{kT}\right),$$

so that I_0 can be written as

$$I_0 = CT^3 \exp\left(-\frac{E_g}{kT}\right), \tag{9.38}$$

where C includes all the terms approximately independent of T. Therefore

$$\frac{1}{I_0}\frac{dI_0}{dT} = \frac{d}{dT}(\ln I_0) = \frac{d}{dT}\left(\ln C + 3\ln T - \frac{E_g}{kT}\right) = \frac{3}{T} + \frac{E_g}{kT^2}. \tag{9.39}$$

For Si ($E_g = 1.1$ eV) at 300°K, the relative change in I_0 is about 15% per °K.

Under reverse voltage the leakage current $-I_{GR_0}$ of (9.37) increases with T because of n_i. Using a logarithmic derivative again, we find half the relative change obtained for I_0 in (9.39), i.e. about 7.6% per °K for Si. Measured values (which add the contributions of $-I_{GR_0}$ and $-I_0$) are around 9% per °K. From (9.36)

$$V_A = \frac{\eta kT}{q} \ln \frac{I}{I_0}. \tag{9.40}$$

The dependence of V_A on T at a constant current I, can therefore be expressed by

$$\left.\frac{\partial V_A}{\partial T}\right|_{I=\text{const}} = \eta \frac{k}{q} \ln \frac{I}{I_0} - \frac{\eta kT}{q} \frac{1}{I_0} \frac{dI_0}{dT} = \frac{V_A}{T} - \frac{\eta kT}{q} \frac{1}{I_0} \frac{dI_0}{dT}. \tag{9.41}$$

Substituting (9.39) into (9.41) yields

$$\left.\frac{\partial V_A}{\partial T}\right|_{I=\text{const}} = -\frac{(\eta/q)(3kT+E_g)-V_A}{T} \text{ V °K}^{-1}. \tag{9.42}$$

For a Si diode with $\eta \simeq 1.2$ we get about -2.4 mV °K^{-1} for $V_A = 0.7$ V at 300°K. About the same result is obtained for Ge or GaAs diodes. The fact that V_A drops at a constant rate with increased T when the diode is fed by a constant current source is used for temperature measurements, especially in the low-temperature range around 100°K.

9.5 Punch Through, Avalanche and Zener Breakdowns. Zener Diodes

When the applied reverse voltage is increased more and more, any diode finally breaks down and the reverse current increases to a value limited only by the external circuit. The breakdown may have one of three forms:

(a) Punch Through

Such a breakdown occurs in a diode of which at least one side is narrow and has low doping. In this case the depletion layer extends mostly into the low-doped side, and if that is narrow a voltage is soon reached at which the depletion reaches the far ohmic contact. Further voltage increase creates a field at the contact which responds by supplying all the current allowed by the outside circuit resistance. For that extra voltage the diode acts as a short circuit.

Punch-through voltage is determined by doping and bulk-region thickness and can be found from the depletion-layer equations. If the current after punch through is limited so that no overheating occurs, the diode will recover all its properties when the reverse voltage is reduced again. As we shall see, punch through may also occur in certain transistors.

(b) Avalanche

This is the most common breakdown mechanism in diodes (and transistors). Even before the depletion layer reaches the ohmic contact, the maximum reverse field in the junction may reach such values (about 200 kV cm^{-1} in Ge, 200–1000 kV cm^{-1} in Si depending on doping) that some of the minority carriers, participating in the normal leakage current, are accelerated to kinetic energies high enough for them to ionize a semiconductor atom when they collide with it (mean free path between collisions is about 10 nm and is longer the lower the doping). Ionization here means transferring a valence electron to the conduction band, thereby creating a new hole and electron. These are now also accelerated in opposite directions, colliding and ionizing again and again. Hence the name 'avalanche'.

The leakage current crossing the junction is therefore multiplied by a factor M to give a value of

$$I_0' = MI_0. \tag{9.43}$$

To obtain the dependence of M on the junction reverse voltage, we define an *ionization coefficient* α which is the number of ionizations per unit length at a given field. In some semiconductors, including Si, α is different for electrons and holes. In GaAs it is about equal. To simplify our treatment we shall assume that $\alpha_e \simeq \alpha_h = \alpha$. Obviously α grows fast with the field. The exact dependence has been measured for the more important semiconductors.

Consider the depletion layer at a reverse field that is still below multiplication level. The leakage current components are shown in Figure 9.6(a), and one may write $J_0 = J_{h_0} + J_{e_0}$, where index 0 indicates pre-multiplication values. At higher reverse fields α grows and the J_0 components are multiplied to something like the form shown in Fig. 9.6(b).

Let $x = 0$ represent the multiplication-zone boundary on the N side (from which the minority holes come) and $x = W$ the boundary on the P side (from which the minority electrons are swept across). We also assume α to be constant in this zone.

Hole flow at point x is $(1/q)J_h(x)$ which, by ionization, creates $(\alpha/q)J_h(x)\,dx$ additional holes inside a distance dx. Adding to that the holes generated by electrons flowing in the opposite direction, the total hole flow increase in a

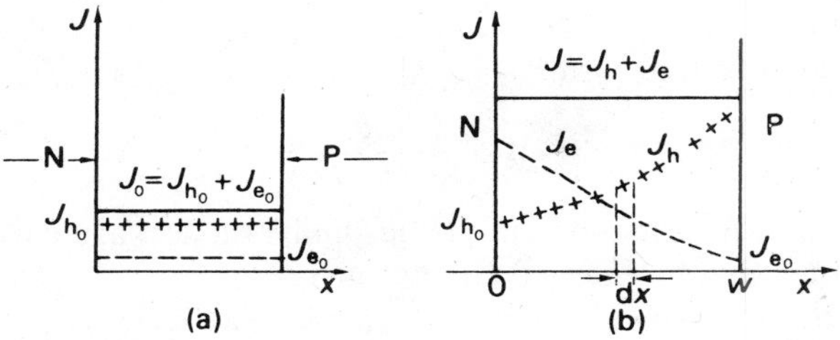

Figure 9.6. Multiplication and leakage current density components in a reversed-biased junction: (a) before multiplication; (b) after multiplication starts.

distance dx is

$$\frac{1}{q}\,dJ_h = \frac{\alpha}{q}\,J_h(x)\,dx + \frac{\alpha}{q}\,J_e(x)\,dx = \frac{\alpha}{q}\,[J_h(x) + J_e(x)]\,dx.$$

But the total current J_0' must be the same at any x assuming a constant cross section:

$$J_0' = J_h(x) + J_e(x) = \text{constant with } x.$$

The boundary condition to this differential equation in $J_h(x)$ is $J_h(0) = J_{h_0}$ at $x = 0$. Therefore the solution is

$$J_h(x) = \alpha J_0' x + J_{h0}$$

and similarly for $J_e(x)$.

For the constant α assumption, therefore, $J_h(x)$ and $J_e(x)$ should be drawn as straight lines in Fig. 9.6(b).

At $x = W$, $J_h(W) = J_0' - J_{e_0}$. Substituting this in our $J_h(x)$ expression, for $x = W$, we get

$$J_0' = \frac{J_{e0} + J_{h0}}{1 - \alpha W} = \frac{J_0}{1 - \alpha W}$$

where J_0 is the leakage current density before multiplication started. The multiplication factor M will therefore be

$$M = \frac{J_0'}{J_0} = \frac{1}{1 - \alpha W}.$$

The quantity αW gives the number of ionizations in the distance W, which depends on the field and hence on the reverse voltage V, as approximately

$$\alpha W = C V^m$$

where m has been determined empirically to be between 3 and 6, depending on semiconductor material and its doping.

In this equation C is a constant which can be expressed in terms of the breakdown voltage, denoted by BV and given by the condition $M=\infty$, i.e. $\alpha W=1$, from which $C=(BV)^{-m}$. Substituting C into the M expression gives it in the commonly used form:

(9.44)
$$M=\frac{1}{1-(V/BV)^m}.$$

When V reaches BV the diode no longer limits the leakage current, which is then determined by the external circuit only.

For a given semiconductor in which the avalanche field E_{BV} is known, the breakdown voltage can easily be found by substituting E_{BV} for E_{max} (the field at the junction) in (8.21) and separating out V_t, which is then the breakdown voltage:

(9.45)
$$BV=\frac{\varepsilon\varepsilon_0}{2q}\frac{N_A+N_D}{N_A N_D}E_{BV}^2.$$

If, as is common, one junction side has much higher doping, say $N_A \gg N_D$, then (9.45) becomes

(9.46)
$$BV\simeq\frac{\varepsilon\varepsilon_0}{2q}\frac{E_{BV}^2}{N_D}.$$

Since E_{BV} is a property of the material, the breakdown voltage can be controlled through N_D, the doping on the lower doped side. In diodes used for high-voltage rectification, which must withstand voltages of up to 2 kV, one junction side is left almost intrinsic.

Actually (9.45) or (9.46) give us a very rough estimate only since α is not a constant but a very sensitive function of the field E. One can approximate the experimentally measured values of $\alpha(E)$ for Si by the functional form

$$\alpha=a\exp(bE)\ [\mathrm{cm}^{-1}]$$

$a=33;\ 0.125\ [\mathrm{cm}^{-1}]$; $b=1.6\times10^5;\ 2.72\times10^{-5}$ [cm/V] for electrons and holes respectively. If one considers a single-sided P^+N junction with E changing linearly from E_{BV} to zero along a depletion distance W, then the avalanching condition becomes (for $\alpha_e \simeq \alpha_h \simeq \alpha$)

$$\int_0^W \alpha\,dx=1$$

which results in (see Problem 9.25)

(9.47)
$$E_{BV}=\frac{1}{b}\ln\left(\frac{qN_D b}{\varepsilon\varepsilon_0 a}+1\right).$$

Substituting E_{BV} into (9.46) gives a more accurate value of the breakdown voltage.

The temperature coefficient for avalanche field is positive, i.e. BV grows with T. This results from the reduction of the mean distance between collisions when the thermal vibrations of the atoms increase their amplitude. Higher fields are then necessary for the carriers to accumulate sufficient kinetic energy for ionization (the same thing happens with increased doping). For avalanche to occur, the depletion layer in which it takes place must be wider than the mean distance between collisions. Otherwise, the carriers will drift out of the high-field zone before they have a chance to collide and ionize. This means that at least one junction side must not be too highly doped. Therefore, the avalanche mechanism is responsible for breakdowns at about 6 V and up (eq. 9.46) in Si.

(c) Zener Breakdown

If the doping density on both junction sides is high, a different breakdown mechanism occurs, known as field, or Zener breakdown, after its discoverer. The depletion layer is now too narrow for avalanche to develop and the maximum junction field may grow as high as a few MV cm^{-1}. At such a combination of high field and narrow depletion layer (narrower than about 10 nm), electrons can tunnel directly from the valence band on the P side to the conduction band on the N side.

Tunnelling is a quantum-mechanical effect in which an electron confined by a potential barrier, higher than its energy, can still pass through that barrier if it is narrow enough, i.e., less than about 10 nm. The solution, ψ, to Schrödinger's equation inside that barrier, is an exponential function fast decaying with distance into the barrier. For very narrow barriers it doesn't decay quite to zero before the other side is reached, and ψ stops decaying and becomes oscillatory again. Since $|\psi|^2$ there is larger than zero, there is a finite probability that the electron will appear on the far barrier side.

The energy-band picture of such a reversed-biased junction is shown in Fig. 9.7. The doping of the P side is high enough to bring E_F near E_V. The N side is degenerate with E_F inside the conduction band. When a reverse voltage V_z is applied, valence band electrons can directly tunnel into the empty conduction band states opposite them on the N side without first being excited into the conduction band on the P side (i.e. without going over the potential barrier).

Zener breakdown fields are reached at voltages below about 5 V, since at the high doping densities used the depletion layer is so narrow that few volts suffice.

The temperature coefficient of the Zener voltage is negative because E_g goes down slowly with increased temperature.

When the breakdown is between 4 and 6 V, both avalanche and Zener mechanisms may operate together, resulting in a temperature coefficient

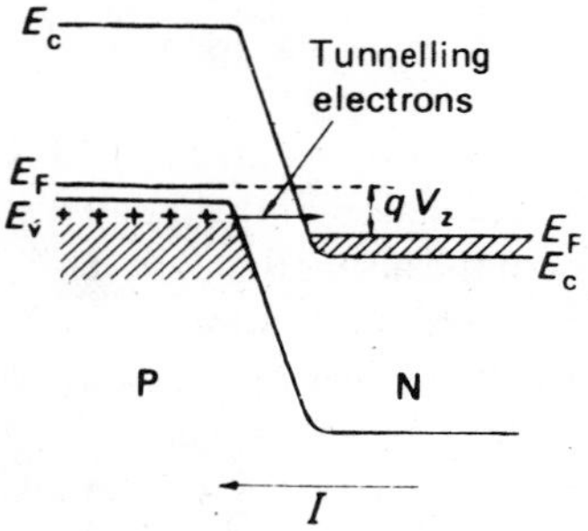

Figure 9.7. Energy bands of a junction in Zener breakdown.

which is around zero.

The real diode characteristic in both voltage polarities looks like Fig. 9.8(a).

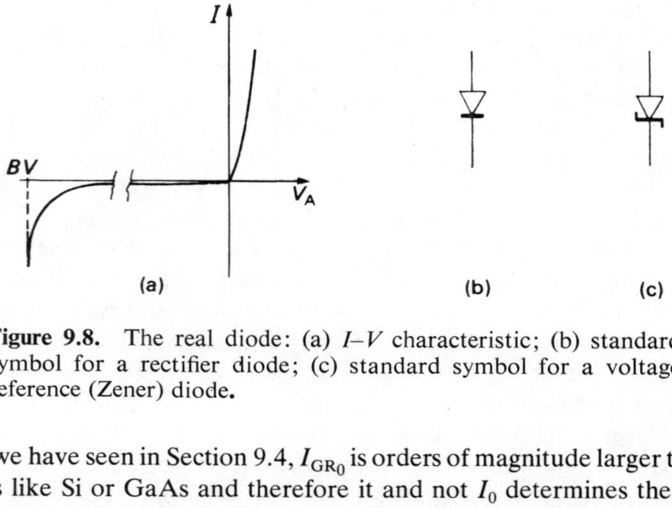

Figure 9.8. The real diode: (a) I–V characteristic; (b) standard symbol for a rectifier diode; (c) standard symbol for a voltage reference (Zener) diode.

As we have seen in Section 9.4, I_{GR_0} is orders of magnitude larger than I_0 in materials like Si or GaAs and therefore it and not I_0 determines the leakage current. Notice also from (9.37) that I_{GR_0} slowly grows with reverse voltage since W_{dep} grows with it. The leakage current of a real diode may also have a surface component that leaks around the junction through contaminations on the surface or through a thin semiconductor surface layer that is usually rich in localized states.

The relative importance of bulk and surface leakage components depends on the way the junction is protected where it emerges from the bulk into the surface. The junction built-in field attracts ionized dust particles there which create leakage paths. In Si diodes, made by diffusion through an SiO_2 mask, that region is already covered and protected by the oxide when the junction forms; The oxide also greatly reduces the number of localized states near the surface.

Such Si diodes are therefore called *passivated*. The leakage current in such good diodes remains very small almost up to the point of breakdown and the characteristic has a sharp bend in it there. Such a characteristic is called *hard*. Bad junctions have *soft* breakdown characteristics with a gradually increasing leakage current long before final breakdown is reached, indicating small, premature local breakdowns at weak spots in the junction area or periphery. Silicon diodes, especially made to operate in the breakdown range, are used as *voltage references* in rectification and control circuits. They are historically called Zener diodes, although in most of them the avalanche mechanism predominates. The desired breakdown (i.e. reference) voltage V_z is obtained by proper selection of the doping levels. Once in breakdown that voltage remains almost constant, independent of the current, so long as the permitted power dissipation, $P=IV_z$, as given by the manufacturer, is not exceeded. Such diodes should have hard characteristics, indicating uniform breakdown in the junction area with no hot-spot formation. They are available with 0.25 W to 50 W allowed dissipation (with the higher power diodes necessitating metal heat sinks for better heat removal).

Typical parameters for Motorola 50 W Zener diode 1N2820, at 30°C diode case temperature, are

Nominal Zener voltage (at $I_z=520$ mA)	$V_z=24$ V
Differential impedance at this current (breakdown curve slope)	$Z_z=\Delta V_z/\Delta I_z \leqslant 2.6\ \Omega$
Differential impedance at $I_z=5$ mA (indicating breakdown bend sharpness)	$Z_z \leqslant 80\ \Omega$
Maximum allowed current at 75°C case temperature	$I_z=1.75$ A
Forward voltage drop at $I_F=10$ A	$V_F \leqslant 1.5$ V
Zener voltage temperature coefficient	$0.08\,\%\ °C^{-1}$
Leakage current at 18.2 V	$I_R \leqslant 5\ \mu A$.

Reference diodes with near zero temperature coefficients can be achieved by connecting the positive coefficient reference diode in series with a forward-biased diode whose temperature coefficient is negative (eq. (9.42)).

In diodes intended for rectifying work, which utilize the nonlinearity in the diode characteristic around $V=0$, a low forward voltage drop V_F at the maximum operating current I_F is very important, since it reduces the power lost in the diode and its cooling requirements. In the reverse direction it is important for those diodes that their leakage currents remain smaller than specified up to a given peak inverse voltage.

Typical parameters for Philips BYX45-600 Si rectifying diode are

Crest working reverse voltage	V_{RWM} max. 600 V
Average forward current	$I_F(AV)$ max. 1.5 A

Nonrepetitive peak forward current ($T_j = 150°C$)	I_{FSM} max. 40 A
Forward voltage at $I_F = 5$ A; $T_j = 25°C$	$V_F < 1.45$ V
Peak reverse current at $V = V_{RWM}$, $T_j = 125°C$	$I_R < 100$ μA

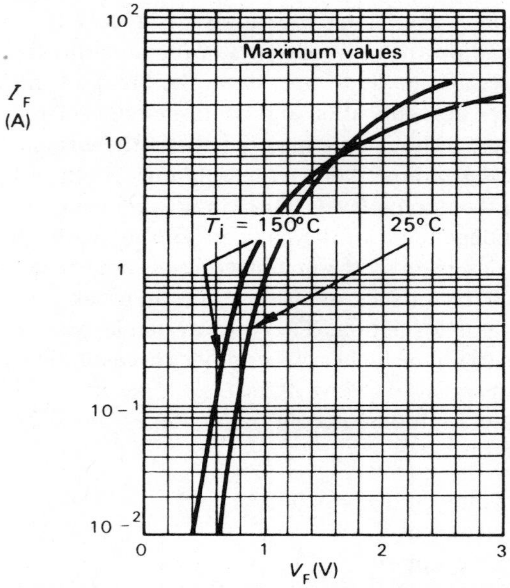

Figure 9.9. Rectifying diode BYX45 (Philips) forward characteristics.

Figure 9.9 shows the forward I–V characteristic of this diode at two junction temperatures using a semilogarithmic scale. Maximum V_F values are given (typical values are lower). Only regions II and III of Fig. 9.5 are covered here. At low currents the dependence on V_F is exponential, yielding a straight line in the figure. Above about 1 A, the ohmic drops in the bulk regions outside the junction start to become significant, especially when the device temperature is high, and the characteristic becomes gradually ohmic, i.e. curved on a semilogarithmic scale. At low currents the temperature coefficient is negative, becoming less so with increasing current as predicted by (9.42). At still higher current, about 8 A, this coefficient becomes positive as expected of a mainly ohmic voltage drop which grows due to reduced mobility at the increased temperature.

9.6 The Varactor, or Variable Capacitance Diode

If the reverse voltage $-V_A$, applied to a diode, is increased by $-\Delta V_A$, the two depletion-layer parts, of widths d_n and d_p, given by (8.19), will widen by Δd_n and Δd_p respectively. This will increase the space charge on one side by $+\Delta Q$ and on the other side by $-\Delta Q$ as shown by Fig. 9.10.

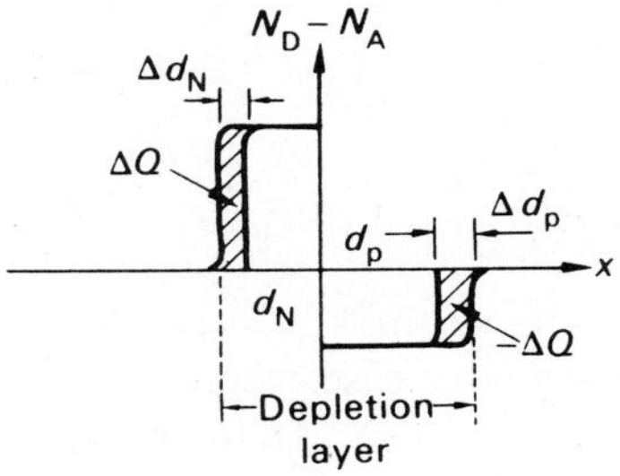

Figure 9.10. Effects of reverse bias increase by $-\Delta V_A$ on depletion-layer width and depletion charge.

The increment ΔQ is given by

$$|\Delta Q| = |qN_D \, \Delta d_n| = |qN_A \, \Delta d_p|.$$

This is exactly the response expected of a parallel-plate capacitor with plates a distance $d = d_n + d_p$ apart. Actually the analogy is only accurate for the differential capacitance $\Delta Q/\Delta V_A$, since the distance d changes with V_A. We therefore define junction capacitance C_j as the differential capacitance presented by the junction when a small a.c. voltage of amplitude dV_A is superimposed on the d.c. bias of $-V_A$:

(9.48) $$C_j \triangleq \left. \frac{dQ}{dV_A} \right|_{V_A}.$$

From Fig. 9.10 and the analogy to the parallel-plate capacitor:

(9.49) $$C_j = \frac{A\varepsilon\varepsilon_0}{d},$$

where A is the junction area.

Substituting d from (8.20) gives:

(9.50) $$C_j = A \left(\frac{q\varepsilon\varepsilon_0 (N_A + N_D)}{2V_t} \right)^{1/2} \left[\left(\frac{N_D}{N_A} \right)^{1/2} + \left(\frac{N_A}{N_D} \right)^{1/2} \right]^{-1}.$$

If one junction side has much higher doping, like $N_A \gg N_D$, this becomes

(9.51) $$C_j = A \left(\frac{q\varepsilon\varepsilon_0 N_D}{2V_t} \right)^{1/2}, \qquad N_A \gg N_D.$$

The same results would have been obtained by using (9.48) with Q given by (8.18).

Since for reverse bias,

$$V_t = V_B + V_A = V_B\left(1 + \frac{V_A}{V_B}\right)$$

C_j can be expressed as

$$C_j = \frac{C_j(0)}{[1+(V_A/V_B)]^{1/2}} \simeq \frac{B}{V_A^{1/2}}, \qquad V_A \gg V_B. \tag{9.52}$$

$C_j(0)$ is the junction capacitance for $V_A = 0$ and B is a constant.

In the linear graded-junction case, where depletion-layer width is proportional to $[1+(V_A/V_B)]^{1/3}$ (Problem 8.14), the junction capacitance is given by

$$C_j = \frac{C_j(0)}{[1+(V_A/V_B)]^{1/3}} \simeq \frac{B_1}{V_A^{1/3}}, \qquad V_A \gg V_B. \tag{9.53}$$

The junction capacitance always drops with increased reverse bias. Measurements of C_j as a function of $-V_A$ (usually made at a signal frequency around 1 MHz) enable us to get information on the doping profile shape near the junction and also measure the diffusion voltage V_B. To do that we plot log C_j against log $|-V_A|$ as is done in Figure 9.11(a) for $|-V_A| \gg |V_B|$. By eqs. (9.50)–(9.53), this is a straight line whose slope is $-\frac{1}{2}$ for the step junction, $-\frac{1}{3}$ for a linear graded one, or something in between for a real junction obtained by diffusion. To obtain V_B, we use (9.52) and draw C_j^{-2} against $-V_A$ as is done in Fig. 9.11(b). A straight line is obtained which, when extrapolated to $C_j^{-2} \to 0$, gives V_B (in a linear graded junction one should draw C_j^{-3}).

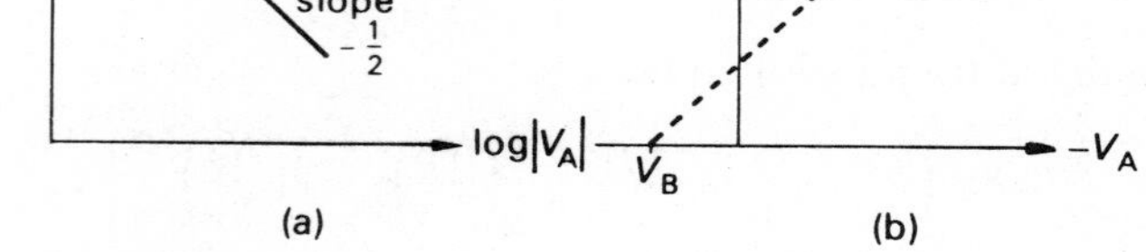

Figure 9.11. Junction capacitance measurements:
(a) Obtaining the junction type by the slope: —— step junction with $-\frac{1}{2}$ slope: ------ linear junction with $-\frac{1}{3}$ slope;
(b) Obtaining V_B for a step junction.

Reversed-bias junction diodes are often used as small signal capacitors whose capacitance can be electrically controlled by their d.c. bias. Diodes especially made for this purpose are called *tuning diodes* or *varactors*. They are used for electronic tuning of high-frequency resonant circuits to the desired frequency as needed, e.g., in selection of the proper television channel. Other uses are in microwave amplification (parametric amplifiers) or generation (frequency multipliers) as will be described in Chapter 20.

A typical tuning diode $C_j(V)$ characteristic is shown in Fig. 9.12 for Philips BB105B diode intended for TV uses up to 860 MHz. Its maximum reverse voltage is -28 V and even at $T_j = 60°C$ its leakage current is still smaller than 0.5 μA.

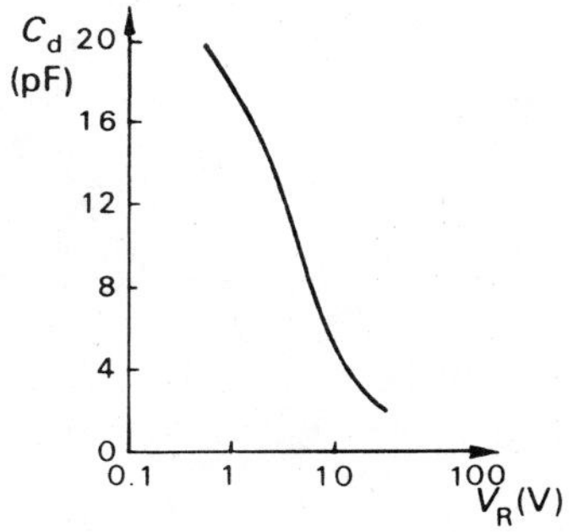

Figure 9.12. Junction capacitance versus voltage for Philips tuning diode BB105B.

9.7 The Schottky-barrier Diode

Schottky-barrier diodes, also known as metal–semiconductor diodes, are based on the rectifying properties of the Schottky barrier, which forms when metals of certain work functions are deposited on the semiconductor surface, as explained in Chapter 8. Upon application of a forward bias the barrier height to majority carriers in the semiconductor is lowered, as shown in Fig. 8.11, and use of Boltzmann's statistics to calculate the number of those that have high enough energy to cross it gives the current that will flow as

$$I = I_s\left(\exp\frac{qV_A}{\eta kT} - 1\right),$$

i.e., an equation similar to that of the PN-junction diode. There are four main differences between Schottky-barrier and PN-junction diodes

(a) In a PN diode the reverse leakage current I_s is the result of *minority* carriers diffusing to the depletion layer edges to be swept across or recombine. Therefore it is very temperature sensitive. Here it is the result of *majority* carriers that can overcome the barrier. This would give a much higher value for I_s and around room temperature that value would not be as sensitive to temperature as in the PN junction.

(b) There are different barriers to electrons in the semiconductor (for the N-type diode case shown in Fig. 8.11) and the holes (empty states) on the metal side. Upon application of a forward bias, the majority electrons in the semiconductor are indeed injected over the reduced barrier into the metal, but holes from the metal, which must overcome a barrier of $E_g - \phi_B$, are not. Thus, it is mostly injection from the semiconductor into the metal that accounts for the forward current and there is very little excess minority charge accumulated in the semiconductor. This enables Schottky-barrier diodes to switch very quickly from forward conduction to reverse blocking, as we shall learn in Chapter 11.

(c) The majority electrons injected over the barrier into the metal have much higher energy than the rest of the metal electrons which are in thermal equilibrium with the metal lattice atoms. Those electrons are therefore called *hot*, and the diodes are sometimes referred to as *hot electron diodes*.

(d) Since under forward bias the injection is only from the semiconductor side, there is very little recombination in the depletion region and the ideality factor η in this diode equation is very nearly 1 (1.03 is a practical value) while in a PN junction in Si, for example, it is around 1.2 and as high as 2 at low forward voltage.

Two main practical results are associated with those differences. The first is that the current in the Schottky-barrier diode grows much faster with forward voltage than in the PN-junction diode. This is shown schematically in Fig. 9.13. The second is related to their relative switching speeds and will be described in Chapter 11.

The capacitance–voltage relation of a Schottky diode built on the surface of a semiconductor is often used to determine its doping dependence on depth $N(x)$. The structure resembles a single-sided step junction (like P^+N) with the depletion layer extending into the substrate only. Using (9.48) with $dQ = qN(x)dx$ one obtains

$$N(x) = \frac{C'}{q\varepsilon\varepsilon_0}\left(\frac{d\frac{1}{c'}}{dV}\right)^{-1} \quad \text{where } C' \triangleq \frac{C_j}{A} \text{ and } x = \frac{C'}{\varepsilon\varepsilon_0}$$

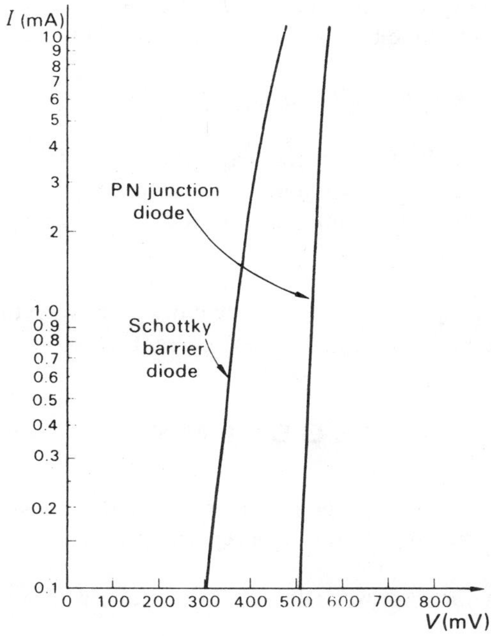

Figure 9.13. Comparison of Schottky-barrier and PN-junction diode characteristics.

QUESTIONS

9.1 How will the characteristic of a real P^+N diode be affected if the N side is made wider and wider?

9.2 Subjecting a semiconductor to energetic radiation, like that encountered in a radioactive vicinity, creates crystal faults with consequent severe reduction in lifetimes. Suppose a normal diode has been so treated. How will it affect its characteristics?

9.3 Given a P^+N diode, which of its properties will change if the P side doping were to be raised even further? Which will change if its N side doping is increased?

9.4 The temperature coefficient of two similar P^+N diodes of the same doping densities, one with a wide N region and the other with a narrow one, were compared. It was found that they behaved the same at 1 mA current but became quite different at 100 mA. Can you explain this?

9.5 Why is the junction capacitance not measured with a forward bias? Can a junction diode be used as a capacitor in an a.c. circuit?

9.6 Why do we not define junction capacitance as $C = Q/V$?

9.7 Draw schematically the expected capacitance of a $P^+N^-N^+$ diode as a function of the reverse voltage. Assume that the N^- region is sufficiently narrow for it to be punched through long before avalanche fields are reached.

9.8 Discuss the compromises needed when designing a rectifying diode for both high voltage and high forward current.

PROBLEMS

9.9 Show that eq. (9.19) for the general ideal diode case contains both the wide- and narrow-diode results as special cases.

9.10 Calculate the breakdown voltage of a Si diode whose parameters are:

$$N_A = 10^{19}\ \text{cm}^{-3} \qquad W_n = 90\ \mu\text{m}$$

$$N_D = 10^{14}\ \text{cm}^{-3} \qquad W_p = 10\ \mu\text{m}.$$

For additional material parameters refer to Appendix 3. Assume that the field at which avalanche starts is 250 kV cm^{-1}. Which type of breakdown will develop?

9.11 A P^+N Ge diode must withstand a breakdown voltage of 30 V. Suggest doping densities for the two junction sides. Assume 200 kV cm^{-1} as the avalanche field for Ge.

9.12 Plot the avalanche breakdown voltage of a P^+N Si diode as a function of N_D on a log–log scale, for N_D values between 10^{15} and 10^{18} cm^{-3}. Assume an average avalanche field of 300 kV cm^{-1}. This graph was used to evaluate the doping uniformity across a large Si wafer on which ten separate diodes were made by heavy diffusion of boron atoms into ten specific locations on the wafer to a depth of a few microns. Subsequent measurement of the breakdown voltages yielded the following results (in volts):

70, 75, 50, 60, 45, 55, 68, 72, 65, 68.

What is the range of doping densities encountered on that wafer?

9.13 Calculate the capacitance per unit area of the diode in Problem 9.10 at zero and near breakdown voltages.

9.14 A Ge diode has 10^{18} cm^{-3} donors on the N side. What is the excess hole concentration near the edge of the depletion layer on the N side when a forward voltage of 78 mV is applied? At what forward voltage will high injection effects start to become important?

9.15 The following data are given for a wide Ge diode at 300°K:

$$\tau_h = \tau_e = 10\ \mu s \qquad N_D = 10^{16}\ \text{cm}^{-3}$$

$$D_h = 44\ \text{cm}^2\ \text{s}^{-1} \qquad N_A = 10^{19}\ \text{cm}^{-3}$$

$$D_e = 70\ \text{cm}^2\ \text{s}^{-1} \qquad A = 1.25 \times 10^{-4}\ \text{cm}^2.$$

Calculate the current through that diode when a voltage of 200 mV is applied in the forward and in the reverse directions. Calculate also the width of the depletion layer, the junction capacitance and the maximum field when the reverse voltage is applied.

9.16 A P$^+$N diode is given in which $W_n \ll L_h$. Show that electron current in such a forward-biased diode is negligible compared to the hole current and, using the neutrality condition, show also that the field in the bulk N region is approximately given by

$$E = \frac{kT}{q}\frac{1}{W_n}\frac{\hat{p}_n(0)}{N_D + \hat{p}_n(x)}, \tag{9.54}$$

where x is measured from the depletion-layer edge.

9.17 Show that the width of the depletion layer, in a P$^+$N narrow diode, depends on the forward current I_F according to

$$d = \left(\frac{2\varepsilon\varepsilon_0}{qN_D}\frac{kT}{q}\ln\frac{qAN_AD_h}{I_FW_n}\right)^{1/2}. \tag{9.55}$$

Calculate C_j at a forward bias of $4kT/q$ and $8kT/q$ for the diode given in Problem 9.15, and compare it to $C_j(0)$ and $C_j(-8kT/q)$. What are your conclusions regarding the change in C_j with forward current?

9.18 Estimate I_s and η at 25°C for the diode whose V–I characteristic is given in Fig. 9.9, for the 0.01 A to 1 A range. Using these values find dV_A/dT at 0.1 A and at 1 A. What is the measured increase in I_s when the temperature grows to 150°C?

9.19 Figure 9.14 shows three basic single-phase rectifying circuits. Assuming ideal diodes (i.e. zero forward voltage drop and zero reverse leakage current), draw the current wave forms through the load R_L as functions of time for $V_0 \cos \omega t$ input voltage.

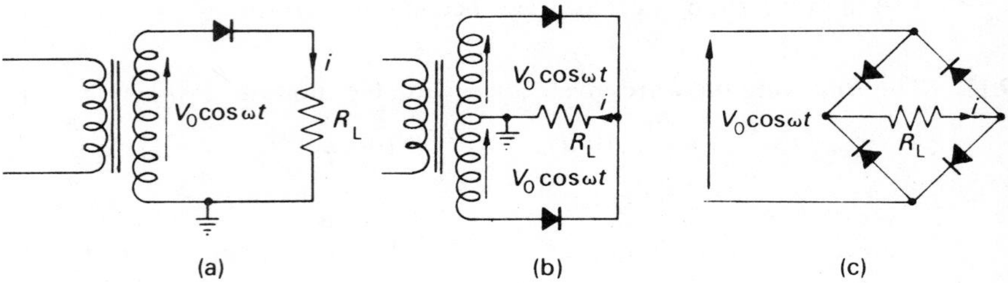

Figure 9.14. Basic rectifying circuits: (a) half-wave rectifier; (b) full-wave rectifier with center tapped transformer; (c) full-wave bridge rectifier.

9.20 Approximate the $C_j(V)$ curve of the tuning diode of Fig. 9.12 by a straight line on a log–log scale and determine the functional dependence of C_j on V for that diode in the range 2–28 V. At what bias will the diode resonate with a 5 nH coil (a) at 750 MHz and (b) at 850 MHz?

9.21 In a P^+N diode of 10^{-3} cm² area the junction capacitance was measured as a function of the reverse voltage V_R:

V_R (V)	0.1	0.5	1.0	1.5	2.1	2.5
C_j (pF)	20.0	14.5	11.8	10.2	9.0	8.4

Find (a) the doping density in the N region, and (b) the junction built-in (diffusion) voltage V_B.

9.22 Calculate the components of the reverse currents (diffusion and generation–recombination) for the following two step junction diodes at 5 V reverse bias and 300°K:

(a) A Ge diode whose parameters are given in Problem 9.15.

(b) An Si diode of the same doping densities and area and with $\tau_e = \tau_h = 1\,\mu s$, $D_h = 15\,cm^2/s$, $D_e = 30\,cm^2/s$.

9.23 In a narrow P^+N diode the doping density N_D on the N side is a function of x, the distance from the junction. Show that under low-level forward injection the excess holes are given by

$$\hat{p}_n(x) = \frac{I}{qAD_hN_D(x)} \int_x^{W_n} N_D(x)\, dx \tag{9.56}$$

(assuming the depletion layer under forward bias is very narrow and can be neglected).

Use this result to find $\hat{p}_n(x)$ for the special case of exponential doping

$$N_D(x) = N_D(0) \exp\left(-\eta \frac{x}{W_n}\right),$$

where $N_D(0) \ll N_A$ and η is a constant. Draw $qAD_h\hat{p}_n(x)/(IW_n)$ as a function of x/W_n for $\eta=0$ (step junction) and $\eta=6$. Which diode necessitates higher forward voltage for the same current?

9.24 Prove eq. (9.50) directly from (9.48) without the use of the parallel-plate capacitor analogy.

9.25 Show that R_t in (9.31) reverts to

$$R_t = \frac{n_i}{2(\tau_{e0}\tau_{h0})^{1/2}} \exp \frac{qV_A}{2kT} \tag{9.57}$$

if one does not assume $\sigma_e = \sigma_h$ in (9.26) but only that they are not very different.

9.26 Prove eq. (9.47). *Hint*: Use Poisson's equation to relate E, N_D and x. Calculate E_{BV} and BV for $N_D = 10^{15}$ cm^{-3}.

9.27 Compare a P$^+$N Si diode breakdown voltage as calculated from (9.46) and (9.47) to the experimentally suggested equation

$$BV = 60\left(\frac{E_g}{1.1}\right)^{3/2}\left(\frac{10^{16}}{N_D}\right)^{3/4} \tag{9.58}$$

(E_g in eV; this equation gives approximately correct values for Si, Ge, GaAs and GaP). Do it for $N_D = 10^{15}$, 10^{16} and 10^{18} cm^{-3}. Assume $\alpha_e \simeq \alpha_h = 30 \exp(1.6\times10^{-5}E)$ [cm^{-1}].

SEMICONDUCTORS AND DIODES IN OPTOELECTRONICS 10

Semiconductors in general, and semiconductor diodes in particular, have found very important uses in *optoelectronics*, the field in which the electronic device is designed to interact with electromagnetic radiation in the visible (λ between 0.4 μm to 0.7 μm approximately), the infrared or i.r. ($\lambda > 0.7$ μm) and ultraviolet or u.v. ($\lambda < 0.4$ μm) ranges.

Those optoelectronic uses can be categorized in five main subfields:

(a) light detection
(b) direct conversion of solar to electric energy
(c) light-emitting devices, liquid crystals and displays
(d) lasers
(e) fibers and the optical communication system.

The semiconductor material used and the required doping are determined by the relevant light wavelength λ, while the detailed device structure is usually designed to obtain the highest efficiency in the intended use.

In this chapter we shall cover the operating principles of various devices in these fields and touch upon some of their design problems. Additional information on optoelectronic semiconductor devices can be found in References 7, 8 and 9.

10.1 Light–Semiconductor Interaction

Interaction between electromagnetic light photons and a semiconductor means that the photons are either absorbed or emitted by the semiconductor. Appreciable, and therefore useful, absorption results from the generation of hole–electron pairs (low obsorption can also result from other mechanisms). This puts an upper bound on λ to which a specific semiconductor can react usefully, which is the wavelength at which the photon energy equals the band gap. At longer λ the semiconductor becomes transparent, or almost so, and can no longer be used with that light (there are special extrinsic detectors designed for the far i.r., as mentioned later in this section, that are exceptions to this).

The energy E of the photon is related to its wavelength λ by

$$E=hf=h\frac{c}{\lambda}=\frac{1.24}{\lambda\ (\mu\mathrm{m})}\ \mathrm{eV}. \tag{10.1}$$

Equating E to the band gap E_g yields the maximum useful wavelength:

$$\lambda_{max}=\frac{1.24}{E_g\ (\mathrm{eV})}\ \mu\mathrm{m}. \tag{10.2}$$

Table 10.1 lists λ_{max} for some useful semiconductors. As E_g usually becomes smaller with increasing temperature, it is important to list the operating temperature too.

Table 10.1.

Semiconductor material	λ_{max} (μm)	Working temperature (°K)
ZnS	0.35	300
CdS	0.52	300
GaP	0.55	300
GaAs	0.88	300
Si	1.2	300
Ge	1.8	300
InAs	3.0	77
InSb	5.5	77
Hg/CdTe	8–14	77
Pb/SnTe	8–14	77
Ge:Cu	30	18

The working temperature is determined by a very important consideration: carriers are being continually generated by thermal energy as well as by the incoming light. Thermal generation must therefore be made much smaller than that caused by the absorbed photons for the latter to be noticeable. Otherwise, the detected information will be masked by the noisy background of thermal generation. But the longer λ is the lower must E_g be, and consequently the higher becomes n_i, which represents thermal generation (eq. (7.10) predicts exponential dependence for n_i on E_g). In InSb, for example, the band gap is 0.18 eV at 300°K, which makes n_i so high that it behaves like a good conductor even without intentional doping or the addition of light-generated carriers. On cooling it to 77°K (with liquid nitrogen), E_g is increased to 0.23 eV and n_i decreased by 10^{-6} approximately. Optically generated carriers will now have a strong effect on the conductivity and can therefore be detected. The longer the wavelength the lower the working temperature must be, as can be seen from Table 10.1. For wavelength longer than about 15 μm, in the far i.r., one must resort to liquid hydrogen or even liquid helium (4.2°K) cooling.

The compound semiconductors of three elements included in Table 10.1, like Hg/CdTe (Mercury/Cadmium–Telluride) and Pb/SnTe (Lead/Tin–Telluride) can be grown in a single-crystal form with varying ratios of the compound constituents. Those ratios determine E_g and λ_{max}. If, for example, the amount of CdTe is changed from 19 to 23% the maximum wavelength changes from 8 to 14 μm. If Pb/SnTe includes 27% of SnTe, E_g drops to 0.06 eV and λ_{max} increases to 20 μm.

Devices made from those compounds are mainly intended for military use, since maximum black-body radiation at the temperature of the human body occurs around 10 μm and there is an atmospheric window, i.e., comparatively little atmospheric absorption, in the 8–14 μm range. One can therefore detect from afar anything slightly warmer than its surroundings by its infrared radiation.

The last material in the table, Ge:Cu, is a representative of the so-called *extrinsic photoconductors* group. It differs from the other materials in that the low-energy i.r. radiation does not generate carriers by ionizing a semiconductor valence electron into the conduction band but by ionizing an impurity electron from its impurity level, somewhere in the band gap, into the conduction band. The impurity is chosen so that the energy difference is appropriate for the desired wavelength. Low enough working temperatures must be used so the impurities are not ionized by the thermal energy. Copper, gold or mercury are common impurities used for this purpose in germanium. Light absorption in such materials is proportional to the impurity density and is therefore relatively low.

Most non-military uses are in the visible or near i.r. range of up to about 1.1 μm. We shall therefore concentrate on the materials in the top half of Table 10.1.

Optical irradiation, absorption and carrier generation can be related as follows: Suppose the semiconductor is irradiated by P watts per unit area of optical energy. If the radiation is monochromatic, the photon flux ϕ_0 hitting a unit area per unit time is obtained by dividing P by the energy of a single photon E_{ph}:

$$\phi_0 = \frac{P}{E_{ph}} = \frac{P}{hf} = \frac{P\lambda}{hc}. \tag{10.3}$$

This means that for a constant P, ϕ_0 grows linearly with λ. If no special antireflection coating is used, only a fraction $\eta(\lambda)$ of these photons will penetrate the semiconductor and be absorbed. The rest are reflected at the semiconductor–air interface because of the difference in refractive indices. A single or multilayered antireflection coating is usually used to minimize the reflection in the required range, making $\eta(\lambda)\simeq 1$ there.

Let x represent the depth into the semiconductor from its irradiated surface and $\phi(x)$ the photon flux at this depth (i.e., photons as yet unabsorbed). The carrier generation $g(x)$ at depth x must equal the change of $\phi(x)$ with x on one hand and be proportional to $\phi(x)$ on the other:

$$g(x) = -\frac{d\phi}{dx} = \alpha(\lambda)\phi(x).$$

The proportionality constant, $\alpha(\lambda)$ (cm^{-1}) is called the *absorption coefficient* and depends on the material and on λ.

The solution to this equation is:

$$\phi(x) = \eta\phi_0 \exp(-\alpha x) \tag{10.4}$$

since $\phi = \eta\phi_0$ at $x = 0$.

The absorption coefficients of Si, Ge and GaAs are given in Fig. 10.1 as functions of λ. It is obvious that α becomes negligible once λ exceeds λ_{max} for that particular material. On the short-wavelength side α becomes very large, signifying that practically all the photons are absorbed very near the surface. It should also be noticed that increase of α with photon energy is much faster in GaAs than in Si, near their respective λ_{max}. This is because GaAs is a direct band-gap semiconductor, while Si and Ge are indirect ones and necessitate the participation of phonons in the absorption–generation process.

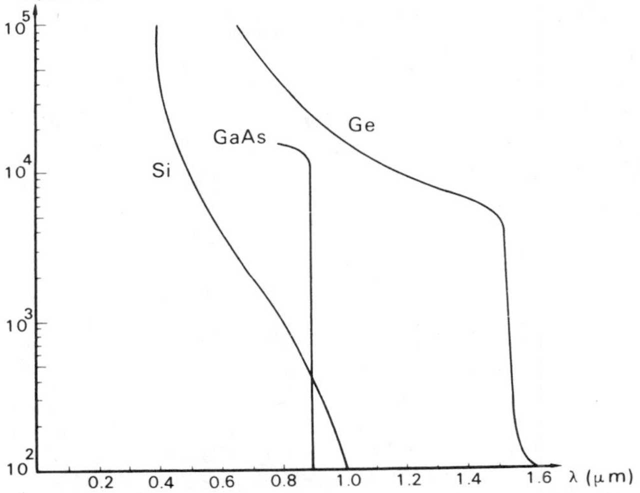

Figure 10.1. Absorption coefficient $\alpha(\lambda)$ for Si, Ge and GaAs at 300°K.

The carrier-generation function $g(x)$ is given by

$$g(x) = -\frac{d\phi}{dx} = \eta\alpha\phi_0 \exp(-\alpha x) \qquad (10.5)$$

and is therefore strongest near the surface and decays exponentially with depth, depending on αx, i.e. on λ.

10.2 Light Detection — the Photoconductive Device

Detailed analysis of an optoelectronic semiconductor device necessitates solution of the continuity equations for holes and electrons, including the enhanced generation $g(x)$, the recombination and the surface effects. This is beyond the scope of this book and we shall restrict our attention to a short qualitative discussion.

In devices intended for light detection, one must use the generated carriers before they recombine and disappear. This means the detecting part of the device must be located in or very near the region where the main absorption occurs. One of the simplest detectors is the *photoconductor*. The photoconductor is built of intrinsic or almost intrinsic semiconductor, has a large light-collecting surface area, and its basic circuit connection is as shown in Fig. 10.2.

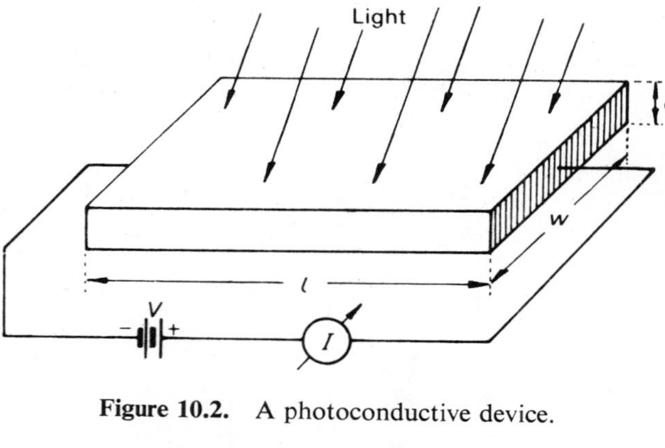

Figure 10.2. A photoconductive device.

The working temperature must be sufficiently low that with no light the number of free carriers is very small, resulting in a high 'dark' resistance. The circuit current I is then very low. Exposure to light increases generation and recombination until new equilibrium is reached at a higher carrier concentration, i.e. at lower resistance and higher current in the external circuit. That current can therefore be used, directly or after amplification, to measure the light intensity, activate a relay or control the opening of a camera lens.

The thickness d of the photoconductive layer in Fig. 10.2 should be large enough to absorb most of the entering photons. The total generation per unit area is, using (10.5),

$$g_t = \int_0^d g(x)\,dx = \eta\phi_0\,[1 - \exp(-\alpha d)]. \tag{10.6}$$

For complete absorption, d must be larger than α^{-1}. But if it is too large, only the top of the photoconductive layer will change its resistance with light, with the bottom part forming a shunt resistance, reducing the overall relative change. One should therefore use $d \simeq 1/\alpha$ (noise considerations give an optimum thickness of $d = 1.25/\alpha$). With such thickness one can use average generation $\bar{g} = g_t/d$ instead of $g(x)$ without too high an error.

The quality of photoconductor operation can be evaluated using two quantities: amplification and response time.

The photoconductive amplification G is defined as:

$$G = \frac{\text{Number of carriers passing between the two contacts in 1 s}}{\text{Number of generated carriers in 1 s}}$$

The numerator in G is I/q. Denoting by σ the conductivity with light, by R the overall resistance and by n the density of carriers, we can express the numerator as

$$\frac{I}{q} = \frac{1}{q}\frac{V}{R} = \frac{V}{q}\frac{\sigma wd}{l} = \frac{V}{q}\frac{(q\mu n)Wd}{l}, \tag{10.7}$$

where $\mu = \mu_e(1 + \mu_h/\mu_e)$. Usually $\mu_e \gg \mu_h$, making $\mu \simeq \mu_e$.

In the static case the generation and recombination rates must be equal, therefore

$$\bar{g} = \frac{\hat{n}}{\tau}, \tag{10.8}$$

where τ is the lifetime.

The denominator in the definition of G is therefore $\bar{g}lwd = \hat{n}lwd/\tau$. Substituting this and (10.7) into the definition yields

$$G = \frac{\mu\tau}{l^2}V. \tag{10.9}$$

G may be put in another interesting form by considering the carrier transit time between contacts, t_d, which is:

$$t_d = \frac{l}{v} = \frac{l}{\mu E} = \frac{l^2}{\mu V}.$$

Therefore

$$G = \frac{\tau}{t_d}. \tag{10.10}$$

To obtain high amplification it is therefore necessary to use a long-lifetime material with $\tau \gg t_d$. t_d can be shortened by increasing V (with a consequent increase in power dissipation).

High τ, however, is detrimental to the response speed, since, if the radiation suddenly stops, the current will decay with $\hat{n}$, i.e., with a time constant τ. Such a device will not be able to respond to light pulses unless their period is longer than τ.

Photoconductive devices, or cells, are used in industry, photography and light-intensity measurements (CdS is the material most commonly used for the visible range, PbS or InSb for the infrared).

Photoconductors are relatively simple to construct, can be made in polycrystalline material and so are also cheap, but they are relatively slow and require an external voltage source.

10.3 The PIN Photodetector

The PIN diode may be used as a detector by operating it in the third quadrant in its characteristic, shown in Fig. 10.3(a) under both dark and light conditions. Fig. 10.3(b) shows its structure. It is operated with reverse bias, smaller than the breakdown voltage, and its detection capability stems from the sharp increase in the reverse current, from I_0 in the dark to $I_0 + I_{ph}$ with light. The device must have a shallow junction followed by a wide depletion layer where most of the absorption and generation should take place. The generated carriers are immediately swept apart by the high reverse field and contribute to I_{ph} with little chance of recombining. The PIN diode, in which even a small reverse voltage suffices to extend the depletion layer across the whole intrinsic region, fits these requirements well. Carriers generated outside the depletion layer but within a diffusion length of it have also a good chance to diffuse towards it and contribute to I_{ph}. Those generated still further away are lost by recombination.

The carrier collecting volume in the PIN structure of Fig. 10.3(b) is therefore $Aw = A(L_e + L_h + d)$, where A is the area. The total photocurrent is:

$$I_{ph} = \int_{\lambda} qA \int_{x \simeq 0}^{W} g(x,\lambda)\, dx\, d\lambda = qA\phi_0 \int_{\lambda} \eta(\lambda)\, [1 - \exp\{-\alpha(\lambda)w\}]\, d\lambda, \tag{10.11}$$

where λ extends over the wavelength range.

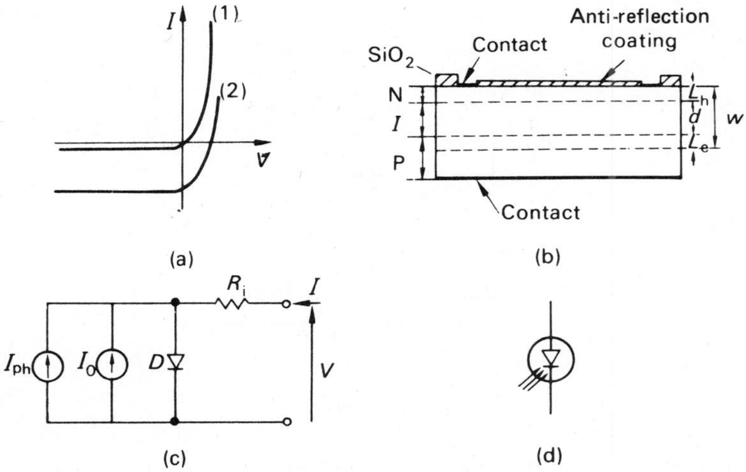

Figure 10.3. The PIN photodetector: (a) the I–V characteristic (1—in the dark, 2—with light); (b) PIN diode structure; (c) the equivalent circuit; (d) standard circuit symbol.

This current has the same direction as the leakage current, i.e. the reverse direction, so the total diode current is

(10.12) $$I = I_0\left(\exp\frac{qV}{kT} - 1\right) - I_{ph}.$$

This characteristic is shown by line (2) in Fig. 10.3(a) and can actually be obtained by shifting the dark characteristic, line (1), down by I_{ph}. All these can be represented by the equivalent circuit of Fig. 10.3(c), in which D represents an ideal diode (under reverse bias when $V<0$) and R_i represents the total internal series resistance of regions outside the depletion layer (bulk of N and P regions, contact resistances).

The field structure inside the diode, which, in the case of the real diode does not have a completely intrinsice I layer but actually has a $P^+N^-N^+$ structure, as shown in Fig. 10.4(a), is determined by Poisson's equation:

$$\frac{dE}{dx} = \frac{q(N_D - N_A)}{\varepsilon\varepsilon_0}$$

and the reverse bias V_R.

Since N_D and N_A change with position, the resulting $E(x)$ changes its slope and is shown in Fig. 10.4(b). The area under $E(x)$ must of course equal V_R.

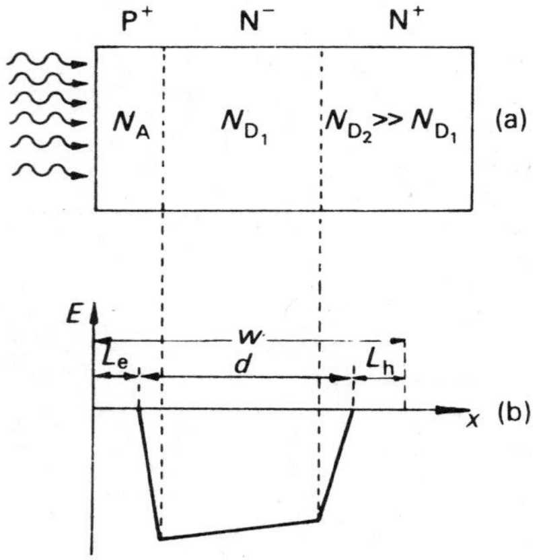

Figure 10.4. The $P^+N^-N^+$ diode and field structure under reverse voltage.

PIN detector response time is limited by the transit time of the generated carriers through the intrinsic region, which is very short because of the high field there. This is true provided the contribution of carriers generated outside the depletion field region is relatively small, since their diffusion times are much longer than the drift time. The diode design should therefore locate the high field region so as to include all the volume where significant generation takes place.

An example of a commercial Si PIN diode is Motorola MRD500, which is packaged in a glass-topped case. This diode can withstand 100 V reverse voltage, although the depletion layer extends through all the I region even at 20 V. At 20 V and 25°C it has a dark (leakage) current of about 2 nA, 4 pF capacitance and less then 10 Ω internal resistance. Its sensitivity is 1.8 μA / (mW cm^{-2}) to black-body radiation (tungsten source at 2870°K) and 6.6 μA / (mW cm^{-2}) to monochromatic radiation at $\lambda=0.8$ μm (which is the maximum-sensitivity wavelength). Irradiation by 1 mW cm^{-2} at 0.8 μm therefore gives $I_{ph}=6.6$ μA. The response time is better than 1 ns.

The basic electrical circuit for the PIN diode is shown in Fig. 10.5. The load resistor R_L may be as high as 1 MΩ, but for fast response it must be small so that the time constant R_LC_j (C_j is diode capacitance) does not inhibit the response. To achieve 1 ns response a 50 Ω load should be used in the case of the MRD500 with subsequent amplification; alternatively a low input impedance (transimpedance) amplifier may be used as a load.

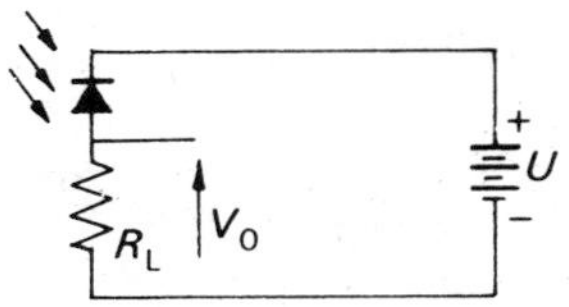

Figure 10.5. The basic electrical circuit for PIN photodetector use.

PN or PIN diodes can also be operated as photodetectors with a built-in amplifying mechanism. I_{ph} can be amplified by adjusting the reverse operating voltage to be near the avalanche breakdown point. I_{ph} will then be multiplied by M, as given by (9.44), which is larger than 1 for that voltage. The amplified current, however, is no longer linearly related to the light intensity and the noise problem is much more severe.

An important subject which concerns all detectors is the minimum detectable signal. This is limited by the detector's own noise (proportional to the dark current I_0 — see Section 15.8) and the background radiation that enters the detector in addition to the desired signal. This important subject, which is not covered here, should not be overlooked when comparing different types of detectors.

10.4 The Photovoltaic Effect

The PN diode can be utilized as a photodetector without any external voltage source, or for direct conversion of optical energy to electrical energy, by employing the *photovoltaic effect.*

The photovoltaic cell is a diode that operates in the fourth quadrant of the irradiated diode I–V characteristic in Fig. 10.3(a). This quadrant is shown enlarged in Fig 10.6(c), together with the equivalent circuit.

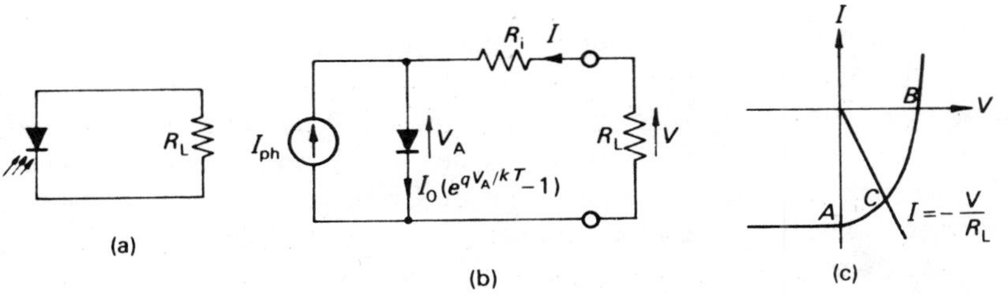

Figure 10.6. The photovoltaic cell: (a) the circuit of the cell (R_L is load resistance); (b) the equivalent circuit; (c) the fourth quadrant, in which the cell operates, and the load line.

The cell may be intended for light measurements only, and in that case a microammeter of very low resistance is used as a load. This can be approximated by a short circuit and if the cell is properly constructed so that its internal resistance R_i is also very small, the output voltage, which equals the diode voltage, is about zero. By (10.12) $I = I_{ph}$, so that it is proportional to the absorbed radiation.

The cell operating point in Fig. 10.6(c) is then the intersection of the diode characteristic with its *load line*, or load characteristic, given by $V=0$. It is marked by A. The cell thus transforms the absorbed optical energy into electrical current through the microammeter. If the circuit of the external cell is left open, i.e. $R_L = \infty$, the load line becomes $I=0$. The operating point shifts to point *B* in Fig. 10.6(c). The open-circuit voltage appearing across the contacts is, by (10.12),

$$V_{oc} = \frac{kT}{q} \ln \left(\frac{I_{ph}}{I_0} + 1 \right). \tag{10.13}$$

This voltage forward biases the diode as I_{ph} must now flow through it. Physically the forward voltage at any load results from (8.28): in the first quadrant this equation predicts an excess of minority carriers near a junction whenever a forward voltage is applied. In the fourth quadrant it predicts that the same excess carriers, if generated by absorbed light, will give rise to a corresponding forward voltage V_F. The total junction voltage $V_t = V_B - V_F$ is still enough to leave a reverse field across the now much narrowed depletion layer. This field sweeps the generated minority carriers across, creating the current generator I_{ph}. The maximum forward voltage V_{oc} when the circuit is open is always less than V_B, since otherwise there will not be a reverse field or I_{ph}.

The relationship (10.13) between V_{oc} and I_{ph} is nonlinear so V_{oc} is not used for light-intensity measurements.

10.5 Optical to Electrical Energy Conversion, the Solar Cell

The most important use of the photovoltaic effect today is for direct conversion of solar energy to electricity. Diodes made for that purpose are called *solar cells*. Only Si cells are commercially available today, though GaAs, because of its higher E_g, yields higher voltage and efficiency. However, the high price and difficult technology of GaAs makes such cells still uneconomic today. To be used as an energy source, the solar cell is connected to a load R_L as in Fig. 10.6(a) and (b). The load characteristic, or load line, is $I = V/R_L$ (the positive polarities of V and I are defined in Fig. 10.6(b)) and the operating point is now point *C*. The total series resistance is $R_L + R_i$, making $V_F = -I(R_L + R_i)$, where V_F is the internal diode forward voltage in

A photovoltaic solar power module made by Ferranti and composed of many interconnected Si solar cells. Reproduced by permission of Ferranti Electronics Ltd.

Fig. 10.6(b). Substituting it in (10.12) and calculating the external voltage $V = -IR_L$,

$$V = \frac{kT}{q}\left(1 + \frac{R_i}{R_L}\right)^{-1} \ln\left(\frac{I_{ph} + I}{I_0} + 1\right). \tag{10.14}$$

The power absorbed in R_L is

$$P = -IV = -CI \ln\left(\frac{I_{ph} + I}{I_0} + 1\right), \tag{10.15}$$

where

$$C = \frac{kT}{q}\left(1 + \frac{R_i}{R_L}\right)^{-1}.$$

In any practical circuit $(I_{ph}+I) \gg I_0$ (though $I<0$ in Fig. 10.6 when the diode operates as a generator), so (10.15) may be simplified to

$$P \simeq -CI \ln \frac{I_{ph}+I}{I_0}. \tag{10.16}$$

P is maximized when its derivative with respect to I equals zero, i.e. when

$$\ln \frac{I_{ph}+I}{I_0} = -\frac{I}{I_{ph}+I}. \tag{10.17}$$

This is a transcendental equation giving I in terms of I_{ph} and I_0. Substituting it in (10.16) gives the maximum available power from the cell:

$$P_{max} = C\frac{I_m^2}{I_{ph}+I_m} = \frac{kT}{q}\frac{R_L}{R_i+R_L}\frac{I_m^2}{I_{ph}+I_m}, \tag{10.18}$$

where I_m is the solution of (10.17).

We see that high power requires low I_0 and R_i. By (9.19) I_0 is reduced if higher doping densities are used and the same is true for R_i. But there is a limit to doping increase, since it also increases the number of crystal defects and so reduces lifetimes, mobilities and diffusion lengths. Consequently I_{ph} of (10.11) starts to drop. A compromise is therefore needed, and most cells built today have very shallow (sometimes only 0.3 μm deep) N layer of about 10^{18} cm^{-3} doping on a P substrate of between 2×10^{15} cm^{-3} to 5×10^{16} cm^{-3} acceptor concentration (5 to 0.5 Ω cm resistivity range).

The shallow junction is necessary so as to locate it where most of the solar-energy spectrum is absorbed – very near the surface. To prevent undue

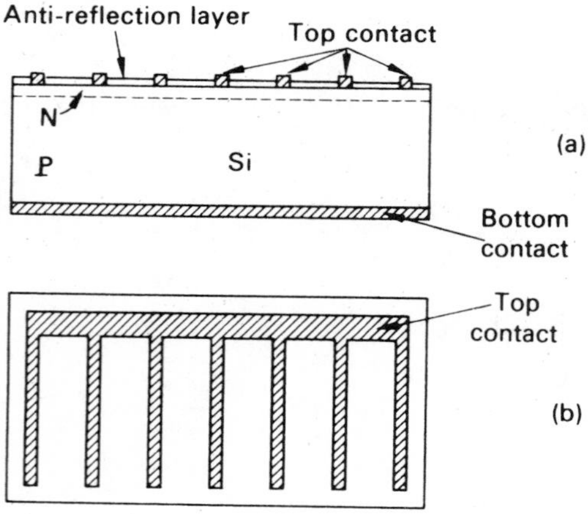

Figure 10.7. A solar cell: (a) cross section; (b) top contact, viewed from above.

increase of R_i because of the thinness of the N layer, a metal net or comb structure with many thin fingers, as in Fig. 10.7, is used for the top contact. This covers about 7% of the Si area (see photo on p.165).

The available sea level solar energy at noon of a bright day is about 70 to 80 mW cm^{-2}. The best commercially available cells today are made in single crystal Si, have efficiencies around 15%, open-circuit voltages of nearly 0.6 V and areas of up to 40 cm^2. They are arranged in large area arrays and connected in series and parallel to obtain useful load voltages and currents. This makes solar cells a comparatively expensive energy source, limited by economic considerations to special uses for which no other source is available, such as in space, or in inaccessible places on earth where automatic equipment must keep operating unattended. The cell arrays are used for continuous battery recharge as long as the sun shines.

Present-day energy research aims at reducing the cost of a cell by shifting from single to polycrystalline silicon (with relatively large crystallites) or by using cheap plastic lenses to concentrate sunlight on a small-area high-quality cell. See Section 21.7 for review of research towards cheap silicon.

10.6 Luminescent Materials

So far only light absorption has been discussed; let us now turn to light emission. This can be achieved in several ways. The first is by using luminescent materials. These are materials in which hole–electron generation or excitation of deep impurity electrons from their normal low-energy level to a higher and empty impurity level (with both in the forbidden gap), is followed by a return to equilibrium via photon emission in the visible spectral range. The exact wavelength, i.e. color, is a characteristic of the material or impurity.

The original excitation can be caused by absorption of higher-energy photons (*photoluminescence*) or by bombardment with high-energy electrons (*cathodo-luminescence*). Recombination and photon emission usually takes place in several stages. An example is the excitation of a valence electron across E_g and high into the conduction band by an ultra-violet photon. Within a very short time ($\simeq 1$ ps) that electron loses its extra kinetic energy by repeated collisions with the lattice and settles in a vacant state at the bottom of the conduction band. The next stage is either a direct radiative recombination or, as is more common, the trapping of the electron in a localized state in the gap, possible re-excitement into the conduction band by thermal energy, trapping again and so on till a hole wanders by and radiative recombination occurs. In such a case the radiated photon is emitted a relatively long time after the original excitation, and such materials are called *phosphors*. ZnS is such a semiconductor, to which Cu, Ag or Mn impurities are added to bring the emission into the visible spectrum with each giving a different color. Materials with instantaneous recombination are used to coat the inside of the glass envelope of fluorescent lamps. These lamps are then filled with gas whose atoms are excited by electrical discharge between internal electrodes. The excited atoms relax by emitting an ultra-violet photon, which is converted by the coating into the visible range with comparatively high overall optical efficiency. An incandescent lamp, on the other hand, radiates mostly in the infra-red (i.e. radiates heat), and its optical efficiency is low.

Phosphors that emit visible light when bombarded by fast electrons are used to coat the screens of cathode ray tubes for television sets and oscilloscopes.

A focused beam of accelerated electrons scans the screen and excites the phosphor coating with subsequent light emission from the scanned spot. Addition of various impurities to the phosphors makes it possible to get a specific color such as red, yellow, green or blue.

10.7 Light-emitting Diodes (LED), Optic Couplers

Light-emitting diodes, or LEDs, utilize the recombination of the excess carriers, injected in a forward-biased diode, to obtain light emission for display purposes. As we have seen in Fig. 6.10(a) and (b), the E–k diagrams of indirect band-gap materials like Si or Ge, is such that conduction electrons and holes have widely different momentum (k) values. Since photons carry practically no momentum, the momentum conservation law makes direct radiative recombination impossible without the participation of several phonons that can carry the excess momentum. This makes radiative recombination a very unlikely process in indirect band gap materials. The recombination there is mainly nonradiative, via recombination centers, and just heats the lattice by generating phonons. In direct band-gap semiconductors, like GaAs, the E–k diagram (Fig. 6.10(c)) is such that both conduction electrons and holes have very low momentum values. Direct radiative recombination is therefore very likely and it is such semiconductors that are used for light generation.

In a forward-biased GaAs diode the injected carriers recombine radiatively but the emission is in the near i.r. (about 0.9 μm). The radiation intensity is proportional to the concentrations of excess minority carriers and therefore to the forward current. It is possible to encapsule a GaAs LED and a Si PIN detecting diode (which is very sensitive at 0.9 μm) in close proximity on the same header, forming an *optical coupler*, also called a photon coupled isolator. This is shown in Fig. 10.8(a). This integrated device is used to replace relays in situations where electrical isolation between the input and output circuits is required. The light-emitting diode and the optical sensor in Fig. 10.8(a) ensures that signal travel will only be from the light emitter to the sensor with no undesired feedback.

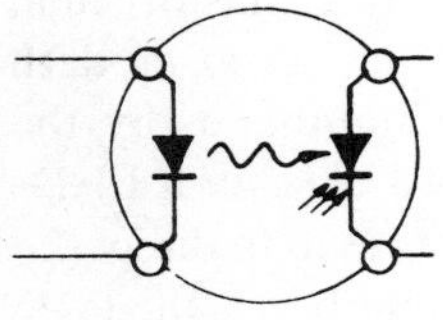

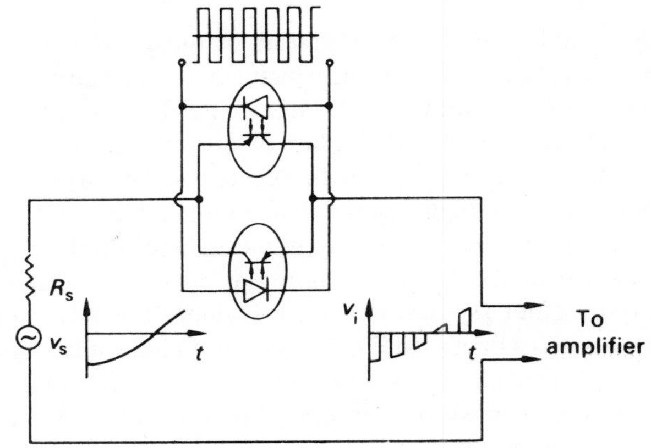

Figure 10.8. Optical coupling: (a) photon-coupled isolator; (b) use of two isolators to obtain a signal-chopping circuit.

Instead of a diode sensor, one can use a phototransistor switch (a combination of sensor and amplifier in the same device as in Fig. 10.8(b)). Optical couplers can be used to build circuits like the one shown in Fig. 10.8(b). This is a chopper circuit, whose purpose is to chop a slowly varying positive or negative input signal provided by the signal source and turn it into an a.c. signal (that can be amplified more easily than the d.c. by the following amplifier). A square chopping wave is applied to the light-emitting diodes of the two couplers causing them to emit corresponding light pulses. The phototransistors are then switched into a high-conduction state, connecting the input signal to the output in turns. By using two couplers, both positive and negative input signals can be chopped. Such chopping, if done by relays, is very limited in frequency and introduces noise into the output due to jitter of the relay contacts. If chopping is done by regular transistors (of which we shall learn in Chapter 14) the capacitive coupling inside the transistor causes spikes, originated by the square chopping wave, to appear in the output as unwanted noise. Here the coupling capacitance inside the isolator is insignificant (about 0.02 pF). Optical couplers are also used for logic-circuit realizations, where the same LED output can activate several PIN diode circuits in parallel.

GaAs LEDs cannot be used for displays since the wavelength is beyond the visible range. But the compound semiconductor $GaAs_xP_{1-x}$ (gallium arsenide phosphide) has a band gap which depends on x, the arsenic percentage. E_g varies from 1.4 eV for pure GaAs ($x=1$) to 2.26 eV for pure GaP ($x=0$). At $x=0.44$ the band gap is still direct, as in GaAs (GaP is indirect), but the emitted light is red and visible. GaP itself may also be used for LEDs, although it is an indirect material, by inclusion of special impurities in it. This gives rise to impurity levels which act as traps and make radiative recombination possible. Addition of CdO or ZnO gives red light with relatively high efficiency. Addition of sulphur or nitrogen shifts the radiation to green with much lower efficiency but the greater sensitivity of the human eye to green more than compensates for that. Parallel connection of many LEDs of small area may be used to display numbers and letters, as is done, e.g. in modern pocket calculators. A common way to display the whole number is by the seven-segment system with each segment possibly composed of several LEDs arranged in a line, as in Fig. 10.9(a). A digital control system is used to direct the current to the desired segment. For example, to obtain the number 3, the logic control feeds positive current into segments 1, 4, 5, 6 and 7 which light up and display the number 3. The cathodes of the LEDs are connected together to a common return terminal. Failure of a single LED will not ruin the display since it will only cause a small break in one segment.

Another common method fcr alphanumeric display is by a matrix of 35 LEDs as shown in Fig. 10.9(b). Logic control passes current only to those LEDs that are needed for a specific number or letter display.

LEDs are also used as pilot lamps. Their advantages compared to other lamps are their high efficiency, long operating lifetimes, mechanical sturdiness and the ability to operate from low voltage supplies, compatible with transistor circuits.

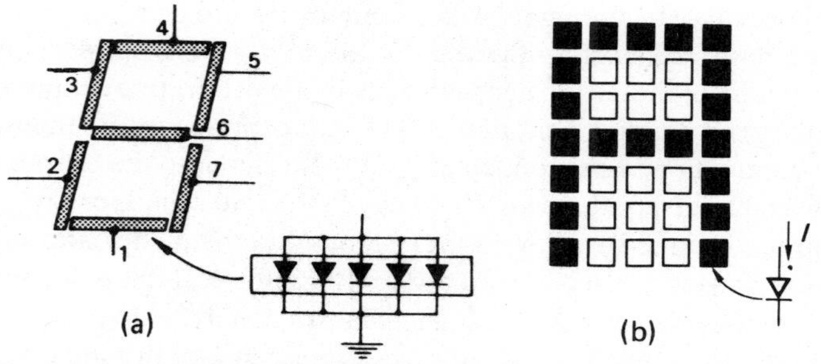

Figure 10.9 (a) The seven-segment system for obtaining numerical display; (b) the 7×5 LED matrix for alphanumeric display with the letter A displayed.

10.8 Liquid Crystal Display (LCD)

Liquid crystals are materials composed of long, rod-like molecules which have both dielectric and optic anisotropies. Their composition is such that in a temperature range of practical interest (say between −10 and +60°C) the intermolecular forces are strong enough to align the molecules in parallel to each other. At a higher temperature, thermal energy overcomes these forces and destroys the ordered structure in the fluid while at a lower temperature the molecules freeze and cannot react to an applied electric field.

A thin display cell is formed by sandwiching the liquid crystal fluid between two optic glass plates A and B as shown in Fig. 10.10 (the cell is hermetically sealed by spacers on all sides). It was found that if the inner surface of the glass

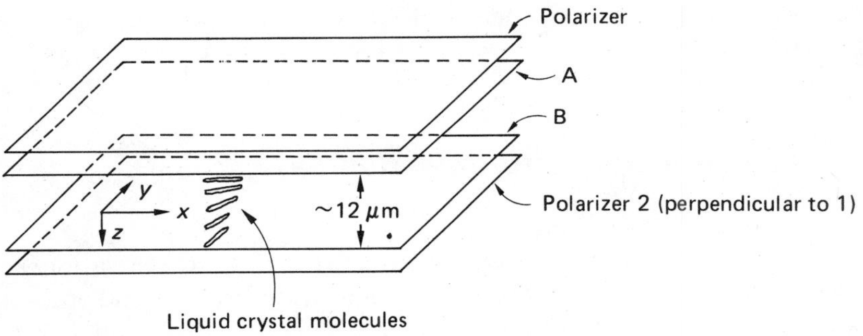

Figure 10.10 The basic twisted nematic liquid crystal cell.

plate is microscopically grooved in a certain direction (by scratching it or evaporating Si0 on it at an angle), the LC molecules in contact with that surface will align in parallel to that direction and exert a force on molecules further away to align too. If glass plates A and B are oriented in perpendicular directions, say x and y, a 90° twist will form in the direction of the LC molecules between the top and the bottom of the cell as shown in the figure.

If polarized light enters the cell through its top cover, it will be guided by the molecules so that when it emerges from the bottom cover its polarization has been also twisted by 90°. If there is a bright reflecting surface behind the cell, the light will be reflected back into it, pass again and re-emerge with its original polarization. When viewed from the top by this light, the cell will show a bright surface. Two crossed polarizers, 1 and 2, are used to obtain properly polarized light from any existing source (daylight, lamp) and allow only it to pass the cell and be reflected back through it.

The conducting electrode and counter electrode made of transparent indium–tin oxide, are evaporated on the glass covers and etched to desired shapes (like the seven segment form). An audio frequency a.c. voltage (5–10 V) applied between those electrodes creates an electric field in the z direction with a resulting torque that tilts the molecules in that direction, thus wrecking their ordered light guiding properties. The entering polarized light will then scatter, lose its polarized nature and will not be reflected back up. The areas covered by the electrodes to which this voltage has been applied will therefore turn dark (a.c. voltage used as d.c. causes electrochemical effects that shorten the cell lifetime). Thus the activated transparent electrodes (in the form of numbers or letters) are displayed as dark shapes on brighter background.

Since the torque on the LC molecules is a field effect (no conductive current) and no internal light source is needed, extremely little battery power is used. LEDs on the other hand, require substantial currents for light emission, but can be viewed in the dark too. There are many types of liquid crystals with varying properties and also other ways in which a cell can be constructed. The one described is the most commonly used for small area displays such as watches or pocket calculators.

10.9 The Semiconductor Injection Laser

In Section 10.7 we discussed radiative recombination near a forward-biased junction in GaAs. With no special geometrical structure and operating conditions intended to prevent optical losses such radiation will tend to have a relatively wide spectral range of a few hundred angstroms around the value corresponding to E_g and it will not be really monochromatic. Also the phase of the emitted photons will be random, i.e., with no relations between the phases of the electromagnetic waves constituting each photon. Such radiation is called *spontaneous* or noncoherent, and is encountered in all normal light sources including LEDs.

Lasing, on the other hand, is an almost pure monochromatic radiation (it has a range of a few angstroms in semiconductors, where lasing results from electron transitions between bands, but only a fraction of an angstrom in other lasers in which the transition is between discrete levels). The phase of the electromagnetic laser wave at any moment is related to its phase a moment before or after. Such radiation is called *coherent* and the device producing it is called a LASER, meaning Light Amplification by Stimulated Emission of Radiation.

The possibility of lasing comes from the quantum-mechanical principle, proved by Dirac, which states that when a photon interacts with an electron, it is equally probably that (a) the photon will be absorbed and the electron will become excited, or (b) if the electron is already excited, the emission of a second photon will be stimulated with the electron dropping from its excited state to a lower-energy one. This second photon has the same λ, phase, polarization and direction of propagation as the first. Thus, the original photon can be amplified.

The question as to whether the original photon will be amplified or absorbed in a semiconductor depends on whether most of the electrons are in excited states or in low-energy states. The first situation is called *population inversion* and cannot normally exist unless special means are used to *pump* or raise the electrons to their excited states before lasing starts. Both absorption and light-stimulation processes are shown schematically in Fig. 10.11.

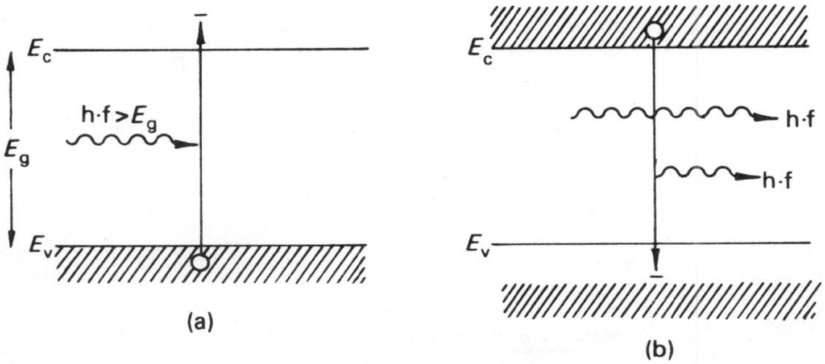

Figure 10.11 Interaction between a photon and a semiconductor (hatched areas represent states occupied by electrons): (a) no population inversion exists. Photon is absorbed causing generation; (b) population inversion exists. The original photon stimulates the emission of a second one.

Population inversion can be achieved near a PN junction by the use of high doping densities and forward currents. The large number of injected carriers creates a region near the junction where there is a very large number of electrons in the conduction band together with a very large number of holes in the valence band, i.e., a population inversion. This situation is shown in Fig. 10.12(a). Some of the injected electrons will start to recombine spontaneously, but the first photons instead of being reabsorbed or radiating away, stimulate the emission of more photons, reach the device wall and are internally reflected back into the junction plane by its mirror-like crystal surface. They now pass again through the region of population inversion stimulating more photons, all coherent with them, and reach the opposite wall. Some are again reflected and so stimulate a stronger and stronger coherent light emission. There is loss of light by radiation to the outside and by reabsorption inside the bulk semiconductor away from the junction, where there is no population inversion. If the loss from these two causes is lower than the light amplification by the stimulated emission, the number of photons and light intensity will keep on growing very fast, while the diode heavy forward current renews the population inversion continuously. The light intensity will stabilize at a value in which the light losses (growing with the intensity) will be exactly balanced by the light amplification. The structure of the basic GaAs injection laser is shown in Fig. 10.12(b).

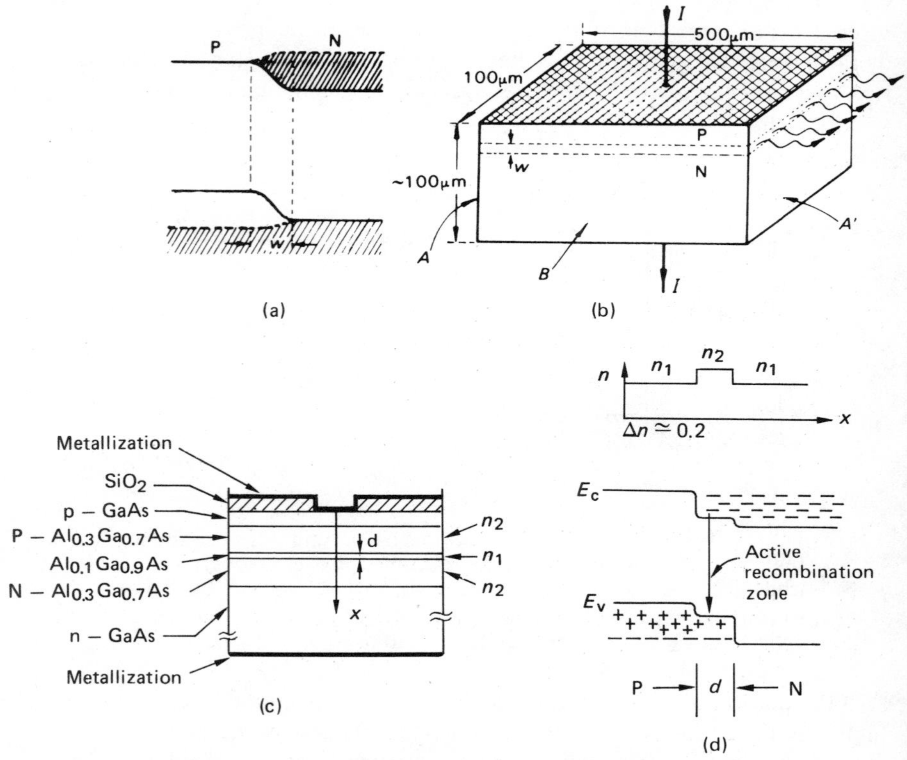

Figure 10.12 The injection laser: (a) a PN junction at high forward injection, creating population inversion near it; (b) basic GaAs laser structure; (c) heterostructure stripe geometry laser; (d) energy bands and refractive index for the heterostructure laser as functions of depth x.

By a suitable choice of the directions of the crystal axes, the two opposing A–A' walls in Fig. 10.12(b) can be cleaved and so be extremely parallel and smooth. When the light strikes those walls from the inside, about 30% of it is reflected back because of the change in the refractive index, and this is enough to overcome the internal losses. The rest is emitted to the outside as coherent light. The B walls are intentionally roughened, otherwise more than one mode of electromagnetic oscillation may build up and the laser may lase at two or more slightly different wavelengths at the same time. Such a structure is called a *Fabry–Perot cavity*. The solution of Maxwell's equations for this cavity predicts which modes of electromagnetic waves can exist in it.

The main difficulty with this basic laser structure is the high current densities needed to pump it up to lasing threshold (40–100 kA cm^{-2} at 300°K but only about 5 kA cm^{-2} at 77°K). They could therefore be operated only at the temperature of liquid nitrogen, and even then only in low-duty cycle-pulse operation and with elaborate heat sinks. New technologies exist today which enable us to grow a multilayered epitaxial structure of $Al_xGa_{1-x}As$, with desired composition and doping, on top of a GaAs substrate. Varying x changes the refractive index n and the band gap E_g slightly, although the single crystal structure continues unbroken. Heterojunctions are formed between the $Al_xGa_{1-x}As$ and the GaAs like those discussed in Section 8.6. Different potential barriers appear in the conduction and in the valence bands. This is utilized in the double heterostructure laser shown in Fig. 10.12(c) and (d) to confine the injected carriers to the immediate junction vicinity. At the same time the change in refractive index confines the emitted light to the same vicinity so that in the thin active region ($d \simeq 0.1$–$0.5\,\mu m$) a very high concentration of electrons, holes and photons builds up. Lasing action therefore starts at a much lower threshold current density than before ($J_{th} \simeq 500\,A/cm^2$ at 300°K). Further reduction of I_{th} is achieved by using a narrow ($\simeq 20\,\mu m$) stripe contact (Fig. 10.12(c)) that concentrates the injected carriers under it. Reliable laser diodes that lase continuously at $\lambda = 0.85\,\mu m$ with $I_{th} = 10$–$20\,mA$ can thus be built. The emitted laser light can be modulated into light pulses by switching the laser current above and below threshold. Modulation frequencies exceeding 2 GHz have been achieved. At such frequencies one must consider the transient occurring when an injection laser is turned on and the photon flux builds up. The emitted light may exhibit self pulsations that depend on the particular diode used.

Injection lasers have been built in a variety of additional direct band-gap semiconductor materials like GaAsP, InGaP, AlGaAs in which PN junctions can also be made, but AlGaAs on GaAs is the best yet. Particularly interesting is the GaInAsP laser on InP substrate which can be made to lase at $\lambda = 1.1 \div 1.6\,\mu m$, a range at which optical fibers (see next section) have their minimum loss. Other types of useful lasers also exist: in solids we have the ruby laser (the first to be built) and in gases the He–Ne ($0.6328\,\mu m$ wavelength) and CO_2 (operating at $10.6\,\mu m$), which is the most powerful laser today.

Lasers have already found a wide use in many fields, such as high accuracy distance measurements and three-dimensional lensless photography (holography). In bio-engineering they are used as sophisticated surgery tools which seal the blood vessels as they cut, in metal working as machine tools for cutting and drilling extremely small holes, and of course in optical communications.

10.10 Fiber Optic Communications

Optical fibers based on silica that have low losses and can act as light guides (i.e. light 'pipes') were invented in 1970 and opened the way to optical communications links like the one shown in Fig. 10.13.

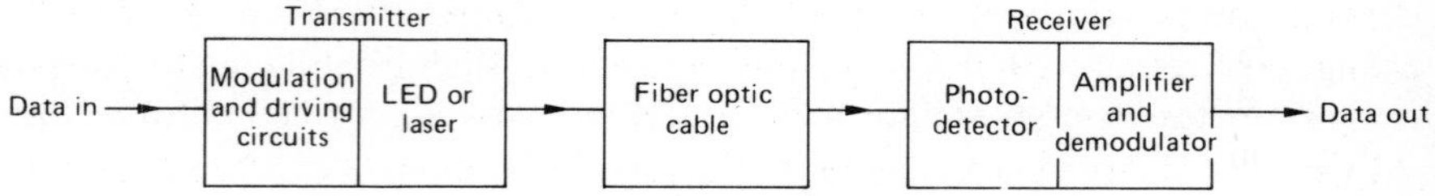

Figure 10.13 Block diagram of an optical communication link.

The light output of an LED or an injection laser, which can be pulse modulated by current control, is coupled into a fiber light guide which guides it to a receiver at the other end. The receiver contains a photodetector, like a PIN or an avalanche photodiode, which transforms the light pulses back to electrical signals. These can then be amplified and processed. The length of the link depends on the transmitted power, the fiber loss in db/km, the fiber dispersion (light velocity dependence on wavelength and propagation mode) and the receiver sensitivity. Links of more than 10 km can be made and repeater stations can be used for longer distances. Such links successfully compete with coaxial cable links. Their attractive properties compared to metal wires are: very large bandwidth, i.e., high pulse rates (in excess of 1 GHz) that can be used to modulate the very high light carrier frequency, immunity to electromagnetic noise pick up and to corrosion, very small size and weight and high ruggedness. Fiber optics are also secure from electromagnetic eavesdropping. On the other hand, it is difficult to splice two fibers together or tap them, coupling into and out of fibers introduces loss and the optical power levels available are low (milliwatts from lasers, microwatts from LEDs).

Optical sources and detectors have already been discussed. Let us now review the fiber properties.

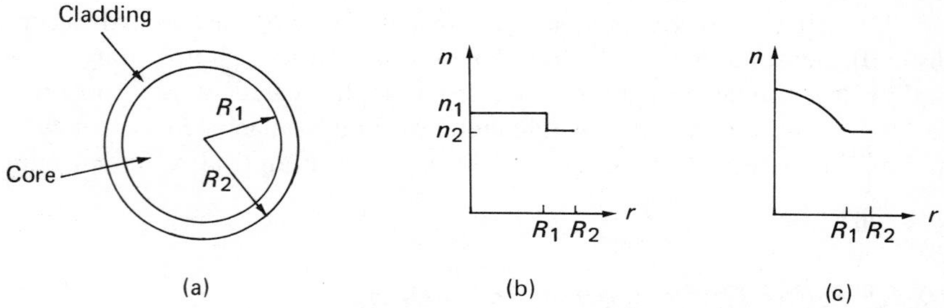

Figure 10.14 The optic fiber; (a) cross section of core and cladding; (b) radial dependence of refractive index n in a step index fiber; (c) radial dependence of refractive index n in a graded index fiber.

The parts of the fiber that are instrumental in light transmission are its core and the cladding around it, both are made of silica (or plastic) and have different refractive indices as shown in Fig. 10.14. (A jacket providing mechanical strength surrounds the cladding but is omitted for clarity.)

Two types of fibers, a step index and a graded index are shown. The step index is simpler so let us consider it first. Figure 10.15 shows two rays, marked I and II, in the core.

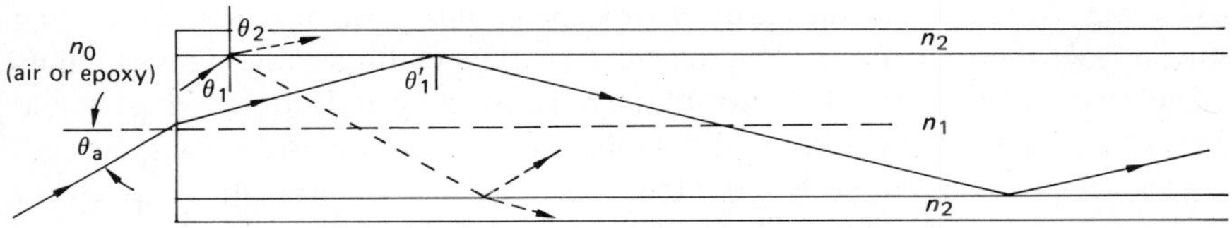

Figure 10.15 Light rays propagating in a step index fiber; ray I (broken line) penetrates the cladding and is absorbed within a short distance; ray II (full line) is totally reflected at the interface and can propagate for a long distance.

When a ray hits the core–cladding interface, it is refracted according to Snell's law

$$\frac{\sin\theta_1}{\sin\theta_2}=\frac{n_2}{n_1} \tag{10.19}$$

where n_1 and n_2 are core and cladding refractive indices respectively. If $n_2<n_1$ then $\theta_1<\theta_2$. So long as $\theta_2\leq\pi/2$, i.e., so long as

$$\theta_1\leq\theta_c=\text{arc sin}\,\frac{n_2}{n_1}. \tag{10.20}$$

then part of the light energy in the ray is refracted and enters the cladding and is absorbed there. This is the case for ray I in Fig. 10.15. After a short distance this ray will lose all its energy and be lost. If θ_1 exceeds θ_c in (10.20), as is the case for ray II in the figure ($\theta'_1>\theta_c$), then this ray suffers total internal reflection at the interface and barring other types of losses it can propagate indefinitely in the core. The fiber material and structure however, are not perfect and have minute irregularities, microbendings and impurities which result in light attenuation with distance. The attenuation is a function of wavelength λ and minimizes at $\lambda=1.55\,\mu$m to about 0.2 db/km for present-day fibers. Around $\lambda=0.85\,\mu$m

(GaAs sources) however, the losses may be several db/km depending on the fiber type. By solving Maxwell's equation for our fiber structure, it is found that only discrete values of θ_1 ($\theta_1 > \theta_c$) can propagate. Each such value corresponds to a separate propagation mode and can exist above a limit wavelength. If a core has a very small diameter ($\sim 3\,\mu$m) then only the lowest mode can propagate. Fibers with larger diameters (55–300 μm) will support multimode propagation. Since each mode is characterized by a slightly different value of θ then in the same fiber length each will be reflected a different number of times and will travel a different total distance. Therefore each mode will suffer a somewhat different attenuation and delay. If a light source with a relatively wide spectrum like LED ($\Delta\lambda \simeq 40-100$ nm) is used, or if the light is pulse modulated (creating sidebands), then each wavelength will be delayed differently. This is called *dispersion* and it distorts the shape of the pulse arriving at the fiber exit. It would look smeared with longer rise and fall times and lower amplitude. Two succeeding pulses may merge together and the receiver will have difficulties in deciding between a 'one' and a 'zero'. Dispersion is reduced if an almost monochromatic source, like a laser, is used instead of an LED, or a single mode fiber is used. Both attenuation and dispersion set limits to the maximum length of fiber links that can be operated without repeating stations (that detect, amplify, reshape and retransmit the light pulses). In the graded index fiber of Fig. 10.14(c), the ray is reflected back towards the axis gradually. Here higher order modes have longer paths to travel in the lower index region where the light velocity (c/n) is higher. This results in less dispersion and consequently higher pulse rates can be used.

Coupling the Fiber to a Source and Detector

Each optic fiber has a maximum light acceptance angle θ_m from which rays from the outside can penetrate its face and propagate with an angle θ_1 exceeding θ_c given by (10.20). Referring to Fig. 10.15 for the step index case, light with $\theta_a < \theta_m$ will be accepted. The *numerical aperture* (N.A.) of the fiber is defined as

$$\text{(10.21)} \qquad \text{N.A.} \triangleq \sin\theta_m$$

Using (10.19) for the air (or epoxy) to fiber interface:

$$\frac{n_0}{n_1} = \frac{\sin(\pi/2 - \theta_c)}{\sin\theta_m} = \frac{\cos\theta_c}{\sin\theta_m} = \frac{\sqrt{1-\sin^2\theta_c}}{\sin\theta_m}.$$

Substituting $\sin\theta_c$ from (10.20) and assuming $\Delta n = n_2 - n_1 << 1$

$$\text{(10.22)} \qquad \text{N.A.} = \frac{n_1}{n_0}\sqrt{1-\left(\frac{n_2}{n_1}\right)^2} \simeq \frac{1}{n_0}\sqrt{2n_1\Delta n}.$$

Thus a glass fiber with $n_1 = 1.5$, $\Delta n = 0.005$ and $n_0 = 1$ (air) will have N.A. $= 0.12$ which corresponds to an acceptance angle of $\theta_m = 7°$. Larger Δn with N.A.$\simeq 0.3$ can be obtained if plastic cladding is used. It is often necessary to use miniature lenses to redirect light emitted by a LED or a laser into the small acceptance angle of the fiber. Source, lens and fiber can then be connected together with epoxy cement ($n \simeq 1.5$) as shown in Fig. 10.16.

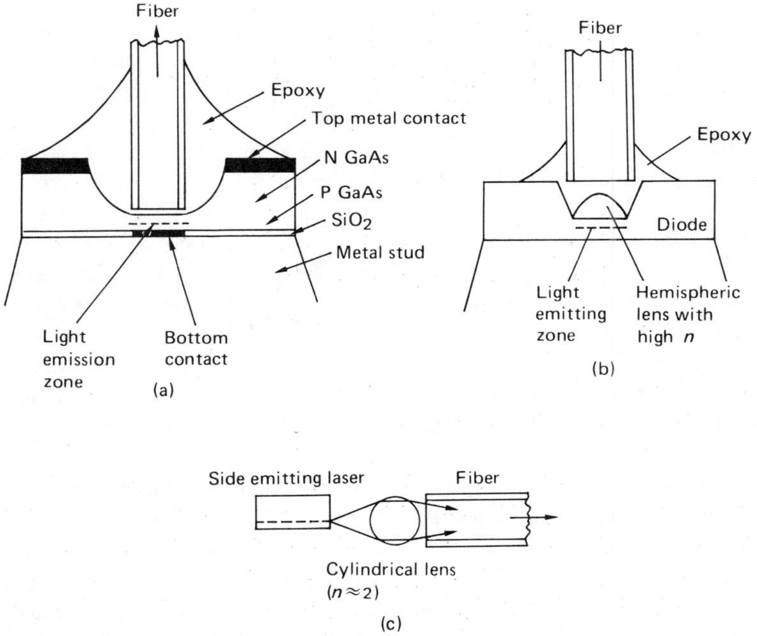

Figure 10.16 Possible ways to couple fibers to sources: (a) fiber coupling to surface emitting diode (Burrus method); (b) use of a hemispherical lens; (c) use of cylindrical lens for side emitting laser or LED.

Fiber communication systems using LED sources have been built that operate at 10 Mbit/s with 12 km spacing between repeaters. The distance goes down to about 8 km at 100 Mbit/2 but can be increased if lower loss fibers (or sources that operate at wavelength corresponding to loss minimum, like GaInAsP LED or lasers) are used. This considerably exceeds coaxial cable capabilities and is only about 1% the weight. Optical communication system components are continuously perfected, become more economic and reliable, and with perfection of tapping and splicing will probably become the most often used system inside buildings and cities.

QUESTIONS

10.1 A photovoltaic Ge detector is positioned behind a window made of thin Si. To what wavelength range will the detector respond?

10.2 What are the differences between the absorption properties of direct and indirect band-gap semiconductors around their respective E_g cutoff point.

10.3 What changes in the Si absorption coefficient do you expect if its doping density is increased? Can a doped silicon be completely transparent for photons of lower than its 1.1 eV band-gap energy?

10.4 Why is a silicon solar cell better than a germanium one? (To answer this, check the solar spectrum in Reference 9.)

10.5 Why should a Si solar cell not be made thicker, say a few millimeters thick, so as to absorb more of the infrared solar energy at which its absorption coefficient is low?

10.6 What is an extrinsic photoconductor? Remembering the solid solubility limitation on doping densities, do you expect the same sensitivity from extrinsic photoconducting detectors as from intrinsic ones?

10.7 Does the output of a photoconducting detector increase when the external voltage is increased? If so, why not increase the source voltage as high as we want?

10.8 The Si diode of Fig. 10.17 is illuminated from the rear by an incandescent lamp which radiates like a black body at 2000°K. The radiation covers the visible and infrared spectral ranges and maximizes around 1 μm. Discuss the expected output dependence on wavelength and plan your approach for obtaining a numerical solution for the response of the cell to this radiation.

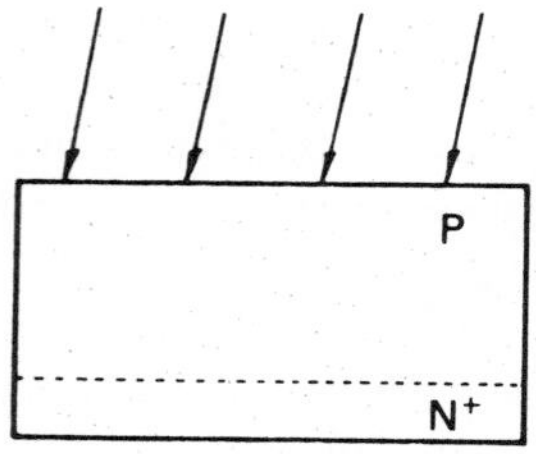

Figure 10.17 A Si diode irradiated from the back.

10.9 An optical detector based on heating, such as a thermocouple or a bolometer, is insensitive to wavelength changes and gives the same reading so long as it is irradiated by the same power. Photon detectors, such as photoconductors or photovoltaic cells, give an output that behaves as in Fig. 10.18 when irradiated by constant power and varying λ. Why?

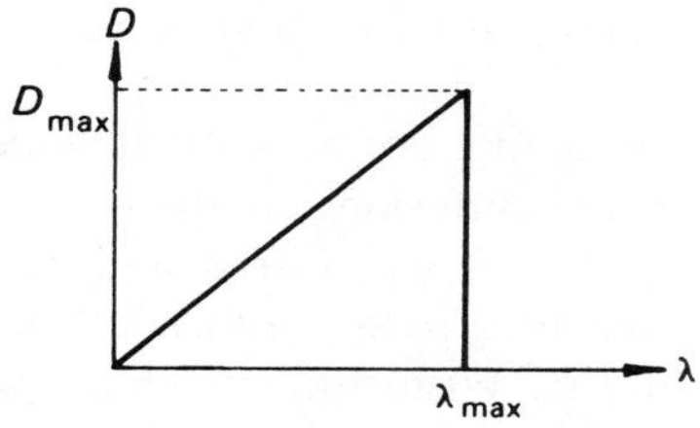

Figure 10.18 The spectral sensitivity curve of an ideal photon detector.

10.10 Referring to the characteristics of Fig. 10.6(c) discuss the limitations on the input impedance of an amplifier that amplifies the signal from a photovoltaic detector.

10.11 How do temperature changes affect an injection laser wavelength and why?

PROBLEMS

10.12 It is required to use a silicon N^+P diode to detect laser radiation at 1.06 μm. The minority diffusion lengths in a given Si sample are $L_h = 1\ \mu$m on the N^+ side and $L_e = 150\ \mu$m on the P side whose doping is $N_A = 5 \times 10^{13}$ cm^{-3}. Assuming an avalanche field of 300 kV cm^{-1}, suggest junction depth, P-region width and biasing conditions for best detector operation. Consult Fig. 10.1 for the absorption coefficient in Si.

10.13 The parameters of a Si solar cell, operated as a normal Si diode in the forward direction, in dark conditions at 30°C, are:
$I_0 = 3.3$ nA
η (the junction ideality factor appearing in exp $(qV/\eta kT) = 1.3$
A(area) $= 1.7$ cm^2
R_i(internal resistance) $= 0.8\ \Omega$.

When the cell is illuminated by sunlight, the short-circuit current is $I_{ph} = 36$ mA. Calculate, for the illuminated cell:

(a) the open-circuit voltage V_{oc};
(b) the relationship between I and R_L, where R_L is the external load;
(c) the maximum output power P_{max} and the optimum operating conditions I_m, V_m, and R_{Lm} for that maximum power;
(d) The fill factor defined as F.F. $= I_m V_m / I_{ph} V_{oc}$.
(e) The output power for $R_L = 0.5 R_{Lm}$ and $R_L = 2R_{Lm}$.

10.14 Obtain an expression for I_{ph} of N^+ on P Si diode with junction depth d, cell thickness W and diffusion lengths of $L_h < d$ on the N side and $L_e < (W - d)$ on the P side when irradiated by monochromatic light of wave length λ. Assume a perfect antireflection coating and no surface recombination effects. Write the expression for calculating I_{ph} if the diode is irradiated by a known spectral density function $\phi(\lambda)$. Obtain approximate results for irradiation by 1 mW cm^{-2} at $\lambda = 0.6\,\mu$m if $L_e = 50\,\mu$m, $L_h = 1\,\mu$m, $N_D = 10^{18}$ cm^{-3}, $N_A = 10^{16}$ cm^{-3}, $d = 1.25\,\mu$m, $W = 200\,\mu$m, $A = 0.1$ cm^2.

10.15 A GaAs LED ($n = 3.6$) is coupled through air ($n = 1$) to a step index glass fiber ($n = 1.5$). Is the acceptance angle for rays still inside the LED affected by using epoxy ($n \simeq 1.5$) instead of air? What is this angle for $\Delta n = 0.02$?

THE DYNAMIC BEHAVIOR OF A DIODE UNDER SMALL AND LARGE SIGNALS 11

In Chapter 9 we saw that if a reverse d.c. voltage is applied to a PN-junction diode, together with a small a.c. signal, as in Fig. 11.1(a), then the diode can be represented by the a.c. equivalent circuit in Fig. 11.1(b). $C_j(V_0)$ is the junction capacitance with reverse voltage V_0, and R_0 is a shunt resistance representing the reverse leakage current in the junction.

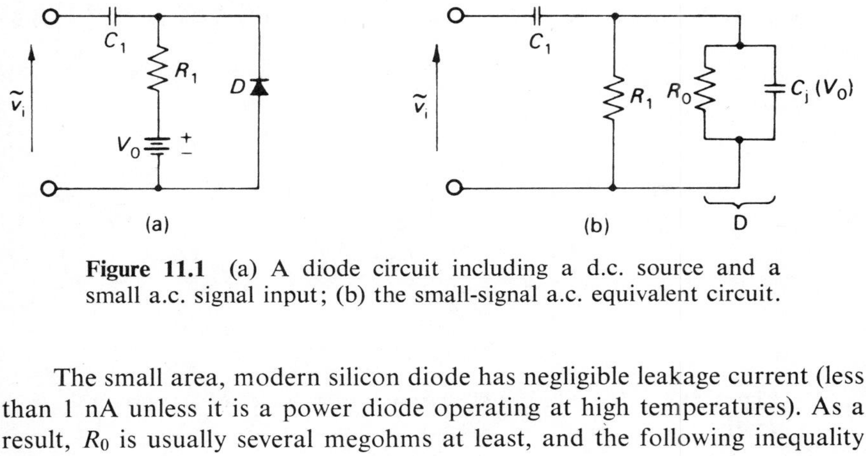

Figure 11.1 (a) A diode circuit including a d.c. source and a small a.c. signal input; (b) the small-signal a.c. equivalent circuit.

The small area, modern silicon diode has negligible leakage current (less than 1 nA unless it is a power diode operating at high temperatures). As a result, R_0 is usually several megohms at least, and the following inequality holds:

$$R_0 \gg \frac{1}{\omega C_j(V_0)},$$

where ω = the angular frequency of v_i. One can therefore usually neglect R_0.

It should also be noticed that the d.c. voltage source V_0 is omitted from the a.c. equivalent circuit since the voltage across it is constant and does not change with the a.c. current, i.e., its a.c. impedance is zero and it is represented by a short circuit.

In this chapter we shall develop an equivalent small-signal model that can represent the diode when operating with a *forward* d.c. bias current and also when it is switched between two d.c. levels. The importance of the results is not limited to diode circuits alone, and most of them can be applied to the transistor case as well.

11.1 Differential Resistance of a Forward-biased Diode

If a forward d.c. current I on which a small a.c. component i is superimposed flows through a diode, the impedance to the a.c. signal is composed of both ohmic and capacitive parts. The capacitance is the sum of the junction capacitance and the effect of the excess charges of the minority carriers stored in the neutral regions of the diode. These charges must grow or diminish to facilitate the changes in the alternating current. The resistive component, which is the only important part when the signal frequency is low, is obtained directly from the diode equation:

$$I = I_0 \left(\exp \frac{qV_A}{kT} - 1 \right)$$

and is given by the slope of this characteristic at the bias point $I = I_E$ as shown in Fig. 11.2.

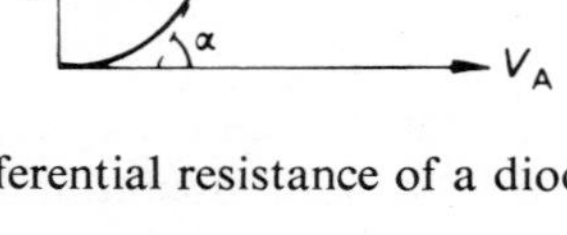

Figure 11.2. The differential resistance of a diode at bias current $I = I_E$.

If $V_A > kT/q$, i.e. if the applied d.c. voltage V_A is more than about 0.1 V at 300°K, then the small-signal resistive component, also called the differential resistance of the diode, is given by

$$\tan\alpha = \frac{1}{r_e} = \frac{dI}{dV_A}\bigg|_{I_E} = \frac{I_0 q}{kT} exp(qV_A/kT) \simeq \frac{qI_E}{kT}$$

or

$$r_e = \frac{kT}{qI_E}, \tag{11.1}$$

where $\tan\alpha$ is the slope of the characteristic at $I = I_E$, and r_e is proportional to the reciprocal bias current. If, as we have seen in Chapter 9, there are generation–recombination centers in the junction, causing a slower increase of the diode current with voltage, the exponent in the diode equation will be $qV_A/\eta kT$ ($\eta \simeq 1.2$) then r_e will be larger by the factor η. This is the usual case in Si.

The capacitive component in the diode impedance under forward bias and the switching times are strongly connected with the average time it takes a minority carrier to cross the diode, i.e. the transit time. We shall therefore first look at this problem.

11.2 Transit Time of Minority Carriers in a Diode – Diffusion Capacitance

Let us consider a P^+N diode where the thickness w of the N region is somewhat smaller than the diffusion length L_h of holes injected in the junction. This is the case of a general diode somewhat on the narrow side, and includes the narrow-diode case. It is the more interesting case when one considers the holes transition time across the N region and can be directly applied to the bipolar transistor. (In a thick diode, this time is obviously infinite: all the injected holes recombine before they reach the far ohmic contact.)

From the results of Chapter 9 on such forward-biased diodes, the concentration of injected holes depends on the distance x from the junction as in Fig. 11.3, where the excess hole concentration at each point is given by (9.18):

$$\hat{p}_n(x) = \hat{p}_n(0)\,\frac{\sinh(w-x)/L_h}{\sinh w/L_h}$$

where

$$\hat{p}_n(0) = \bar{p}_n\left(\exp\frac{qV_A}{kT} - 1\right).$$

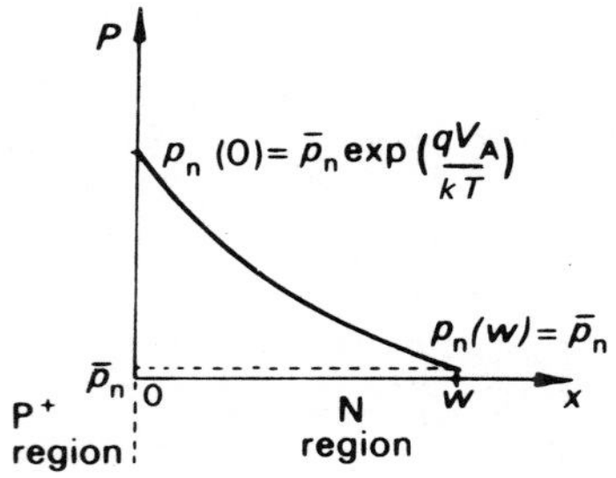

Figure 11.3. Concentration of minority carriers in a diode under forward bias.

Since we are dealing with a P^+N diode, the electronic current component injected from the N to the P region can be neglected (again, this is appropriate to the transistor case; also one can easily generalize to any PN step junction, as we shall see).

If the diode area is A, the total excess minority charge in the N region will be

$$\hat{Q}_h = qA \int_0^w \hat{p}_n(x)\, dx = \frac{qA\, L_h\, \hat{p}_n(0)}{\sinh w/L_h}\left(\cosh \frac{w}{L_h} - 1\right). \tag{11.2}$$

(Remember that the N region remains neutral, and therefore this charge is compensated by an equal charge of excess electrons, the majority carriers, which will be drawn into the N region from the opposite side, through the ohmic contact at $x = w$.)

The holes move in the x-direction because of diffusion, and this movement results in a hole current of

$$I_h(x) = -qAD_h \frac{d\hat{p}_n(x)}{dx} = \frac{qAD_h\hat{p}_n(0)}{L_h} \frac{\cosh (w-x)/L_h}{\sinh w/L_h}. \tag{11.3}$$

At $x = 0$, $I_h(0)$ is equal to the total current crossing the junction (since $I_e(0)$ is negligible) while at $x = w$, $I_h(w)$ represents the hole current reaching the far-side ohmic contact to the N region:

$$I_h(w) = \frac{qAD_h\hat{p}_n(0)}{L_h} \frac{1}{\sinh w/L_h}.$$

If v is the average hole velocity due to diffusion, then $dt = dx/v$ is the time it takes to cross a distance dx. The total transit time τ_B across the N region will then be

$$\tau_B = \int_0^w v^{-1}\, dx = \int_0^w \left(\frac{I_h(x)}{qA\hat{p}_n(x)}\right)^{-1} dx, \tag{11.4}$$

where the general relation $I_h = qA\hat{p}_n v$ was used.

Substituting $\hat{p}_n(x)$ and $I_h(x)$ and performing the integration, we get

$$\tau_B = \tau_h \ln\left(\cosh \frac{w}{L_h}\right), \tag{11.5}$$

using the relation $L_h = \sqrt{(D_h \tau_h)}$.

If $L_h \geqslant w$, as we have assumed at the beginning, the function $\cosh(w/L_h)$ is only slightly larger than 1 and we can represent it by

$$\cosh \frac{w}{L_h} \simeq 1 + \delta, \qquad \delta \ll 1.$$

Using this approximation, the logarithm in the expression for τ_B can be approximated by

$$\ln\left(\cosh \frac{w}{L_h}\right) = \ln(1+\delta) \simeq \delta.$$

(A measure of the error in the two approximations can be obtained by taking the limit $L_h = w$ and then the approximations give $\delta = 0.54$, while the exact form (11.5) yields 0.44. For smaller values like $w = \frac{1}{2}L_h$ the error is already only +6.3%.)

Therefore,

$$\tau_B \simeq \tau_h \delta = \tau_h\left(\cosh \frac{w}{L_h} - 1\right) \tag{11.6}$$

But using $\hat{Q}_h$ in (11.2) and I_h in (11.3), we also get

$$\frac{\hat{Q}_h}{I_h(w)} = \tau_h\left(\cosh \frac{w}{L_h} - 1\right);$$

therefore τ_B can be expressed as

$$\tau_B = \frac{\hat{Q}_h}{I_h(w)}. \tag{11.7}$$

On the other hand, the difference in hole currents at $x=0$ and $x=w$ must be equal to the number of holes recombining in a unit time in the whole N region:

$$I_h(0) - I_h(w) = \frac{\hat{Q}_h}{\tau_h}.$$

Substituting $I_h(w)$ from this expression into (11.7), one gets

$$\hat{Q}_h = \frac{I_h(0)}{1/\tau_h + 1/\tau_B} = \tau_F I_h(0) = \tau_F I_E, \tag{11.8}$$

where τ_F is defined as

$$\frac{1}{\tau_F} \triangleq \frac{1}{\tau_h} + \frac{1}{\tau_B} \tag{11.9}$$

and I_E is the total current in the diode.

Equation (11.7) holds for any narrow diode. If $I_h(w)/q$ holes leave the N-region each second and their average transit time through it is τ_B, then the stored charge $\hat{Q}_h$ equals $\tau_B I_h(w)$ irrespective of the exact doping profile provided the diode is narrow enough for recombination to be neglected.

As already mentioned, $\hat{Q}_h$ is the excess minority charge stored in the neutral region of the N side, together with an equal amount of excess majority charge. This charge is necessary for the flow of current I_E through the junction. In order to make any change in that current these charges must first be changed. But such charge–current relations imply a capacitive reactance, which is represented in the model by a capacitor known as the *diffusion capacitance* of the diode:

$$C_{diff} = K\frac{dQ_h}{dV_A} = K\tau_F\frac{dI_E}{dV_A} = K\frac{\tau_F}{r_e} = K\tau_F\frac{qI_E}{kT} \tag{11.10}$$

K is a numerical factor, which accounts for the fact that not all the excess minority charge leaves the neutral region through the junction at which it entered, when the current is decreasing after first being increased. A detailed calculation for a small-signal case shows that $K = \frac{2}{3}$ for a narrow step-junction diode, so we may assume $K \simeq 1$ (τ_F itself is usually known only approximately).

The important conclusion from (11.10) is that the diffusion capacitance is directiy proportional to the forward current and increases with it.

The complete diode model for a small a.c. signal, when the diode is forward biased at a d.c. current I_E, looks therefore as in Fig. 11.4. r_e and C_{diff} depend (inversely) upon I_E, and C_j is the junction depletion layer capitance at the forward voltage V_A, corresponding to I_E. The capitance $C_j(V_A)$ is therefore somewhat larger than $C_j(0)$ and increases slowly with the square root of the logarithm of I_E (see Problem 9.17 for its expression).

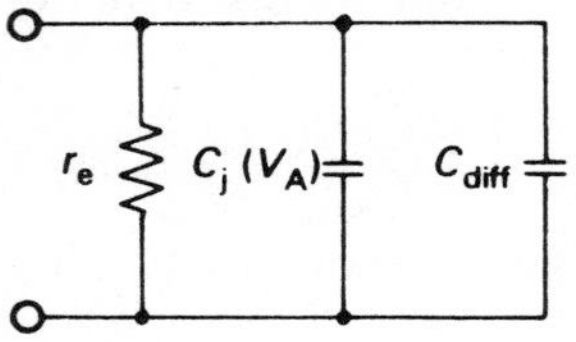

Figure 11.4. Small-signal model of a diode under forward bias.

So far we have considered a general step-junction diode which is not too narrow and not too wide. It is easy to extend the discussion to include these two extreme cases, which are of great practical importance.

In a narrow diode $L_h \gg w$ and then (11.6) yields for the transit time:

$$\tau_B = \tau_h \left[\cosh \frac{w}{L_h} - 1\right] = \tau_h \left[\left(1 + \frac{w^2}{2L_h^2} + \ldots\right) - 1\right] \simeq \frac{\tau_h w^2}{2L_h^2} = \frac{w^2}{2D_h}. \tag{11.11}$$

This expression is very important in determining the frequency limitations of a bipolar transistor, as we shall learn later.

In such a narrow diode one can completely neglect the recombination, i.e. assume $\tau_B \ll \tau_h$, and then $\tau_F \simeq \tau_B$ and the diffusion capacitance, which is proportional to τ_F, is then proportional to the square of the width w of the neutral N region.

In a wide diode, where $L_h \ll w$, the injected holes will recombine before reaching the far-side ohmic contact. From (11.5), which also applies to this case, we find $\tau_B \to \infty$ and hence $\tau_F = \tau_h$. The diffusion capacitance will no longer depend on the width of the neutral N region, but only on the lifetime of the minority carriers and the current.

Let us now consider transit times and diffusion capacitance in a narrow P^+N diode with variable doping in the neutral region.

Such a diode is very important because it represents the emitter–base junction of a present-day bipolar transistor. However, since it is a much more complicated structure to analyze, we shall restrict our attention to mainly qualitative reasoning.

We have seen in Chapter 4 that variable doping in a semiconductor, $N_D(x)$, causes a built-in field E to form in the N region, whose magnitude is given by (4.26), if one assumes $\bar{n} \simeq N_D(x)$. In Problem 4.12 it was shown that if

$$N_D(x) = N_{D_0} \exp\left(-\eta \frac{x}{w}\right),$$

then

$$E = \frac{kT}{q} \frac{\eta}{w},$$

where N_{D_0} is the donor concentration at the depletion layer edge, and decays exponentially with distance towards the ohmic contact at $x = w$, and η is a constant. This is a close approximation to the real doping profile in the base of a transistor. The field E, being caused by the majority carriers in equilibrium, is not disturbed by the minority carriers injected into the base at $x = 0$ and drifting towards $x = w$. The field direction is such as to increase the velocity of the injected minority carriers and so drastically reduces their transit time (see Problem 11.15). The minority charge, stored in the neutral N region for a given value of current, will be reduced and with it the diffusion capacitance, as can be seen from eqs. (11.17), (11.9) and (11.10). The reduction might be by more than an order of magnitude, and it is therefore very important to have a steep doping gradient (high η), and consequently a high built-in field, in the base of transistor intended for high-frequency operation where transit times must be short.

11.3 Diode Switching

Let us consider a diode connected as in Fig. 11.5 (which is not a practical switching circuit, but one intended only for explaining the effects).

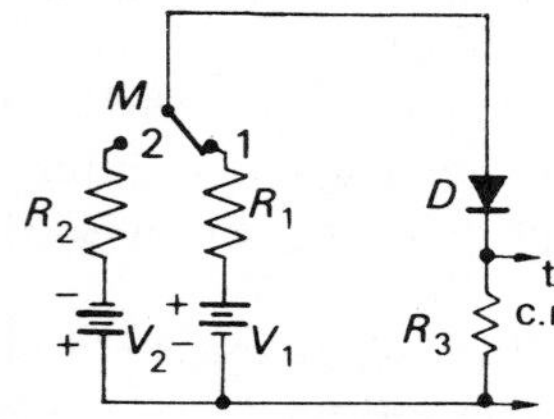

Figure 11.5. A basic circuit for switching a diode.

Suppose the switch M is at position 1 at $t \leq 0$. A forward current I_F then flows through the diode. If at $t=0$, M is switched to position 2, the oscilloscope will measure the current change through R_3 and it will look like Fig. 11.6(a): For a short time marked t_{rr} and called the reverse recovery time, the diode conducts in the reverse direction instead of blocking, as we would expect it to. For part of that time, t_S, called the storage time, the reverse current is constant at $-I_R$ and the diode acts as a practical short circuit.

The flow of a high reverse current for a short period t_{rr} following the switching from a forward current I_F is caused by the formation of an excess minority (and consequently also majority) charge in the neutral regions of the diode neighboring the depletion layer. This 'recovery' period depends on the magnitude of the excess charge, i.e. on the forward current, and on the reverse current I_R, i.e. on the speed at which this charge is removed. In a P^+N diode this is mostly the excess hole charge shown in Fig. 11.6(c), and given by (9.18). As long as $\hat{p}_n(0) > 0$ the diode equation predicts the existence of a forward voltage V'_A across the junction:

$$\hat{p}_n(0) = \bar{p}_n\left(\exp\frac{qV'_A}{kT} - 1\right).$$

If one writes down Kirchhoff's voltage law for the circuit of Fig. 11.5, with the switch at position 2, the expression for I_R given in (11.12) is obtained. I_R is determined by the parameters of the external circuit, V_2, R_3, R_2 and is therefore constant as long as there is an excess charge near the edge of the depletion layer with V'_A positive and low. The concentration of excess carriers goes gradually down, as represented by the series of curves in Fig. 11.6(d),

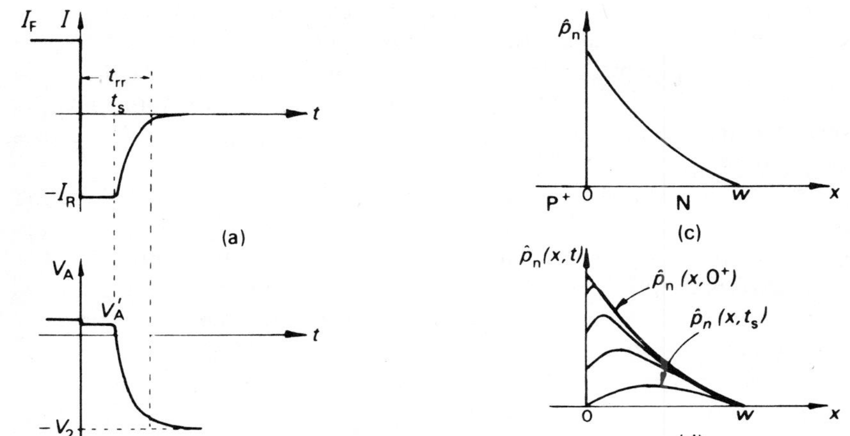

Figure 11.6. (a) Current through the switching diode; (b) voltage across the diode; (c) concentration of minority carriers as a function of distance from the junction in the N region at $t=0$; (d) changes in the minority concentration during the storage period $0<t<t_S$.

since holes are leaving via the junction, carrying the reverse current. At the same time, the excess majority charge of electrons leaves the N region through the far ohmic contact so that Kirchoff's current law is also fulfilled and the N region remains neutral. Actually, it is the diffusion capacitance that is being discharged. Some of the excess charge will be lost by recombination before it has the chance to flow out. Because the voltage V_A across the diode, when conducting in the forward direction or during the storage period, is low compared to V_1 or V_2 (no more than a fraction of a volt), the currents I_F and I_R will be determined by the outside voltage sources and resistors:

$$I_F=\frac{V_1-V_A}{R_1+R_3}\simeq\frac{V_1}{R_1+R_3}, \qquad I_R=\frac{V_2+V_A'}{R_2+R_3}\simeq\frac{V_2}{R_2+R_3}. \tag{11.12}$$

The magnitude of the reverse current I_R, constant during $0\leq t<t_s$, determines the slope of $p_n(x,t)$ around $x=0$ in Fig. 11.6(d), since at any time one has:

$$I_R=-qAD_h\left.\frac{\partial\hat{p}_n(x,t)}{\partial x}\right|_{x=0}=\text{constant}.$$

This period is called the storage period. It will end, at $t=t_S$, when the hole concentration at the depletion layer edge reaches zero. At this point the reverse current starts to go down quickly since there are no longer enough holes to carry it. The slope of $\hat{p}_n(x,t)$ at $x=0$ goes to zero, and the depletion layer starts to expand into the formerly neutral, low doped (compared to the P^+) N region, sweeping the mobile charge carriers out of it and building up to the static value appropriate to the externally applied reverse voltage $-V_2$. At this point it is the depletion-layer capacitor that is being charged. The total time from the instant of switching $t=0$ to the moment at which the junction reverse voltage reaches 90% of its final value is what is called the reverse recovery time t_{rr}.

One should therefore calculate t_{rr} in two stages. First the storage period when the excess charge is removed. This continues, with rough approximation, till the fraction of charge left is about $(1+I_F/I_R)^{-1}$ (see Problem 11.14 at the end of this chapter). Second, the depletion capacitance charging time is added. To get the storage time, let us start from the time-dependent continuity equation for holes

$$\frac{\partial \hat{p}_n(x,t)}{\partial t} = -\frac{\hat{p}_n(x,t)}{\tau_h} - \frac{1}{q}\frac{\partial J_h(x,t)}{\partial x}. \tag{11.13}$$

This is a partial differential equation in two variables whose solution is complicated. The problem may be simplified by considering the total excess hole charge, $\hat{Q}_h(t)$, stored in the neutral region at any time t and thus getting rid of the position variable x. This is a well-known method of dealing with switching effects in semiconductor devices such as transistors and is called the *method of charge control parameters*. To do this, let us multiply (11.13) by the diode area A, and integrate it with x changing between 0 and w while t is kept constant:

$$\frac{\partial}{\partial t}\int_0^w qA\hat{p}_n(x,t)\,dx = -\frac{1}{\tau_h}\int_0^w qA\hat{p}_n(x,t)\,dx - \int_0^w \frac{\partial[AJ_h(x,t)]}{\partial x}dx.$$

But the integral of $qA\hat{p}_n$ gives the total excess hole charge $\hat{Q}_h$ at t; therefore

$$\frac{d\hat{Q}_h(t)}{dt} = -\frac{\hat{Q}_h(t)}{\tau_h} - [I_h(w,t) - I_h(0,t)].$$

Using (11.7) for $I_h(w,t)$ and substituting τ_F from (11.9), the last expression can be written as

$$\frac{d\hat{Q}_h(t)}{dt} + \frac{\hat{Q}_h(t)}{\tau_F} = I_h(0,t). \tag{11.14}$$

During the storage period $0 \leq t < t_s$, $I_h(0,t) = -I_R = \text{constant}$; therefore the solution of (11.14) is

$$\hat{Q}_h(t) = c \exp\left(-\frac{t}{\tau_F}\right) - I_R\tau_F.$$

The integration constant c can be found from the consideration that $\hat{Q}_h(t)$ cannot change suddenly at $t=0$, i.e.

$$\hat{Q}_h(0^-)=\hat{Q}_h(0^+)=I_F\tau_F$$

from which $c=\tau_F(I_F+I_R)$. Substituting, we finally get

$$\hat{Q}_h(t)=\tau_F(I_F+I_R)\exp\left(-\frac{t}{\tau_F}\right)-I_R\tau_F. \tag{11.15}$$

If we assume a triangular shape for the concentration, as in Problem 11.14 of this chapter, then

$$\frac{\hat{Q}_h(t_s)}{\hat{Q}_h(0)}=(1+I_F/I_R)^{-1},$$

from which

$$t_s=\tau_F \ln\left[(1+I_F/I_R)\left(1+\frac{1}{1+I_R/I_F}\right)^{-1}\right]. \tag{11.16}$$

In a wide diode $\tau_F=\tau_h$, of course.

Using the same approach one can calculate the transient period when the current is switched from one value to another, both in the forward direction.

Some references neglect the second, depletion-capacitance charge part, but assume the storage period ends when $\hat{Q}_h(t_s)=0$. Then from (11.15)

$$t_s\simeq\tau_F \ln(1+I_F/I_R).$$

The forward voltage V'_A across the diode during the storage period can be approximately calculated if one assumes that $\hat{p}_n(x,t)$ remains exponential as long as $t<t_s$ (i.e., we neglect the change of slope of $\hat{p}_n(x,t)$ at $x=0$ after the switching). With this assumption, simple integration of $\hat{p}_n(x,t)$ yields

$$\hat{Q}_h(t)=qA\int_0^w \hat{p}_n(0,t)\exp\left(-\frac{x}{L_h}\right)\mathrm{d}x$$

$$=qAL_h\left[1-\exp\left(-\frac{w}{L_h}\right)\right]\bar{p}_n\left[\exp\left(\frac{qV'_A(t)}{kT}\right)-1\right],$$

from which, by substituting $\hat{Q}_h(t)$ from (11.15), and $\bar{p}_n=n_i^2/N_D$,

$$V'_A(t)=\frac{kT}{q}\ln\left[\frac{\tau_F(I_F+I_R)\exp(-t/\tau_F)-I_R\tau_F}{qAL_h[1-\exp(-w/L_h)]n_i^2}N_D+1\right]. \tag{11.17}$$

This is a small positive quantity which gradually goes down from the value appropriate to I_F to zero which it reaches when $t=t_s$. The shape of $V'_A(t)$ is also shown in Fig. 11.6(b).

At $t=t_S$ the charging of depletion-layer capacitance C_j starts. This, as we have seen in Chapter 9, is a nonlinear capacitance which depends on the voltage across it. The time it takes to charge it from zero to $-V_2$ can be calculated exactly for a step junction, but a simpler expression of good accuracy can be obtained if we just take the average junction capacitance, $\overline{C}_j(0,-V_2)$, between the extreme voltage limits and use it to obtain the charging time constant $R\overline{C}_j$, where R is the resistance through which the charging current passes.

For a step junction,

$$(11.18)\quad \overline{C}_j(0,-V_2)=-\frac{1}{V_2}\int_0^{-V_2}\frac{C_j(0)}{(1-V/V_B)^{1/2}}\,dV=2C_j(0)\left[\frac{1+V_B/V_2}{(1+V_2/V_B)^{1/2}}-\frac{V_B}{V_2}\right].$$

Usually V_B, the absolute value of the junction diffusion voltage, is small compared to V_2, and then

$$(11.19)\qquad \overline{C}_j(0,V_2)=2\left[C_j(-V_2)-C_j(0)\frac{V_B}{V_2}\right].$$

The time it takes to charge $\overline{C}_j$, through R, to 90% of $-V_2$, is found from

$$-0.9V_2=-V_2\left[1-\exp\left(-\frac{t(90\%)}{R\overline{C}_j}\right)\right]$$

to be

$$t(90\%)=2.3R\overline{C}_j.$$

The diode manufacturers usually measure the reverse recovery time t_{rr} by applying a square-wave input voltage through a known resistor, so that $I_F \simeq I_R$, and include it in their data sheet. If a constant d.c. voltage is added in series with the square wave, t_{rr} may be measured for any desired ratio of I_F/I_R. Typical data, for a very high speed diode, are given in Fig. 11.7.

One should also notice that there is also a switching transient when the voltage is switched from reverse to forward direction, because the depletion-layer capacitance has to be discharged and diffusion capacitance charged before the steady-state forward current I_F is established.

The effect of a finite recovery time has very important implications on the uses and limitations of diodes for rectification and switching. When rectifying, it is obvious that if the voltage to be rectified is of high frequency, and therefore short period, of the same order of magnitude as the recovery time, then there will not be any rectification: during the first, positive, half cycle, the diffusion capacitance will charge and during the second, negative, half cycle, it would discharge and the diode would operate as if it were a capacitor and not a rectifying element. Each diode has therefore an upper limit to the frequency at which it can be used for rectification (or for demodulation of r.f. waves in case of diodes intended for r.f. detection). The rectification efficiency of a diode, which usually operates as a line-frequency rectifier or as a low-frequency switch, may drop to 50% when the frequency is increased to a few kilohertz.

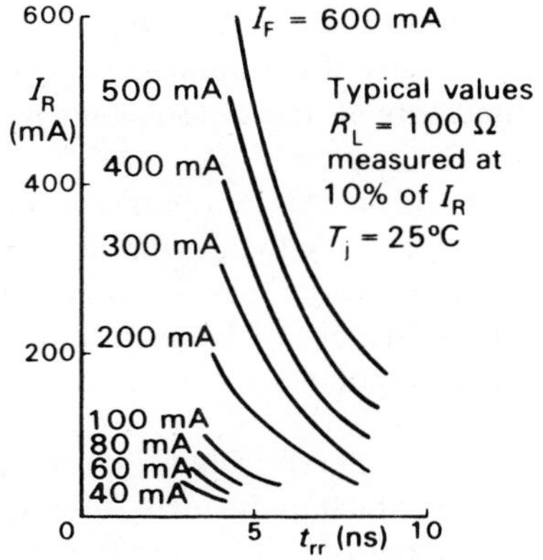

Figure 11.7. Recovery time as a function of forward and reverse currents for Philips BAV10 ultra high-speed Si planar expitaxial diode (R_L=total series load).

When used as a switch, the diode must react quickly to fast pulses by going from conduction to cut-off, and the finite recovery time will limit the maximum pulse rate.

As an example, let us look at the circuit shown in Fig. 11.8(a) which is known as the 'min. of' circuit because its output U_0 always follows the lowest of the four (or more) input voltages.

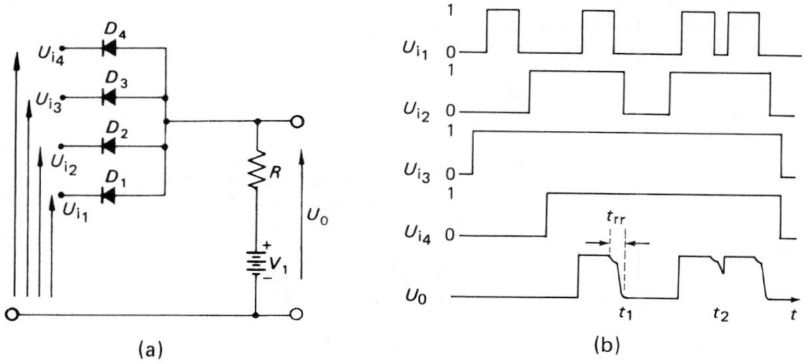

Figure 11.8. The effect of finite recovery time: (a) the 'min. of' circuit which can perform the logic 'AND' operation; (b) digital inputs and output. Note loss of '0' at t_2 because of t_{rr}.

If U_{i_1} is the lowest, the current flows from the source V_1 through R, into the diode D_1 and the output potential is

$$U_0 = U_{i_1} + V_A(D_1) \simeq U_{i_1}.$$

The rest of the diodes will be cut off, since their cathode potentials are higher than that of their common anode which is about equal to U_{i_1}. If now U_{i_2} drops suddenly below U_{i_1}, then D_2 starts to conduct but D_1 continues to conduct too during its recovery time forcing the output voltage to be higher than it should be.

The circuit performs the logic 'AND' operation when used with digital inputs, as shown in Fig. 11.8(b). Using logic symbolism, the output should be $U_0(t) = U_{i_1} \cdot U_{i_2} \cdot U_{i_3} \cdot U_{i_4}$. For diodes with finite recovery time t_{rr} the output pulse in U_0 continues t_{rr} seconds beyond t_1 at which time it should have dropped. If the input pulses come too close together, as at time t_2, then the output may miss a zero and be in error.

Fast switching diodes must therefore have a very short recovery time. This is achieved by reducing τ_F which, in its turn, is reduced by shortening the minority carriers' lifetime. Three orders of magnitude reduction (to less than 1 ns) can be obtained by intentional inclusion of heavy-metal dopant atoms, such as gold in silicon, which creates several permitted energy levels deep in the forbidden gap. These levels act as recombination centers in which a free carrier can be caught, losing its energy and momentum gradually, and finally recombining. The 'price' to be paid for the addition of the gold atoms is mostly an increase in reverse voltage leakage current with associated increased noise output and some reduction in the reverse breakdown voltage.

Another type of diode, intended for detection (i.e. rectification) of ultra high frequency (UHF) waves in the microwave range (several GHz), are the Schottky-barrier diodes (Chapter 8, Fig. 8.11 and Section 9.7). When forward voltage is applied to these diodes, carriers are injected from the semiconductor into the metal only, as depicted in the energy-level diagram of Fig. 11.9.

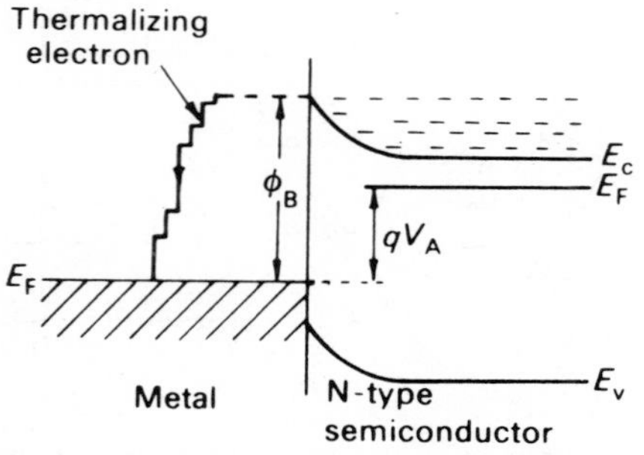

Figure 11.9. Energy-level diagram of a Schottky-barrier diode under forward bias.

The injected carriers, electrons in the figure, find themselves in the metal with a much higher kinetic energy than that of the electrons in the metal. The energy of these is about E_F, which corresponds to a thermal equilibrium between the free electron population and the thermal vibrations of the metal's crystal lattice structure, with both having the same temperature T. The injected electron is therefore much 'hotter' at the moment of injection than the crystal lattice and most other electrons. These hot electrons lose their excess energy very quickly by repeated collisions with phonons, the vibrational waves of the metal crystal lattice. This is called *thermalization*. If about 100 collisions are needed to dissipate the excess energy, and the average time between collisions is about 10^{-13} s, then the total time for thermalization is about 10^{-11} s. As soon as the electron has lost its excess energy, it cannot flow back into the semiconductor if the diode is switched into a reverse bias, because of the energy barrier ϕ_B. Therefore the recovery time of the Schottky-barrier diodes, also called hot-carrier diodes, is of the order of 10^{-11} s, and they are suitable for work at UHF or for very fast switching.

QUESTIONS

11.1 Measurement of r_e of a diode, as a function of the direct current through it, shows first a reduction with the current, as expected, but then the measured value starts to increase again, finally becoming more or less a constant. Why?

11.2 You have performed in the lab a series of measurements of I versus V on a diode in the forward direction. What is the best way to plot the results graphically so that you can find r_e and η easily? How will you plot them if you want to obtain I_0 from the same data?

11.3 What is the transit time through the neutral P region of an N^+P diode with $W_P \ll L_e$?

11.4 How will narrowing of the neutral regions of the diode (decreasing $W_{P,N}$ compared to $L_{h,e}$) affect its diffusion capacitance? What effect will shortening of the lifetime have?

11.5 Why is the diffusion capacitance not important when considering diodes for operation in a line frequency rectifying circuit?

11.6 Draw a circuit performing the function of 'max. of' (i.e. logic 'OR' function) based on principles similar to the 'min. of' circuit of Fig. 11.8.

11.7 Estimate the average free distance between collisions for an electron in the metal of a metal–semiconductor (Schottky-barrier) diode? What is the approximate value of its recovery time?

11.8 In Fig. 11.6(b), a distinct kink is observed in the forward voltage of a diode at the instant of switching. Explain it on the basis of the concentration functions of the minority carriers just before and just after switching as seen in Fig. 11.6(d).

PROBLEMS

11.9 An N^+P silicon diode with the following parameters is given:

$$N_D^+ = 10^{20}\ \text{cm}^{-3},\quad W_N = 2\ \mu\text{m},\quad D_e = 20\ \text{cm}^2\ \text{s}^{-1},$$
$$N_A = 10^{16}\ \text{cm}^{-3},\quad W_p = 100\ \mu\text{m},\quad D_h = 10\ \text{cm}^2\ \text{s}^{-1},$$
$$A = 10^{-3}\ \text{cm}^2,\quad T = 300°\text{K},\quad \tau_e = \tau_h = 0.2\ \mu\text{s}.$$

(a) Find the concentration of electrons on the P side as a function of distance from the junction, when a current of 1.2 mA is flowing.
(b) What is the electronic charge stored in the neutral P region?
(c) Calculate the small-signal equivalent circuit of the diode at this current.

11.10 The diode of Problem 11.9 is used as a rectifier for the square wave of Fig. 11.10. Calculate the recovery time, and estimate the maximum frequency of the square wave for which the diode can still be used.

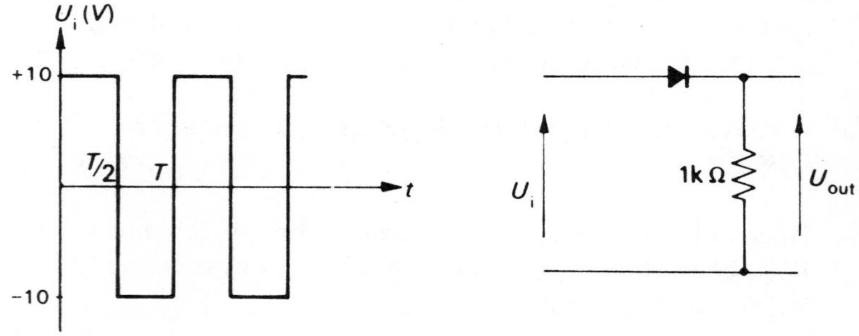

Figure 11.10. A rectifying circuit for Problem 11.10.

11.11 A P^+N step junction diode with wide N region has the characteristic

$$I = I_o[\exp(qV/1.5kT) - 1].$$

The junction capacitance at zero voltage is $C_j = 400$ pF. The diode is connected as in Fig. 11.11, where C is a large capacitor which can be considered an effective short circuit at the input signal frequency, which is 1 MHz. The input signal amplitude is a few millivolts.

(a) Calculate R in Fig. 11.11, for which the diode impedance, measured at 1 MHz, will be $Z_D = 0.0529 - 0.174j\ \Omega$.
(b) What is the direct current through the diode?
(c) What is the diode's impedance at 1 kHz?
(d) What is the hole lifetime in the N region? (*Hint*: first calculate the diffusion capacitance.)

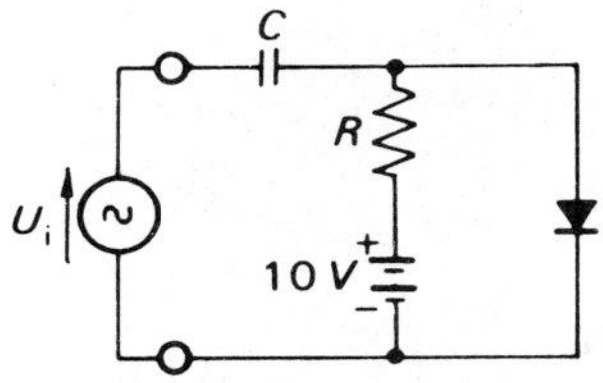

Figure 11.11. The circuit for Problem 11.11.

11.12 The admittance of a P^+N Ge diode, with a wide N region, was measured at 1 kHz, as a function of the forward current, and the following results were obtained:

I_A(mA)	1	2	3	5
Y_D(mmho)	$38.5+0.107j$	$77+0.1883j$	$115+0.2725j$	$192+0.431j$

Find the junction capacitance $C_j(0)$ and the diffusion capacitance at $I_A = 10$ mA.

11.13 The circuit of Fig. 11.12 is used as electronic attenuator for the a.c. small signal input $v_i(t)$. The attenuation is a function of the d.c. source current. Assuming the two capacitors C are large, and act as effective shorts, find the transfer function v_o/v_i as a function of I_{dc}.

At what value of I_{dc} will a -15 dB attenuation be obtained?

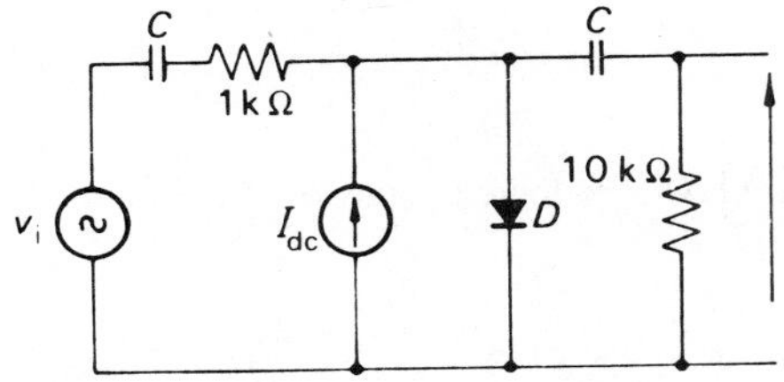

Figure 11.12. A diode attenuator of Problem 11.13.

11.14 Prove that the fraction of excess charge left at $t=t_S$, when switching a narrow P^+N diode into the reverse direction, is $(1+I_F/I_R)^{-1}$. (*Hint*: assume triangular carriers concentration with the forward and reverse currents proportional to $\partial\hat{p}_n/\partial x\,|_{x=0}$ at $t=0$ and $t=t_S$, respectively, i.e.. assume $\hat{p}_n(x,t)$ at any fixed time t forms a triangle whose base is the width w of the N side, the other two sides having slopes corresponding to I_F at $t<0$ and to I_R at $t>0$.)

11.15 Use the results of Problem 9.23, together with (11.4) for τ_B, to show that the transit time in a narrow P^+N diode with an exponential doping on the N side given by

$$N_D(x)=N_{D_0}\exp\left(-\eta\frac{x}{w}\right)$$

is

$$\tau_B=\frac{\hat{Q}_S}{I_h}=\frac{1}{D_h}\int_0^w\left[\frac{1}{N_D(x)}\int_x^w N_D(x)\,dx\right]dx=\frac{w^2}{D_h}\frac{\eta-1+e^{-\eta}}{\eta^2}.$$

For $\eta=6$, how much shorter will τ_B be compared to a step diode with constant N_D and the same dimensions?

11.16 Draw the expected output U_0 of the logic circuit for the inputs as shown in Fig. 11.13. What logic operation does it perform? What effect will t_{rr} of the diodes have on the output at point t_1?

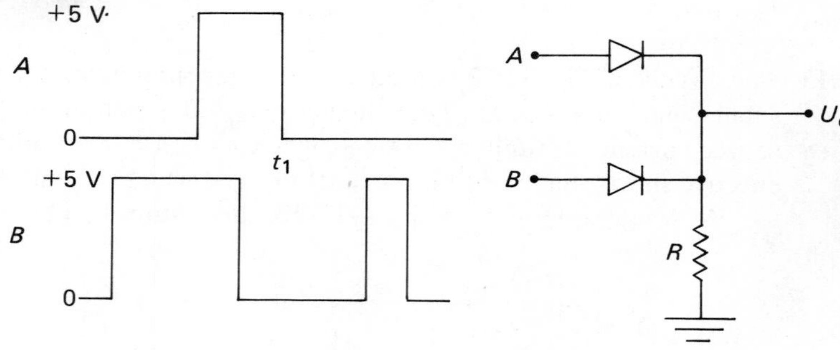

Figure 11.13 A logic circuit for Problem 11.16.

12 THE FIELD EFFECT TRANSISTORS (FETs)

We shall now meet for the first time an amplifying semiconductor device. This is a more complicated device of which the junction is just one part.

The whole development of electronics in the twentieth century started, and was made possible, by the invention of the first electronic amplifier, the vacuum triode, at the beginning of the century. The transistor, invented by the middle of the century, largely replaced the vacuum tube and started a new era in electronics.

The field effect transistors or FETs comprise the first transistor family that we shall tackle, its structure and operation being simpler than those of the second big family, the bipolar transistors, to which we shall get in Chapters 14 and 15.

Our purpose now is to describe the various FET structures and develop from them the terminal current–voltage relationships, i.e. the electrical characteristics. These will then be used in the next chapter to obtain an equivalent circuit for the transistor, which is very useful in transistor network analysis and design. Overall network properties, like amplification as a function of frequency, or input and output impedances and their dependence on the transistor parameters, can then be found.

The input signal voltage creates a field in the FET which controls its current. This is the *field effect*. FETs are divided into two groups.

(a) Those in which the signal controls a PN junction gate, known as JFET.
(b) Those in which the signal controls by means of an Insulated Gate, known as IGFET. Since the gate electrode is usually metal, the insulator used is oxide (i.e. SiO_2) and the semiconductor is Si, they are also known as MOS transistors or MOST (or MOSFET).

12.1 The Junction Field Effect Transistor (JFET)

The structure of a basic *JFET* is shown in Fig. 12.1.

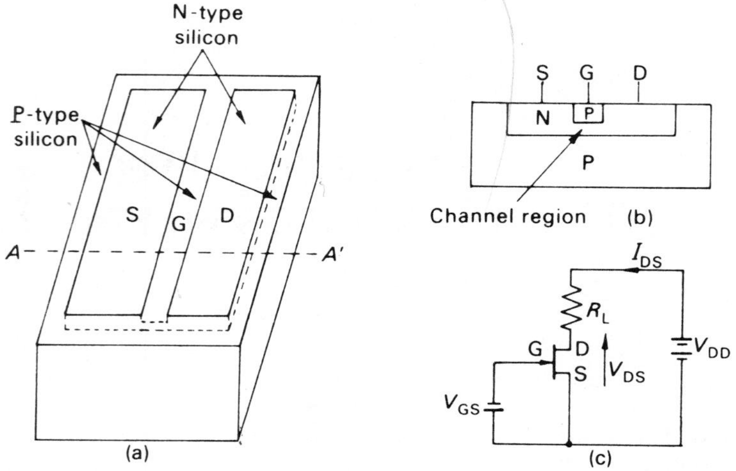

Figure 12.1. The (N channel) JFET: (a) viewed from above; (b) *A–A′* cross section; (c) N channel JFET circuit symbol and basic amplifying stage.

This is not the only possible structure but the principle is always the same: The current between the terminals identified in the figure as Source (S) and Drain (D) is controlled by the signal, which is applied, in series with a reverse bias voltage, between the Gate (G) and the source. In Fig. 12.1(b) we see that the source to drain current, I_{DS}, must flow through a region called the *channel*, which is N-type Si in this case. The majority electrons are the current carriers (P channel JFET is similar, with the P and N regions interchanged). Applying a reverse voltage V_{GS} between the P gate and the N source creates a depletion layer which extends into the channel, provided its doping level is lower than in the gate region. This reduces the free channel cross section available for majority flow, thereby reducing I_{DS} even if V_{DS} increases. Even at this early stage it can be seen that one of the important properties of the FET is its high input impedance. V_{GS} applied across a reverse-biased junction is loaded by the small junction capacitance only (of the order of 1 pF for the dimensions normally used). The d.c. leakage current in Si can be neglected at normal working temperatures. Most JFET uses today are as an input stage to an amplifier where its high input impedance, difficult to achieve by bipolar transistor circuits, is of great advantage.

Figure 12.1(c) shows an elementary amplifying stage and the circuit symbol for N channel JFET (the arrow, representing the gate-source diode direction, is reversed for P channel).

To find the dependence of I_{DS} on V_{GS} and V_{DS}, let us concentrate on the channel region only. This is shown magnified in Fig. 12.2 with its dimensions. The hatched areas represent the depletion layer at some specific values of the voltages. For simplicity let us assume a gate which is symmetrical as to its top and bottom. The channel length, always taken in the direction of current flow, and usually smaller than the width, is L. The width, normal to the paper, is W. The free channel height is $2a$ minus the width of the depletion layer $H(y)$, at top and bottom.

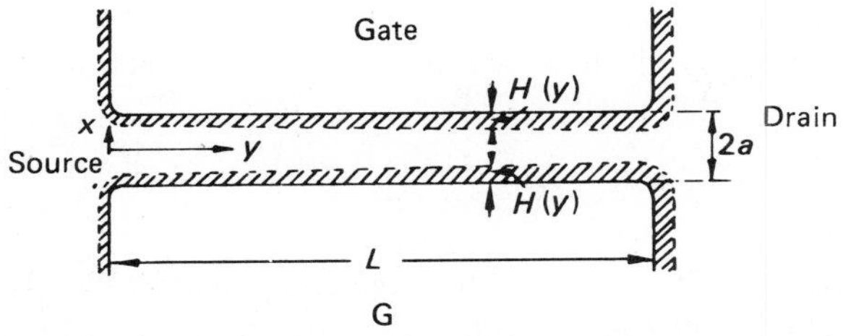

Figure 12.2. The channel region and its dimensions.

The free channel height is therefore $2[a-H(y)]$ and is a function of the position y even if V_{GS} is constant. This is so because the electrons flowing from source to drain create a voltage drop $V(y)$, along the channel, which varies from zero at the source to V_{DS} at the drain. The potential difference between the equipotential gate and the channel at some point y is therefore $V_{GS}-V(y)$ ($V_{GS}<0$ for N channel).

The width of the depletion layer is given by (8.22a):

$$H(y)=\sqrt{\left(\frac{2\varepsilon\varepsilon_0}{qN_D}\right)}\sqrt{-[V_{GS}-V(y)]}. \tag{12.1}$$

The current density J_{DS} in the channel is

$$J_{DS}=\sigma E(y)=-\sigma\frac{dV(y)}{dy}=-qn\mu_e\frac{dV(y)}{dy} \tag{12.2}$$

and the total current at y (A = area):

$$I_{DS}=AJ_{DS}=2[a-H(y)]WJ_{DS}. \tag{12.3}$$

Substituting $n=N_D$, J_{DS} and $H(y)$ into (12.3) yields

$$I_{DS}=-2WqN_D\mu_e\,\{a-[-\frac{2\varepsilon\varepsilon_0}{qN_D}\,(V_{GS}-V(y)]^{1/2}\,\}\,\frac{dV(y)}{dy}. \tag{12.4}$$

We can now separate variables y and V and integrate along the channel

$$\int_0^L I_{DS}\,dy = -2WqN_D\mu_e \int_{\substack{V=0\\(y=0)}}^{\substack{V=V_{DS}\\(y=L)}} \{a-[-\frac{2\varepsilon\varepsilon_0}{qN_D}(V_{GS}-V)]^{1/2}\}\,dV.$$

The current I_{DS} must be the same at any cross section y. Performing the two integrations and rearranging gives

$$(12.5)\quad I_{DS} = -\frac{2WqaN_D\mu_e}{L}\{V_{DS}-\tfrac{2}{3}\left(\frac{2\varepsilon\varepsilon_0}{qN_Da^2}\right)^{1/2}[(-V_{GS}+V_{DS})^{3/2} - (-V_{GS})^{3/2}]\}.$$

The coefficient on the right has the dimensions of conduction and is denoted by G_0:

$$(12.6)\qquad G_0 \triangleq \frac{2WqaN_D\mu_e}{L}.$$

When the reverse voltage across the depletion layer $V_{GS}-V(y)$ reaches a value V_p, called the *pinch-off voltage*, the channel becomes completely depleted from that point y. The pinch-off voltage V_p can be found from (12.1) by demanding $H(y) = a$:

$$(12.7)\qquad V_p \triangleq V_{GS}-V(y)\Big|_{H(y)=a} = -\frac{qa^2N_D}{2\varepsilon\varepsilon_0}.$$

Using the definition of G_0 and V_p in (12.5) gives it in the accepted form

$$(12.8)\qquad I_{DS} = -G_0\left\{V_{DS}+\tfrac{2}{3}V_p\left[\left(\frac{V_{GS}-V_{DS}}{V_p}\right)^{3/2} - \left(\frac{V_{GS}}{V_p}\right)^{3/2}\right]\right\}.$$

For an N channel transistor V_{GS} and V_p are negative and V_{DS} is positive. I_{DS} appears negative because the accepted current direction is $-y$, i.e. opposite to the electron flow. The signs are reversed for the P channel.

The characteristic (12.8) holds only for drain voltages below pinch-off, i.e. for $|V_{GS}-V_{DS}| < |V_p|$. Plotting I_{DS} against V_{DS} with V_{GS} as a parameter, we get the set of characteristics shown on the left of the dashed line in Fig. 12.3(a). This line corresponds to the pinch-off condition. The corresponding V_{DS} is called the saturation voltage and is given by

$$(12.9)\qquad V_{DS}(\text{sat}) = V_{GS}-V_p.$$

Beyond pinch-off the depletion layer looks like the hatched region in Fig. 12.3(b): The channel end is now pinched off for a very short distance. At the beginning of the pinched region $V(y) = V_{DS}(\text{sat})$ and at its end $V(y) = V_{DS}$.

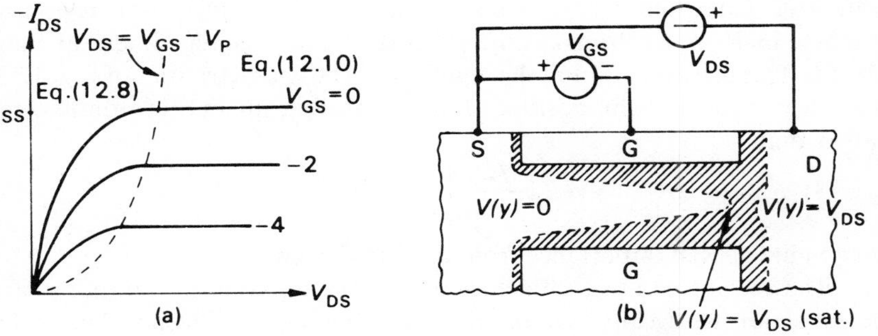

Figure 12.3. (a) The JFET drain characteristics determined by (12.8) up to the pinch-off point; (b) the depletion layer for $V_{DS} > V_{DS}(\text{sat})$.

Increase of V_{DS} beyond $V_{DS}(\text{sat})$ has almost no effect on the current, since all the excess voltage drops on that short pinched-off region at the channel end, where a very high field builds up in the y direction. Electrons arriving from the source enter the pinched region and are immediately accelerated to their saturation drift velocity (about 10^7 cm s^{-1}), so that further increase of V_{DS} and the field cannot move them any faster. Neither can it increase the flow of electrons from the source, because that is controlled by $V(y)$ and V_{GS}, which remain fixed with $V(y) = V_{DS}(\text{sat})$ at the entrance to the pinched region.

The current for $V_{DS} > V_{DS}(\text{sat})$ is therefore constant and given by (12.8) with V_{DS} replaced by $V_{DS}(\text{sat})$ of (12.9). Thus I_{DS} becomes saturated at

$$I_{DS}(\text{sat}) = -G_0\left\{V_{GS}\left[1 - \tfrac{2}{3}\left(\frac{V_{GS}}{V_p}\right)^{1/2}\right] - \frac{V_p}{3}\right\}. \tag{12.10}$$

The drain characteristics in the saturation region are thus straight horizontal lines on the right of the dashed line in Fig. 12.3(a).

Another property of the transistor which will be needed in the next chapter, when we discuss equivalent circuit and amplification, is the *transconductance* g_m defined as

$$g_m \triangleq \left|\frac{\partial I_{DS}}{\partial V_{GS}}\right|_{V_{DS}=\text{constant}} \tag{12.11}$$

This measures the vertical distance between the characteristics.

In the saturation region we get from (12.10) and (12.11)

$$g_m = G_0\left[1 - \left(\frac{V_{GS}}{V_p}\right)^{1/2}\right]. \tag{12.12}$$

The real JFET differs from our ideal characteristics in two respects. The first is that I_{DS} above saturation is not completely constant but grows slowly with V_{DS}. This results from a slight lengthening of the pinched-off region with increase in V_{DS}, which makes the effective channel length somewhat shorter than L. This increases G_0 and through it I_{DS}. The characteristics of Fig. 12.3(a) will then have a slight positive slope, indicating an output admittance g_0 larger than zero:

$$g_0 \triangleq \left| \frac{\partial I_{DS}}{\partial V_{DS}} \right|_{V_{GS}=\text{constant}} . \tag{12.13}$$

Finite g_0 is of importance from the circuit viewpoint.

The second point of difference is that the top and bottom parts of the gate junction are usually asymmetrical and obtained by diffusion. They behave somewhat differently from our assumed symmetrical step junction. A useful approximation for the characteristics of a real JFET above saturation is

$$I_{DS}(\text{sat}) = I_{DSS}\left(1 - \frac{V_{GS}}{V_p}\right)^2, \tag{12.14}$$

where $I_{DSS} = I_{DS}(\text{sat})$ for $V_{GS}=0$ (see Fig. 12.3(a)).

Figure 12.4 shows typical characteristics of the Philips N channel transistor BF245C. It has the following parameters at the operating point of $V_{GS}=0$; $V_{DS}=15$ V:

$$V_p \simeq -6.5 \text{ V}, \qquad g_0 \simeq 25\ \mu\text{A V}^{-1},\ g_m = 5 \text{ mA V}^{-1}.$$

It can be seen that generally the characteristics of the real transistor behave as expected.

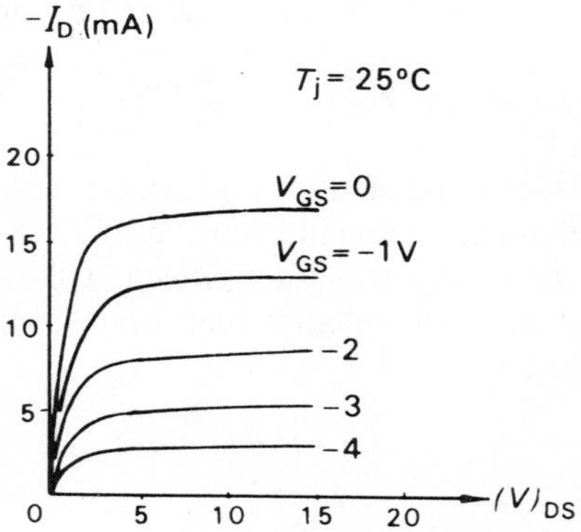

Figure 12.4. The characteristics of Philips BF245C N channel JFET.

During the last few years a special type of JFET was developed in GaAs using a Schottky-barrier gate. This transistor is very useful for microwave amplification and we shall discuss it in Chapter 20.

Conclusions

12.2 The Principle of the Insulated Gate Field Effect Transistor (IGFET)

This transistor is of much greater importance today than the previously mentioned one. Basically it is similar to the JFET but control of the channel conductance is achieved by the field of a parallel-plate capacitor with oxide (SiO_2) insulation instead of by junction capacitance. Because of its structure, shown in Fig. 12.5, it is usually abbreviated MOST (metal-oxide semiconductor transistor).

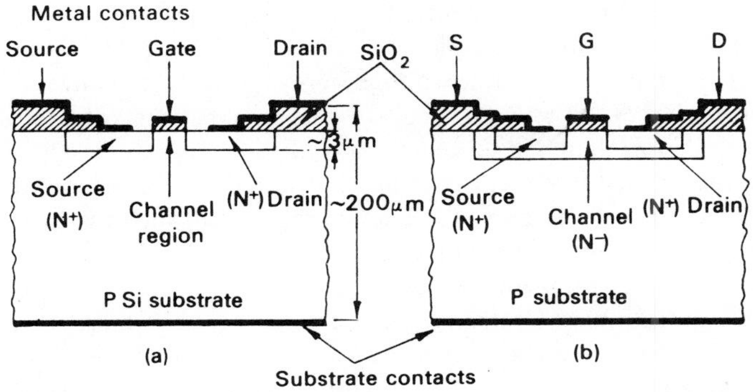

Figure 12.5. A cross section through an N channel MOS transistor: (a) of the enhancement type; (b) of the depletion type.

We shall concentrate on the N channel type, remembering that it is also possible to make a P channel transistor, in which the N and P regions are interchanged and the current and voltage polarities reversed.

The N channel is made by diffusing phosphorus (a donor) at high concentration into a P substrate of about 5 Ω cm resistivity. The diffusion is done through holes in a SiO_2 mask on the Si surface so that only specific regions of the substrate become N^+. These are the source and drain regions, which are separated by a narrow stripe of between 3 and 10 μm of P region. This later serves as the channel. On top of the channel a very thin (about 0.1 μm) SiO_2 layer is now formed by oxidizing the Si at high temperature. The oxide is an excellent electrical insulator with a dielectric constant of about 3.85. A metal layer, usually Al, is vacuum evaporated on top of the oxide to serve as the gate terminal. It forms the top plate of the gate capacitor, the Si substrate being the other plate. Al metal contacts to the source and drain regions are made at the same time. It should be noticed that everywhere, except over the channel, the oxide thickness is high (up to 1.5 μm), so that Al conducting stripes can pass over it on their way to contact holes in the oxide without influencing the Si below them. The big advantage of MOSFET over JFET is in this construction, which requires relatively few process steps and permits the interconnection of many such transistors, made at the same time on the same substrate, by Al conductors on top. Very complicated circuits, called MOS integrated circuits, can be made in this way (Chapter 18). Before starting a detailed analysis let us go over the physical principles underlying the operation of the MOST.

With no gate-to-substrate bias the channel region in Fig. 12.5(a) remains P type. Application of positive drain voltage with respect to the source will not result in any current between them since the drain (N type) to channel (P type) junction is under reverse bias. The source-to-substrate junction, on the other hand, becomes very slightly forward biased, but no current can flow since the drain junction is in series and reversed. Substrate and source are therefore at practically the same voltage here (though this is not always the case as we shall see). Applying a positive gate-to-substrate voltage repels the positive holes from the channel region and attracts negative electrons there. A very thin layer, just under the gate oxide, will then be inverted into N type, with electrons as the free carriers. The source and drain thus become connected by the inverted N channel and current starts to flow between them. Increase of the gate voltage increases the charge stored in the gate capacitor, i.e., the concentration of electrons in the channel. Its conductivity will grow and so will I_{DS}. In such a transistor, shown in Fig. 12.5(a), the gate voltage is essential first to invert the channel region into N type and then to progressively increase its conductivity. Consequently it is called an N channel enhancement MOST. Another type of MOS transistor that operates in the depletion mode is shown in Fig. 12.5(b). In this type the channel region is already made N^- in the manufacturing process so that a source–gate current can flow at zero gate bias. Negative bias repels electrons from the channel and reduces its conductivity and current as in the JFET case. But unlike it a positive bias can also be applied, increasing the conductivity even more than at $V_{GS}=0$, with no danger of gate current.

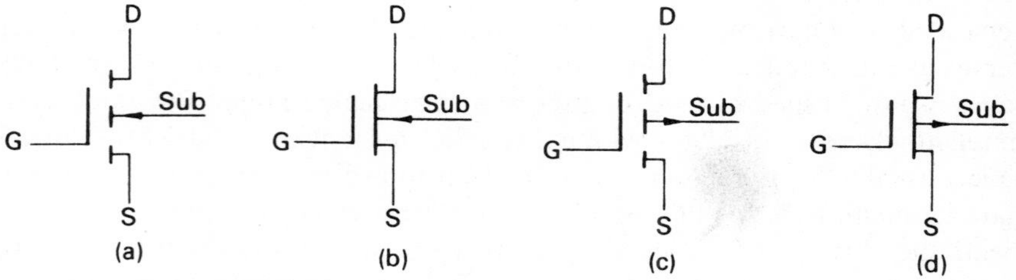

Figure 12.6. Standard circuit symbols for MOST (S=source, G=gate, D=drain, Sub=substrate): (a) N channel enhancement; (b) N channel depletion; (c) P channel enhancement; (d) P channel depletion.

The standard circuit symbols for the various MOS transistors are given in Fig. 12.6. The arrows point to the forward directions of the junctions formed between the substrate and the inverted channel regions.

The analysis of MOS transistors will be divided into two parts. First, the simpler MOS capacitor will be analyzed. This capacitor is the main part of the MOST and an important device in its own right. We shall then use the results to obtain the transistor properties.

12.3 The MOS Capacitor

The MOS capacitor has an Al metal plate for one electrode and the Si substrate, say P, for the other. They are separated by the oxide insulator as in Fig. 12.7(a).

The energy levels in A1, $Si0_2$ and Si are shown in Fig. 12.7(b) when separate, all referred to the free electron energy level outside, E_0 (note the large band gap of the oxide). When the capacitor is formed, the Fermi levels align themselves in equilibrium (see Section 8.5), but the relative differences in affinities are maintained, causing the band bending shown in Fig. 12.7(c).

Fermi level alignment involves charge movement (through the outside circuit between the Si and the metal) and the formation of potential difference, making the material with the higher work function, here Si, negative with respect to the metal by

$$V_{MS} = \frac{1}{q}\phi_{MS} = \frac{1}{q}(\phi_M - \phi_S) \tag{12.15}$$

where ϕ_M and ϕ_S are the respective metal and Si work functions in eV. Part of V_{MS} drops on the oxide insulator (the exact value depending on oxide capacitance and semiconductor doping) causing its energy bands to slope. Since no charge can move inside the oxide the bands' slope, i.e., the electric field, is uniform there. The rest of V_{MS} drops on the semiconductor causing charge movement and band bending. Since the Si is negative and the metal positive in Fig. 12.7(c), the positive holes are repelled from the semiconductor–oxide interface leaving behind a depleted surface layer of thickness d with a net negative acceptor charge $-Q_B$. The positive hole charge, moving through the outside circuit, appears on the metal as Q_M.

In real MOS capacitors the initial bending is even stronger, because the oxide usually contains some positive charge, Q_{OX} for two reasons. The first is that incomplete oxidation near the oxide–silicon interface leaves some of the silicon bonds dangling, which causes some positive charge there. This charge, known as *surface-states charge*, depends on the crystal orientation and on the oxidation procedure, but is always positive. A second source of positive charge

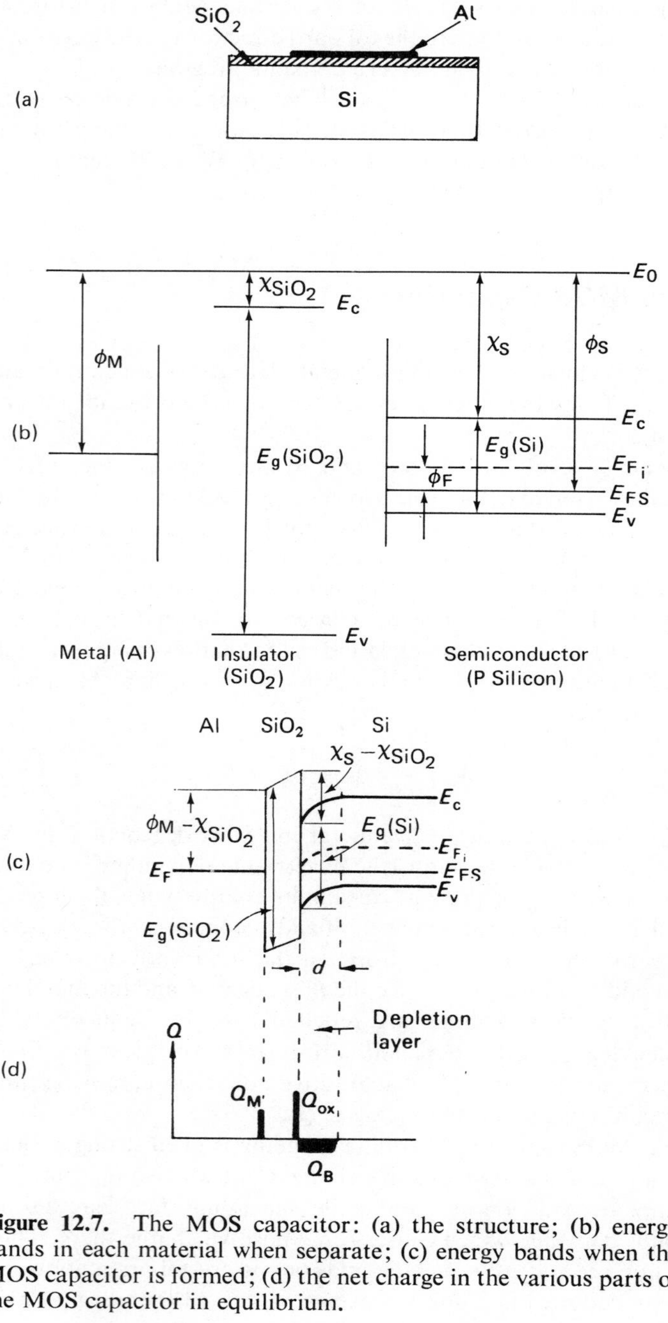

Figure 12.7. The MOS capacitor: (a) the structure; (b) energy bands in each material when separate; (c) energy bands when the MOS capacitor is formed; (d) the net charge in the various parts of the MOS capacitor in equilibrium.

is unwanted sodium contamination of the oxide. Sodium ions may enter the oxide because of insufficient pre-cleaning or use of sodium-containing furnace materials. They have relatively high mobility in the oxide, especially at elevated temperatures. Application of d.c. voltage to the capacitor will, therefore, shift this charge with time, changing the band bending and thus the MOST properties. This kind of oxide instability was very troublesome in early MOS development until the reason was found and mainly eliminated.

The total positive oxide charge Q_{OX}, shown in Fig. 12.7(d), further increases the negative semiconductor bulk charge Q_B which must now compensate for both ϕ_{MS} and Q_{OX} effects. This implies stronger band bending and may even invert the silicon surface to N-type without any additional bias (inversion means that E_{FS} comes nearer to E_c than to E_v on the Si surface). This 'built-in' inversion is usually unwanted and may be prevented by using substrates of higher acceptor doping.

The bands may be made flat by applying a certain voltage between metal (negative) and Si. This voltage is called the *flat band voltage*, V_{FB}, and is equal to

$$V_{FB} = V_{MS} - \frac{Q_{ox}}{C_{ox}}, \tag{12.16}$$

where V_{MS} is given by (12.15) and is negative for Al on Si with numerical values given in Table 12.1. Q_{ox} is the positive oxide charge near the SiO_2–Si interface and C_{ox} is the oxide capacitance, both per unit area.

Table 12.1

Material	Energy gap (eV)	Affinity (eV)	Work function (eV)	Dielectric constant
Al			$\phi_M = 4.1$	
Si	$E_g = 1.12$	$\chi_S = 4.15$	$\phi_S = \chi_S + \frac{E_g}{2} + E_{F_i} - E_F$	11.8
$Si0_2$	$E_g \simeq 8$	$\chi_{Si0_2} = 0.95$		3.85

For *P*-type Si doped with $N_A = 10^{15}$ cm^{-3} at $T = 300$°K, one gets $V_{MS} = -0.85$ V. For *N*-type Si of the same doping $V_{MS} = -0.27$ V. Typical values for Q_{ox} are $5\times10^{11}q$ [C/cm^2] for Si of ⟨111⟩ orientation and less than $10^{11}q$ [C/cm^2] for ⟨100⟩ orientation.

Applying a more negative voltage than V_{FB} reverses the band bending, making the Si even more P type at the surface. This is called *accumulation*, since holes accumulate there, and is shown in Fig. 12.8(a). When in accumulation the MOS capacitor may be used for a.c. circuit purposes like any other parallel-plate capacitor. Its capacitance is

$$C = AC_{ox} = \frac{A\,\varepsilon_{ox}\varepsilon_0}{t_{ox}}, \tag{12.17}$$

where A is the area and t_{ox} is the thickness of the oxide layer.

Applying a positive voltage to the metal with respect to the Si does the reverse: It increases band bending and negative charge in the Si. E_F must remain flat, since no current can flow through the oxide, but the metal and Si Fermi levels become separated by the applied voltage V. The increased bending will eventually bring E_{Fi} below E_{FS} as shown in Fig. 12.8(b). The Si at the interface has now become N-type, i.e. inverted.

The start of strong, i.e., effective, inversion occurs when Si band bending at the surface relative to deep in the substrate (where the bands are flat again) is $2\phi_F$, where $\phi_F = E_{F_i} - E_F$ depends on the substrate doping and is given by (7.13) or (7.14). Further increase of the external voltage V will bring E_c very near or even below E_{FS} on the Si surface. Since the free electron concentration depends exponentially on $E_e - E_{FS}$ (eq. 7.8), this means that the free electron charge will start to increase very fast once effective inversion is achieved. This charge is represented by Q_e in Fig. 12.8(c). A corresponding positive charge Q_M appears

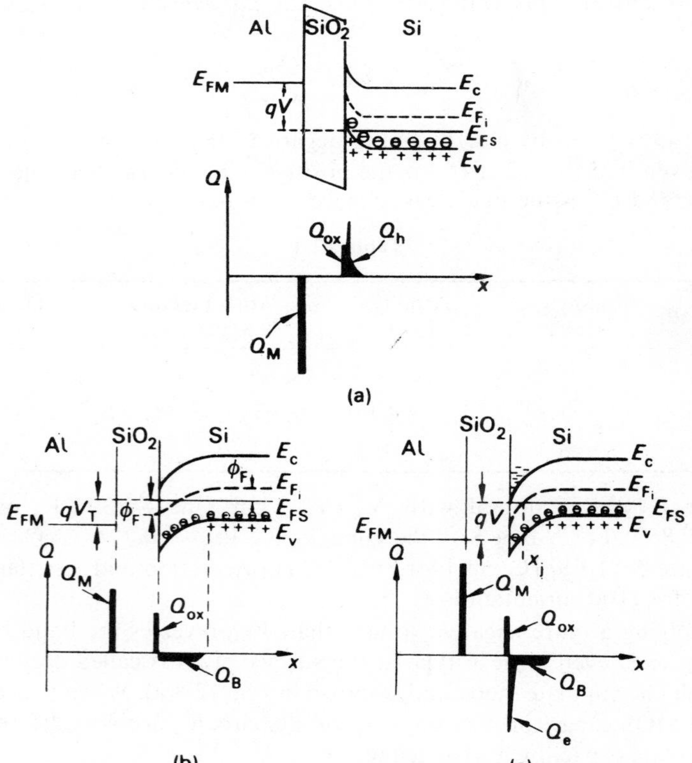

Figure 12.8. Band bending and charges in MOS capacitors: (a) in accumulation; (b) at the beginning of effective inversion; (c) in strong inversion.

on the metal, satisfying

$$Q_M + Q_{ox} = Q_B + Q_e \tag{12.18}$$

as in any other capacitor.

It should be noticed that Q_e represents the charge of minority carriers in the substrate, which accumulate at the Si surface. The electrons are thermally generated continuously and the band bending means that a field exists near the surface which pushes them towards it, and holes away from it, so that no recombination is possible. This continues till the negative charge, corresponding to the applied voltage, has built up and additional electrons are now repelled. But thermal generation is relatively slow, so that application of a positive voltage step will first increase the bending and the depletion-layer charge, Q'_B, much beyond the final steady state to a value given by $Q_M + Q_{ox} = Q'_B$. As Q_e builds up, Q'_B reduces to the steady-state value of Q_B in (12.18).

When the capacitance is measured by using a small a.c. signal on top of an inverting d.c. bias, Q_e will be unable to follow the fast signal if its frequency is above 50 Hz or so. The corresponding charge variation will then occur on the Al plate on one side and in the substrate majority carriers, i.e. holes, on the other. Since the holes reside beyond the depletion layer, this will give a smaller capacitance than that of (12.17), as if the depletion capacitance were in series with the oxide capacitance. As the depletion layer grows with increasing d.c. bias, the measured differential capacitance will drop till effective inversion is reached at a certain voltage called the *threshold voltage* V_T. Any further increase of the d.c. bias will now increase Q_e, the electronic charge, without further changing the thickness of the depletion layer. The measured a.c. capacitance will now become approximately constant. This is shown in the capacitance versus d.c. bias curves of Fig. 12.9. The three regions of

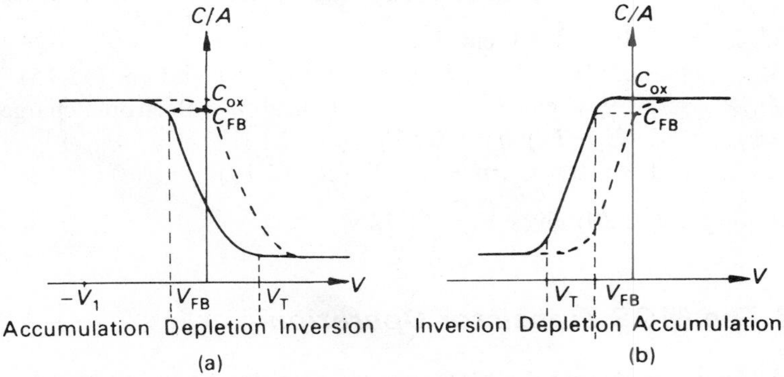

Figure 12.9. The $C(V)$ curves of MOS capacitors measured at 1 MHz (—— real capacitor; ------ ideal capacitor with $\phi_{MS}=0$, $Q_{ox}=0$); (a) capacitor built on a P-type substrate; (b) capacitor built on an N-type substrate.

accumulation, depletion and inversion are marked. The full line represents the high frequency (usually 1 MHz) measured capacitance.

The dashed line in the figure shows the calculated curve for an ideal capacitor with zero ϕ_{MS} and Q_{ox}, i.e., with originally flat bands. The voltage shift between this and the real $C(V)$ curve measures the flat band voltage of (12.16). Such measured $C(V)$ curves are very useful in obtaining information on semiconductor surface properties.

At the onset of effective inversion Q_B is determined by the thickness of the depletion layer d_{dep} when the voltage across it (the band bending between the silicon surface and its bulk) is

$$V_S = \left| \frac{2\phi_F}{q} \right| = \frac{2kT}{q} \ln \frac{N_D}{n_i}$$

where $\phi_F = E_{Fi} - E_F$ is in electron volts.

Using the junction equation (8.22) we get

$$Q_B = \pm q N_{A,D} d_{dep} = \pm [2q \varepsilon_{si} \varepsilon_o N_{A,D} V_S]^{1/2} \tag{12.19}$$

The charge Q_B is negative in P substrate (negatively charged acceptors) and ϕ_F is positive then. In N-type substrate it is the other way around. The threshold voltage for inversion is the sum of V_{FB}, the voltage drop $2\phi_F/q$ across the silicon depletion layer and the voltage drop across the oxide necessary to support the depletion charge $-Q_B$ ($Q_e \simeq 0$ at the threshold):

$$V_T = V_{MS} - \frac{Q_{ox}}{C_{ox}} + \frac{2\phi_F}{q} - \frac{Q_B}{C_{ox}}. \tag{12.20}$$

This equation can be used for both N and P substrates if the correct signs are used for the various terms.

For example, an MOS capacitor made on <100> N substrate, doped with $N_D = 10^{15}$ cm^{-3}, with Al metal on oxide insulator 0.1 μm thick, will have

C_{OX}	=	3.46×10^{-8} F cm^{-2}	
V_{MS}	=	-0.27V	(Table 12.1 and eq. (12.15)
Q_{OX}	=	$10^{11}q$ C cm^{-2}	(typical; q = electronic charge)
$2\phi_F/q$	=	$2\,(E_{F_i} - E_F)/q = -0.58$V	(eq. 7.13)
Q_B	=	1.4×10^{-8} C cm^{-2}	(eq. 12.19)

Substituting in (12.20) gives $V_T \simeq -1.72$ V.

12.4 The MOS Transistor Operation

All that was said of the MOS capacitor applies to the MOST too, with one exception: upon inversion it is no longer necessary to wait for thermal generation to supply the minority carriers, since they are immediately supplied by the source and drain, which are of opposite type to the channel zone and bound it on both sides. The mobile carrier charge in the channel can then follow the gate voltage even if it varies at high frequency. Up to inversion, however, capacitor and MOST behave similarly and the results obtained for V_T and its constituents applies to both.

When V_{GS} exceeds V_T an inverted channel forms between source and drain. Let us now look for the conductivity of that channel in order to relate I_{DS} to V_{GS} and V_{DS}, i.e., to find the MOST characteristics.

We refer again to the N channel case (P substrate) shown in Fig. 12.10.

The following assumptions and approximations are very useful for obtaining simple, but still sufficiently accurate expressions:

(a) The source is externally shortened to the substrate (this limitation will be removed later).

(b) A constant average mobility $\bar{\mu}_e$ is assumed in the inverted channel. Its measured value is about half the bulk mobility because of the additional carrier scattering near the Si–SiO_2 interface.

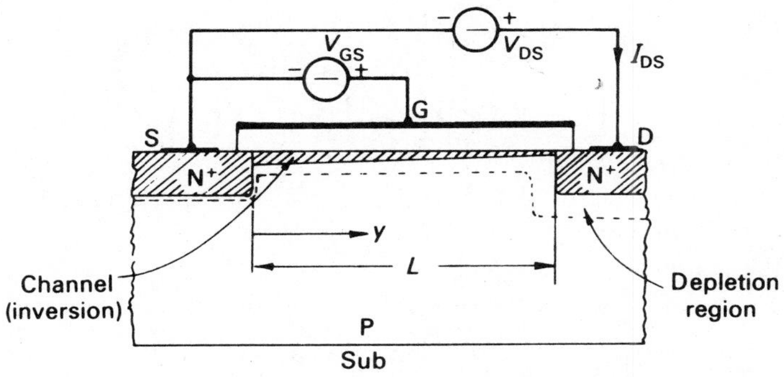

Figure 12.10. N channel MOST together with external voltage sources for operation (N regions are shown as hatched areas).

(c) The potential gradient in the drain–source direction in the channel is much smaller than in the perpendicular direction caused by the gate. This assumption enables us to consider the mobile charge at each value of y (see Fig. 12.10) along the channel, as dependent on the gate-to-channel potential difference there only.

(d) The existence of a drain–source current implies that there exists a voltage drop along the y direction of the channel. The reverse voltage from channel to substrate therefore changes from V_B (the source junction diffusion voltage) at $y=0$ to $V_B + V_{DS}$ at the drain end at $y=L$. This makes

Q_B, the depletion-layer charge, and therefore V_T, y dependent. Nevertheless, we assume V_T to be constant with y since Q_B depends on the square root of the reverse voltage and therefore changes slowly. This assumption becomes progressively worse as the substrate doping (and Q_B with it) are increased. (See Problems 12.21, 12.22 and 12.23 for the case when this assumption is removed.)

Using these assumptions let us now proceed. The mobile electronic charge per unit area in the channel at point y is given by C_{ox} multiplied by the excess of the gate-to-channel voltage at that point over V_T necessary to bring it to inversion threshold:

$$Q_e(y) = C_{ox}[(V_{GS} - V_T) - V(y)]. \tag{12.21}$$

If the channel width (normal to the plane of the paper) is W, the current in the y direction will be

$$I_{DS} = W\bar{\mu}_e Q_e(y)\left[-\frac{dV(y)}{dy}\right].$$

Substituting $Q_e(y)$, separating variables and integrating along the channel, we obtain

$$\int_{y=0}^{L} I_{DS}\, dy = -W\bar{\mu}_e C_{ox} \int_{V=0}^{V_{DS}} (V_{GS} - V_T - V)\, dV,$$

where all voltages are relative to the source. I_{DS} is independent of y, so the integration will give

$$I_{DS} = -\frac{W\bar{\mu}_e C_{ox}}{L}\left[(V_{GS} - V_T)V_{DS} - \frac{V_{DS}^2}{2}\right]. \tag{12.22}$$

The negative sign means again that for N channel the conventional current flows in the $-y$ direction. The same equation with a plus sign and negative values of V_{GS}, V_{DS} and V_T fits the P channel case. This characteristic is correct only in the range

$$0 \leqslant V_{DS} \leqslant V_{GS} - V_T. \tag{12.23}$$

The upper limitation is similar to JFET pinch-off and can be understood by checking the shape of $V(y)$ along the channel. Integrating I_{DS} up to point y only gives

$$I_{DS} = -\frac{W\bar{\mu}_e C_{ox}}{y}\left[(V_{GS} - V_T)V(y) - \frac{V^2(y)}{2}\right]. \tag{12.24}$$

This is a quadratic equation in $V(y)$ if I_{DS} is specified. The solution for two

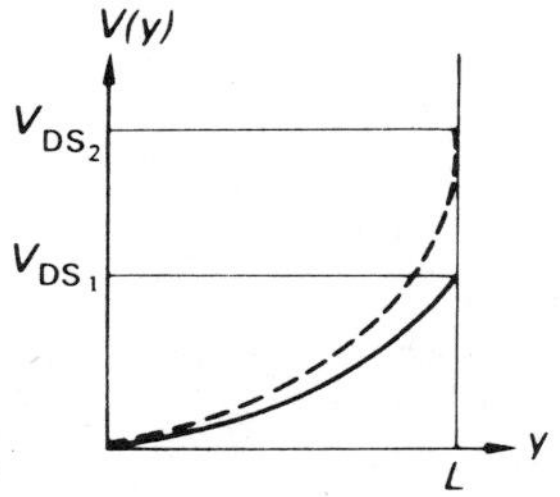

Figure 12.11. $V(y)$ along the channel: —— for $V_{DS1} < V_{GS} - V_T$; ------ for $V_{DS2} = V_{GS} - V_T$.

values of V_{DS}, below and at the point of channel pinch-off, are shown in Fig. 12.11.

Since V_{GS} is fixed, the higher $V(y)$ is, the smaller becomes the potential difference between gate and channel at point y and with it $Q_e(y)$ of (12.21). To retain the same current independent of y, the velocity of the reduced charge must increase. This velocity is proportional to the field dV/dy, which must therefore increase. When $V_{DS} = V_{GS} - V_T$, the gate-to-channel voltage at the drain end is just sufficient to bring the channel there to inversion threshold, and no excess voltage is left to support $Q_e(L)$, which becomes negligible there. To retain I_{DS}, the field must become infinite as shown in the figure; this, of course, is impossible. The velocity of the carriers saturates, but more important, our assumption (c) breaks down since dV/dy can no longer be neglected. Channel pinch-off and current saturation occur at $V_{DS} = V_{GS} - V_T$ and any further increase of V_{DS} will simply increase the field at the pinched-off end without increasing the current, since the charge Q_e is already moving at its scattering limited velocity.

The current in saturation is given by (12.22) with $V_{DS} = V_{GS} - V_T$:

$$I_{DS}(\text{sat}) = -\frac{W\bar{\mu}_e C_{ox}}{2L}(V_{GS} - V_T)^2, \qquad V_{DS} \geqslant V_{GS} - V_T. \tag{12.25}$$

(P channel saturates when $V_{DS} \leqslant V_{GS} - V_T$ with all terms negative.)

I_{DS} in saturation is no longer linearly related to V_{GS}. The sign of V_T determines whether the transistor operates in the enhancement or in the depletion mode. For N channel, requiring positive V_{GS} for increased conduction, the meaning of $V_T < 0$ is that at $V_{GS} = 0$ a channel already exists (because of ϕ_{MS} and Q_{ox}) and current will flow immediately V_{DS} is applied.

The drain characteristics, shown in Fig. 12.12(a), are of such a transistor with $V_T = -5$ V. This transistor can operate in both enhancement and depletion modes, depending on the polarity of V_{GS}. Figure 12.12(b) shows the characteristics of another transistor with $V_T = +1$ V. This will operate only if $V_{GS} > +1$ V, i.e., only in the enhancement mode. Such N channel transistors

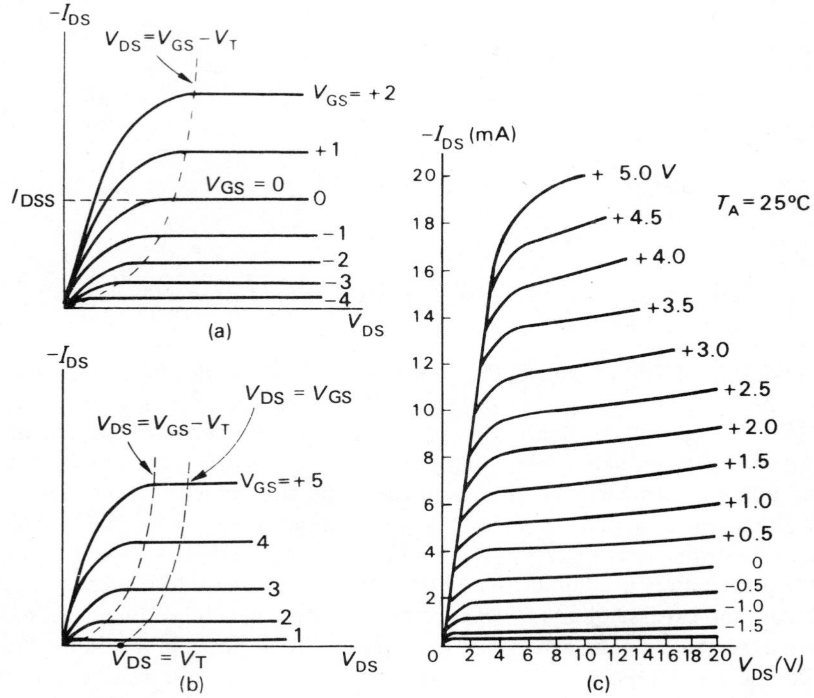

Figure 12.12. N channel MOST drain characteristics: (a) anticipated characteristics for $V_T=-5$ V; (b) anticipated characteristics for $V_T=+1$ V; (c) Motorola transistor 2N3797 with $V_T \simeq -5$ V.

can be obtained in spite of Q_{ox} and ϕ_{MS} effects if N_A in the channel is increased by ion implantation. P channel transistors are always of the enhancement type, since for them $V_T < 0$, requiring an even more negative V_{GS} to conduct.

For comparison purposes typical characteristics of Motorola N channel MOST number 2N3797 are also shown in the figure. The one deviation from our expected characteristics that stands out is the finite output resistance, given by the positive slope of the I_{DS}–V_{DS} curves above saturation. As in the case of the JFET, this current increase results from the reduction of the effective channel length with increased V_{DS} (due to lengthening of the pinched off region).

One can roughly model this effect by assuming the length of the pinched off region ΔL is equal to the length of a depletion region between the highly doped drain whose potential is V_{DS} and the low doped substrate at the drain end of the channel where the potential is $V_{GS}-V_T$. Use of (8.22a) then yields:

$$\Delta L = \left[\frac{2\varepsilon\varepsilon_0}{qN_{sub}}\right]^{1/2} [V_{DS}-(V_{GS}-V_T)]^{1/2}.$$

The effective channel length becomes $L_{\text{eff}} = L - \Delta L$ resulting in increase of drain current with drain voltage according to (12.25).

The maximum permissible drain and gate voltages are limited. If V_{DS} is too high (more than 25 V for 2N3797), avalanche breakdown may develop in the reverse-biased drain junction, with a sharp increase in I_{DS}. The gate in an MOS transistor needs special protection against overvoltage. The gate capacitance in discrete, and even more so in integrated MOS circuits, is usually so small and the leakage resistance so high ($>10^{12}\,\Omega$) that even a small static charge, accumulating on the gate if left disconnected, may be enough to cause gate oxide breakdown with irreparable transistor damage. Discrete MOST are therefore carefully packaged with the gate and source leads shorted together. In integrated circuits the gates of the input transistors are protected by a diode in parallel which enters into controlled avalanche or punch-through breakdown (which is nondestructive) before a dangerous gate voltage is reached.

The MOST transconductance, needed for equivalent circuit and amplification calculation, is defined as before by (12.11). Using (12.25) we then obtain for the saturation region:

$$g_m = \frac{W\bar{\mu}_e C_{ox}}{L}(V_{GS} - V_T). \tag{12.26}$$

g_m grows with V_{GS} and is proportional to the W/L ratio, called the *aspect ratio*, of the transistor. The minimum value of L is limited by drain–source punch-through effects and is about 3 μm today. For high g_m the oxide thickness should be kept low (C_{ox} high), compatible with the input voltage requirements. Usually it is chosen between 50 and 100 nm. The thinner the oxide the more difficult it is to make with reasonable yield, i.e., free of holes.

Under first approximation, the input impedance to the MOST is composed only of the gate capacitance $C_{gs} \simeq LWC_{ox}$ (LW is the area) in series with the channel resistance to the source. The last, however, is small and can usually be neglected compared with C_{gs} reactance. More accurate calculation of C_{gs}, taking account of the potential variation along the channel, yields (see Problem 12.20)

$$C_{gs} = \tfrac{2}{3}LWC_{ox}. \tag{12.27}$$

A measure of the maximum frequency at which the MOST can operate may be obtained from the ratio g_m/C_{gs} (s^{-1}). The a.c. component of the output current is $g_m v_{gs}$, where v_{gs} is the a.c. voltage between gate and source in the input. Assuming an amplifer made of identical transistors, one following the other, the output current of the first must charge the input capacitance of the second, C_{gs}, to a voltage of at least v_{gs} (so that at this maximum frequency the amplification is 1). The minimum charging time will therefore be given by the necessary charge, $v_{gs}C_{gs}$, divided by the charging current:

(12.28) $$T_{\min} = \frac{v_{gs} C_{gs}}{v_{gs} g_m} = \frac{C_{gs}}{g_m} \text{ s.}$$

$T_{\min}$ represents the minimum signal period (i.e. $f_{\max}^{-1}$) or the minimum pulse width if the transistor is intended for switching. Problem 12.21 demonstrates that $T_{\min}$ is also of the order of magnitude of the carrier transit time through the channel.

Substituting (12.26) and (12.27) into (12.28) shows that $T_{\min}$ is proportional to $L^2/\bar{\mu}$. One should therefore prefer N channel (since $\bar{\mu}_e \simeq 2\bar{\mu}_h$) and minimum channel length L for fast switching. This analysis neglected parasitic effects like drain junction capacitance and series resistances of drain and source, which may increase $T_{\min}$ by an order of magnitude. The parasitics will be discussed in the next section.

Finally it should be stressed that in both junction and MOSFET the current is carried by majority carriers only, i.e., by electrons in N channel and by holes in P channel. Minority carrier generation and lifetime, which are important in devices such as diodes or bipolar transistors, have little effect on their performance. Thus they are better suited to operation in an environment where there is a radiation hazard, such as in outer space, where the radiation causes the lifetime to deteriorate with time.

Additional material on field-effect devices can be found in Reference 10.

12.5 Additional Information Relevant to MOS Transistors and Capacitors in Integrated Circuits

When MOS integrated circuits are described in Chapter 18, it will be seen that many MOS transistors must operate with a reverse voltage V_{sub} between their source and substrate. This must influence expression (12.19) of Q_B, where the reverse voltage across the inverted channel to substrate junction was taken as only $V_S = 2\phi_F/q$ volts. This should now be changed to $V_S + V_{sub}$, so that Q_B in P-type substrate becomes

$$Q_B = -[2qN_A\varepsilon_{si}\varepsilon_0(V_S + V_{sub})]^{1/2}.$$

Substituting Q_B in eq. (12.20) gives

(12.29) $$V_T = V_{MS} - \frac{Q_{ox}}{C_{ox}} + \frac{2\phi_F}{q} + \frac{1}{C_{ox}}[2qN_A\varepsilon_{si}\varepsilon_0(V_{sub} + V_S)]^{1/2} = V_{T_0} + \Delta V_T,$$

where V_{T_0} is the value of V_T for $V_{sub} = 0$.

A common practice is to approximate V_T by

(12.30) $$V_T = V_{T_0} + \Delta V_T,$$

where V_{T0} is the value of V_T for $V_{sub}=0$ and $\Delta V_T \simeq m V_{sub}^{1/2}$ (or with a minus sign for P channel). m is an experimentally determined coefficient of about 1/2 but may be as high as 2.

With this approximation we can use all our previous equations, replacing V_T by $V_{T0}+\Delta V_T$.

This change in V_T is known as the *body effect* and will make V_T for a P channel even more negative, reducing I_{DS} for a given V_{GS}. In the case of N channel, ΔV_T is positive, so that the body effect is sometimes used to change the operation of such transistors from the depletion mode (obtained in normal processing which yields a slightly negative V_T) to the enhancement mode ($V_T>0$).

SEM photograph of an MOS transistor with self-aligned polysilicon gate (×1000). Channel length 7 μm. The Microelectronics Laboratory, Technion IIT, Haifa, Israel.

Most integrated circuits (ICs) made today consist of N channel transistors of both enhancement and depletion types. Since $V_T>0$ for the enhancement type, $V_T<0$ for the depletion type and $V_T \gg 0$ under the field oxide (the region between transistors) to prevent possible inversion there by positive interconnect metal lines that run over the field oxide, it is clear that a method for locally controlling V_T is necessary. Equation (12.29) shows that V_T can be controlled by adjusting the surface doping level N_A using ion implant techniques. The original substrate doping, N_{A0}, is kept low (around 10^{15}) to maintain high breakdown voltage and low depletion capacitance for source and drain junctions. Boron implant is then used in selected areas to increase N_A under the field oxide and where gates of enhancement transistors will be. This increases the last term in (12.29) to make $V_T>0$, say +1 V for 0.08 μm of gate oxide. Since the field oxide is an order of magnitude thicker, C_{ox} there is correspondingly smaller and V_T there will exceed 10 V. A second implant of phosphorus is used to reduce the effective N_A under gates of future depletion transistors or even create a thin N layer there. Sometimes two types of enhancement and of depletion transistors with different V_T's are used in the same circuit which necessitates more implant steps, each tailored to a desired V_T group. If a boron implant dose of N_A atoms/cm^2 is implanted in the surface of the channel area which must be depleted by the gate voltage before inversion is achieved, an additional term $-qN_A/C_{ox}$ must be added to (12.20) or (12.29) to give the new threshold voltage.

When very short channels are used (3 μm or less) in high density circuits, a so called *short channel effect* sets in. This happens when channel length becomes comparable to the depletion regions of source and drain junctions. Figure 12.13(a) shows that an appreciable part of the substrate impurity content

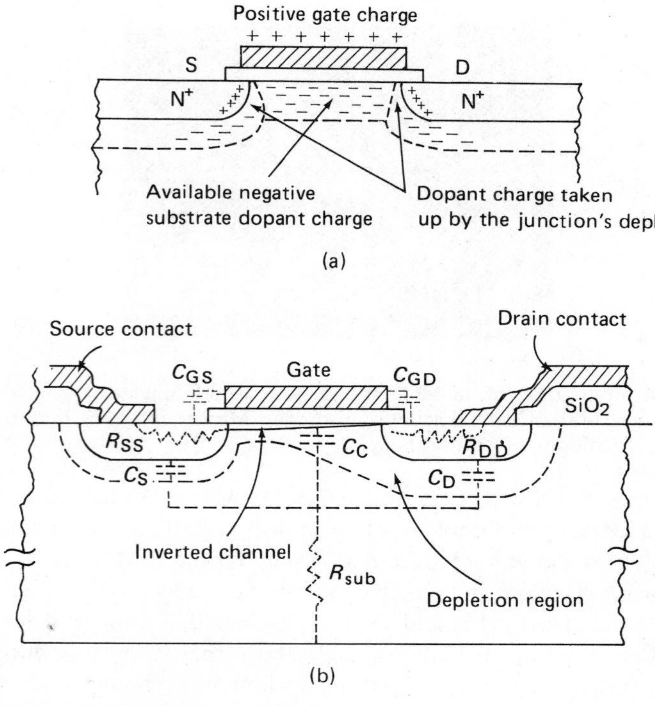

Figure 12.13 Parasitics and second order effects associated with small size integrated MOS transistors: (a) the short channel effect on V_T; (b) MOS parasitic resistances and capacitances.

under the gate becomes part of the junction depletion charge and is no longer affected by the gate potential. As the junction reverse voltage (e.g., the drain voltage) grows, its depletion region extends further under the gate and further reduces the effective value of N_A there with consequent reduction of V_T. This means that even though the transistor is in the saturation region, increased V_{DS} would reduce V_T and increase I_{DS} giving a much steeper slope to the $I_{DS}-V_{DS}$ characteristics, i.e., give lower output resistance ($r_0^{-1}=\partial I_{DS}/\partial V_{DS}$, $V_{GS}=$ const.). It is also obvious from Fig. 12.13(a) that unless substrate doping is increased, the short channel device would be prone to source–drain punch-through at a relatively low drain voltage. This has a bearing on scaling down of MOS transistor dimensions to be discussed in Chapter 18.

The small size of MOS transistor in present day ICs increases the relative importance of parasitics associated with it. These are shown in Fig. 12.13(b). R_{SS} and R_{DD} are resistances in series with source and drain respectively, that represent contact and semiconductor bulk resistance up to the channel entrance (a few tens of ohms each). R_{sub} is the substrate bulk resistance (about 100 Ω). C_{GS} and C_{GD} are capacitances resulting from overlap of the gate electrode over source and drain regions. C_S, C_C and C_D are depletion layers, voltage dependent, capacitances from substrate to source, to inverted channel and to the drain respectively. C_C is the smallest (due to small channel area) and is often negligible. (The MOS effect represented by the intrinsic gate-channel capacitance C_{gs}, channel transconductance g_m and controlled current source $g_m V_{gs}$ are omitted in the figure.)

The parasitics put a limit on the device switching speed, i.e., its ability to change V_{DS} from high to low value or vice versa by gate control of its current. The parasitic capacitances must be charged or discharged to achieve switching by the device current. In (12.28) C_{gs} should therefore be replaced by a much higher total capacitance that includes both intrinsic and parasitic capacitances. This accounts for measured switching speeds that are an order of magnitude slower than expected from (12.28). The main effect of the parasitic resistances is to increase device power dissipation and voltage drops. They are more important in devices designed for linear and MOS power applications.

Another second order effect noticed in MOS ICs is that conduction starts slightly before V_{GS} reaches V_T. Known as *subthreshold conduction*, this results from defining V_T as threshold for *strong* inversion. Actually some mobile channel charge forms the moment E_{FS} in Fig. 12.8(b) crosses to the upper side of E_{Fi}. Detailed theory shows that this charge and the resulting current increase exponentially with V_{GS} in the range $|V_T|-0.5<|V_{GS}|<|V_T|$. I_{DS} is practically zero for $|V_{GS}|\le|V_T|-0.5$ and is still very small at $V_{GS}=V_T$.

12.6 The Charge Coupled Device (CCD)

The MOS capacitor is often used today in a dynamic and not a static fashion. This is done by applying a voltage pulse to the capacitor with the proper polarity for inversion. The pulse causes deep depletion in the semiconductor as shown in Fig. 12.14(a).

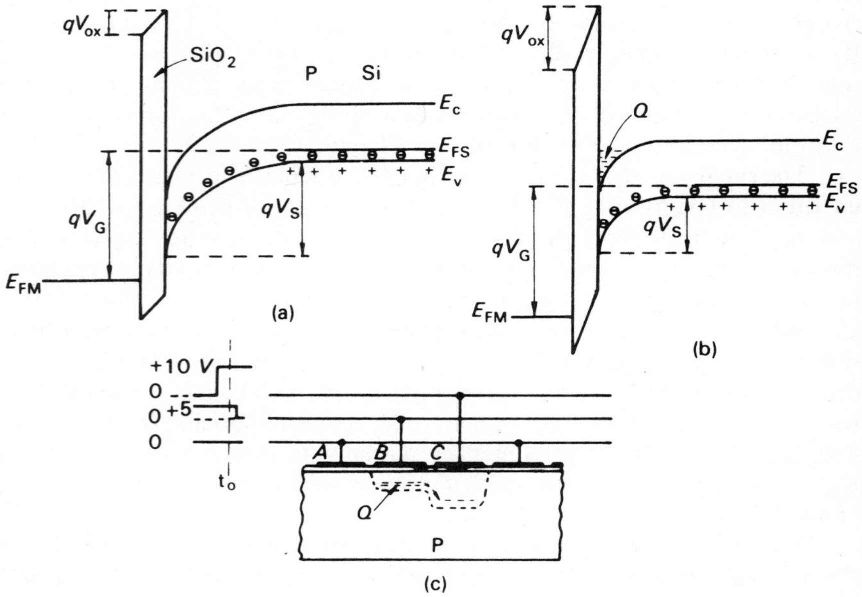

Figure 12.14 Energy bands in MOS capacitor in a dynamic mode of operation (V_G=voltage applied between gate and substrate): (a) immediately after a strong inverting voltage pulse has been applied; (b) while storing a charge packet Q; (c) charge transfer from capacitor B to capacitor C.

For a limited time (up to a few milliseconds) the number of thermally generated minority carriers tending to accumulate at the interface can be neglected. If some minority charge Q is injected at the interface from a neighboring capacitor during that time, it can be stored in the capacitor (Fig. 12.14b) for a certain delay time and then moved on by applying a more positive potential to a neighboring capacitor on the other side. A charge packet Q can thus be moved along a line of MOS capacitors, one behind the other, by applying a series of synchronized pulses between each of them and the substrate as shown in Fig. 12.14(c). This is known as a charge-coupled device (CCD).

The applied voltage V_G is the sum of the voltage drops on the oxide, V_{ox}, and on the silicon V_S. The last is called the *surface potential* and represents the voltage drop from surface to bulk. V_S can be related to V_G and Q (the stored minority charge) by:

$$V_G = V_{FB} - \frac{Q_B'}{C_{ox}} - \frac{Q}{C_{ox}} + V_S, \tag{12.31}$$

where the depletion-layer charge is (for $|V_S| \gg V_B$)

$$Q'_B = \pm qN_{A,D}d_{dep} = \pm(2qN_{A,D}\varepsilon_{si}\varepsilon_0 |V_S|)^{1/2}.$$

For P substrate: Q (electrons) <0 and $Q'_B<0$. Since V_{FB}, C_{ox} and N_A are fixed, increase of the stored electronic charge reduces V_S for a given V_G. CCDs will be further discussed in Chapter 18.

12.7 MOS Transistors as Memory Elements

MOS transistors are the common building blocks for integrated semiconductor memories. The gate–channel capacitance can be either charged or not (like in the CCD) controlling the drain–source conduction. The memory lasts as long as the charge on the gate can be retained. Gate oxide is an almost perfect insulator but the gate must be charged through another MOS transistor (acting as on–off switch) whose drain is connected to the gate with both having the same voltage. Leakage in the drain junction would dissipate the stored gate charge within a few milliseconds unless a periodic refresh charging is done. This is the basis of dynamic memories which are therefore more complicated circuitwise.

A special structure of an MOS transistor that once charged can retain its gate charge for years is also in use [Ref. 26] and is known as *F*loating gate *A*valanche injection *MOS* or FAMOS. The gate in the FAMOS, shown in Fig. 12.15(a) is made of doped polysilicon completely embedded in SiO_2 and electrically unconnected, i.e., its potential is 'floating'.

The substrate doping is chosen so that with the floating gate neutral $V_T<0$ (depletion N transistor) and the device conducts. (P channel FAMOS is also made.) With a negative charge on the gate there is no channel inversion and the device is off. Charging of the gate is done by a high drain–source pulse which accelerates the channel electrons in the pinched-off, high field region to such high energies above the Si conduction band bottom that they can pass over into the oxide conduction band, Fig. 12.15(b), cross the thin gate oxide and accumulate in the floating gate (edge effects cause the electrical field lines in the pinched-off region to pull electrons towards the gate). A device so treated would become nonconducting. A P channel enhancement FAMOS gate can be charged negatively (into conduction) by avalanching the drain junction thereby, again, creating hot (high energy) electrons that can cross over to the gate. Once on the gate the charge cannot escape for years at normal operating voltages and temperatures. A matrix of FAMOS devices with proper connections for sources and drains (so that gates can be charged selectively), forms an *E*rasable *P*rogrammable *R*ead *O*nly *M*emory (EPROM). Such a memory can be totally erased by illuminating it with ultra violet light whose photons have enough energy to raise the electrons on the gate over the oxide barrier $q\phi_B$ (Fig. 12.15(b)) so they can escape back into the substrate (there is no drain-induced

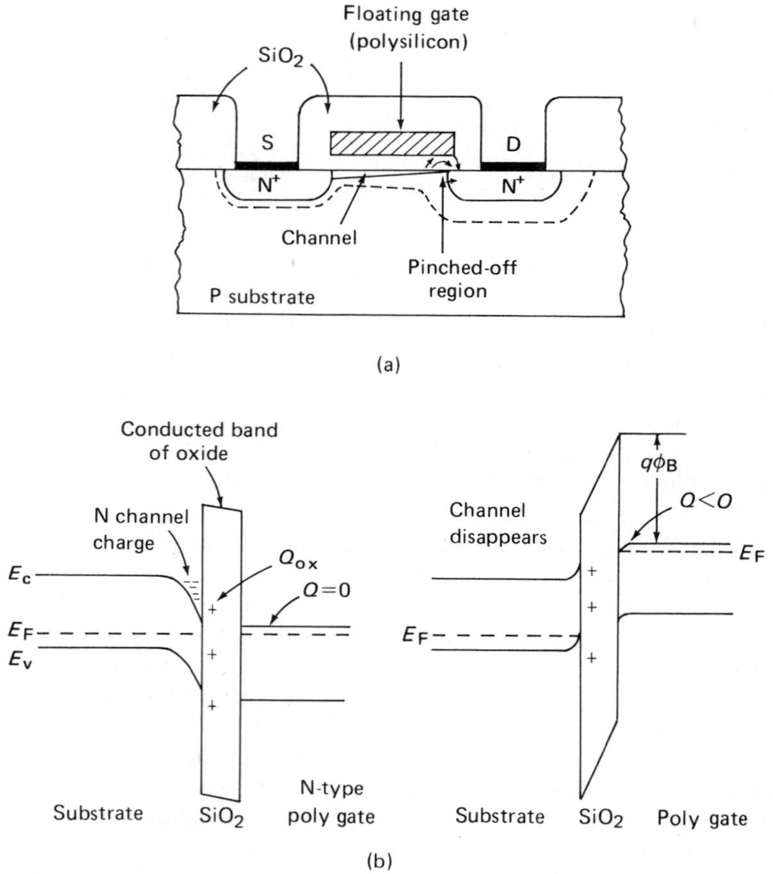

Figure 12.15 A FAMOS device: (a) basic structure (field lines are marked around the pinched off region); (b) energy band picture for uncharged and charged gate states.

field pulling them into the gate now as was during the charging). A more elaborate FAMOS structure with two stacked gates [Ref. 26] is shown in Fig. 12.16. It can be both electrically charged and discharged selectively, i.e., it can be programmed, erased and reprogrammed many times.

The lower, floating, gate can be charged by directing hot electrons from the pinched-off region towards it with positive pulses (about 20 V) simultaneously applied to drain and top control gate. Electron removal, or erasure, is achieved by applying a positive pulse train (about 25V) to the top gate with source, drain and substrate grounded. Figure 12.16(b) shows the way the pulse voltage V_G divides itself: a small part, V_{S1}, is used for inverted channel formation on the substrate, two parts, V_{ox1} and V_{ox2} drop on the two oxide layers and the largest

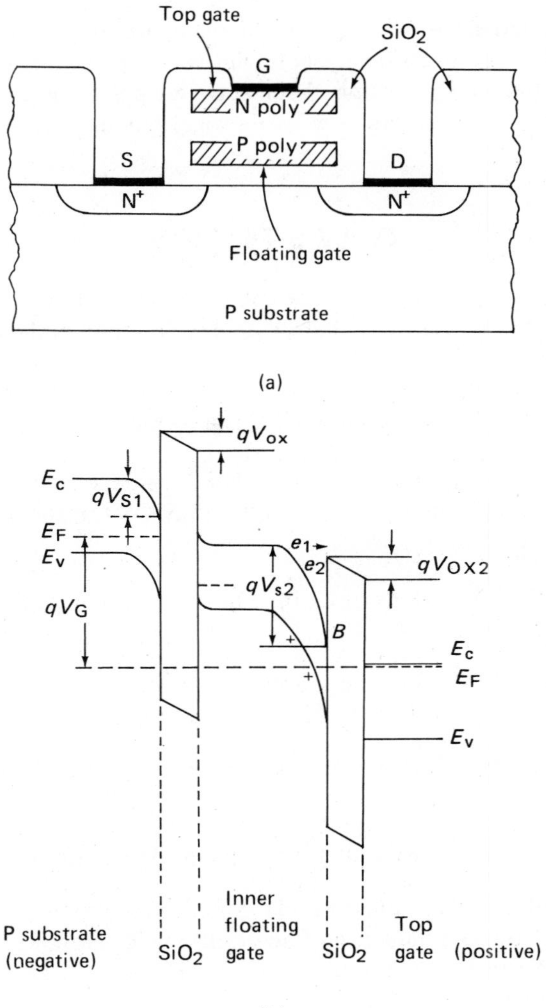

Figure 12.16 Electrically Erasable reprogrammable (E^2FAMOS) version of FAMOS [Ref. 26]: (a) cross section; (b) band diagram during erasure.

part, V_{S2}, goes to deep deplate the P-type polysilicon floating gate on the side facing the top gate. The field created in the floating gate is sufficient to cause avalanche. The free electrons created by this avalanche are directed towards the top gate. Some of these electrons, marked e_1 in the figure, have high enough energy to go into the conduction band of the top oxide layer and cross into the top gate, thereby gradually removing the stored negative charge. Most of the avalanche created electrons, marked e_2 in the figure, stay in the polysilicon and would form another inversion layer at point *B*, except for the pulses being short with recombination eliminating them between pulses. Erasure is thus performed and the memory can now be reprogrammed.

QUESTIONS

12.1 For high sensitivity to input signal in JFET, would you use a higher or a lower doping density in the channel region than in the gate region?

12.2 What polarity should the gate–source voltage have in a P channel JFET? What polarity should the drain–source voltage have?

12.3 Would the input impedance of a JFET be effected by V_{GS} and if so. how? Does the input impedance to an MOS transistor behave in the same way?

12.4 Check the dimensions of G_0 in (12.6) and show that they are those of conductance.

12.5 How would you find the output resistance from characteristics such as those shown in Fig. 12.12(c)?

12.6 Do minority carriers participate in current carrying in JFET? in MOS?

12.7 Can one build a JFET that operates in the enhancement mode?

12.8 The oxide in a P channel MOST contains sodium ions that can move slowly under the influence of an electric field. How will this affect the characteristics of such a transistor if a positive d.c. voltage is applied to its gate for some time?

12.9 It is claimed that an MOS transistor will sustain higher gate voltage if the oxide thickness is increased to 200 nm or more. Do you recommend building such transistors? Will they have any drawbacks?

12.10 How are the drain characteristics of N and P channel MOS transistors affected by:

(a) change of the silicon oxide to silicon nitride which has higher dielectric constant;

(b) increase of t_{ox};

(c) increase of substrate doping?

12.11 Explain why the carrier transit time through the channel should be related to the maximum frequency at which the transistor can operate.

12.12 What effect would changing the polysilicon gate doping from P- to N-type have on a P channel MOS circuit?

PROBLEMS

12.13 A P channel JFET made in Si, has a channel which is 3 μm high, 8 μm long and 400 μm wide. The doping density in the channel is $N_A = 10^{15}$ cm^{-3} and in the gate is $N_D = 10^{18}$ cm^{-3}. Hole mobility in the channel is 400 cm^2 V^{-1} s^{-1}.

(a) Calculate the pinch-off voltage.

(b) Find the drain–source voltage at which I_{DS} will saturate for $V_{GS} = 1.0$ V. What is this current?

12.14 A small a.c. signal is applied between source and drain of a JFET, operated with a fixed gate voltage. Show that the transistor presents a resistance of $r_0 = 1/g_m$ to that signal. g_m is the transconductance in saturation for the same gate voltage. Show that this is correct for the MOST too.

12.15 Calculate the threshold voltage of a P channel MOST with Al gate made on a <111> surface with substrate doping of 3×10^{15} cm^{-3}. Do this for two values of the gate oxide thickness: 80 nm and 120 nm. Use the information in Table 12.1 and correct ϕ_{MS} to account for the different substrate doping.

12.16 Repeat Problem 12.15 but for an N channel made on <100> surface and 100 nm oxide thickness. Do this for two substrate doping densities of 5×10^{14} cm^{-3} and 10^{16} cm^{-3}.

In what mode will the transistor operate in each case?

12.17 Equation (12.25) points to a convenient method of measuring V_T and the coefficient $W\bar{\mu}_e C_{ox}/(2L)$ if the characteristics are available. Find this method and use it to measure those parameters for transistor 2N3797 (Fig. 12.12) whose characteristics are given in Fig. 12.12(c).

12.18 Find the output resistance and the transconductance of transistor 2N3797 around the operating point of $V_{GS} = 2.0$ V and $V_{DS} = 10$ V.

12.19 The small-signal resistance between source and drain of an MOS transistor was measured with a bridge as shown in Fig. 12.17 for two gate voltages $V_{GS_1} = 2$ V and $V_{GS_2} = 5$ V. The values of 1 kΩ and 500 Ω were obtained respectively. Can you use those results to find V_T of the transistor? In what mode does it operate?

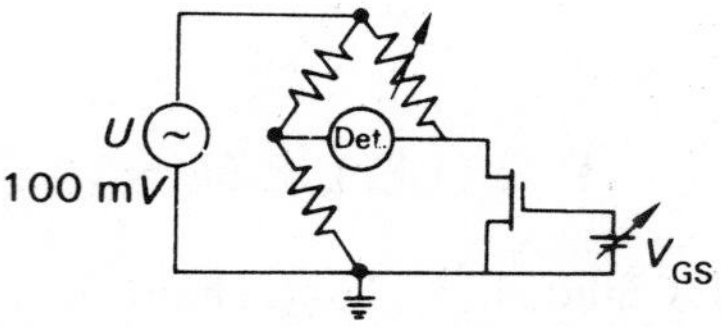

Figure 12.17 Small-signal source–drain resistance measurement for Problem 12.19.

12.20 The mobile charge $Q_e(y)$ per unit area in an N channel MOST is given by (12.21). Use the expression of $V(y)$ in (12.24) to show that the small-signal (differential) capacitance measured between gate and source in saturation is actually

$$C_{gs} = \frac{dQ_t}{dV_{GS}} = \tfrac{2}{3} WLC_{ox},$$

where Q_t is the total mobile charge in the channel (excluding the pinch-off region). Assume the channel length is always L and $V(y) = V_{GS} - V_T$ for $y = L$.

12.21 Show that the transit time from source to drain in a MOST operated in saturation is $2C_{gs}/g_m$.

Assume C_{gs} as in Problem 12.20, constant mobility in the channel and zero transit time through the pinched-off region. Repeat the derivation using a linear approximation to the voltage $V(y)$ in the channel and compare it to the previous result.

12.22 An N channel MOS is given with a reverse substrate bias $|V_{sub}|$, gate voltage V_{GS} and drain voltage V_{DS} (all voltages taken with respect to the source). Show that if assumption (d) in Section 12.4 is removed, the expression obtained for V_T is

$$(12.32) \quad V_T = V_{FB} + V_B + \frac{1}{C_{ox}} (2q\varepsilon_0\varepsilon_{si}N_A)^{1/2}[V_B + |V_{sub}| + V(y)]^{1/2}$$

where $V_B = |2\phi_F/q|$, $V_{FB} = V_{MS} - Q_{ox}/C_{ox}$ (the Flat Band voltage) and

$V(y)$ is the channel (at point y) to source voltage. This replaces equation (12.20). The expression for I_{DS} in the linear region that replaces (12.22) is then

(12.33)

$$I_{DS} = -\frac{W\bar{\mu}}{L}\left\{ C_{ox}\left[(V_{GS}-V_{FB}-V_B)V_{DS} - \frac{V_{DS}^2}{2} \right] - \frac{2}{3}(2q\varepsilon_0\varepsilon_{si}N_A)^{1/2} \left[(V_B+V_{DS}+V_{sub})^{3/2} - (V_B+V_{sub})^{3/2} \right] \right\}$$

This current saturates at a drain–source voltage of

(12.34)

$$V_{DS}(\mathrm{sat}) = V_{GS} - V_{FB} - V_B + \frac{q\varepsilon_0\varepsilon_{si}N_A}{C_{ox}^2}\left\{ 1 - \left[1 + \frac{2C_{ox}^2}{q\varepsilon_0\varepsilon_{si}N_A}(V_{GS}-V_{FB}+V_{sub}) \right]^{1/2} \right\}$$

instead of at $V_{GS} - V_T$ when a constant V_T is assumed.

12.23 Compare threshold voltages calculated from (12.20) and (12.30) to that found from the more accurate expression (12.20) for an N channel MOS with $N_A = 2\times10^{16}$ cm^{-3}, $Q_{ox} = 8\times10^{10}q$, Al gate with 70 nm gate oxide. Do it for the two values: $V_{sub} = 0$ and $V_{sub} = 5$V.

12.24 Compare $I_{DS}(\mathrm{sat})$ and $V_{DS}(\mathrm{sat})$ obtained from the accurate expressions of Problem 12.22 to those obtained from eq. (12.22) for the numerical values given in Problem 12.23 and $W/L = 10$, $\bar{\mu} = 600$ cm^2/vs with $V_{sub} = 0$. Notice that the accurate expressions always yield smaller values, i.e., lower current and lower saturation voltage.

12.25 The gate oxide thickness of the device described in Problem 12.23 is scaled down by $k = 2$. By how much should V_{sub} be scaled in order to obtain $V'_T = V_T/2$ where V'_T is the scaled device threshold and V_T is the original threshold?

12.26 Find the range of hole charges, Q_h, that can be stored in a MOS capacitor (per unit area) if the substrate is N, doped with $N_D = 10^{15}$ cm^{-3}, the oxide thickness is 100 nm, the gate pulse voltage is $V_G = -10$ V and V_S should be at least -2 V. Assume $Q_{ox} = 5\times10^{10}q$ C cm^{-2} and that the gate metal is Al.

AMPLIFICATION AND SWITCHING: TRANSISTOR MODELS AND EQUIVALENT CIRCUITS 13

By now we have met the first active types of semiconductor devices capable of analog amplification or of acting as switches in digital circuits. Before continuing with more devices we should consider the operation of a single amplifying stage to see how best to define the device parameters and build a model that will help us in the complete circuit analysis. Such an analysis is essential to find the amplifier frequency response, the time-domain response to some input function, the effect of the amplifier on the signal source or the way it is affected by the load. In digital circuits the active devices are used as controlled current switches. A model must be developed for such a switch so that we can calculate switching speeds or power used. Now that we know at least one active device, the FET, it is possible to do this.

13.1 The Meaning of Amplification

A device capable of amplification is a device that can convert power obtained from a power supply (usually a d.c. source) to power at the input signal frequency. The device input port (like the gate of a FET) is connected to the signal source which produces the signal as some low-amplitude, low-power time function. The device delivers the same signal, at higher amplitude and power level, to a load connected to its output port. It is possible to obtain voltage, current or power amplification. Power amplification is always obtained with an efficiency of less than one, i.e., the d.c. power supplied to the device is always larger than the signal power at the output. The difference is dissipated in the amplifying device in the form of heat.

One of the limitations of any device is the maximum power it can dissipate safely: this must be got rid of by convection to the outside ambient at a sufficient rate to keep its internal temperature below some specified maximum. Practically all the higher-power semiconductor devices are limited by the maximum junction temperature and so are assembled on some kind of a metal heat sink which assists the transfer of the dissipated heat to the outside.

Usually the amplified signal is required to be a faithful copy of the input time function. Otherwise we say that it is *distorted*. No distortion occurs if the input and output of the device are linearly related. Complete linearity, however, is never found in a real device, but it is possible to assume linear characteristics around some operating point, provided the signal is small enough. Thus, even in the MOS transistor case, where (12.25) predicts a quadratic relationship between I_{DS} and V_{GS}, we get for very small gate voltage change $dV_{GS} = v_{gs} =$ the signal:

$$dI_{DS} = \left.\frac{\partial I_{DS}}{\partial V_{GS}}\right|_{V_{DS}=\text{constant}} dV_{GS} = g_m v_{gs} \tag{13.1}$$

i.e., we obtained a linear relationship between the output current change and the input voltage change.

In this chapter we shall examine both the small signal and the large signal (switching) cases. The transistors we shall meet, have three terminals. Their basic small signal amplifying circuit is constructed as shown in Fig. 13.1(a), where T is the device.

A d.c. power supply feeds current to the device through a series load resistor R_L, connected to the output terminal 3. The input is applied at terminal 2 as a time-dependent voltage or current signal of low amplitude. The amplifying capability of T is its ability to control the load current I_L by the signal, forcing it to change with the signal. The load current I_L, through R_L, will then contain a d.c. component I_{dc}, and an a.c. component i_{ac} which follows the signal. As the power supply keeps its constant d.c. voltage output even though the current taken from it is varying, it can be concluded that it presents a zero impedance to the a.c. current component. As far as i_{ac} is concerned, point A in the figure is shorted to ground. An a.c. voltage $i_{ac}R_L$ will therefore develop across the load R_L, i.e., between point B and ground. This is the amplified output.

One can, of course, ask: why would the signal output power, fed into R_L (i.e., $i_{ac}^2 R_L$), be higher than the signal input power fed at terminal 2? The answer to that is found in the structure of the amplifying device T. In each such a device the power supply voltage creates a high-field region in the current path, as shown in Fig. 13.1(b). In a FET this would be the pinched-off region. The input terminal 2, on the other hand, is connected to a region of high sensitivity, where the relatively weak field of the signal can control a large current. In a FET

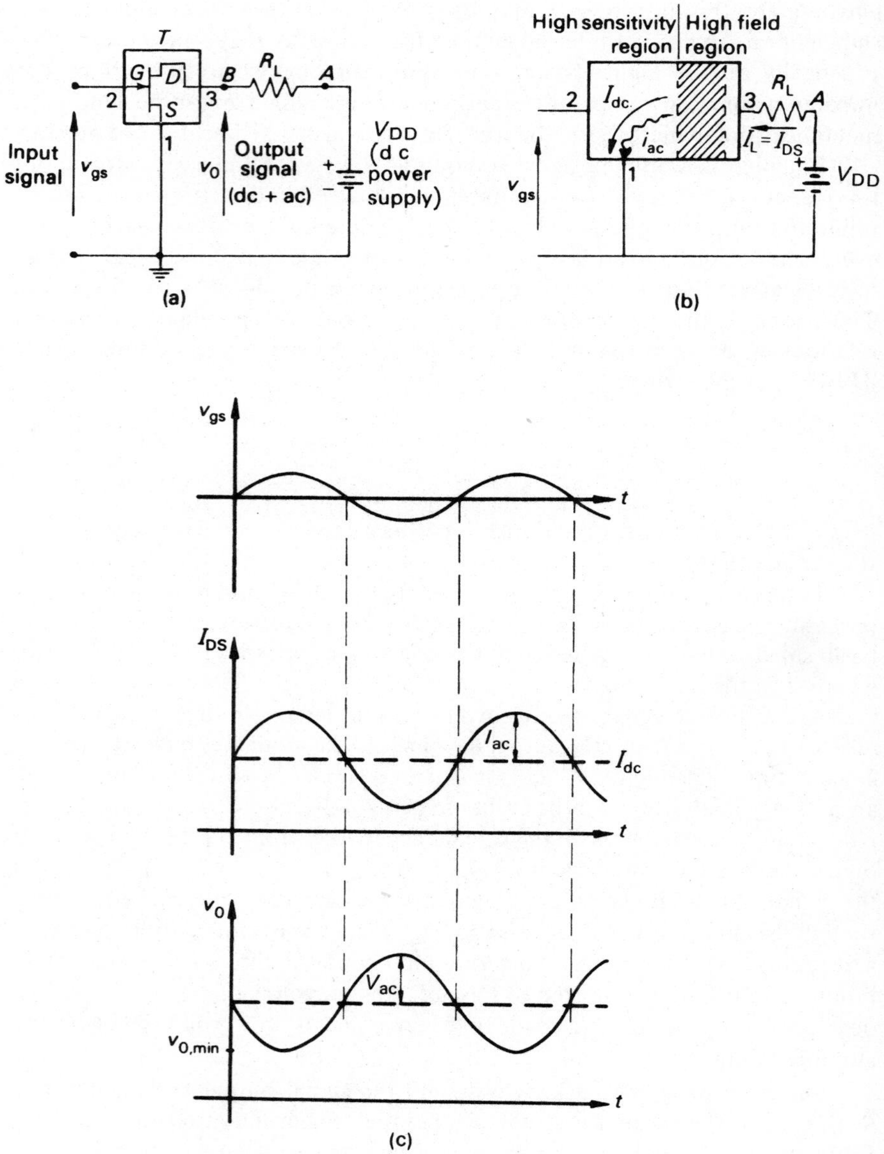

Figure 13.1. An amplifier stage based on device T (e.g. FET): (a) the circuit; (b) the energy conversion region inside the device; (c) input signal v_{gs}, device current I_{DS} and high field region voltage V_0.

the gate voltage controls the voltage drop along the channel from source to pinch-off point, which is $V_{GS}-V_T$. Since the channel resistance is very low, a small change in V_{GS} results in a large current change.

In bipolar transistors the input impedance is low, so again a small input voltage change would result in a high current change. The current carriers taking I_{dc} and i_{ac} must pass the high field region and are quickly accelerated to their saturation velocity in the semiconductor. Thus, they acquire kinetic energy from the power supply. The a.c. current component passing through R_L causes voltage fluctuations across it, and therefore across the high field region in T, as seen in Fig. 13.1(c). But if the power supply voltage is high enough, the voltage across T would still be sufficient to cause velocity saturation even at its minimum swing point $V_{0,\min}$. Thus the output voltage fluctuations across R_L and T have very little effect on i_{ac}, determined in the high-sensitivity region by the input, even if R_L is high. The a.c. signal input power into the FET will be

$$\tilde{P}_{in}=\frac{[\Delta(V_{GS}-V_T)]^2}{r_{ch}}=\frac{(\Delta V_{GS})^2}{r_{ch}}=\frac{v_{gs}^2}{r_{ch}}=g_m v_{gs}^2,$$

where r_{ch} is the source-to-pinch-off-point channel resistance,equal to g_m^{-1} (Problem 12.14). The output signal power is

$$\tilde{P}_{out}=i_{ac}^2 R_L=(g_m v_{gs})^2 R_L,$$

which gives a power amplification of

$$G=\frac{\tilde{P}_{out}}{\tilde{P}_{in}}=g_m R_L.$$

It should be noted that i_{ac} is generated inside the device T and *not* in the power supply. The high-field region is where energy conversion takes place: from the d.c. power to carrier kinetic energy and from this to a.c. output power. The i_{ac} and v_{ac} components are in antiphase across the high field region, as can be seen from Fig. 13.1(c), indicating that this is where the a.c. output signal power is generated.

The d.c. current and voltage components determine the d.c. power taken by the device. Subtracting $i_{ac}^2 R_L$ (which the device supplies to R_L) gives the power dissipated by the device as heat.

13.2 A Basic Amplifying-stage Circuit

The familiar N channel JFET can be connected as a basic amplifying stage in the circuit shown in Fig. 13.2(a). A bias voltage source, V_{BB}, is connected to the gate in series with the signal source, to insure that the device operates in the desired region of the characteristics (e.g., to make sure that the gate junction is always reverse biased). This is the simplest way to connect a bias source, but we shall shortly see that it can also be done without a separate power supply.

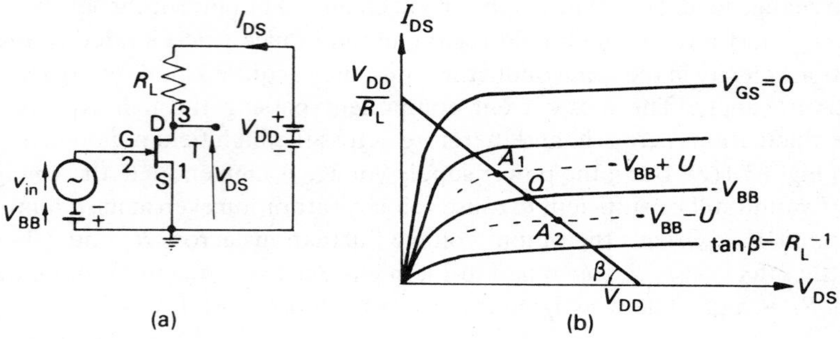

Figure 13.2. An elementary JFET amplifying stage: (a) the circuit; (b) the characteristics of the amplifying device.

A typical set of output characteristics for the transistor T is given in Fig. 13.2(b). The first step in our analysis is to find the d.c. *operating point*, also called the *quiescent point*, Q, in which T operates when the input signal v_{in} is zero.

From Kirchhoff's voltage law, applied to the output circuit loop:

$$V_{DD} = I_{DS}R_L + V_{DS}. \tag{13.2}$$

This is the *load-line* equation. In the I_{DS}–V_{DS} coordinates of Fig. 13.2(b) it represents a straight line, passing through the points ($V_{DS} = V_{DD}$, $I_{DS} = 0$) and ($V_{DS} = 0$, $I_{DS} = V_{DD}/R_L$), with a slope of $-1/R_L$. At the operating point Q both (13.2) and the relevant transistor characteristic curve must be satisfied. Therefore Q is given by the intersection of the load line and the curve $V_{GS} = V_{BB}$, which is the relevant device characteristic for the circuit of Fig. 13.2(b). When the input signal, $v_{in} = U \sin \omega t$ is applied, V_{GS} varies periodically between $V_{BB} + U$ and $V_{BB} - U$, i.e., between points A_1 and A_2 on the load line (whose equation must be satisfied at any instant). Once the d.c. operating point has been determined, the transistor parameters, representing the linearized characteristics in that vicinity, can be found, either from the manufacturer's data or from direct measurements.

In the case of Fig. 13.2(b) the amplified signal amplitude is just the change in V_{DS} between points Q and A_1 or Q and A_2.

A more practical circuit for the basic amplifying stage is shown in Fig. 13.3 and we shall use it as the example for obtaining the model and performing the analysis. The bias here is supplied automatically by the d.c. component of the transistor current flowing through R_3. The capacitors C_1 and C_2 are so chosen that they represent effective short circuits to the a.c. current component in the relevant signal frequency range ($1/\omega C_1 \ll R_3$; $1/\omega C_2 \ll R_2$).

We must now distinguish between the d.c. circuit necessary for finding Q, in which the capacitors act as open circuits, and the a.c. circuit for finding the amplification (in which both capacitors and power supplies represent short circuits).

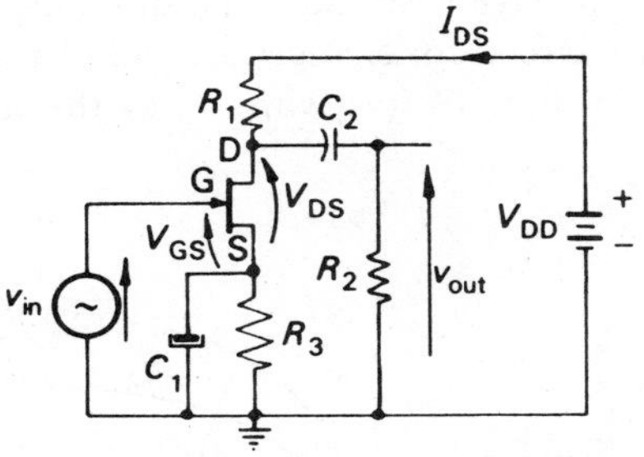

Figure 13.3. A more practical circuit for JFET amplifying stage with self bias:
$V_{DD}=20$ V, $R_2=50$ kΩ, $C_1=40\ \mu$F
$R_1=2.2$ kΩ, $R_3=390\ \Omega$, $C_2=0.25\ \mu$F.

The d.c. circuit is presented in Fig. 13.4(a). To find Q we must write the static (d.c.) load-line equation. From the d.c. circuit,

$$V_{DD}=I_{DS}(R_1+R_3)+V_{DS}. \tag{13.3}$$

Figure 13.4. The d.c. circuit of Fig. 13.3: (a) the d.c. circuit, $v_{in}=0$; (b) finding the quiescent point Q.

This is the dashed straight line in Fig. 13.4(b) and has a slope of $-(R_1+R_3)^{-1}$. The relevant characteristic is determined by the input circuit of Fig. 13.4(a):

$$V_{GS}=-I_{DS}R_3. \tag{13.4}$$

This is also entered in Fig. 13.4(b) as the second dashed curve, relating values of V_{GS} to I_{DS}. The intersection gives Q, whose coordinates represent the d.c. current and voltage across the transistor.

(It is also possible to construct a set of I_{DS}–V_{GS} characteristics, with V_{DS} a parameter, in which (13.4) is a straight line, and find Q by its intersection with the load line curve).

To analyze the a.c. behavior we must first draw the effective a.c. circuit, which represents the real circuit for changes around Q at the signal frequency. This circuit is shown in Fig. 13.5(a) with v_{in} as the input and v_{out} as the amplified output.

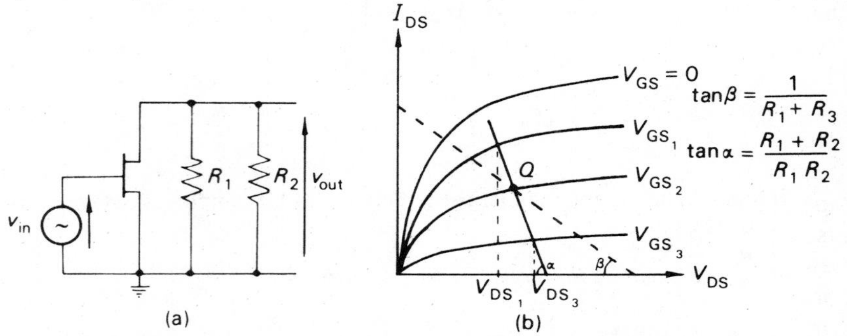

Figure 13.5. The a.c. circuit of Fig. 13.3: (a) the effective circuit at the signal frequency; (b) the static (dashed) and dynamic (full) load lines.

Because of the shorting effect of C_1, the input is effectively connected between gate and source and the signal causes the operating point to oscillate around Q. This time, however, the oscillations are not along the static load line (13.3), since as Fig. 13.5(a) tells us, the a.c. load resistance is the parallel connection of R_1 and R_2 and not the series connection of R_1 and R_3 as in the d.c. case. We therefore draw a new load line through Q, called the dynamic load line, which is relevant only for the frequency range at which the a.c. circuit of Fig. 13.5(a) holds. The dynamic line slope is $-[R_1R_2/(R_1+R_2)]^{-1}$.

Were we to connect v_{DS} to the x input of an oscilloscope and another voltage, proportional to i_{DS} (i.e., instantaneous values), to the y input, we would indeed obtain a straight line at angle α (provided the same overall amplification was used for each oscilloscope input). This measurement cannot be repeated in a static fashion. Once the frequency has been reduced, as when v_{in} is changed manually from one value to the next, we find that Q moves along the static load line at angle β.

Using Fig. 13.5(b) we can get a graphical answer for the amplification A:

$$A = \frac{v_{out}}{v_{in}} = \frac{V_{DS_1} - V_{DS_3}}{V_{GS_1} - V_{GS_3}}. \tag{13.5}$$

It should be noted that A is a negative number, i.e., v_{out} and v_{in} are in antiphase: when v_{in} becomes more positive, v_{out} becomes less so and vice versa (see also Fig. 13.1(c)).

13.3 The Small-signal Transistor Model

Graphical analysis using characteristics is needed only in power-amplifying stages where the input amplitude is already large enough for the characteristics of Fig. 13.5(b) to be useful. As can be seen, the curve of V_{GS1} is not exactly parallel to that of V_{GS3} and the distances from Q to V_{GS3} and V_{GS1} along the dynamic load line are not exactly equal. This means that for an input v_{in} that is a pure sine wave, the output v_{out} will be distorted, i.e., contain harmonics. This is called *nonlinear distortion.* Graphical work with the characteristics must then be done if the exact output shape and distortion are required. Another way is to express the characteristics analytically (e.g., eq. 12.25), or by tables of coordinate points, and use special nonlinear computer programs. This falls outside the scope of this book, which is not a textbook on circuit analysis, and we shall limit ourselves to the small-signal case, when v_{in} is just a fraction of a volt, sometimes a few millivolts or even microvolts. It is impractical then to use a graphical approach as the characteristics cannot be distinguished if the steps between them become too small. It is much more practical to describe the device by a linear equivalent circuit, or model, determine its parameters and then go on to perform a computerized (or manual) analysis, using known linear network theory. Linearization is possible, since for very small signals the characteristics may be taken as linear, parallel and equidistant in the close vicinity of Q. There is also no basic difficulty in including the effects of the capacitors in the linear network, if the frequency range is such that open- or short-circuit approximations are no longer valid.

It should be stressed again that we require our model to represent the device only in the vicinity of the quiescent point Q, which must first be found by a graphical method (as shown) or by nonlinear computer techniques. The model parameters will usually be functions of the position of Q.

Let us now look at the enlarged vicinity of Q in the characteristics shown in Fig. 13.6(a) and (b). The first may represent a JFET, MOST or vacuum tube, which are all controlled by the input voltage which is represented by variations of V_{GS}. The second set of characteristics represents the bipolar transistor case, covered in the next chapters, which is current controlled. We shall develop the models for both cases.

The input signal amplitude is either v_{in} (in a FET) or i_{in} (in a bipolar transistor). $\overline{QA}$ is a section of the dynamic load line which makes an angle α (see Fig. 13.5) with the negative voltage axis. For a small signal the characteristics can be taken as parallel straight lines, equidistant for constant input steps. They are inclined at an angle γ to the positive V axis. This angle is related to the output conductance g_0 defined by (12.13):

$$g_0 = \tan \gamma = \left.\frac{\partial I}{\partial V_{GS}}\right|_{V_{GS} \text{ or } I_B = \text{constant}} . \tag{13.6}$$

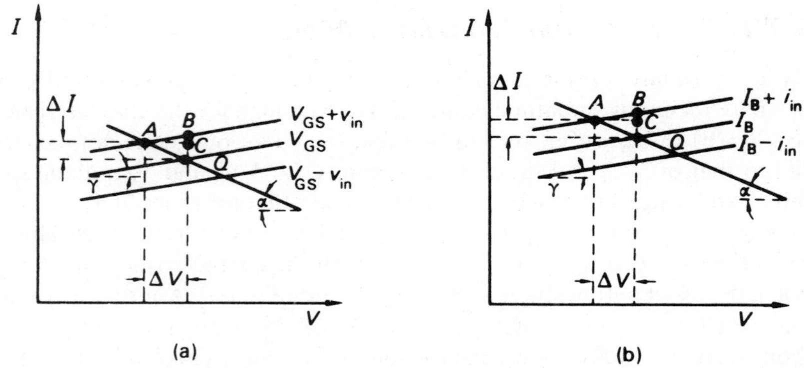

Figure 13.6. Enlarged section of the characteristics and dynamic load line around Q: (a) typical characteristics of JFET, MOST or vacuum tube; (b) typical characteristics of a bipolar transistor.

For the case of Fig. 13.6(a) we shall also need the transconductance g_m defined in (12.11), which, in terms of our characteristics, is

$$g_m = \left.\frac{\partial I}{\partial V_{GS}}\right|_{V = \text{constant}} . \tag{13.7}$$

In the case of Fig. 13.6(b) we can similarly define a forward current gain β:

$$\beta = \left.\frac{\partial I}{\partial I_B}\right|_{V = \text{constant}} . \tag{13.8}$$

From inspection of Fig. 13.6 it can be seen that g_m or β measure the vertical distance (V=constant) between neighboring characteristics:

$$g_m = \frac{\overline{QB}}{v_{in}}, \qquad (v_{in} = \Delta V_{GS}),$$

$$\beta = \frac{\overline{QB}}{i_{in}}, \qquad (i_{in} = \Delta I_B).$$

When fed by the signal, the amplifying devices produce an output current change, ΔI, associated with a voltage change ΔV in the external circuit. From the triangle ABC in Fig. 13.6(a),

$$\Delta I = \overline{QB} - \overline{BC} = g_m v_{in} - \Delta V \tan \gamma = g_m v_{in} - g_0 \Delta V. \tag{13.9}$$

This equation describes the output part of the device model shown in Fig. 13.7(a), for which the same relations, (13.9), hold. Similarly, in the bipolar

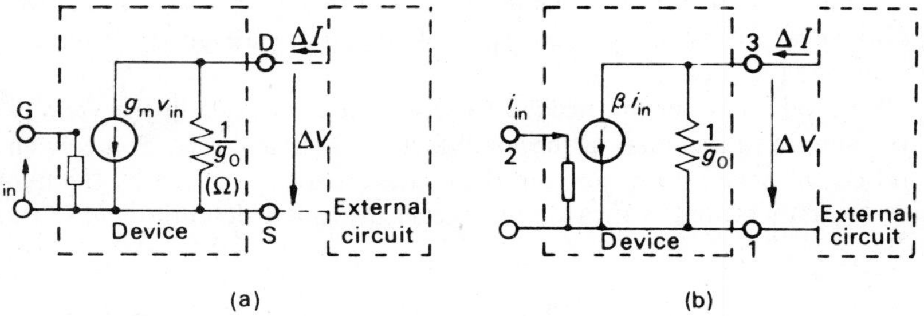

Figure 13.7. The output part of the small signal device model: (a) for devices whose characteristics are given by Fig. 13.6(a); (b) for the bipolar transistor whose characteristics are given by Fig. 13.6(b).

case with β and i_{in} replacing g_m and v_{in} in (13.9), the partial model will be that of Fig. 13.7(b). If the external load connected to the device output has the admittance $y_L = \Delta I/\Delta V$, then, on substituting y_L into (13.9), the output voltage can be expessed as

(13.10) $$v_{out} = -\Delta V = -v_{in}\frac{g_m}{g_0 + y_L},$$

from which the stage amplification can be immediately obtained. The models of Fig. 13.7 are not complete. We started from the device output characteristics which do not include information regarding its input behavior. In the MOST case, for example, we already know that between the gate G and source S there exists a capacitance C_{gs} equal to two thirds of the oxide gate capacitance (Problem 12.20). A similar input capacitance exists in the JFET or vacuum-tube cases and should replace the empty rectangle in Fig. 13.7(a) (the bipolar case will be treated in the next chapters). Additional interelectrode parasitic capacitances may also appear in the model. Thus production tolerances on the MOST gate metallization result in that metallization covering a little of the drain area, adding C_{gd}. The reverse-bias drain-to-substrate junction must also be represented by its voltage-dependent junction capacitance C_{ds}. The resulting MOST model (appropriate for the JFET and vacuum tube too) is shown in Fig. 13.8. For more exact modelling, which is necessary in computer-aided IC design, the device parasitics of Fig. 12.13(b) should be included too.

An amplifying (or active) device model always includes an internal current (or voltage) source, controlled by that part of the signal voltage (or current) that is applied to the device input terminals. The internal source has an associated output conductance g_0 which in the FET case results from channel length modulation by the drain voltage (current sources with parallel conductance can be replaced by voltage sources with series resistance, according to well known network theorems).

In the model of Fig. 13.8 the input–output phase inversion is automatically taken care of by the respective polarity directions assigned the input and the controlled source.

The model parameters needed to represent the device in the vicinity of Q are sometimes included in the manufacturer's data sheets. Some, such as g_0 and g_m, may be estimated from the characteristics supplied by the manufacturer (or measured with a curve tracer) using the definitions (13.6) and (13.7).

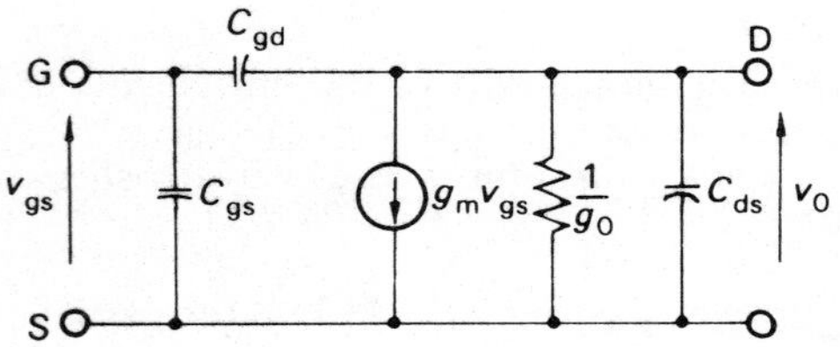

Figure 13.8. The MOS transistor small-signal model (source shorted to substrate).

All the parameters can also be computed from the knowledge of he physical parameters of the device, such as the material, geometry and doping profiles, provided Q is known. Thus g_m may be computed for the MOST using (12.26), C_{gs} may be found from the oxide thickness and area, and g_0 from channel shortening effect $L_{eff} = L - \Delta L$ (exact modelling necessitates solution of the field equations in the pinched-off region in two or three dimensions). We can measure g_0 from the output characteristic's slope.

To demonstrate the equivalent circuit construction and model parameter determination and use, we shall take as an example the Philips N channel JFET BF245B, connected as in the circuit of Fig. 13.3. The relevant components and power-supply values are given in the figure. The transistor characteristics are shown in Fig. 13.9.

The first step in the analysis is to draw the static load line (13.3) and the self-bias curve (13.4). Their intersection yields the quiescent point Q as

$$I_{DS} = 3.9 \text{ mA}, \qquad V_{DS} = 10 \text{ V}.$$

The self-bias resulting from the passage of I_{DS} through R_3 is $V_{GS} \simeq -1.5$ V.

The dynamic load line is now drawn (dashed straight line through Q) with a slope determined by $R_1 R_2/(R_1 + R_2) \simeq 2.1$ kΩ.

We are now ready to determine the transistor model parameters in the vicinity of Q. We obtain g_m from the vertical distance between two characteristics in Fig. 13.9, e.g., between points B and Q:

$$g_m = \left.\frac{\Delta I}{\Delta V_{GS}}\right|_{V_{DS}=\text{constant}} = \frac{(5.7-3.9)10^{-3}}{(-1)-(-1.5)} = 3.6 \text{ mmho}.$$

g_0 is obtained from the slope of the $V_{GS} = -1.5$ V characteristic at Q:

$$r_0 = \frac{1}{g_0} = \left.\frac{\Delta V_{DS}}{\Delta I_{DS}}\right|_{V_{GS}=\text{constant}} \simeq 40 \text{ k}\Omega.$$

The manufacturer's data sheets give the following capacitance values, at the operating point of $V_{DS} = 20$ V, $V_{GS} = -1.0$ V:

$$C_{gs} = 4 \text{ pF}, \qquad C_{gd} = 1.1 \text{ pF}, \qquad C_{ds} = 1.6 \text{ pF}.$$

These values must be corrected for our operating point, which is $V_{DS} = 10$ V, $V_{GS} = -1.5$ V. The correction factors can be estimated by assuming that all the JFET junctions behave like step junctions and their capacitances change with voltage according to the step-junction law (9.52):

$$C(V) = \frac{C(0)}{(1+V/V_B)^{1/2}},$$

where V is the magnitude of the reverse voltage and V_B is the junction diffusion voltage (about 0.7 V in Si). Thus

$$\frac{C_{gs}(-1.5)}{C_{gs}(-1.0)} = \left[\frac{1+1.0/0.7}{1+1.5/0.7}\right]^{1/2} = 0.88 \qquad \text{or} \qquad C_{gs}(-1.5) \simeq 3.5 \text{ pF}.$$

Similarly $C_{gd}(-10) \simeq 1.5$ pF, $C_{ds}(-10) \simeq 2.2$ pF.

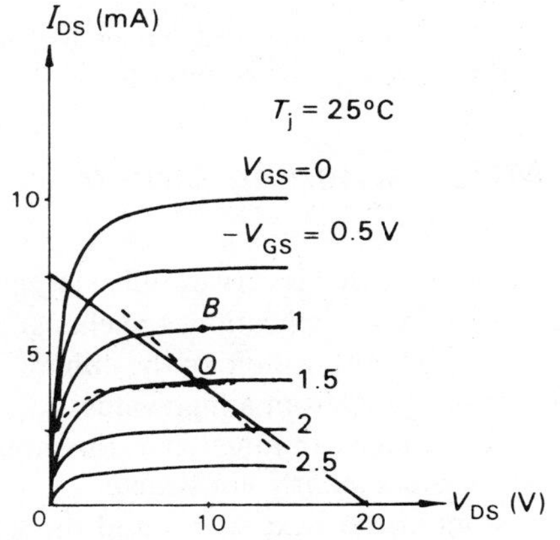

Figure 13.9. Finding the operating point Q for transistor BF245B in the circuit of Fig. 13.3.

The complete small-signal equivalent circuit of the transistor and the amplifying stage is shown in Fig. 13.10. Only the power supply, represented by a short circuit, has disappeared. Nodes *G*, *D*, *S* are the respective transistor model terminals. This circuit can be used to calculate the circuit properties up to very high frequencies, so long as we are dealing with small signals. If a linear network computer program is available, we have only to number the nodes and supply the values of the components as the program data (remembering that $g_m v_{gs}$ is a current source controlled by the voltage between nodes *G* and *S*). We can then ask for the computation of the desired network function, such as the voltage transfer ratio v_{out}/v_{in} or the input and output impedances. Such computation can be done at a single frequency or for a range of frequencies. We can also ask for the time response to a step function (provided it is a small step, otherwise parameter variation with the operating point must be included and a nonlinear circuit program needed). We can also look for the effects of a change in some circuit component, like the effect of changing C_1 on the frequency response or include the device parasitics like source and drain series resistances.

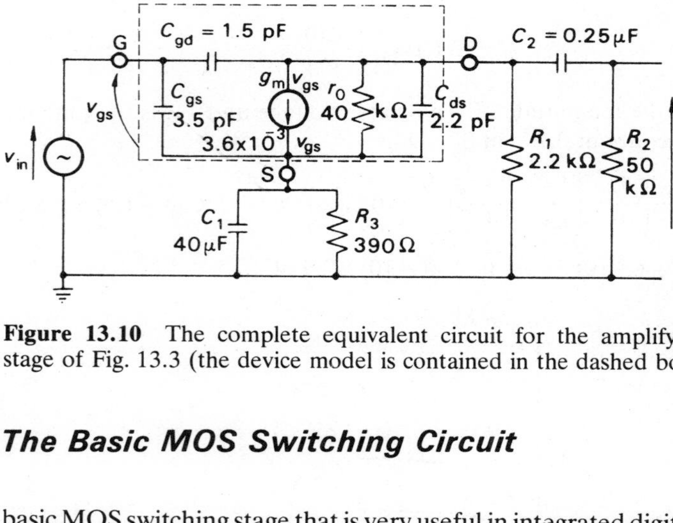

Figure 13.10 The complete equivalent circuit for the amplifying stage of Fig. 13.3 (the device model is contained in the dashed box).

13.4 The Basic MOS Switching Circuit

A basic MOS switching stage that is very useful in integrated digital circuits, is shown in Fig. 13.11(a). For logic applications the change in the input v_i from $v_i < V_{T1}$ to $v_i > V_{T1}$, where V_{T1} is the threshold of the enhancement transistor Q_1, should switch the output voltage v_o from a high value $v_{oH} > V_{T1}$ to a low value $V_{oH} < V_{T1}$. Thus this output voltage can function as the input that would switch the next logic stages which are similarly constructed.

The gates of transistors in the next stages and the connections to them combine with the drain junction capacitance of Q_1 to give a total capacitance C_o as indicated on Fig. 13.11(a). C_o must be charged or discharged for v_o to change.

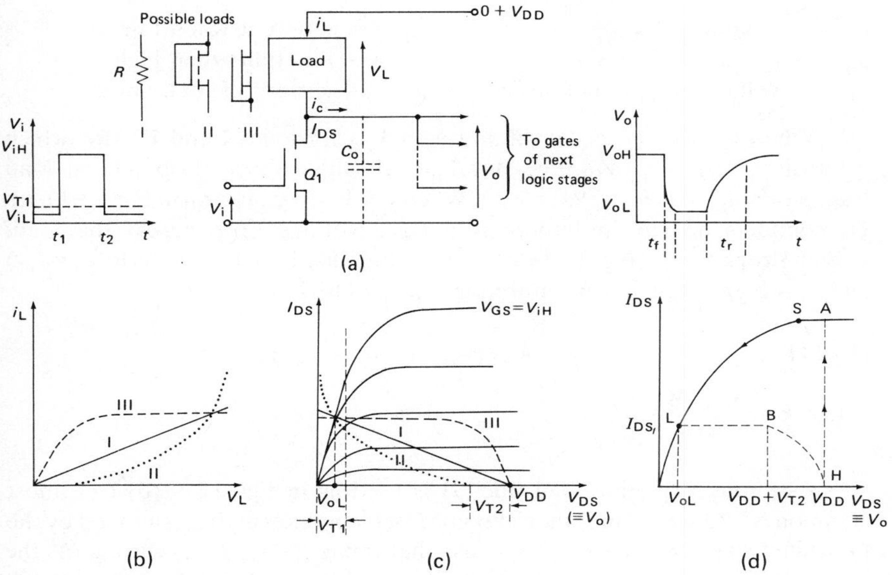

Figure 13.11 The basic MOS switching circuit (inverter): (a) the circuit with its input and output voltages; (b) three possible characteristics for a load device: I – ohmic; II – enhancement MOS with $V_{GS} = V_{DS}$; III – depletion MOS with $G_{GS} = 0$; (c) the three load characteristics as load lines for Q_1; (d) NMOS inverter switching path.

The question that arises is what load device to choose for fastest switching. Three possible loads with their current–voltage characteristics are indicated in Fig. 13.11(b). Curve I represents an ohmic resistor (we shall later see that such a load is unrealistic for integrated circuits). Curve II represents current–voltage relation of an enhancement transistor (similar to Q_1 but with different dimensions) with its gate permanently shorted to its drain, i.e., $V_{GS} = V_{DS}$. This characteristic was indicated by a dotted line in Fig. 12.12(b). Such a load is the easiest and cheapest to include in an IC and has been used a lot in P-channel metal gate ICs in the past. As we shall see it suffers from a slow v_o rise time, τ_r in Fig. 13.11(a). Curve III represents current–voltage relation for a depletion transistor used as load with its gate permanently shorted to its source ($V_{GS} = 0$) (such $V_{GS} = 0$ characteristic was indicated in Fig. 12.12(a)). Use of such a load requires positive V_{T1} for Q_1 and negative V_{T2} for the load (for N channels). This can be controllably managed in ICs today by ion implantation. The three load lines are superimposed on the characteristics of Q_1 in Fig. 13.11(c). Let us now consider separately the static operating points for the two values of v_i and the dynamic switching between them. We shall use the following nomenclature (refer to Fig. 13.11):

v_{iL}	→ v input when low	v_{oL}	→ v output when low
v_{iH}	→ v input when high	v_{oH}	→ v output when high
v_L	→ voltage across load device	i_L	→ current of load device

When $v_i < V_{T1}$, Q_1 is cut off and $v_{oH} = V_{DD}$ for loads I and III (for which $v_L = 0$ at $i_L = 0$). $v_{oH} = V_{DD} - V_{T2}$ for load II (the voltage drop on the load transistor at $i_L = 0$ is $V_{DS} = V_{GS} = V_{T2}$). When $v_i > V_{T1}$, e.g., $v_i = v_{iH}$ in Fig. 13.11(a), Q_1 conducts heavily and there is a large voltage drop across the load. v_o then drops to v_{oL} (Fig. 13.11(c)) for all three loads. When v_{DS} is low ($= v_{oL}$) and v_i is high, Q_1 is not in saturation and by (12.22)

$$I_{DS1} = k_1[2(v_{iH} - V_{T1})v_{0L} - v_{0L}^2] \tag{13.11}$$

where $k_1 = \dfrac{C_{ox}\mu W_1}{2L_1}$.

Assuming depletion load line III is used as in Fig. 13.11(d) (the most common NMOS structure) then at point L, Q_1 conducts and v_{iH} (supplied by the preceding stage) equals $V_{DD} \gg V_{T1}$. At that point $v_o = v_{oL} \ll V_{T1}$ cutting off the following stage. Then $v_L = V_{DD} - v_{oL} \gg |V_{T2}|$ and the depletion load transistor is saturated:

$$i_L = k_2(0 - V_{T2})^2 = k_2 V_{T2}^2 \tag{13.12}$$

where $k_2 = \dfrac{C_{ox}\mu W_2}{2L_2}$.

Under static conditions $i_c = 0$ and $i_L = I_{DS1}$. With C_{ox} and μ the same for both transistors, we get from (13.11) and (13.12):

$$\frac{k_2}{k_1} = \frac{W_2/L_2}{W_1/L_1} = \frac{1}{V_{T2}^2}[2(V_{DD} - V_{T1})v_{oL} - v_{oL}^2] \tag{13.13}$$

The required ratio of W/L for the two transistors is now known for specified values of v_{oL} and V_{DD} for a given technology (i.e., known values of V_{T1} and V_{T2}). At point H, Q_1 is cut off ($v_{iL} = v_{oL} \ll V_{T1}$ from the preceding stage) and the output is high $v_{oH} = V_{DD}$. It is clear that the output of our circuit is low when its input is high and vice versa. The circuit is therefore called an *inverter* and is the basic building block of most digital circuits.

The Dynamic Switching Process

The load lines of Fig. 13.11(c) show how the operating point of Q_1 shifts with v_i but do not give information about switching speeds. This question shall be considered now for the NMOS enhancement–depletion inverter whose characteristic is shown in Fig. 13.11(d).

Down switching: During this period the operating point follows the path H→A→S→L and C_o discharges through Q_1 which carries both the discharge current i_c and the load current i_L:

$$I_{DS}(Q_1) = i_L - i_c = i_L - C_o \frac{dv_o}{dt}$$

$i_L = F(v_L) = F(V_{DD} - v_o)$ where F represents the load characteristic $I-V$ relation.

Throughout this switching i_L is much smaller than i_c and can be neglected.

At point A, $V_{DS}(Q_1) = V_{DD} > V_{GS}(Q_1) - V_{T1} = V_{DD} - V_{T1}$ and Q_1 is saturated, giving

$$k_1(V_{DD} - V_{T1})^2 \simeq -C_o \frac{dv_o}{dt};\quad V_{DD} - V_{T1} \leq v_o \leq V_{DD}.$$

Therefore,

$$\tau_1 = t(S) - t(A) = \frac{C_o}{k_1(V_{DD} - V_{T1})^2} V_{T1}.$$

At point S, $v_o = V_{DD} - V_{T1}$ and Q_1 becomes unsaturated. $v_o(t)$ will then be the solution of

$$-C_o \frac{dv_o}{dt} \simeq k_1[2(V_{DD} - V_{T1})v_o - v_o^2].$$

Solving for v_o by separation of variables with the initial condition $v_o = V_{DD} - V_{T1}$ at $t = 0$ (t is now measured from $t(S)$) gives

$$(13.14)\quad t = \frac{C_0}{2k_1(V_{DD} - V_{T1})} \ln \frac{2(V_{DD} - V_{T1}) - v_o}{v_o};\quad v_{oL} \leq v_o \leq V_{DD} - V_{T1}.$$

Substituting $v_o = v_{oL}$ gives $t(L) - t(S)$. The fall time τ_f is approximately $\tau_1 + t(10\%)$ where $t(10\%)$ is the value given by (13.14) for $v_o = 0.1 V_{DD}$.

We see that the down switching speed depends primarily on Q_1 which is therefore called the *pull down* transistor.

Upward switching = At time t_2, Q_1 is cut off and i_L charges C_o. v_o follows the path L→B→H in Fig. 13.11(d).

$$(13.15)\quad v_o(t) = v_{oL} + \frac{1}{C_o} \int_{t_2}^{t_2+t} i_L dt;\quad i_L = F(v_L) = F(V_{DD} - v_o(t)).$$

Obviously, the fastest switching would occur for a load which provides the highest i_L for any v_L. In fact a current source would be best. Examination of Fig. 13.11(b) shows clearly that the depletion load transistor III that resembles a current source will be the fastest, an enhancement type load II will be the slowest and a resistive load I will be in between. A resistive load, however, is ruled out since I_{DS} in a dense IC should be the smallest possible (to reduce heat dissipation) and may be of the order of 10 μA while V_{DD} may be 5 V. An ohmic resistance of half a megaohm is therefore needed which cannot be made by compatible IC technology. Let us then concentrate on the depletion load III that has replaced the enhancement load in present day N channel MOS IC technology (NMOS).

To solve (13.15) one must use different expressions for i_L for saturation (between L and B in Fig. 13.11(d)) and nonsaturation (between B and H):

$$i_L = k_2(-V_{T2})^2 \qquad \text{for } V_{DS}(\text{load}) = v_L = V_{DD} - v_o > 0 - V_{T2}, \text{ i.e., } v_o < V_{DD} + V_{T2}$$

$$i_L = k_2[2(-V_{T2})(V_{DD} - v_o) - (V_{DD} - v_o)^2] \quad \text{for } v_o > V_{DD} + V_{T2} \ (\textit{remember}: V_{T2} < 0).$$

Since the load transistor controls the speed of upward switching, it is called the *pull up* transistor.

Solving (13.15) by considering the derivative dv_o/dt and substituting the saturation value of i_L, one obtains (with t now measured from t_2):

$$t = \frac{C_o}{k_2 V_{T2}^2}(v_o - v_{oL}) \qquad \text{for } v_o \leq V_{DD} + V_{T2} \text{ (between points L and B).}$$

Point B is reached at $t = \tau_1$, $v_o = V_{DD} + V_{T2}$ and the load transistor comes out of saturation. Substituting the unsaturated expression of i_L and solving (13.15) again:

$$t = \tau_1 + \frac{C_o}{2k_2(-V_{T2})} \ln \frac{v_o - (V_{DD} + 2V_{T2})}{V_{DD} - v_o} \qquad \text{for } v_o \geq V_{DD} + V_{T2} \quad \text{(between points B and H).}$$

Defining risetime τ_r as the time needed for v_o to reach 90% of its final value (0.9 V_{DD}) we get

$$\tau_r = \frac{C_o}{k_2}\left[\frac{V_{DD} + V_{T2} - v_{oL}}{V_{T2}^2} - \frac{1}{2V_{T2}} \ln \frac{-2V_{T2} - 0.1V_{DD}}{0.1V_{DD}}\right]. \tag{13.16}$$

Thus for $C_o = 1$pF, $k_1 = 0.1$mA/V^2, $V_{T1} = 1.2$V, $V_{T2} = -1.5$V, $V_{DD} = 5$V, $v_{oL} = 0.2$V, then $k_2 = 0.066$mA/V^2 from (13.13) and $\tau_f = 4.3$ ns, $\tau_r = 30.4$ ns from (13.14) and (13.16), respectively.

For fast switching C_o must be kept to the minimum. C_o increases with the fan out (number of gates connected to our output node) which limits fan out for a given speed. Also note that there is a trade-off between faster switching speed and lower power dissipation: for a given C_o and V_{DD}, C_o will charge and discharge faster if currents are higher, i.e., the dissipation is higher.

QUESTIONS

13.1 What, in your opinion, are the possible effects that increasing the power supply voltage will have on the maximum value of R_L that can be used in Fig. 13.1 and on the resulting amplification?

13.2 Can you obtain current amplification if $R_L = 0$ in Fig. 13.1? Can you obtain power amplification under this condition?

13.3 Why should one determine the quiescent point Q before proceeding with the details of the small-signal model?

13.4 Estimate the maximum input signal amplitude for which one can still use a small-signal model, for the MOS transistor characteristics of Fig. 12.12(c), when the operating point is $V_{DS} = 10$ V, $I_{DS} = 10$ mA, and when $V_{DS} = 10$ V, $I_{DS} = 1$ mA.

13.5 Draw a load line for $R_L = 1$ kΩ through $Q(10\text{ V}, 10\text{ mA})$ in Fig. 12.12(c) and assume a sine-wave input of 3 V amplitude. Plot, point by point, the corresponding output current wave form using graphical technique and observe the distortion.

13.6 It is required to measure the a.c. amplitude of the output of the amplifier in Fig. 13.3 with a voltmeter. Are there any limitations on the voltmeter internal resistance?

13.7 Which of the two parameters, g_m and g_o, can be more easily and accurately estimated from the device characteristics of Fig. 13.9? Apply this to the problem of whether to prefer a voltage source with series resistance or a current source with parallel resistance for the transistor model in the usual case of $R_L \ll 1/g_o$.

13.8 Can you envisage a case in which the dynamic load line in a circuit such as Fig. 13.3 will have smaller slope than the static load line ($\alpha < \beta$ in Fig. 13.5)?

PROBLEMS

13.9 Use the characteristics of Fig. 13.9 and the dynamic load line in it to obtain the value of the amplification at the medium-frequency range graphically. Compare to the result obtained in Section 13.4.

13.10 A cross section of a MOST is shown in Fig. 13.12. The transistor is symmetrical (drain and source can be interchanged). Additional relevant data are as follows:

$W = 500\ \mu m$ (channel width)
$\bar{\mu}_h = 250\ cm^2\ V^{-1}\ s^{-1}$
$V_T = -2.5$ V
$t_{ox} = 90$ nm (gate oxide thickness)
$\varepsilon_{ox} = 3.85$.

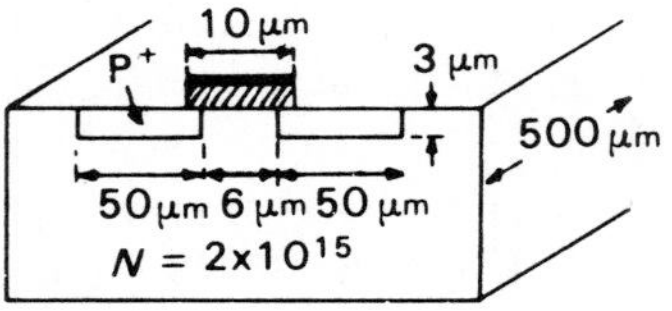

Figure 13.12 Cross section of the MOST in Problem 13.10.

Both drain and source can be assumed degenerate (P^+).

(a) Determine V_{GS} necessary to operate the transistor at a quiescent point of $I_{DS} = 2$ mA in the current-saturation region while using the minimum possible value of V_{DS}.

(b) Calculate the small-signal transistor model parameters (assume step junctions and $g_0 \simeq 0$).

13.11 Compare the risetimes of an NMOS inverter using two enhancement transistors with that of the same inverter but with the load MOST replaced by a resistor equal in value to dV_{DS}/dI_{DS} of the load MOST, operating with $V_{GS} = V_{DD} - V_T$.

13.12 The circuit of Fig. 13.13 is used as a buffer, enabling a small, low-current MOS inverter I to drive a relatively large load capacitance C without slowing down the switching operation too much. Calculate the rise time of the output voltage (0 to 90% of the final value) and fall time (to 10% of initial value) for the given circuit parameters.

Estimate the maximum frequency that can be used for an input square wave if the output must reach (or exceed) 3 V on the high side and be equal to or smaller than 0.5 V on the low side. Draw a sketch of the output voltage at that frequency.

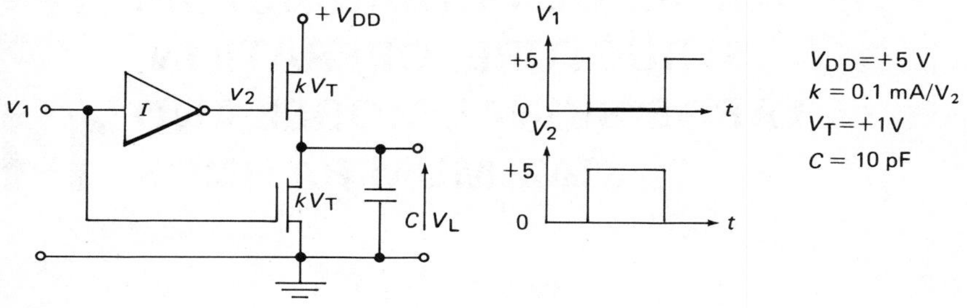

Figure 13.13 The circuit for Problem 13.12. (*I* is an ideal inverter.)

THE BIPOLAR TRANSISTOR: STRUCTURE, OPERATION, LARGE-SIGNAL MODEL AND MAXIMUM RATINGS 14

Bipolar transistors comprise the second family of active devices in use today. They exist both as discrete components and in integrated circuits, i.e., circuits made of many transistors, diodes and resistors, built and operated as single big devices.

The internal currents in a bipolar transistor are carried by both minority and majority carriers, depending on the device zone, hence the name.

In this chapter we shall first go over the physical structure of the bipolar transistor and its operating principles. We shall then develop the equations governing its characteristics and obtain its large-signal model with parameters depending on the operating point. This model will then be applied to analyzing transistor operation in the switching mode.

Finally, we shall discuss the maximum permissible current, voltage and power ratings of the transistor and their relations to its physical structure.

In Chapter 15 we shall discuss the small-signal model and frequency behavior of this transistor.

14.1 Bipolar Transistor Structure

A bipolar transistor is a three-zone structure with two parallel junctions very near each other, built in a single-crystal silicon (or Ge) wafer. The two possible three-zone structures, NPN and PNP, are shown in Fig. 14.1. Both are in use and their circuit symbol is included in the figure.

In the following we shall discuss the PNP transistor. The results will be applicable to the NPN as well provided all the voltage and current polarities are reversed.

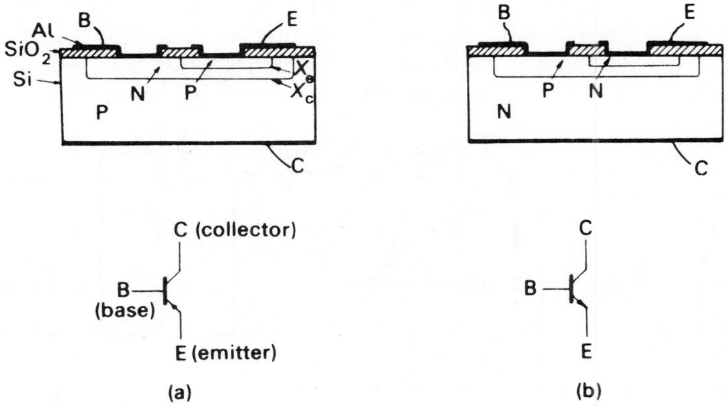

Figure 14.1. Cross section of a planar bipolar transistor: (a) PNP transistor and circuit symbol; (b) NPN transistor and circuit symbol.

The majority of transistors made today are of the Si *planar type* shown in Fig. 14.1. They are made by allowing N-type impurities to diffuse into a P-type Si substrate (for a PNP transistor) through an SiO_2 mask on the substrate surface. A hole in the mask determines the area into which the donor atoms penetrate the substrate at the high temperatures used for diffusion. The diffusion duration and temperature determine the depth (a few microns) of the region which will be thus converted into N-type. A second, shorter diffusion through a second mask, with a smaller hole, is now performed, this time with an acceptor-type impurity. This transforms back some of the N region into P, creating the PNP structure of Fig. 14.1(a). The impurity profile obtained after these two diffusion processes is shown in Fig. 14.2(a). The depths at which N_A equals N_D are X_c resulting from the first diffusion and X_e resulting from the second. These are the depths of the junctions. The net impurity profile $|N_A-N_D|$, also given in Fig. 14.2(a), shows that three distinct regions P, N and P, with two parallel and planar junctions, have been obtained, giving the cross section of Fig. 14.1(a). More details of the planar production process will be described in Chapter 16.

This process, developed in the late 1950s, has been a breakthrough in transistor technology. Before this, most transistors were made in Ge using the alloy-junction process (Section 8.1), in which the parallelism and the absolute distance between the two junctions could not be well controlled, in contrast to diffusion and even more so to modern ion-implant techniques. Alloying results in a step junction with approximately uniform doping on each side of the junction, as shown in Fig. 14.2(c). Notice the wider distance between the junctions which is necessary, in view of the poor control, to prevent accidental shorting. The figure contains typical doping densities (using a log scale) and junction depth values.

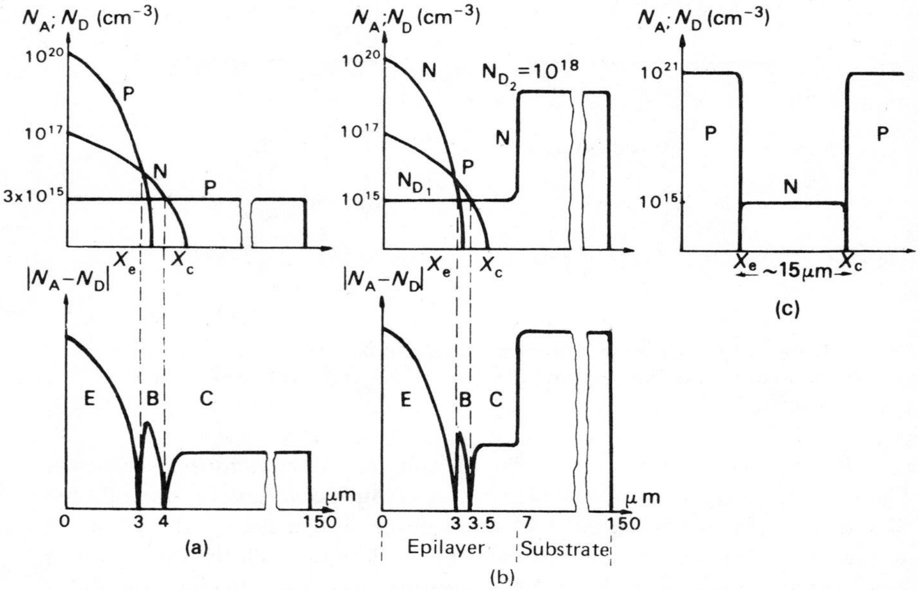

Figure 14.2. Impurity profile in three typical transistor types: (a) a planar PNP transistor obtained by two consecutive diffusions into a uniformly doped substrate; (b) planar epitaxial structure of an NPN transistor, obtained after two diffusions into N-type epitaxial layer (doping N_{D1}), first grown on low-resistivity N-type Si substrate (doping N_{D2}); (c) a PNP structure obtained by alloying.

In a more complicated structure the diffusions are done into a thin, high-resistivity epitaxial layer, first grown on a low-resistivity substrate (Chapter 16). This is called a *planar expitaxial transistor.* The impurity profile of such an NPN transistor is shown in Fig. 14.2(b). Its advantage lies in reducing the parasitic series resistance of the substrate (which takes most of the transistor volume and is necessary for mechanical strength) through which its current must flow, as we shall see.

The alloy junction and the planar transistors differ in their impurity profiles. Taking into account the varying profile of the planar types would rather complicate the resulting equations without contributing much to the physical understanding of transistor operation. We shall therefore analyze the alloy type assuming uniform doping density in each region. To simulate the planar transistor better we shall assume, however, that the emitter's doping is much higher than in the base which, in its turn, is higher than in the collector. This will give us all the important transistor properties. We shall later discuss the additional effects of the varying profile.

Referring to Fig. 14.1, the substrate is called a *collector* (C). The first diffusion creates an opposite impurity zone called the *base* (B). The second diffusion reconverts part of the base back to the substrate type, forming a zone called the *emitter* (E). Aluminum metal contacts are made to each transistor zone and these are later connected to three external terminals built into the transistor header on which the semiconductor chip is mounted during final encapsulation and sealing.

14.2 The Principles of Bipolar Transistor Operation

To understand how the transistor operates let us connect it to two power supplies, with the polarities indicated in Fig. 14.3. The junction at X_e, between emitter (E) and base (B), is forward biased by V_{EE} while that at X_c, between collector (C) and base (B), is reverse biased by V_{CC}. This is called a *common base* (CB) connection, and with such a bias the transistor is brought into its active zone where it operates as an amplifier (this is only one of several possible connections and operating zones).

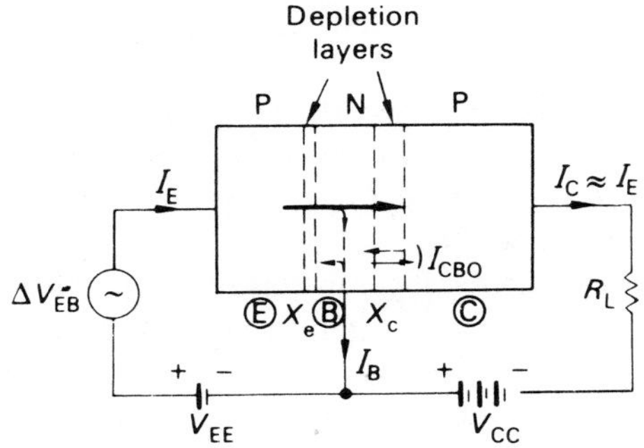

Figure 14.3. A PNP transistor biased for amplification in the common-base connection:
——> hole-flow direction;
------> electron-flow direction.

Because of the forward bias at X_e, carriers are injected across the junction. Since emitter doping is chosen to be much higher than that of the base (see Fig. 14.2) the injection will be mostly of holes, injected from the P emitter to the N base. The collector–base junction at X_c is reverse biased by V_{CC} and a depletion layer forms on both its sides. We would have expected that only an insignificant leakage current would flow through it, arising from the minority carriers arriving from each side and being swept across. This would indeed have been the case had the base been much wider than the diffusion length L_h of the injected holes. The *transistor effect* is a consequence of the base width being much narrower than L_h, a few percent at the most. In this case the injected minority holes diffuse across the base and upon reaching the edge of the depletion layer on the other side they are immediately swept across into the collector, adding to the normal minority leakage current marked I_{CBO} in Fig. 14.3.

Due to the base narrowness almost all the injected holes reach the collector junction before they have a chance to recombine with one of the base majority electrons. The few that do recombine account for one part of the small base current I_B in Fig. 14.3. The rest of I_B comes from electrons which leave the base by being injected into the emitter, across the forward-biased emitter junction. As already mentioned, the fact that $N_A \gg N_D$ insures that almost all the current through that junction is carried by holes flowing the other way. As a result the collector current I_C is only slightly smaller than the emitter current I_E, while I_B is about two orders of magnitude lower.

The diffusion of minority holes through the base is maintained by their large concentration gradient: They are injected in large quantities across the forward-biased emitter–base junction and are swept out by the reverse field across the collector–base junction, which acts as a sink for them. The high reverse field created by V_{CC} accelerates the holes to high velocities, thus raising considerably the impedance through which the current I_E can flow. In the input circuit I_E flows from the low-voltage supply, V_{EE}, through the low forward resistance of the emitter–base junction. Across the high-field collector junction the impedance level is raised so the current, now called I_C, can pass through a high load resistance R_L.

The collector–base depletion layer is thus the high-field region mentioned in Section 13.1, where energy is converted from the d.c. power supplied by V_{CC} to a.c. output signal power controlled by the input current change ΔI_E.

A change ΔV_{EB} in the emitter–base input circuit will cause a large change ΔI_E in I_E, exponentially related to V_{EB}. The power supplied to the forward-biased emitter junction, whose resistance is r_e (eq. 11.1), is $(\Delta I_E)^2 r_e$. ΔI_E approximately equals the collector current change ΔI_C that flows through R_L. The resulting a.c. power gain is

$$G = \frac{P_o}{P_i} = \frac{(\Delta I_C)^2 R_L}{(\Delta I_E)^2 r_e} \simeq \frac{R_L}{r_e}. \qquad (14.1)$$

For ΔI_E around $I_E = 1$ mA, r_e is about 25 Ω. If V_{CC} of 15 V is used with $R_L = 10$ kΩ, for example, G may reach a value of about 400.

From (14.1) it is clear that gain will be obtained only if ΔI_C is nearly equal to ΔI_E, i.e. recombination in the base must be minimized. In Si this means a base width of around 1 μm or less. In Ge, with longer minority diffusion length, the transistor effect will still be useful at base widths around 15 μm. If the base is much wider than the diffusion length, the device behaves like two diodes connected in opposite directions instead of like a transistor.

It was mentioned that with no base recombination and no reverse injection of electrons from base to emitter, I_B would be zero. But this is correct only for the static (d.c.) case. Any change in the total excess hole charge in the base, brought about by a change in the injected hole current, must be compensated by an equal negative electronic charge entering the base from the base terminal, so that base neutrality is maintained. When the transistor conducts, the base is thus 'charged' by equal numbers of excess holes and electrons, above the equilibrium values. In the static case holes keep flowing into and out of the base continuously. No new electrons enter the base, however, except to replenish the few that recombine or get injected into the emitter. I_E and I_C may therefore be high while I_B remains very small. The currents in Fig. 14.3 satisfy $I_E = I_C + I_B$. It is only when the excess base charge changes that both I_E and I_B change by the same amount to supply this charge.

This means that amplification can also be obtained if the signal is applied as base current, with the emitter acting as a terminal common to both input and output circuits.

In this common-emitter (CE) connection, shown in Fig. 14.4, a change of I_B causes the number of electrons in the base to change. The base becomes slightly more (or less) positive and hole injection from the emitter immediately follows suit (because of the change in V_{EB}) and returns the base neutrality. Since the ratio of ΔI_E to ΔI_B is maintained, ΔI_E and ΔI_C are much larger than ΔI_B and current amplification results. The CE connection of Fig. 14.4 gives power amplification too and, as we shall see, is more useful than the CB connection because of a more convenient ratio of input to output impedances.

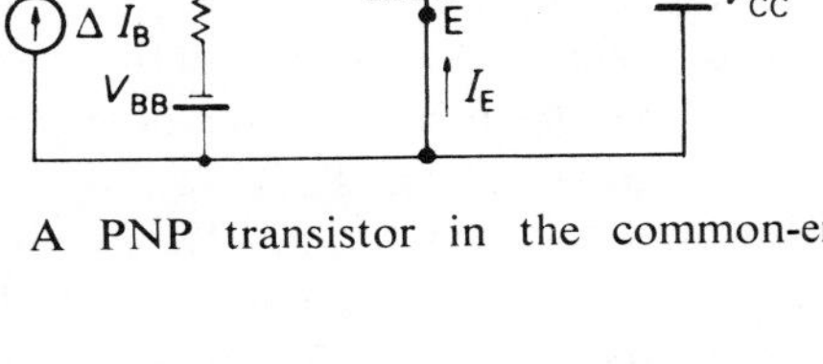

Figure 14.4. A PNP transistor in the common-emitter (CE) connection.

Our discussion attributed minority movement through the base to diffusion only. This is strictly correct for the uniform base doping of Fig.

14.2(c) only. Such a transistor is sometimes referred to as *diffusion transistor* (though it is made by alloying and not diffusion). In the planar transistor, (Fig. 14.2(a) and (b)) there is a doping density gradient in the base resulting in a built-in field in the base (Problem 14.13). The injected minority carriers are then helped by this field in their movement towards the collector and their current then contains both drift and diffusion components. Such transistors are sometimes referred to as *drift transistors*. As already mentioned, our analysis will center on the simpler diffusion transistor.

14.3 The Ebers–Moll Equations and the Large-signal Transistor Model

The CB connection is a very convenient starting point for obtaining the transistor current–voltage characteristics and for constructing a model of it. Once this model is established it can be applied to any arbitrary connection.

In developing the transistor equations it should be remembered that junction voltages determine minority-carrier concentrations at the edges of the depletion layer, according to (8.28). Outside the depletion layer the base is neutral and minority-carrier flow through it is governed by diffusion. The characteristics will be found by relating the voltage-dependent carrier concentrations in the base to the current flow in it.

Referring to the PNP transistor, with x measured from the edge of the emitter junction into the base, as in Fig. 14.5(a), we know that

$$\hat{p}_n(0) = \bar{p}_n\left(\exp\frac{qV_{EB}}{kT} - 1\right) \qquad \text{at } x=0, \tag{14.2a}$$

$$\hat{p}_n(W) = \bar{p}_n\left(\exp\frac{qV_{CB}}{kT} - 1\right) \qquad \text{at } x=W, \tag{14.2b}$$

where W is the neutral base width.

If $V_{CB} < 0$ the collector acts as a sink and $p_n(W) = 0$ (or $\hat{p}_n(W) = -\bar{p}_n$). If $V_{EB} > 0$ at the same time then $\hat{p}_n(0) \gg \bar{p}_n$ and the hole concentration will vary with x as shown schematically by Fig. 14.5(a) (notice the similarity to the forward-biased narrow diode).

In the more general case, when V_{EB} and V_{CB} may have either polarity, eqs. (14.2) give the boundary values for the holes in the base.

The minority concentrations in the emitter and the collector sides of the junctions (which are electrons) will also be determined by the junction equations at the respective edges of the depletion layer:

$$\hat{n}_{\mathrm{pE}}(0)=\bar{n}_{\mathrm{pE}}\left(\exp\frac{qV_{\mathrm{EB}}}{kT}-1\right), \tag{14.2c}$$

$$\hat{n}_{\mathrm{pC}}(0)=\bar{n}_{\mathrm{pC}}\left(\exp\frac{qV_{\mathrm{CB}}}{kT}-1\right). \tag{14.2d}$$

Here the index E refers to the emitter and C to the collector.

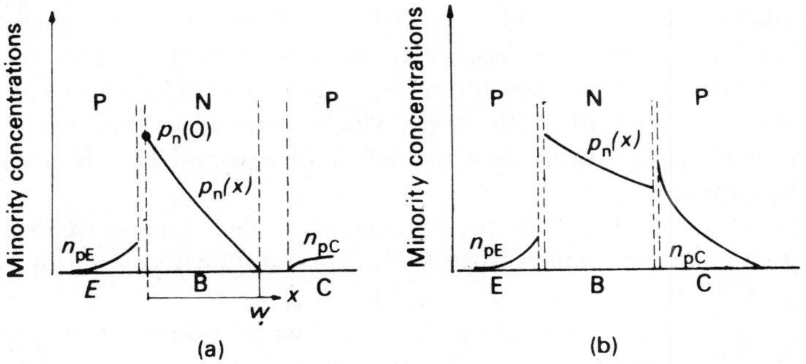

Figure 14.5. Minority carriers distribution in a PNP transistor: (a) with emitter junction forward biased ($V_{\mathrm{EB}}>0$) and collector junction reverse biased ($V_{\mathrm{CB}}<0$); (b) with both junctions forward biased ($V_{\mathrm{EB}}> V_{\mathrm{CB}}>0$).

The detailed shape of the curves of Fig. 14.5 at any value of x can be found as in the general-diode case of Chapter 9. We start from the continuity equation (9.2) and hole-diffusion current equation in the base, (9.4), which then yield the diffusion equation (9.5), repeated here for convenience:

$$\frac{\mathrm{d}^2\hat{p}_{\mathrm{n}}(x)}{\mathrm{d}x^2}-\frac{\hat{p}_{\mathrm{n}}(x)}{L_{\mathrm{h}}^2}=0, \tag{9.5}$$

where $\hat{p}_{\mathrm{n}}(x)$ is the excess holes at point x in the base.

The general solution was

$$\hat{p}_{\mathrm{n}}(x)=C_1\exp\left(-\frac{x}{L_{\mathrm{h}}}\right)+C_2\exp\left(+\frac{x}{L_{\mathrm{h}}}\right). \tag{9.6}$$

Use of the boundary values of (14.2a) and (14.2b) enables us to find C_1 and C_2. Substituting them in (9.6) we get:

$$\hat{p}_{\mathrm{n}}(x)=\bar{p}_{\mathrm{n}}\left(\exp\frac{qV_{\mathrm{EB}}}{kT}-1\right)\frac{\sinh\,[(W-x)/L_{\mathrm{h}}]}{\sinh\,(W/L_{\mathrm{h}})} \tag{14.3}$$

$$+\bar{p}_{\mathrm{n}}\left(\exp\frac{qV_{\mathrm{CB}}}{kT}-1\right)\frac{\sinh\,(x/L_{\mathrm{h}})}{\sinh\,(W/L_{\mathrm{h}})}.$$

The hole current anywhere in the base is then given by

$$J_h(x) = -qAD_h \frac{d\hat{p}_n(x)}{dx}. \tag{9.4}$$

Thus, the injected hole current entering the base will be found by taking (9.4) at $x=0$ while the flow of holes out of the base will be obtained by taking it at $x=W$.

When a junction is forward biased and electrons are also injected from the base into the emitter or collector, their concentration there and their flow can be found in a similar way by solving the diffusion equation for electrons, using the proper boundary conditions for each region, (14.2c) or (14.2d). If both emitter and collector regions are wide compared to the local electron diffusion length L_e in them, then the forms of n_{pE} and n_{pC} shown in Fig. 14.5(b) are obtained.

The electron contribution to the current in each junction can now be found by an equation analogous to (9.4). The total currents, I_E and I_C, are the sum of the hole and electron contributions.

If this long but essentially straightforward work is done it finally yields

$$I_E = I_{ES}\left(\exp\frac{qV_{EB}}{kT} - 1\right) - \alpha_R I_{CS}\left(\exp\frac{qV_{CB}}{kT} - 1\right), \tag{14.4a}$$

$$I_C = -\alpha_F I_{ES}\left(\exp\frac{qV_{EB}}{kT} - 1\right) + I_{CS}\left(\exp\frac{qV_{CB}}{kT} - 1\right), \tag{14.4b}$$

$$I_B = -(I_E + I_C), \tag{14.4c}$$

where the currents are defined as positive when flowing into the transistor. The definitions of the various parameters are:

$$I_{ES} \triangleq \frac{qAD_{hB}\bar{p}_{nB}}{L_{hB}} \coth\frac{W}{L_{hB}} + \frac{qAD_{eE}\bar{n}_{pE}}{L_{eE}}, \tag{14.5a}$$

$$I_{CS} \triangleq \frac{qAD_{hB}\bar{p}_{nB}}{L_{hB}} \coth\frac{W}{L_{hB}} + \frac{qAD_{eC}\bar{n}_{pC}}{L_{eC}}. \tag{14.5b}$$

$$\alpha_F \triangleq \frac{1}{I_{ES}} \frac{qAD_{hB}\bar{p}_{nB}}{L_{hB}} \left(\sinh\frac{W}{L_{hB}}\right)^{-1}, \tag{14.6a}$$

$$\alpha_R \triangleq \frac{1}{I_{CS}} \frac{qAD_{hB}\bar{p}_{nB}}{L_{hB}} \left(\sinh\frac{W}{L_{hB}}\right)^{-1}. \tag{14.6b}$$

From (14.6) we see that these parameters are interrelated by

$$\frac{\alpha_F}{\alpha_R} = \frac{I_{CS}}{I_{ES}}. \tag{14.7}$$

The capital letters in the indices of (14.5) and (14.6) indicate the transistor region to which it refers. Thus D_{hB} means hole diffusion constant in the base and $\bar{n}_{pE}$ means the equilibrium electron concentration in the P-type emitter.

Equations (14.4) are known as the *Ebers–Moll* (E–M) *equations* after the scientists who first developed them.

The currents I_{ES} and I_{CS} are not included in the usual manufacturer's data sheet but can be easily measured in the laboratory: (14.4a) shows that shorting collector to base ($V_{CB} = 0$), measuring I_E against forward V_{EB} and plotting it on a semilog scale in the range $V_{EB} \gg kT/q$ (but still below the high injection level) will yield I_{ES}. Similarly shorting emitter to base and using (14.4b) yields I_{CS} (notice the similarity to I_0 measurement in the diode case). The index S therefore refers to the shorting condition under which they are measured.

A bipolar transistor model based on the E–M equations can be obtained with the following considerations: The diffusion equation (9.5) leading to $\hat{p}_n(x)$, is linear; so is (9.4) giving I_h. One can therefore decompose the minority concentrations for any kind of biasing into two separate groups, each corresponding to different biasing conditions, as shown in Fig. 14.6(a) and (b).

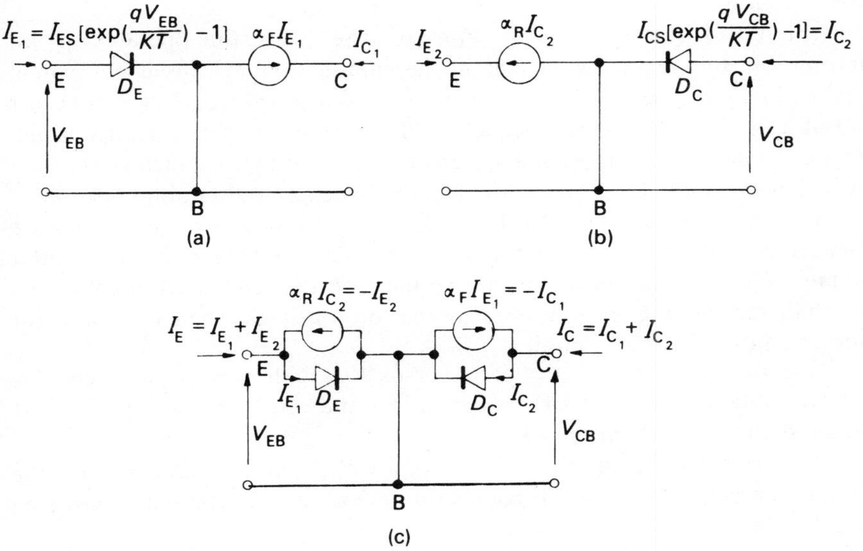

Figure 14.6 The Ebers–Moll model for the PNP transistors: (a) partial model representing forward transistor operation; (b) partial model representing reverse transistor operation; (c) complete d.c. model obtained by parallel connection of (a) and (b).

The forward, or active mode, transistor operation of Fig. 14.6(a), with injecting emitter ($V_{BE}>0$) and collecting collector ($V_{CB}<0$), is represented by the first term in each of the eq. (14.4(a) and (b). the reverse mode of Fig. 14.6(b), with injecting collector ($V_{CB}>0$) and collecting emitter ($V_{EB}<0$), is represented by the second term in each of those equations. Due to the linearity between minority concentrations and currents, the two partial models of Fig. 14.6(a) and (b) can be combined in parallel, adding the minority concentration and currents, as shown in Fig. 14.6(c) which represents the complete E–M equations (14.4) for large signals and any biasing combination.

An NPN transistor can be described by the same equations (14.4) provided only that we reverse the positive polarity definitions of I_E, I_C, I_B, V_{EB} and V_{CB}. The NPN model will then look like Fig. 14.6(c) but with outward-flowing I_E and I_C and with the terminal voltages defined as positive when the base is the more positive electrode.

It can be seen from either the model or eqs. (14.4) that there are three transistor operating regions in the CB connection.

(a) Cut-off region with $V_{EB}<0; V_{CB}<0$. In this region both diodes are reverse biased and only leakage current flows. In the brackets appearing in (14.4) the exponential can then be neglected compared with unity. As we shall see, transistor operation in the switching mode utilizes this region as the 'off' position.

(b) Active region $V_{EB}>0$; $V_{CB}<0$. The transistor operates as an amplifier in this region. A change in the emitter current caused by a small change in V_{EB} appears with practically the same amplitude in the collector but at a much higher impedance level. This current, flowing through a high load resistance R_L, creates a voltage change across it that is much larger than the original change V_{EB}, with consequent voltage and power amplification.

(c) The saturation region $V_{EB}>0$; $V_{CB}>0$. Here both junctions are forward biased, each taking a fraction of a volt. The total collector–emitter voltage $V_{CE}=V_{CB}-V_{EB}$ is almost zero but high transistor currents flow. As we shall see this region is utilized as the 'on' position when the transistor operates in the switching mode.

The output characteristics of I_C versus V_{CB} with I_E as a parameter are directly obtained from (14.4) or the model and are shown in Fig. 14.7(a), where the three zones are marked.

If I_C is drawn versus $V_{CE}=V_{CB}-V_{EB}$ with I_B as a parameter, then the output characteristics of a CE connection are obtained. These are shown in Fig. 14.7(b).

It should be noted that V_{CE} does not change its polarity when one passes from the active to the saturation region, even though V_{CB} does change it. This is because $|V_{EB}|>|V_{CB}|$ in saturation due to a higher emitter doping density compared to that of the collector. The transistor input characteristics of I_E versus V_{EB} with V_{CB} as a parameter (for CB connection) or I_B versus

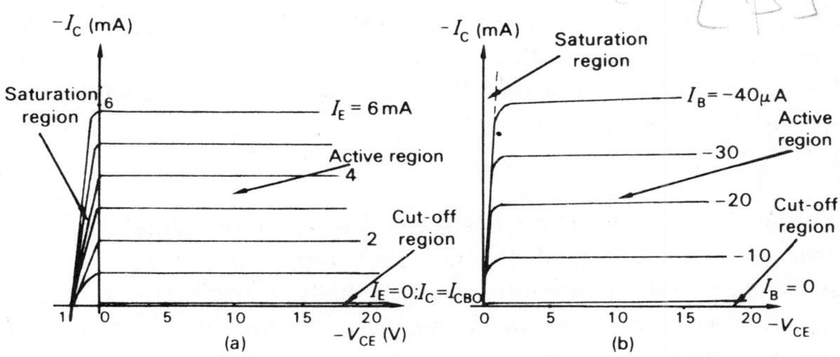

Figure 14.7 PNP transistor output characteristics obtained from the Ebers–Moll equations: (a) in the CB connection; (b) in the CE connection.

V_{BE} with V_{CE} as a parameter (for CE connection) can also be obtained from the E–M equations and resemble the diode I–V characteristic. They can be used to estimate the transistor input resistance at low frequencies.

The equations and model of Fig. 14.6(c) contain some inaccuracies resulting from the fact that α_F, α_R and the effective base width depend to some extent on the voltages and currents at the operating point of the transistor. Those effects will be dealt with in the next section. Their effect on the characteristics of Fig. 14.7 is to introduce a slight upward slope (i.e., a finite output resistance) and make the characteristics somewhat non parallel and non equidistant (i.e., equal steps of ΔI_E or ΔI_B do not result in equal steps of ΔI_c if we look at a wide range of I_c). This is especially pronounced in the characteristics of the CE connection since, as we shall see in the next section, small changes in α_F have a very strong effect on them.

Another important limitation of our model arises from the fact that the internal capacitances were not included. As such, the model is limited to d.c. or low-frequency work only. When interest is in switching speeds, time response to pulse inputs, or high-frequency amplification those capacitances must be included as will be done in the next sections.

14.4 The Dependence of Ebers–Moll Parameters on the Transistor Structure and Operating Point

Equations (14.6) relate α_F and α_R and the reverse saturation currents to transistor dimensions and impurity profile. These equations are mathematically complicated and it is difficult to foresee physically the effects that a change in some parameter, such as minority lifetime in the base, would have.

To get a deeper physical understanding of the various engineering compromises involved in the design of a transistor for a specific use, let us take the PNP transistor, connected with a common base and biased into the active region ($V_{EB} > 0$, $V_{CB} < 0$). For such biasing it is easily shown (Problem 14.14) that eqs. (14.4) are reduced to

$$-I_C = \alpha_F I_E + I_{CBO}. \tag{14.8}$$

We shall now 'enter' the transistor and see how α_F is determined. Figure 14.8 (a) shows the various components of the junction currents. I_{CBO} is the collector–base leakage with open emitter and is usually negligible in Si transistors.

Let us define a *base transport factor*, b, as the ratio of hole current $I_h(W)$ reaching the collector junction and collected by it, to the hole current $I_h(0)$ injected into the base by the emitter. $I_e(0)$ is the electron current injected from base into emitter so that the total emitter current is the sum $I_E = I_e(0) + I_h(0)$.

From the figure and the definition of b, I_C can be related to the internal currents:

$$\begin{aligned} -I_C &= I_h(W) + I_{CBO} = bI_h(0) + I_{CBO} = b\frac{I_h(0)}{I_E} I_E + I_{CBO} \\ &= b\frac{I_h(0) I_E}{I_h(0) + I_e(0)} + I_{CBO}. \end{aligned} \tag{14.9}$$

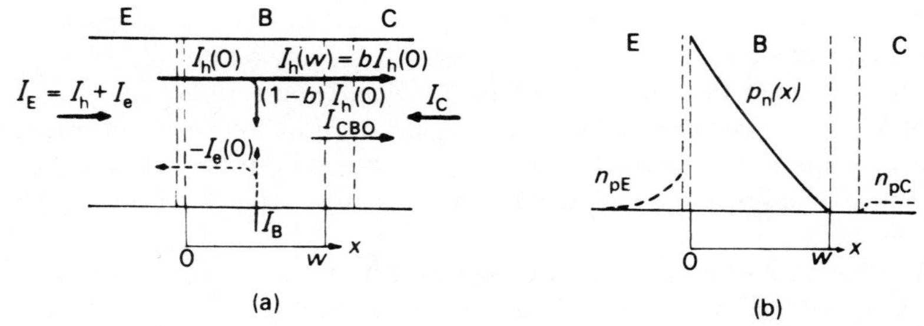

Figure 14.8. A PNP transistor in the active region: (a) the various current components; (b) minority carriers distributions.

Let us define the emitter injection efficiency, γ, as

$$\gamma \triangleq \frac{I_h(0)}{I_h(0) + I_e(0)} = \frac{1}{1 + I_e(0)/I_h(0)}. \tag{14.10}$$

Comparing (14.8) with (14.9) and 14.10) it is clear that $\alpha_F = \gamma b$.

Two additional factors should, however, be included in α_F to account for transistor operation at extremely low currents and at voltages near to breakdown.

At very low I_E, most of it is due to the generation recombination current I_{GR} (described in Section 9.4) which adds to the total I_E, making

$$\frac{I_h(0)}{I_E}=\frac{I_h(0)}{I_h(0)+I_e(0)+I_{GR}}=\gamma\frac{1}{1+I_{GR}/(I_h(0)+I_e(0))}=\gamma\delta.$$

The factor δ reduces α_F at low I_E. It tends to 1 at larger emitter–base forward voltage, since the diffusion components $I_h(0)$ and $I_e(0)$ grow much faster with V_{EB} than I_{GR} so δ has to be considered at low currents only. Also if V_{CB} is high enough to start avalanche multiplication in the collector-junction depletion layer, then the multiplication factor M (Section 9.5) must be included in α_F too. The general expression for α_F is therefore:

(14.11) $$\alpha_F=\gamma b\delta M.$$

In normal operation both δ and M are 1 so we shall concentrate on γ and b and relate them to the transistor structure.

(a) The Emitter Injection Efficiency γ

From the general diode eq. (9.19) one can immediately write down the ratio of injected electrons to injected holes:

$$\frac{I_e(0)}{I_h(0)}=\frac{(D_{eE}/N_A L_{eE})\coth(W_E/L_{eE})}{(D_{hB}/N_D L_{hB})\coth(W_B/L_{hB})},$$

where W_E, N_A, L_{eE} and D_{eE} are the emitter width, doping and the minority diffusion length and constant in it. W_B, N_D, L_{hB} and D_{hB} are the same parameters for the base.

This expression can be simplified, since transistor effect demands a very narrow base, i.e. $W_B \ll L_{hB}$, making $\coth(W_B/L_{hB})\simeq L_{hB}/W_B$. Also the heavy doping of the emitter results in very low minority lifetime and mobility there, making $L_{eE}=\sqrt{(D_{eE}\tau_{eE})}$ short compared to W_E. We therefore also have $\coth(W_E/L_{eE})\simeq 1$.

Substituting the simplified expression for $I_e(0)/I_h(0)$ into the definition (14.10) of γ, we obtain

(14.12) $$\gamma\simeq\frac{1}{1+(D_{eE}W_B N_D/D_{hB}L_{eE}N_A)}.$$

As we shall see, high amplification requires that α_F be as near 1 as possible. To increase γ it is clear from (14.12) that the emitter doping N_A must be several orders of magnitude larger than the base doping N_D. Re-examination of Fig. 14.2 shows that this requirement is fulfilled by both planar double-diffused transistors and the alloy-junction type.

When I_E grows very large we finally enter the high injection phase. The excess hole density in the base becomes comparable or even exceeds N_D in it. To retain base neutrality an equal amount of excess electrons flows in from the base terminal. The total density of majority carriers in the base becomes higher than the former N_D value, replaces it in (14.12) and results in a decrease of γ. This is less pronounced in the planar drift transistor due to its higher base doping near the emitter junction.

(b) The Base Transport Factor b

The concentration profile of minority holes across the base in the active region, $p_n(x)=\hat{p}_n(x)+\bar{p}_n$, is shown in Fig. 14.8(b) and obtained by using (14.3) for $\hat{p}_n(x)$, neglecting exp (qV_{CB}/kT) for $V_{CB}<0$:

(14.13)
$$p_n(x)=\hat{p}_n(x)+\bar{p}_n = \bar{p}_n\left[\frac{\sinh\,[(W_B-x)/L_{hB}]}{\sinh\,(W_B/L_{hB})}\left(\exp\frac{qV_{EB}}{kT}-1\right)-\frac{\sinh\,(x/L_{hB})}{\sinh\,(W_B/L_{hB})}+1\right].$$

Hole flow at point x is given by

(14.14)
$$I_h(x)=-qAD_{hB}\frac{dp_n}{dx}=\frac{qAD_{hB}\bar{p}_n}{L_{hB}\sinh\,(W_B/L_{hB})}\cdot\left[\cosh\frac{W_B-x}{L_{hB}}\left(\exp\frac{qV_{EB}}{kT}-1\right)+\cosh\frac{x}{L_{hB}}\right].$$

From the two terms in the square brackets only the first is the result of emitter injection. The second represents hole leakage at the collector junction (notice it is maximum for $x=W_B$ and exists even if $V_{EB}=0$). The transport factor b refers only to the change in the first term, for injected holes, when x changes from 0 to W_B:

(14.15)
$$b=\frac{I_h(W_B)}{I_h(0)}=\frac{1}{\cosh\,(W_B/L_{hB})}.$$

To make b as nearly 1 as possible, we must have $W_B \ll L_{hB}$, which we already know from the physical discussion. Equation (14.15) may then be simplified by retaining only the first two terms of the hyperbolic cosine series expansion

(14.16)
$$b\simeq\frac{1}{1+\frac{1}{2}(W_B/L_{hB})^2}.$$

An interesting physical insight into b is gained if it is expressed in terms of the transit time τ_B of the minority carriers through the base. τ_B is given by eq. (11.6), and substituting it into (14.15) we get

(14.17)
$$b=\frac{1}{1+\tau_B/\tau_{hB}},$$

where τ_{hB} is the minority lifetime in the base. Obviously we must have $\tau_B \ll \tau_{hB}$ for b to be nearly 1. In other words, the transit time should be so short that the injected carriers have little chance to recombine in the base.

It is known that temperature increase causes τ_{hB} to increase too. Both b and α_F will therefore grow a little with T.

Most transistor circuits utilize the CE connection. Biasing into the active or the cut off regions requires $V_{CB}=V_{CE}-V_{EB}<0$. Therefore neglecting exp (qV_{CB}/kT) compared to -1 in eqs. (14.4) and substituting

$$I_{ES}\left(\exp\frac{qV_{EB}}{kT}-1\right)$$

from (14.4a) and (14.4c) into (14.4b) yields:

$$I_C=\frac{\alpha_F}{1-\alpha_F}I_B-\frac{1-\alpha_R\alpha_F}{1-\alpha_F}I_{CS}. \tag{14.18}$$

The coefficient of I_B is the forward-current gain in the Ce connection and is usually denoted by either β_F or h_{FE}. The second term is the *c*ollector–*e*mitter leakage with *o*pen base and therefore denoted by I_{CEO}.

$$\beta_F \equiv h_{FE} \triangleq \frac{\alpha_F}{1-\alpha_F}, \tag{14.19}$$

$$I_{CEO} \triangleq \frac{1-\alpha_R\alpha_F}{1-\alpha_F} I_{CS}, \tag{14.20}$$

so that for the active region ($I_c<0$; $I_B<0$), (14.18) has the form

$$I_C=h_{FE}I_B-I_{CEO}. \tag{14.21}$$

It is obvious that a very small change in α_F will result in a large change in h_{FE}, since α_F is nearly 1. The small changes in the constituents of α_F with current or temperature that we have discussed are shown schematically in Fig. 14.9(a). Their strong influence on h_{FE} can be seen in Fig. 14.9(b), which shows h_{FE} for a typical Si transistor.

At very low currents h_{FE} is down to half its maximum value due to the reduced δ. At high current it is reduced again because of high-injection effects on γ. The effect of the temperature on b is also obvious. The large h_{FE} changes must be taken into consideration when designing circuits using the CE connection so as to prevent circuit malfunction at the extreme ends of the operating range.

I_{CEO} in (14.21) is negligible for silicon transistors at normal temperatures, therefore changes of h_{FE} with I_c appear as unequal spacings between the characteristics of Fig. 14.7(b).

(c) The Base Spreading Resistance

Examination of the transistor cross section of Fig. 14.1 shows that base current must flow some distance from the base terminal B to the actual base

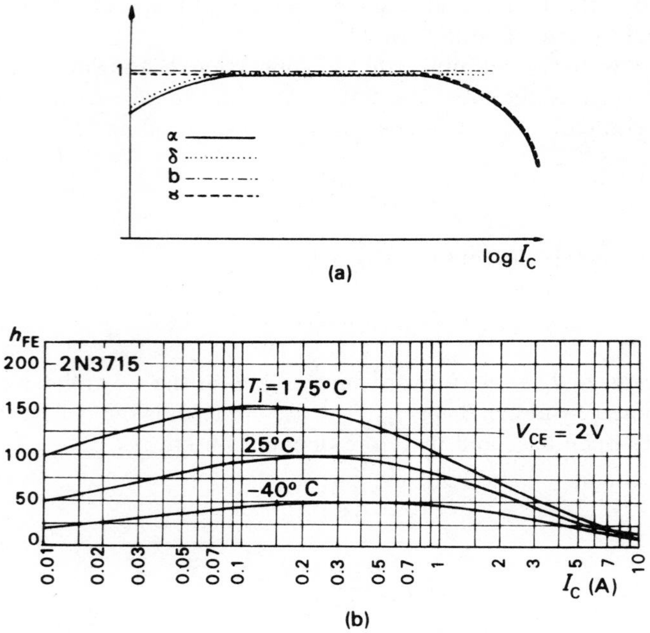

Figure 14.9. (a) The dependence of α_F constituents on I_C (or I_E); (b) h_{FE} dependence on I_C and temperature for a typical Si transistor (Motorola 2N3715).

location between the two junctions which we shall call B′. Since the base is thin and not highly doped this results in a parasitic resistance, denoted $r_{b'b}$ and called *base spreading resistance*, which should be added to the transistor model in series with the base. $r_{b'b}$ adversely affects transistor operation at very high frequencies and increases base-emitter voltage drop at the high base currents of power and switching transistors. Good transistor design therefore aims at reducing it to a minimum of around 10Ω for such transistors, however it may reach 60Ω or more in some. $r_{b'b}$ is included in the fuller model of Fig. 14.11. Actually this resistance may change with transistor currents and frequency because of lateral voltage drop in the base. An average value can then be used.

(d) The Transistor Output Resistance

When the transistor operates in its active region its collector–base junction is reversed biased. The collector voltage which determines the depletion region width of that junction thereby affects the actual base width. Fig. 14.10 shows the change in minority-carrier distribution in the base caused by a change of V_{CB}

which, in its turn, changes the effective base width W_B. For a PNP transistor V_{CB} is negative, and increasing its magnitude by a negative dV_{CB} increases the width of the depletion layer and decreases W_B as shown. If I_E (given by the slope of $\hat{p}_n(x)$ at $x=0$) is kept constant, the excess hole charge in the base $\hat{Q}_h$ will diminish with a consequent reduction in hole recombination in the base. This increases the base transport factor b and increases I_C for the same I_E.

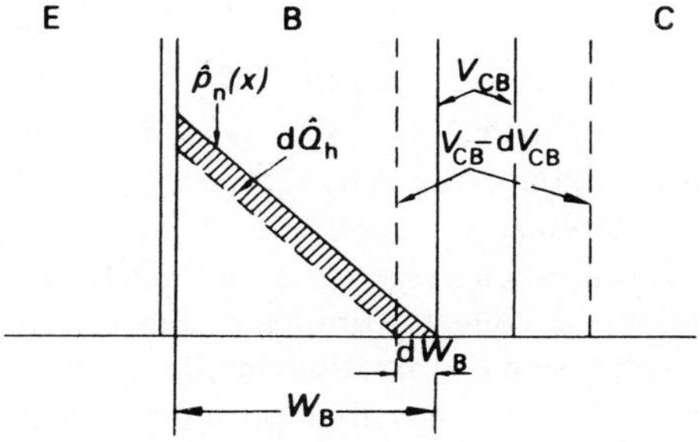

Figure 14.10. Minority charge in the base of a PNP transistor for two values of V_{CB}. I_E is kept constant.

The resistance r_c is defined by

$$\frac{1}{r_c} \triangleq \frac{dI_C}{dV_{CB}}\bigg|_{I_E} = I_E\frac{d\alpha_F}{dV_{CB}} = I_E\frac{d(\gamma b)}{dV_{CB}} = I_E\gamma\frac{d(b)}{dV_{CB}}, \tag{14.22}$$

where we used the fact that $\alpha_F=\gamma b$ in the active region. γ is independent of V_{CB} but b is affected by it:

$$\frac{d(b)}{dV_{CB}} = \frac{d(b)}{dW_B}\frac{dW_B}{dV_{CB}}.$$

Substituting (14.15) for b and remembering that $W_B \ll L_h$ yields for the first factor

$$\frac{d(b)}{dW_B} = -\frac{1}{L_h}\frac{\sinh(W_B/L_h)}{\cosh^2(W_B/L_h)} = -\frac{b}{L_h}\tanh\frac{W_B}{L_h} \simeq -\frac{bW_B}{L_h^2}.$$

The second factor, dW_B/dV_{CB}, depends on the doping density profile on both sides of the collector junction. For a step junction such as is found in an alloy transistor, with N_D doping concentration in the base and N_A in the collector, we get from (8.19a):

$$\frac{dW_B}{dV_{CB}} = \frac{d}{dV_{CB}}(W_{BO}-d_n) = -\left(\frac{\varepsilon\varepsilon_0}{2qV_{CB}}\frac{N_A}{N_D(N_A+N_D)}\right)^{1/2}.$$

Substituting all this into (14.22) yields for the step junction

$$\frac{1}{r_c} = I_E \gamma b \frac{W_B}{L_h^2}\left(\frac{\varepsilon\varepsilon_0 N_A}{2qN_D(N_A+N_D)V_{CB}}\right)^{1/2}$$

$$(14.23) \qquad = \frac{I_C W_B}{L_h^2}\left(\frac{\varepsilon\varepsilon_0 N_A}{2qN_D(N_A+N_D)}\,\frac{1}{V_{CB}}\right)^{1/2},$$

or for the general junction

$$(14.24) \qquad \frac{1}{r_c} = -\frac{I_C W_B}{L_h^2}\,\frac{dW_B}{dV_{CB}}.$$

For a planar Si transistor with $L_h = 15\ \mu$m, $W_B = 1\ \mu$m, $V_{CB} = 10$ V, $I_C = 1$ mA and assuming that on the average $N_D \simeq 2N_A = 10^{16}$ cm^{-3}, so that we can use the step junction equations, we get $r_c = 6.75$ MΩ. This large value of r_c explains why the CB output characteristics look perfectly horizontal. r_c should be added in parallel to the collector branch of Fig. 14.6(c) when the model is used to represent small signal operation in the active region. In saturation ($V_{CB} > 0$) and in cutoff ($I_c \simeq 0$), r_c has no importance and anyway (14.24) do not hold.

14.5 The Transistor Switch

For large signal operation, such as encountered when the transistor switches from cutoff to saturation or vice versa and where the interest lies in the switching speed, one must also include junction and diffusion capacitances as well as the base spreading resistance in the transistor model of Fig. 14.6(c). From Chapter 11 we know that junction capacitance depends on the junction voltage while diffusion capacitance depends on stored excess charges in the neutral region (i.e., on the junction currents). The large-signal model, including $r_{b'b}$ and those capacitances, is shown in Fig. 14.11.

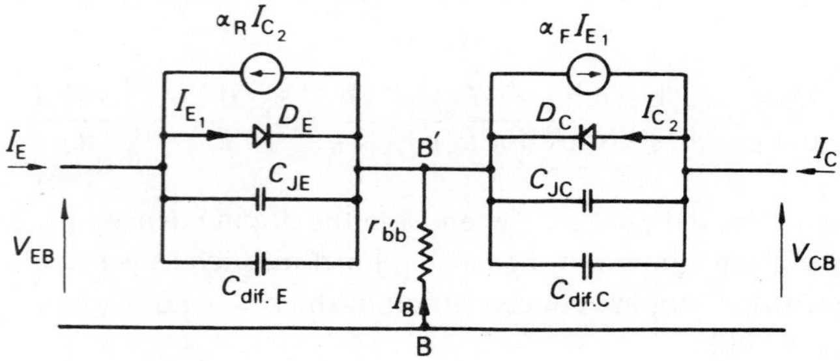

Figure 14.11. The large-signal model including capacitive and base resistance effects.

From eqs. (9.52) and (9.53) we know that the general form for junction capacitance is

$$C_j(V) = \frac{C_j(0)}{(I - V/V_B)^n},$$

where $C_j(0)$ is the zero voltage capacitance, V is the external junction voltage (positive or negative), V_B is the magnitude of the junction built-in voltage (about 0.7 V for Si) and n is usually between $\frac{1}{2}$ and $\frac{1}{3}$.

The diffusion capacitance is related to the excess stored charge as given by (11.10). In the active mode this charge is stored in the base (Fig. 14.5(a)), but in saturation a large part of it is also stored in the collector (Fig. 14.5(b)).

Figure 14.11 then represents the large-signal nonlinear model of the transistor and is useful in computer-aided simulation of the circuit operation of digital bipolar transistors, which usually extends over all three regions: cutoff, active and saturation.

This model is too cumbersome for manual use, especially as digital circuits are no longer built from discrete components but from complete integrated-circuit building blocks, so the analysis must include many interconnected bipolar transistors, diodes and resistors, each with its associated capacitances and nonlinear effects. A nonlinear computer program, such as SPICE, is therefore a must for such circuits, and there is no sense in wasting a lot of effort on approximate manual quantitative analysis of the dynamic switching of a single transistor loaded by an assumed linear and ohmic load. We shall therefore limit quantitative analysis to the two static states of the transistor switch, when it is either on or off, and describe the dynamic switching operation from one state to the other only qualitatively, so that the physical effects of the various model components become clear.

In order to be used as a current switch in digital circuits the transistor is always operated in the CE connection. Only then does it have current amplification $h_{FE} = I_C/I_B$ from base to collector.

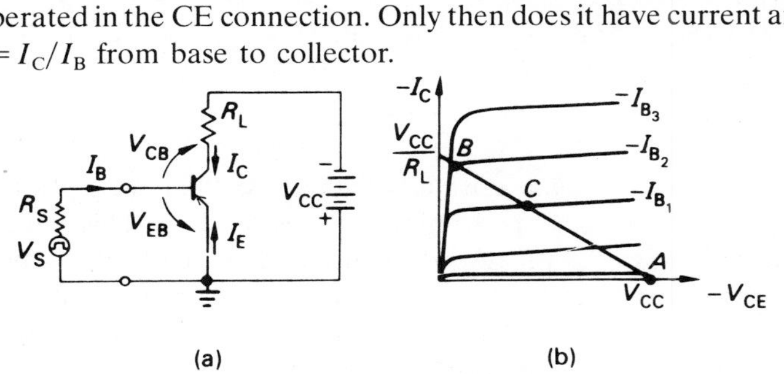

Figure 14.12. PNP bipolar current switch: (a) the circuit; (b) transistor output characteristics and load line.

The basic circuit for a PNP transistor intended to switch the current in a load R_L on and off is shown in Fig. 14.12(a). The relevant common-emitter output characteristics and the load line corresponding to R_L load and V_{CC} supply voltage are shown in Fig. 14.12(b). The larger collector current I_C in R_L is switched by controlling the smaller base current I_B at the input.

To analyze the static 'on' and 'off' states it is sufficient to use the static Ebers–Moll model of Fig. 14.6(c). The positive polarities of voltages and currents in the circuit of Fig. 14.12 conform to that model's conventions.

(a) The 'Off' State

An ideal switch would yield zero current in R_L. Let us see how close the real transistor can come to this for the three possibilities of base–emitter connections shown in Fig. 14.13.

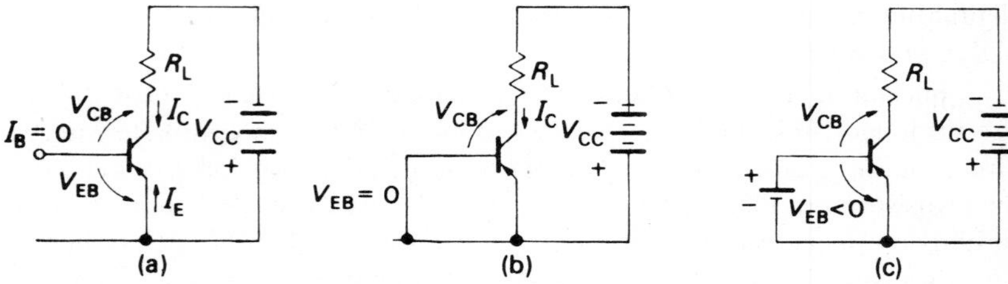

Figure 14.13. Comparing three possible ways to keep the transistor in the off state: (a) open base ($I_B=0$); (b) base–emitter short ($V_{EB}=0$); (c) base–emitter junction reverse biased ($V_{EB}<0$).

The open-base case, the phototransistor. The collector–emitter leakage with open base is denoted by I_{CEO}. From Fig. 14.13(a) it is clear that

$$I_E = -I_C = I_{CEO} \tag{14.25}$$

But (14.18) and (14.20) already gave us I_{CEO}

$$I_{CEO} = \frac{1-\alpha_R\alpha_F}{1-\alpha_F} I_{CS}. \tag{14.20}$$

Actually this open base state leaves the base 'floating', with a potential between that of the collector and emitter (Problem 14.15). This makes the base slightly forward biased with respect to the emitter and reverse biased with respect to the collector. If the collector–base leakage current with open emitter is denoted by I_{CBO} (I_{CBO} is usually given in data sheets) then this current actually leaks into the base across the reverse biased collector junction and serves as effective base current. The transistor amplifies this base current by $\beta_F \equiv h_{FE}$ giving a total current crossing the collector junction of $I_{CBO}+\beta_F I_{CBO}$ or

$$I_{CEO} = (\beta_F+1)I_{CBO} = \frac{I_{CBO}}{I-\alpha_F}. \tag{14.26}$$

(Use of (14.27) to be developed next shows that (14.20) and (14.26) are identical.)

In a typical low-current switching Si transistor I_{CBO} is of the order of 0.1 μA at room temperature and it may grow to around 0.1 mA at high operating temperatures. For $\beta_F \simeq 100$, I_{CEO} may be rather high. We can conclude that making $I_B = 0$ is not a very good way of attaining zero collector current in the 'off' state.

If I_{CBO} is augmented by ΔI_{CBO}, which can be caused by photoelectric generation of electron-hole pairs in, or near, the collector depletion region, then I_{CEO} will increase by $(\beta_F+1)\Delta I_{CBO}$. Therefore an open base transistor with a transparent window over the collector base junction serves as a *phototransistor* which is an excellent photodetector that not only detects optical radiation by increasing the junction current (Chapter 10.3) but also amplifies this increase by β_F+1.

The shorted base–emitter case. The leakage in this case is denoted by I_{CES} (*C*ollector–*E*mitter leakage with *S*horted base). Clearly, from Fig. 14.13(b)

$$V_{EB}=0, \qquad V_{CB}=-V_{CC}.$$

Substituting in (14.4b) with $I_C=-I_{CES}$ yields

$$I_{CES}=I_{CS}=\frac{I_{CBO}}{1-\alpha_R\alpha_F}, \tag{14.27}$$

where use has been made of (14.20) and (14.26).

α_R is much smaller than α_F for several reasons. First, the emitter junction area is much smaller than the collector junction, as can be seen from Fig. 14.1, to insure maximum collection of the emitter current and facilitate base connection. But only a fraction of the current injected by the collector can be collected by the emitter in reverse operation. The rest is lost by recombination. The second reason is the relatively low collector doping which, we now know, will result in low injection efficiency. The third reason is the built-in drift field in the base of a planar-type transistor. This field acts against minority carriers diffusing from the collector towards the emitter, slows them down and so further reduces the base transport factor b in the reverse direction.

Equation (14.27) shows that I_{CES} will be a better solution to cutting off the transistor and is not much larger than I_{CBO}.

Base–emitter junction reverse biased. The leakage current in this case is denoted by I_{CEX}. From Fig. 14.13(c),

$$V_{EB}<0, \qquad V_{CB}=-V_{CC}+V_{EB}<0.$$

Therefore (14.4b) yields

$$I_C=-I_{CEX}=\alpha_F I_{ES}-I_{CS}=(\alpha_R-1)I_{CS}$$

or, when use is made of (14.27),

$$I_{CEX} = (1-\alpha_R)I_{CS} = \frac{1-\alpha_R}{1-\alpha_R\alpha_F} I_{CBO}. \tag{14.28}$$

This is even lower than I_{CBO} and is the best biasing for attaining the 'off' state.

To get an idea of the numbers involved, if we assume $\alpha_F = 0.98$; $\alpha_R = 0.1$, we get

$$I_{CEO} = 50 I_{CBO},$$
$$I_{CES} = 1.1 I_{CBO},$$
$$I_{CEX} = 0.998 I_{CBO}.$$

(b) The 'On' State

When the transistor switch is in the 'on' state it should behave like an ideal short as nearly as possible. V_{CE} in Fig. 14.12 should be about zero so that $|I_C|$ is maximized. Obviously, $|I_B|$ must be relatively large too. (It should be remembered that in a PNP transistor the normal direction of I_B flow is out of the transistor and it is therefore a negative number in the Ebers–Moll equations, as is I_C too.)

In obtaining the relations between V_{CE}, I_C and I_B we must distinguish between two cases:

(a) $|I_B|$ is too small to bring the transistor into saturation and only sufficient to bring it into the active region, with $V_{EB} > 0$ but V_{CB} still negative so that the magnitude of $|V_{CE}| = |V_{CB} - V_{EB}|$ is still large.

(b) $|I_B|$ is large enough to cause saturation with $V_{EB} > 0$, $V_{CB} > 0$.

Case (*a*) has been covered in Section 14.4 and resulted in eq. (14.21):

$$I_C = h_{FE} I_B - I_{CEO}.$$

h_{FE} is a large number so I_{CEO} can be neglected in comparison to the $h_{FE} I_B$ term. From Fig. 14.12(a) we then get

$$V_{CE} = -V_{CC} - I_C R_L = -V_{CC} - h_{FE} I_B R_L. \tag{14.29}$$

The transistor remains in the active region as long as

$$|I_B| < \frac{1}{h_{FE}} \frac{V_{CC}}{R_L}. \tag{14.30}$$

This is the situation when $I_B = -I_{B_1}$ in Fig. 14.12(b). The operating point is still at point C in the figure and the remaining V_{CE} is much too large. Increasing the base drive to $I_B = -I_{B_2}$ shifts the operation to point B in the figure, which is just on the verge of the saturation region. The inequality (14.30) then becomes an equality.

Equation (14.29), however, no longer holds because our original assumption of $V_{CB}<0$ is not true in saturation and we must return to the original Ebers–Moll equations. We are now entering case (b).

Case (b): $|I_B|$ is now large enough to bring the transistor into saturation. This situation is also shown in Fig. 14.12(b) when $I_B=-I_{B_3}$.

(14.31) $$|I_B|>\frac{1}{h_{FE}}\frac{V_{CC}}{R_L}.$$

In saturation $V_{CB}>0$, $V_{EB}>0$, the unity in the brackets of (14.4) can be neglected and we can use the two equations to express V_{EB} and V_{CB} as functions of I_C and I_E:

$$V_{EB}=\frac{kT}{q}\ln\left[\frac{1}{I_{ES}}\frac{I_E+\alpha_R I_C}{1-\alpha_R\alpha_F}\right], \qquad V_{CB}=\frac{kT}{q}\ln\left[\frac{1}{I_{CS}}\frac{I_C+\alpha_F I_E}{1-\alpha_R\alpha_F}\right].$$

The voltage remaining across our switch is therefore:

$$V_{CE}(\text{sat})=V_{CB}-V_{EB}=\frac{kT}{q}\ln\frac{I_{ES}(I_C+\alpha_F I_E)}{I_{CS}(I_E+\alpha_R I_C)}.$$

Substituting $I_E=-(I_C+I_B)$ and use of (14.7) yields

(14.32) $$V_{CE}(\text{sat})=\frac{kT}{q}\ln\left[\frac{\alpha_R}{\alpha_F}\frac{I_C(1-\alpha_F)-\alpha_F I_B}{-I_B-I_C(1-\alpha_R)}\right]$$

or, in terms of $\beta_F\equiv h_{FE}$ and β_R, which is defined like β_F as $\beta_R\triangleq\alpha_R/(1-\alpha_R)$,

(14.33) $$V_{CE}(\text{sat})=\frac{kT}{q}\ln\left[\frac{\beta_R}{\beta_F}\frac{\beta_F I_B-I_C}{I_B(1+\beta_R)+I_C}\right].$$

It should be noted that since both I_C and I_B are negative quantities, and in saturation eq. (14.31) applies, the argument of the logarithm is always a positive number.

As an example, take a transistor with $\alpha_F=0.98$ ($\beta_F=49$) and $\alpha_R=0.1$ ($\beta_R=0.11$) connected as in Figure 14.12(a) with $V_{CC}=12$ V, $R_L=1.2$ kΩ.

If the transistor is an ideal switch it presents a short in the on state with $V_{CE}=0$, and the maximum load current is then

$$I_C(\max)=-\frac{V_{CC}}{R_L}=-10 \text{ mA}.$$

If $V_{CE}(\text{sat})$ is a small fraction of a volt this is also the approximate value of I_C at saturation. The minimum base drive necessary to saturate the transistor is

$$I_B=\frac{I_C}{h_{FE}}\simeq-0.2 \text{ mA}.$$

Increasing the base drive to $I_B = -0.25$ mA (i.e. $I_C/I_B = 40$) will insure that we are inside the saturation region and will leave across our switch a voltage of (at 300°K)

$$V_{CE}(\text{sat}) = -198 \text{ mV}.$$

Increasing the base drive further, to $I_B = -1.0$ mA (i.e. $I_C/I_B = 10$), thus driving it deeper into saturation, reduces V_{CE} to

$$V_{CE}(\text{sat}) = -126 \text{ mV}$$

and our transistor indeed resembles a switch in its closed, or 'on', state.

The measured values for V_{CE}(sat) for real transistors are higher unless the choice of V_{CC} and R_L is such that I_C(max) is small relative to the transistor capabilities. The reason is that the collector bulk resistance R_{CC}, between the collector junction and outside terminal, adds its ohmic voltage drop, $I_C R_{CC}$, to V_{CE}(sat), increasing it to something between 0.25 V and 1.5 V, depending on I_C.

(c) The Dynamic Switching Operation

For reasons stated before, we shall limit the treatment of the transition from 'on' to 'off' state and vice versa to qualitative description. We shall rely on physical effects rather than on mathematics, and strive to understand how the various components of the complete model of Fig. 14.11 affect the dynamic switching.

We shall refer to the circuit of Fig. 14.12(a), which is now fed by a square pulse source $v_s(t)$ as shown in Fig. 14.14. The source is able to drive sufficient base current to saturate the transistor when the input pulse is present.

Let us refer first to Fig. 14.14(a), where the base voltage starts from zero at $t = 0$. We see that there is a short *delay time* t_d before I_C starts to grow. It then grows with a finite *rise time* t_r till it reaches its 'on' state value even though the base drive rise time is assumed zero. At the end of the input pulse, when v_s (and I_B) drop back to zero, again instantly, the collector current I_C continues to flow, almost unchanged, for a period t_s called *storage time*, and only then does it start to drop with a finite *fall time* t_f.

The circuit of Fig. 14.12(a) is that of an inverter, i.e., the phase of the output pulse in V_{CE} is inverted with respect to the input pulse. The sum of t_d and t_r is called *turn on* time and $t_s + t_f$ is called the *turn off* time. Both t_r and t_f are usually defined as the time it takes the output to change from 10% to 90% of its final value. t_d and t_s are then measured from the moment of input change to the beginning of t_r or t_f respectively.

The delay time t_d results from the necessity to charge the emitter junction capacitance, C_{jE} in Fig. 14.11, from zero to about 0.7 V (in Si). Only then does the emitter injection start in earnest and I_C begins to grow.

The rise time t_r results from the necessity to charge the diffusion capacitance $C_{\text{dif.E}}$ and change the voltage across the collector–base junction capaci-

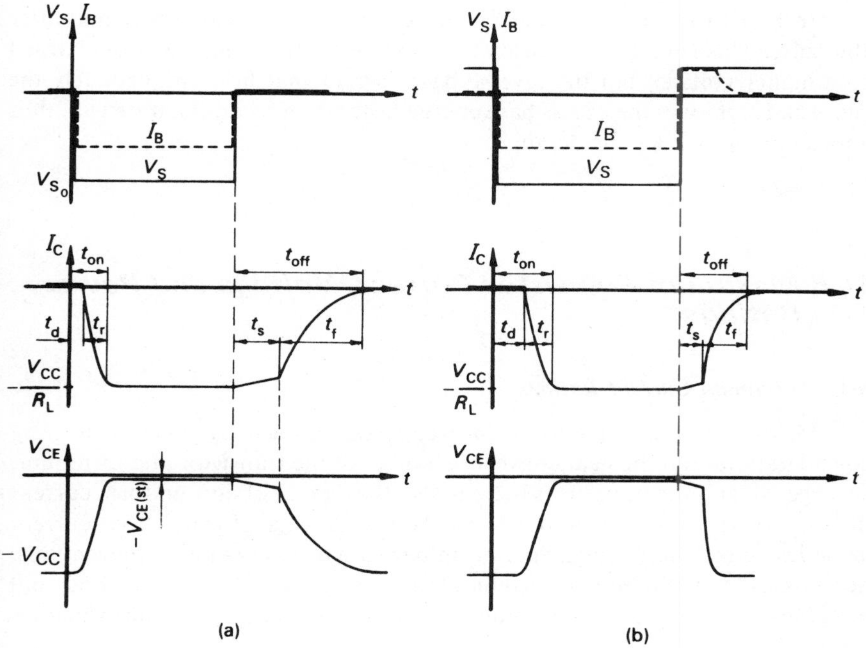

Figure 14.14. Current and voltage wave forms during transistor switching: (a) with base returned to zero potential in the off state; (b) with base returned to reverse potential in the off state.

tance, C_{jC}, from $-V_{CC}+0.7$ at the beginning of t_r to approximately zero at the end of it. the charging current flows through R_L so R_L is included in the time constant affecting t_r.

The storage time t_S arises from reasons similar to those leading to the diode storage effect dealt with in Chapter 11. When the transistor is in saturation there is an excess stored charge of minority carriers in both base and collector (see Fig. 14.5(b). This is represented by the charge in $C_{dif.C}$. This charge must be removed for collector current to start dropping. Base charge can be removed by reversing the base drive current, although in Fig. 14.14(a) this is not done. In this case the storage time will be determined by the base and collector lifetimes (and of course by the initial amount of stored charge, i.e. by the depth of saturation). Intentional gold doping is sometimes used in switching transistors and diodes. Gold atoms provide recombination levels deep in the Si forbidden gap and reduce the lifetime to the nanosecond range, reducing t_S with it.

The fall time t_f, like the rise time, is required for changing the charge in C_{jC} and removing the rest of the stored charge.

In Fig. 14.14(b) v_S provides a reverse base–emitter bias before and after the pulse. This lengthens the delay time somewhat (C_{jE} must now be charged to a higher voltage) but the reverse base current that flows immediately the pulse ends removes the excess base charge faster than recombination can, thus shortening t_s and t_f considerably.

14.6 Maximum Transistor Current, Voltage and Power Ratings

(a) *Maximum Current Ratings*

Maximum collector current is usually determined by junction heating considerations and the heat convection ability of the transistor and its mount. In large area power transistors there is also the danger of non-uniform current distribution across the emitter area. Hot spots may form where current densities exceed the average. Special emitter structures are used to prevent this. Sometimes manufacturer's current limitations arise from the method and materials used for interconnecting the transistor chip to the encapsulation terminals.

Another reason for recommending maximum operating current is the sharp drop in h_{FE} (Fig. 14.9) beyond that point. The base–emitter junction is especially vulnerable to overheating because of its much smaller area and metal contact (which helps in heat removal) than the collector's area and contact.

(b) *Maximum Power Dissipation*

The danger of collector junction overheating is most severe when both high-current and high-voltage conditions exist. The dissipated power that must be removed is approximately the product of the average values of I_C and V_{CE}. Transistor data sheets include the maximum collector dissipation rating, $P_{D,max}$, at a given transistor case temperature T_C. This power is obtained from the heat-flow equation:

$$T_{j,max} - T_C = \theta_{jc} P_{D,max}, \tag{14.34}$$

where θ_{jc} (°C W^{-1}) is the *thermal resistance* from collector junction to transistor case (which depends on the method of its mounting inside it) and $T_{j,max}$ is the maximum allowable junction temperature.

The same equation may be applied to any semiconductor device. Thus, if $T_{j,max} = 175$°C for a Si power transistor and the internal thermal resistance is 10°C W^{-1} then, for a case temperature of 50°C, the maximum allowable dissipation is

$$P_{D,max} = \frac{175 - 50}{10} = 12.5 \text{ W}.$$

If heat convection from the case to the air surrounding it is less efficient (e.g. the transistor is mounted on a smaller heat sink) then the case may heat up to 100°C. By (14.34) the allowed dissipation must then be reduced to 7.5 W only.

Under pulse operation, with pulse width τ and pulse repetition rate $1/T$, the dissipation rating may sometimes be increased with respect to continuous-wave (CW) operation. This is possible because the device cools somewhat between pulses. The allowed increase depends on the *duty cycle* τ/T and on the device *thermal time constant*, which is the product of its thermal resistance and thermal capacitance (J °C^{-1}). This time constant must be longer than τ (so the device will not reach steady-state temperature during the pulse) for the allowed dissipation to be increased.

(c) Maximum Voltages and Breakdown

In some high-frequency alloy junction transistors, with narrow, low-doped bases, punch-through breakdown may limit the maximum collector voltage. The collector junction depletion layer extends then through the whole base, reaching the emitter junction on the other side if V_{CE} is high enough. Further increase of V_{CE} will forward bias the emitter junction, causing a sharp current increase which is limited only by the external circuit. If no overheating occurs, however, the transistor suffers no permanent damage.

Punch-through breakdown does not usually occur in planar type transistors because the base impurity density obtained by diffusion (Fig. 14.2) is everywhere higher than the collector's, causing the depletion layer to extend mostly into the collector. Increasing the collector voltage we shall finally get to junction fields where avalanche multiplication starts. The current is then multiplied by the factor M, which grows very fast with the voltage (Section 9.5). The common-base characteristics at high voltages have the form shown in Fig. 14.15(a) and BV_{CBO} (*B*reakdown *V*oltage between *C*ollector–*B*ase with *O*pen emitter) is reached when $M \simeq \infty$. This voltage is determined by the base and collector doping densities and the avalanche-causing field in the material (eq. 9.45). The manufacturers usually commit themselves to some stated V_{CB} at which I_{CBO} is still below some specified value (such as 1 μA).

In the CE connection, Fig. 14.15(b), on the other hand, the collector–emitter leakage current with open base, I_{CEO}, is given by (14.26). When multiplication exists, however, the effective α_F is multiplied by M (eq. 14.11), which changes I_{CEO} into

$$I_{CEO} = \frac{I_{CBO}}{1 - \alpha_F M}. \quad (14.35)$$

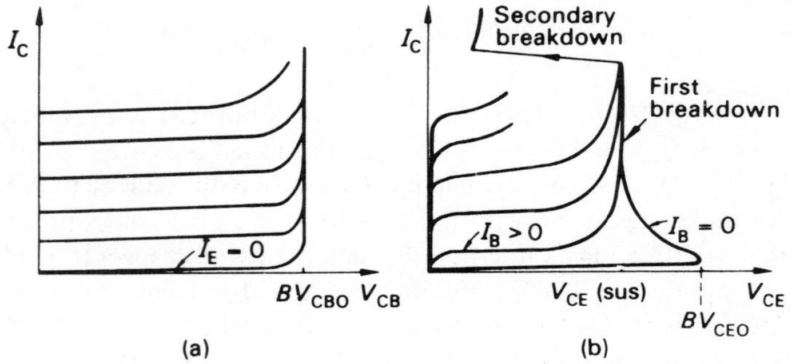

Figure 14.15. Transistor characteristics in the breakdown range: (a) in the common-base connection; (b) in the common-emitter connection.

Since α_F is nearly 1 it is enough for M to be only slightly larger than 1 for I_{CEO} to become infinite, i.e. for breakdown. V_{CE} at which M reaches this value with normal active-region base current, is called the *sustaining voltage* and denoted by V_{CE}(sus). It is shown in Fig. 14.15(b).

When $I_B = 0$ the breakdown voltage, BV_{CEO}, is reached when I_{CEO} in (14.35) is infinite, i.e. when:

$$\alpha_F M = \frac{\alpha_F}{1-(BV_{CEO}/BV_{CBO})^m} = 1,$$

where (9.44) has been used for M. Therefore

$$BV_{CEO} = BV_{CBO}(1-\alpha_F)^{1/m} \simeq \frac{BV_{CBO}}{(\beta_F)^{1/m}}. \tag{14.36}$$

BV_{CEO} is also marked in Fig. 14.15(b). Since $\beta_F \gg 1$ it is decidedly lower than BV_{CBO}. The reason that it is higher than V_{CE}(sus) is that at $I_B = 0$ I_C is also very small, which reduces the effective α_F (and β_F) because of the factor δ in (14.11). A larger value of M (and therefore of V_{CE}) is then necessary to cause breakdown. When multiplication starts to build up, or at higher I_B, δ increases to 1 and M, necessary for breakdown, is lowered and reached at V_{CE}(sus).

It is clear that high-voltage transistor operation necessitates use of low collector doping densities in the transistor design since this increases BV_{CBO}. Reduced collector doping, however, increases its parasitic bulk resistance between the junction and the outside terminal (Fig. 14.1). This is why the planar epitaxial transistor of Fig. 14.2(b) was developed. Here low-collector doping is maintained only near the collector junction, while most of the collector bulk (necessary for mechanical strength) has high doping and low resistivity. Such a structure is essential for a switching transistor that must withstand high voltage in its 'off' state and must present low saturation voltage in its 'on' state.

Emitter–base junction breakdown occurs at rather low reverse voltage in planar transistors, due to the relatively high doping densities on both sides of that junction (Fig. 14.2a, b). One should not apply more than a few volts of reverse voltage to it without an external series resistance high enough to protect against excessive current and damage if breakdown occurs. Further discussion of heat induced damage encountered in power transistors is given in Chapter 19 on Power Devices.

QUESTIONS

14.1 Which parameters of the diffusion process should be changed if the substrate resistivity is increased and one wants to maintain the same junction depth?

14.2 Why are double diffused planar transistors not made directly in very low resistivity substrate?

14.3 What design considerations determine the optimum epitaxial layer thickness and resistivity when one designs a planar epitaxial transistor for a given BV_{CBO} and minimum $V_{CE}(\text{sat})$?

14.4 Can the transistor of Fig. 14.3 operate as an amplifier if both junctions are forward biased?

14.5 Compare from the viewpoint of their output resistance the two transistors whose impurity profiles are given by Fig. 14.2(a) and (c).

14.6 Referring to Fig. 14.1(a) and to the location of the base contact in it, discuss the possible effects of lateral voltage drop between base contact and junction, when the transistor operates at high base (and collector) currents. (This effect is called current crowding.)

14.7 Assuming the areas of the collector and emitter junctions to be the same, will the ratio of β_F/β_R be higher or lower in an alloy junction transistor compared to a planar one?

14.8 Include parasitic collector bulk resistance in Fig. 14.11 and in eq. (14.33).

14.9 Draw an equivalent electrical circuit to the transistor thermal circuit if it is known that it dissipates P_D watts, its collector junction to case thermal resistance is θ_{jc}, and the transistor header is mounted on an

Al heat sink with a thin mica disc insulator in between. The mica thermal resistance is θ_{ch} and the heat sink to surrounding atmosphere resistance is θ_{ha}. How would P_D be affected if T_j and T_a (ambient) were fixed but the heat sink surface area were increased?

14.10 A resistance R is connected between transistor base and emitter. Estimate the collector leakage current and breakdown voltage (denoted by I_{CER} and BV_{CER} respectively) compared to I_{CEO}, I_{CBO}, BV_{CEO}, BV_{CBO}.

14.11 Which of the two transistor types, planar or alloy junction, has the higher r_c? Base your answer on the impurity profiles shown in Fig. 14.2. How will a reduction in the base lifetime affect r_c?

PROBLEMS

14.12 The impurity profile obtained after base diffusion in a planar transistor production is given by

$$N_D(x) = \frac{Q_0}{\sqrt{(\pi D t)}} \exp\left(-\frac{x^2}{4Dt}\right).$$

The diffusion is of arsenic (donor) into boron (acceptor) doped Si substrate and x is the depth from the surface. It is known that
$Q_0 = 10^{16}\ \text{cm}^{-2}$ (constant depending on previous process)
$t = 4$ h (diffusion duration)
$D = 5 \times 10^{-14}\ \text{cm}^2\ \text{s}^{-1}$ (diffusion constant of As at the diffusion temperature)
$N_A = 10^{15}\ \text{cm}^{-3}$ (substrate doping density).
Calculate the collector junction depth.

14.13 The emitter in the transistor of Problem 14.12 is obtained by an additional short boron diffusion which makes a second junction at $x = 1\ \mu$m. Since arsenic diffuses much more slowly than boron, it can be assumed that the collector junction depth remains unchanged. Measuring y from the emitter junction into the base,

(a) calculate the base doping density N_B $(y=0)$ near the emitter;

(b) approximate the base doping profile by the function

$$N_B(y) = N_B(0) \exp\left(-\eta \frac{y}{W}\right),$$

where W is base width and η a constant to be determined from knowledge of $N_B(0)$ and $N_B(W)$ (= the collector doping) and find the built-in field in the base.

14.14 Show that eq. (14.8) results from the Ebers–Moll equations applied in the active region.

14.15 An NPN transistor is connected as shown in Fig. 14.13(a) (with V_{CC} of an opposite polarity, of course) and with its base left open. Calculate the base potential with respect to the emitter in terms of the Ebers–Moll parameters.

14.16 The d.c. circuit of a given transistor is as shown in Fig. 14.16. Use the Ebers–Moll equations (14.4) to obtain a set of simultaneous equations from which the operating point (I_C and V_{CE}) may be found.

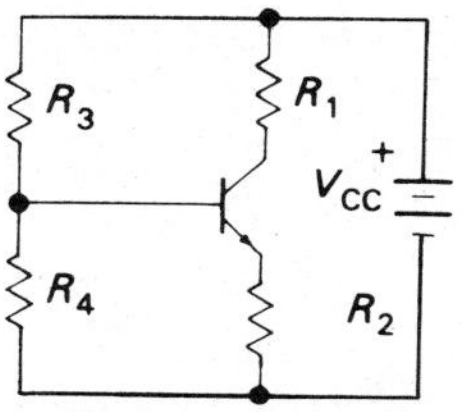

Figure 14.16. A typical NPN transistor amplifier d.c. circuit.

14.17 The information given in Table 14.1 applies to an NPN transistor at its extreme working temperature range

Table 14.1

T_j (°C)	h_{FE}	μ_e (cm^2 V^{-1} s^{-1}) in base
−40	50	1100
+25	100	800
+175	150	400

Assume an injection efficiency of 1 and that α_F is determined by the base transport factor only.

(a) What is the transit time across the base at 25°C if it is known that base width is 1 μm?

(b) What is the ratio of minority lifetime in the base at −40°C and +175°C to its value at 25°C?

14.18 Draw the energy bands in equilibrium for the three transistors whose impurity profiles are shown in Fig. 14.2. Draw the bands across an alloy junction transistor biased into (a) the active zone, (b) the cut off zone.

14.19 Find an expression for I_{CER} (Question 14.10) in terms of the Ebers–Moll parameters. Show that it tends towards I_{CEO} if $R \to \infty$ and towards I_{CES} if $R \to 0$.

14.20 A given NPN transistor has $\alpha_F = 0.96$, $\alpha_R = 0.15$. The parasitic collector bulk resistance is 10Ω. The transistor is connected as in Fig. 14.16 with $V_{CC} = 9$ V, $R_1 = 3$ kΩ, $R_2 = 0$, $R_4 = \infty$.

(a) Find R_3 necessary to bring the transistor to the threshold of saturation (assume $V_{BE} = 0.7$ V independent of base current).

(b) Find V_{CE} for R_3 of one third the value found in (a).

14.21 A Ge power transistor is operated at $V_{CE} = 5$ V, $I_C = 1.5$ A. The junction-to-case thermal resistance is 6°C W^{-1}. The transistor is mounted on a heat sink with a thin mica insulator of 0.5°C W^{-1} thermal resistance between them. Find the maximum allowable heat-sink-to-air resistance for an ambient temperature of 35°C and a maximum allowable junction temperature of 90°C.

14.22 A current I_B is driven into the base of an NPN transistor whose collector is left open. Use the E–M equations to obtain an expression for V_{CE} under those conditions (called the offset voltage) and for the slope $(\partial V_{CE}/\partial I_C)|_{IC=0}$ in terms of α_F, α_R and I_B. Calculate their values for $kT/q = 0.026$ V, $\alpha_F = 0.98$, $\alpha_R = 0.2$, $I_B = 0.1$ mA. Assume $I_B >> I_{ES}$.

14.23 It is argued that an heterojunction bipolar transistor with a wide band gap (AlGaAs) emitter and a narrower band gap base and collector (GaAs) makes possible a transistor which has both a very high β and a very low $r_{b'b}$. Point out why this can be done and why it is difficult to achieve in the homojunction case.

THE BIPOLAR TRANSISTOR: SMALL-SIGNAL LOW- AND HIGH-FREQUENCY MODELS 15

Bipolar transistors are widely used in linear circuits, i.e. as small-signal amplifiers. In such circuits the transistor is always biased into its active operating region by a suitable d.c. circuit, containing power supplies and resistors. This circuit is so designed as to keep the transistor in the active region even though some of the parameters representing it may change within an acceptable range. These changes may be due to temperature variations or to production spread. Even when the worst combination of parameters and temperature extremes exists, the operating point must not shift too far, and never into the cut off or saturation regions where the transistor behavior is extremely nonlinear.

Once the operating point has been determined, the transistor can then be represented by a small-signal model whose equivalent a.c. small-signal circuit can then be drawn and analyzed, using linear circuit techniques, since the model parameters can be regarded as constant as far as the small signal is concerned. Various models can be used, depending on the transistor connection, the frequency range of interest and the required accuracy.

15.1 Determination of the D.C. Operating Point

The operating point may be found by a straightforward but difficult method which is sometimes useful for complex circuits involving many interconnected transistors. It usually necessitates a computer. The large-signal Ebers–Moll equations (14.4) are used together with the external circuit equations, relating V_{CB} and V_{EB} or V_{CE} with external currents and power supply voltages. A set of simultaneous equations is thus obtained, from which the junction voltages and currents can be found. The equations, however, are always transcendental (since junction voltages appear both in exponents and out) and can be solved only by numerical or approximate methods.

Let us illustrate this method by a simple example and show how an acceptable approximation can simplify the problem so much as to make it almost trivial.

We want to find the d.c. operating point of the transistor in the circuit of Fig. 15.1 which shows one possible way of biasing the transistor for operating as a small-signal amplifier in the CE connection (another commonly used method will be shown later in Fig. 15.11).

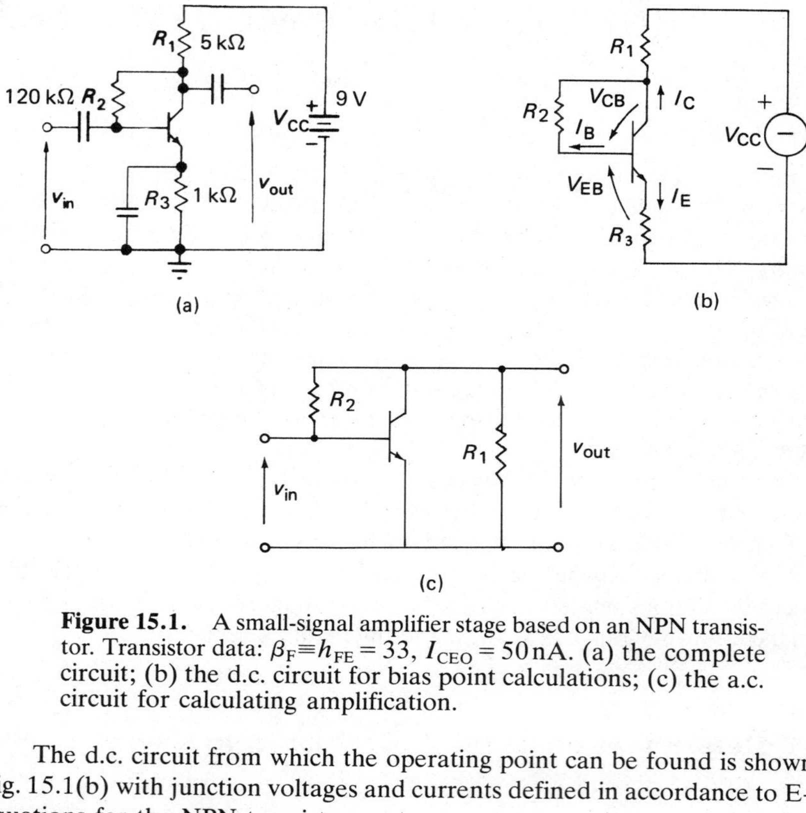

Figure 15.1. A small-signal amplifier stage based on an NPN transistor. Transistor data: $\beta_F \equiv h_{FE} = 33$, $I_{CEO} = 50\,\text{nA}$. (a) the complete circuit; (b) the d.c. circuit for bias point calculations; (c) the a.c. circuit for calculating amplification.

The d.c. circuit from which the operating point can be found is shown in Fig. 15.1(b) with junction voltages and currents defined in accordance to E–M equations for the NPN transistor.

The external circuit has two loops yielding the voltage loop equations:

$$V_{CC} = -I_C R_1 + V_{CE} + I_E R_3 = -I_C R_1 + (V_{EB} - V_{CB}) - (I_C + I_B) R_3$$

$$V_{CB} = I_B R_2$$

These two equations plus the two E–M equations (14.4) enable us to find the four unknowns I_C, I_B, V_{CB}, V_{EB} with the help of a computer.

To proceed manually, we start from the same two external circuit equations together with eq. (14.21) to which the E–M equations reduce in the active region, as shown in the last chapter

$$I_C = h_{FE} I_B - I_{CEO}. \tag{14.21}$$

We also assume that $V_{EB} \simeq 0.7$ V (for Si) since the base-emitter junction forms a forward-biased diode which has an almost constant voltage for a wide range of currents. The three equations can then be readily solved for I_C, I_B and V_{CB} giving

$$I_C = -\frac{V_{CC} - 0.7 + I_{CEO}(R_2 + R_3)/h_{FE}}{R_1 + R_3 + (R_2 + R_3)/h_{FE}} \simeq -0.86\,\text{mA};\; I_B = 26\,\mu\text{A};\; V_{CB} = -3.2\,\text{V}.$$

The effect of I_{CEO} is negligible which is the usual situation for silicon transistors operating near room temperatures. It is enough to know the operating point approximately since the small-signal model parameters vary relatively slowly with the operating point in the active region and this is what makes the model linear for small signals in the first place.

The next step is to represent the transistor in Fig. 15.1(c) around this operating point by an equivalent linear model to facilitate analysis of the a.c. network (notice that the V_{CC} supply is represented by a short in the a.c. circuit since it presents zero resistance to a.c. currents).

15.2 Alternate Two-Port Representations of the Linear Transistor Model

Since the transistor has three terminals, its small-signal ac model can be represented by a two-port with a common input–output terminal, as shown in Fig. 15.2(a) or (b).

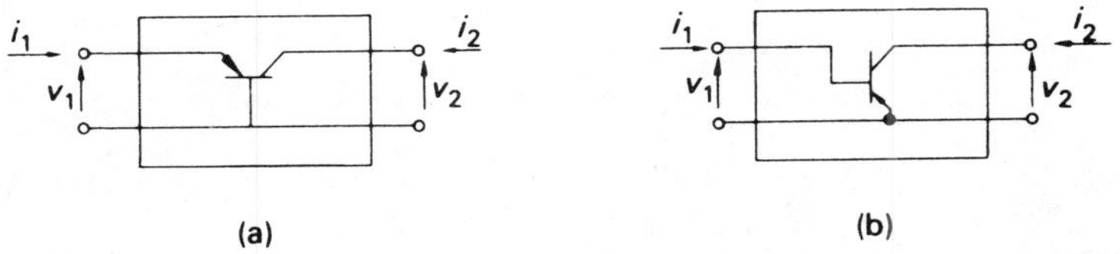

Figure 15.2. Two-port representation of the transistor: (a) in the CB connection; (b) in the CE connection.

v_1, v_2, i_1 and i_2 are the a.c. components only, so that if $v_2=0$, for example, it means that there is an effective short circuit for a.c. across the output (such as would be achieved by a large enough capacitor connected across it). A d.c. circuit, however, must also exist so as to keep the transistor in the desired operating point.

Network theory offers several equivalent possibilities to describe two-port properties. In transistor circuits the h parameters are usually preferred in the low-frequency (audio) range and the y parameters in the high-frequency range. The reason, as we shall see, lies in the relative ease with which they can be measured in those respective frequency ranges. The h parameters for the CB connection are defined as

(15.1a) $$v_1 = h_{ib}i_1 + h_{rb}v_2 \qquad (\text{or } h_{11b}i_1 + h_{12b}v_2),$$

(15.1b) $$i_2 = h_{fb}i_1 + h_{ob}v_2 \qquad (\text{or } h_{21b}i_1 + h_{22b}v_2).$$

(They are similarly defined for the CE or CC connections with an index e or c replacing the b.)

The y parameters for the CE connection are defined as:

(15.2a) $$i_1 = y_{ie}v_1 + y_{re}v_2 \qquad (\text{or } y_{11e}v_1 + y_{12e}v_2),$$

(15.2b) $$i_2 = y_{fe}v_1 + y_{oe}v_2 \qquad (\text{or } y_{21e}v_1 + y_{22e}v_2).$$

Both double-index and triple-index notations are in use, although the former is the more common. The meanings of the indices are related to the two-port functions as follows:

i—input, f—forward
r—reverse, o—output.

Thus, h_{ib} in (15.1a) is measured by the ratio

$$h_{ib} = \left.\frac{v_1}{i_1}\right|_{v_2=0} (\Omega);$$

it therefore means input impedence, hence the index i.

$$h_{rb} = \left.\frac{v_1}{v_2}\right|_{i_1=0}.$$

This represents the reverse voltage transfer ratio (v_1 in the input results from v_2 in the output); hence the index r.

$$h_{fb} = \left.\frac{i_2}{i_1}\right|_{v_2=0}.$$

This gives the forward current transfer ratio, hence the index f. Note that both h_{rb} and h_{fb} are dimensionless.

$$h_{ob} = \left.\frac{i_2}{v_2}\right|_{i_1=0.} \quad (\Omega^{-1}).$$

This is the output conductance, hence the index o.

The second index, b in (15.1a and b), refers to the common-*b*ase connection for which this specific set was measured. The name hybrid (h) parameters stems from the fact that they have different dimensions.

At low frequencies the internal transistor capacitances are too small to have any measurable effect, so the *h* parameters are usually given by real numbers.

The *y* parameters are all admittances. The first index has the same meaning as before while the second, e in (15.2a and b), refers to this specific set being measured for the common-*e*mitter connection. The *y* parameters are all measured under conditions of effective short circuit across the opposite port; thus

$$y_{fe} = \left.\frac{i_2}{v_1}\right|_{v_2=0} \quad (\Omega^{-1})$$

is measured with shorted output. At high frequencies, where these parameters are used, such effective short circuits are easy to accomplish by connecting a relatively small capacitor across the relevant port that acts in parallel with the internal capacitance already present. The *y* parameters are always complex numbers, which depend on the measurement frequency.

Their use over a wide frequency range, therefore, necessitates either eight curves or eight long tables of values covering that range; the calculations must then be done numerically and it is difficult to obtain a generalized picture of the circuit behavior. It is difficult, for example, to predict the effect of a change in the operating-point voltage.

We should therefore endeavor to use these parameters to obtain a more general small-signal model, composed of components such as resistors, capacitors and controlled sources, whose values are related to the *y* or *h* parameters but whose behavior with frequency or with change in operating point is well known and can be predicted. We prefer first to develop such a model from physical considerations and only then to relate it to the *y* or *h* parameters in any desired connection. We can start from the most convenient connection, the CB. Once the parameters are known, it is simple enough to change into any other connection by a set of transfer equations. The method of obtaining such a set for transferring from one set of *y* parameters to any other is described in Appendix 1.

15.3 Transistor Models for CB Connection at Low and High Frequencies

The small-signal physical model can be obtained from the large-signal Ebers–Moll model shown in Fig. 14.11, which degenerates in the active region and at low frequencies to the form of Fig. 15.3(a). The small internal capacitances and $r_{b'b}$ are neglected. They will be added later at high frequencies when their effects become important.

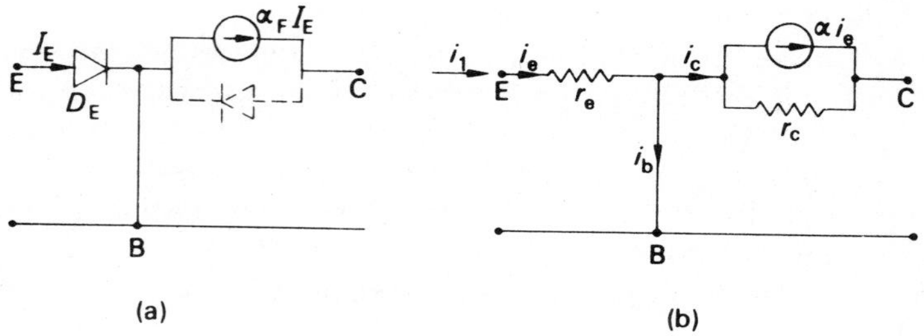

Figure 15.3. Development of the small-signal CB low-frequency model: (a) active region large-signal model; (b) small-signal representation of (a).

Since we are dealing with small signals, the forward-biased emitter–base diode D_E can be replaced by its differential resistance r_e, which depends on I_E according to (11.1). The $\alpha_F I_E$ current source can be replaced by its small-signal equivalent αi_e, where i_e is the a.c. component of I_E (i.e. dI_E) and α is defined as

$$(15.3) \qquad \alpha \triangleq \left.\frac{dI_C}{dI_E}\right|_{V_{CB}=\text{constant}} = \left.\frac{d(\alpha_F I_E)}{dI_E}\right|_{V_{CB}=\text{constant}} = I_E \frac{d\alpha_F}{dI_E} + \alpha_F.$$

Referring to Fig. 14.9 it is obvious that $\alpha = \alpha_F$ when α_F = constant, $\alpha > \alpha_F$ when α_F grows with I_E, and $\alpha < \alpha_F$ when it decreases with I_E. The leakage current, being constant, is of no importance in the a.c. model, but the finite output resistance of a real transistor, r_c, calculated in Section 14.4 is included in it.

Related to r_c there is an additional effect that can be seen from Fig. 14.10: there must be a change in V_{EB} if V_{CB} changes and we want to keep I_E constant. But this is exactly the definition of h_{rb} from (15.1a):

$$h_{rb} = \left.\frac{v_1}{v_2}\right|_{i_1=0} = \left.\frac{dV_{EB}}{dV_{CB}}\right|_{I_E=\text{constant}}.$$

Since, in the active region, the minority distribution in the base is like that of a narrow diode and $I_E \simeq I_h$, we can use (9.15) and rewrite it in the form:

$$(15.4) \qquad V_{EB} = \frac{kT}{q} \ln \frac{W_B I_E}{qAD_h \bar{p}_n},$$

from which

(15.5a) $$h_{rb}=\left.\frac{dV_{EB}}{dV_{CB}}\right|_{I_E=\text{constant.}}=\left.\frac{dV_{EB}}{dW_B}\frac{dW_B}{dV_{CB}}\right|_{I_E}=\frac{kT}{q}\frac{1}{W_B}\frac{dW_B}{dV_{CB}}.$$

If one assumes that $\alpha_0 \simeq b$ with b given by (14.16), then h_{rb} is related to r_c as given by (14.24) as

(15.5b) $$h_{rb}=\frac{\alpha_0 r_e}{r_c}\left[\frac{L_h}{W_B}\right]^2 \simeq \frac{\alpha_0^2 r_e}{2r_c(1-\alpha_0)}=\frac{r_e(1+h_{fe})}{2r_c}.$$

$h_{rb}=8.7\times10^{-4}$ for the example cited in Section 14.4. To add h_{rb} to the model of Fig. 15.3(b) it is necessary to include a controlled voltage source ΔV_{CB} $h_{rb}=v_2 h_{rb}$ in the input circuit. If α_0 represents the a.c. current transfer ratio at low frequency, the CB small-signal circuit model then takes the form of Fig. 15.4(a). The two-port representation by h parameters as defined by eqs. (15.1) is also shown in Fig. 15.4(b). By comparison

(15.6) $$h_{ib}=r_e$$

(15.7) $$h_{ob}=1/r_c$$

(15.8) $$h_{fb}=-\alpha_0.$$

(Were we to include $r_{b'b}$ in our calculations, it would have reduced h_{rb} and increased h_{ob} somewhat.)

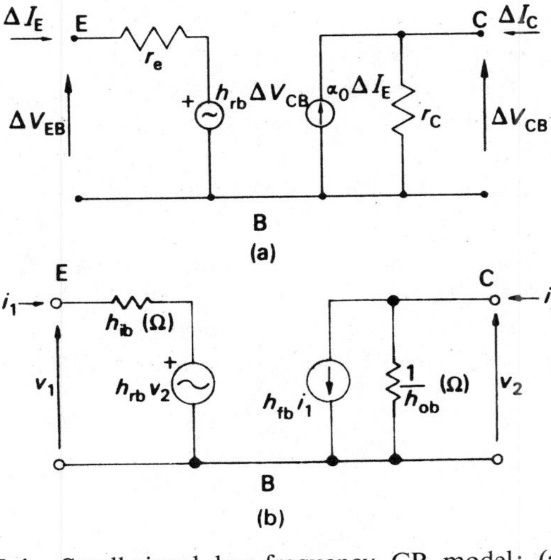

Figure 15.4. Small-signal low-frequency CB model: (a) as developed from physical considerations; (b) as represented by the h parameters in eq. (15.1).

At high frequencies we must add depletion and diffusion capacitances and also $r_{b'b}$, which combines with the capacitances to give a finite RC time constant, limiting the maximum frequency that can be amplified.

Base-width modulation and h_{rb}, which are small to begin with ($h_{rb} \ll 1$), can be neglected because of the shorting effect of the internal capacitances, leaving the circuit of Fig. 15.5 for high frequencies.

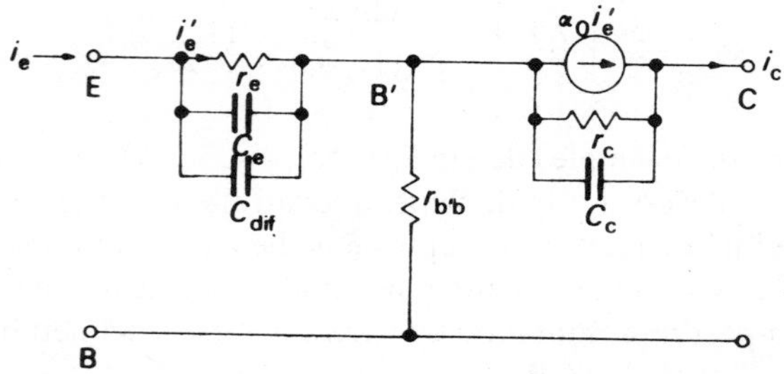

Figure 15.5. High-frequency model for the CB connection.

Diffusion capacitance appears only in the emitter junction, which is forward biased, while only depletion-layer capacitance, C_e, appears in the collector. C_e is a weak function of I_E according to (9.55) and is somewhat higher than $C_e(0)$. C_{dif} is proportional to I_E according to (11.10):

$$C_{dif} = K\frac{qI_E}{kT}\tau_F .$$

Because of the narrow base $\tau_B \ll \tau_h$, making

$$\tau_F = \left(\frac{1}{\tau_B}+\frac{1}{\tau_h}\right)^{-1} \simeq \tau_B ,$$

where τ_B is the minority transit time through the base. In a uniform base transistor $K \simeq \frac{2}{3}$ and C_{dif} is much higher than C_e. In a planar transistor, with a drift field in the base, τ_B is much shorter, reducing C_{dif} to the order of C_e or below.

It should be noticed that the current source in Fig. 15.5 is controlled only by that part of i_e that flows through r_e, marked i'_e. The rest of i_e, the reactive part, flows through the capacitors and the base terminal and has nothing to do with the transistor action. $\alpha_0 i'_e$ in Fig. 15.5 must therefore replace $\alpha_0 \Delta I_E = \alpha_0 i_e$ in Fig. 15.4(a). In order to continue using the total emitter current i_e (which is more convenient) one can define an effective α as follows:

$$\alpha_0 i'_e = \frac{\alpha_0}{1+j\omega r_e(C_e+C_{dif})} i_e \triangleq \alpha i_e .$$

Let us also define an ω_a as

$$\omega_a \triangleq \frac{1}{r_e(C_e+C_{dif})} . \tag{15.9}$$

The effective α is then

(15.10)
$$\alpha \triangleq \frac{\alpha_0}{1 + j\,\omega/\omega_a}\,.$$

When $\omega = \omega_a$, then $|\alpha| = \alpha_0/\sqrt{2}$ and the power amplification (proportional to the current squared) is reduced to half the low-frequency value. That is why ω_a is called the *half-power frequency.*

This model represents the transistor faithfully only so long as the base transit time τ_B is much shorter than the period T of the amplified signal, i.e. $\tau_B \ll T$. At higher frequencies (shorter T) an appreciable phase difference $\omega\tau_B$ appears between the hole current at its point of injection into the base, at $x=0$, and at the point where it leaves the base at $x = W_B$. The ratio of the hole currents at those two points is the base transport factor b which now becomes a complex function of the frequency. This function has an infinite number of poles along the negative real axis. The first and most significant one is at $\omega = \omega_a$.

The expression (15.10) is therefore just a single-pole approximation to the correct form of α (which, circuitwise, can be correctly represented by a distributed RC line only and not by a lumped form). The neglected, far poles have little effect on the magnitude of α but add a significant phase shift to it. A better approximation, therefore, for the effective α includes an additional phase shift factor:

(15.11)
$$\alpha = \frac{\alpha_0 \exp(-jm\omega/\omega_a)}{1 + j\omega/\omega_a}\,.$$

$m \simeq 0.2$ for a uniform base alloy junction transistor, but is much larger and may be as high as 1 for planar transistors with high impurity gradients in their bases.

15.4 Transistor Models for Use in the CE connection

The models of Fig. 15.4 or 15.5 can be used for any transistor connection. They could be drawn sidewise to represent a CE connection. But using them this way is awkward and inconvenient since the internal source is controlled by i_e and not by the input, which is then i_b.

A more convenient model, useful for a wide range of frequencies, can be obtained if we draw the complete CB model (the 'sum' of Figs. 15.4 and 15.5) as shown in Fig. 15.6, and write down the y parameters of the two-port enclosed by the dashed box. The base spreading resistance $r_{b'b}$, which is left outside, will be added later in series with the base terminal.

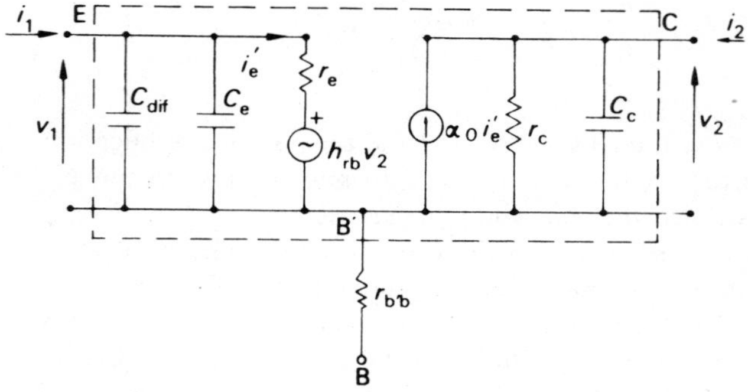

Figure 15.6. The complete CB model.

Using the definitions of the y parameters in (15.2):

(15.12a) $$y_{ib} = \left.\frac{i_1}{v_1}\right|_{v_2=0} = \frac{1}{r_e} + j\omega(C_e + C_{dif}),$$

(15.12b) $$y_{rb} = \left.\frac{i_1}{v_2}\right|_{v_1=0} = -\frac{h_{rb}}{r_e},$$

(15.12c) $$y_{fb} = \left.\frac{i_2}{v_1}\right|_{v_2=0} = -\frac{\alpha_0}{r_e},$$

(15.12d) $$y_{ob} = \left.\frac{i_2}{v_2}\right|_{v_1=0} = \frac{1}{r_c} + \frac{\alpha_0 h_{rb}}{r_e} + j\omega C_c .$$

The transformation from the y_b to the y_e parameters of the CE connection can now be performed following the relations developed in Appendix 1:

(15.13a) $$y_{ie} = \Sigma y_b = \frac{(1-\alpha_0)\,(1-h_{rb})}{r_e} + \frac{1}{r_c} + j\omega(C_e + C_c + C_{dif}),$$

(15.13b) $$y_{re} = -y_{rb} - y_{ob} = \frac{1-\alpha_0}{r_e} h_{rb} - \frac{1}{r_c} - j\omega C_c,$$

(15.13c) $$y_{fe} = -y_{fb} - y_{ob} = \frac{\alpha_0(1-h_{rb})}{r_e} - \frac{1}{r_c} - j\omega C_c,$$

(15.13d) $$y_{oe} = y_{ob} = \frac{1}{r_c} + \frac{\alpha_0 h_{rb}}{r_e} + j\omega C_c .$$

A general equivalent circuit that includes one controlled source and describes any network by its y parameters is shown in Fig. 15.7. It can be easily verified that eqs. (15.2) describe its current–voltage relations.

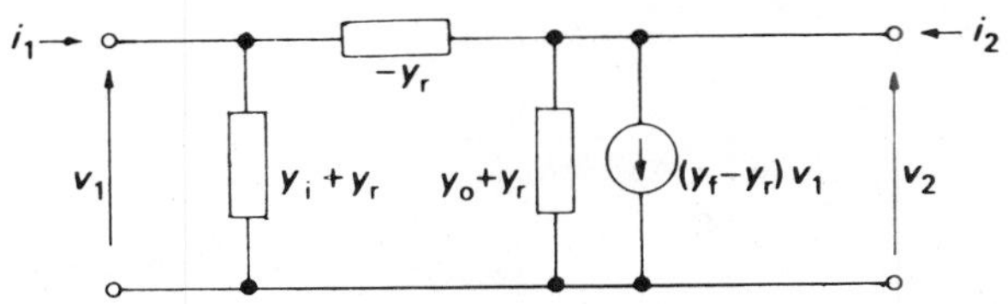

Figure 15.7. A general two-port described by its y parameters.

Using (15.13) for the various y_e parameters and remembering that h_{rb} (of the order of 10^{-4}) can be neglected compared to 1, we then have:

$$y_{ie}+y_{re}=\frac{1-\alpha_0}{r_e}+j\omega(C_e+C_{dif}),$$

$$y_{oe}+y_{re}=\frac{h_{rb}}{r_e},$$

$$y_{fe}-y_{re}=\frac{1}{r_e}\left(\alpha_0-h_{rb}\right)\simeq\frac{\alpha_0}{r_e},$$

$$-y_{re}=\frac{1}{r_c}-\frac{1-\alpha_0}{r_e}h_{rb}+j\omega C_c\simeq\frac{1}{2r_c}+j\omega C_c\,.$$

The approximation in $-y_{re}$ is justified if one uses (15.5b). Substituting all those values in Fig. 15.7 and adding $r_{b'b}$ in series with the base results in the model of Fig. 15.8(a). This is known as the *hybrid π model* of the bipolar transistor.

The big advantage of this model is that all its constituents are simple resistors or capacitors whose frequency behavior is known. It represents the transistor in a wide range of frequencies, from d.c. to an upper limit to be calculated in the next section.

Two commonly used notations for the hybrid π model components are shown in Fig. 15.8(b). Thus $C_{b'e}$ or C_π denotes C_e+C_{dif} and so forth. We shall use the two-index notation.

In the audio frequency range the h_e parameters are also in common use. There is no need to develop them since they can be immediately written down from inspection of the hybrid π model (the capacitors being taken as open circuits at the audio frequencies) keeping in mind the definition in (15.1) of the h parameters,

(15.14a) $$h_{fe}=\left.\frac{i_2}{i_1}\right|_{v_2=0}=\frac{\alpha_0}{1-\alpha_0}=\beta_0\,,$$

(15.14b) $$h_{ie}=\left.\frac{v_1}{i_1}\right|_{v_2=0}=r_{b'b}+\frac{r_e}{1-\alpha_0}=r_{b'b}+r_e(1+h_{fe})\,,$$

(15.14c) $$h_{re} = \frac{v_1}{v_2}\bigg|_{i_1=0} = \frac{r_e(1+h_{fe})}{r_e(1+h_{fe})+r_c} \simeq \frac{r_e(1+h_{fe})}{r_c},$$

(15.14d) $$h_{oe} = \frac{i_2}{v_2}\bigg|_{i_1=0} = \frac{h_{fe}}{r_e(1+h_{fe})+2r_c} + \frac{h_{rb}}{r_e} \simeq \frac{h_{fe}}{r_c}$$

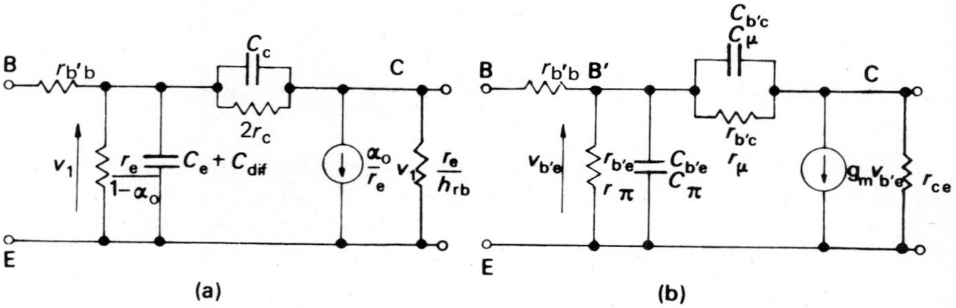

Figure 15.8. The hybrid π model: (a) the values of the various components; (b) two commonly used notations for the components.

This is represented by the model in Fig. 15.9 which has the same form as Fig. 15.4(b) and yields the relations (15.1) for the CE connection.

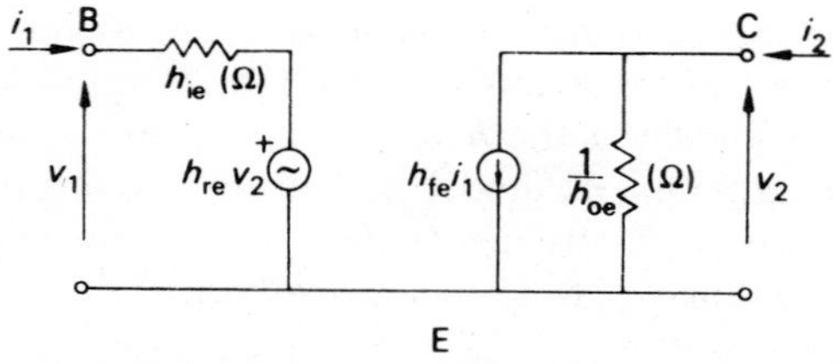

Figure 15.9. *h* parameters low-frequency model for the CE connection.

In many practical situations one may replace the $h_{re}v_2$ source by a short circuit, because of the low value of h_{re} given by (15.14c). Equations (15.14) also explain why h parameters are used: they are measured either by effectively shorting the output ($v_2=0$ for h_{fe} and h_{ie} measurements) or by effectively opening the input ($i_1=0$ for h_{re} and h_{oe}). This is relatively easy to do without posing problems for the d.c. biasing circuit. As the output resistance h_{oe}^{-1} is high (about $10^5\ \Omega$) it is effectively shorted by an a.c. load impedence of about $100\ \Omega$, which is easily obtained at 1 kHz by a 1.5 μF capacitor; since the input resistance h_{ie} is relatively low (about $10^3\ \Omega$), the transistor is effectively open circuited at the input if the small bias current I_B is fed through a series resistance of about $10^5\ \Omega$ or larger.

It can be seen from (15.14) that the h parameters depend on the operating-point current I_C. Typical measured h parameters of a Si transistor are shown in Fig. 15.10. The operating-point voltage V_{CE} has its greatest effect on the collector junction capacitance C_c and has little effect on the low-frequency h parameters, so only current dependence is shown.

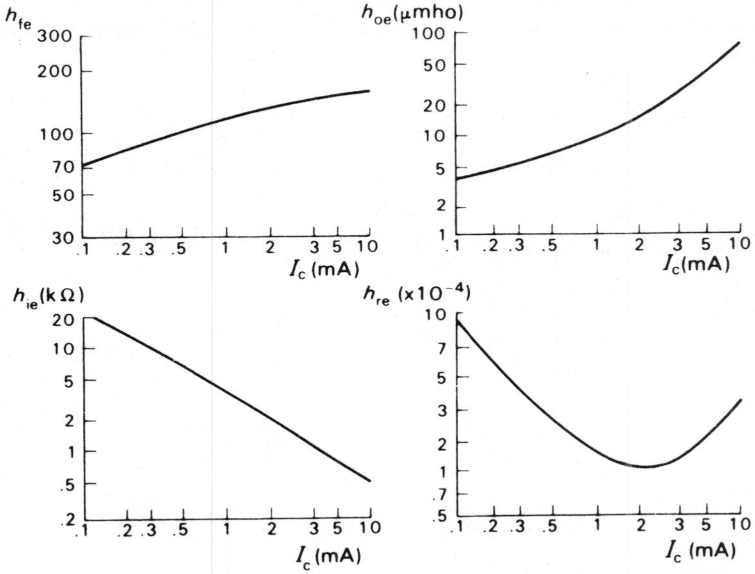

Figure 15.10. Variation with I_C of measured CE h parameters for Motorola 2N3904 transistor. ($T=25°C$, $f=1$ kHz, $V_{CE}=10$ V).

It can be seen from Fig. 15.10 that the measured parameters indeed vary with I_C as expected from eqs. (15.14):

h_{fe} increases with I_C since α_F (and α_0) increase with it (Fig. 14.9) in that range.

h_{ie} decreases because r_e is inversely proportional to I_C (appearing as a straight line with a negative slope on the log-log scale used).

h_{oe} increases since r_c decreases while h_{fe} increases with I_C.

h_{re} includes factors that increase with I_C, such as h_{fe}, and factors that decrease with I_C, such as r_e and r_c.

It is the less accurate expression due to our approximations. However, if (15.14(c)) is used to express h_{re} in terms of the other h_e parameters (neglecting $r_{b'b}$ in h_{ie} expression), one gets $h_{re}=h_{ie}h_{oe}/2h_{fe}$. Calculating h_{re} in terms of the measured h_{ie}, h_{oe} and h_{fe} for $I_c=0.1$, 2, 10 mA, one gets 7×10^{-4}, 1×10^{-4},

1.33×10^{-4} compared to the measured 9×10^{-4}, 1×10^{-4}, 3.5×10^{-4} for the respective currents. The calculated h_{re} has the same general behavior as I_c as measured in Fig. 15.10.

Let us demonstrate by an example how the h parameters are used in a typical circuit problem.

A commonly used audio frequency amplifying stage is shown in Fig. 15.11 together with values of the components. We want to construct the equivalent circuit, using the h parameter data of Fig. 15.10 for the transistor model, and use it to find the voltage amplification v_0/v_i and the input and output resistances.

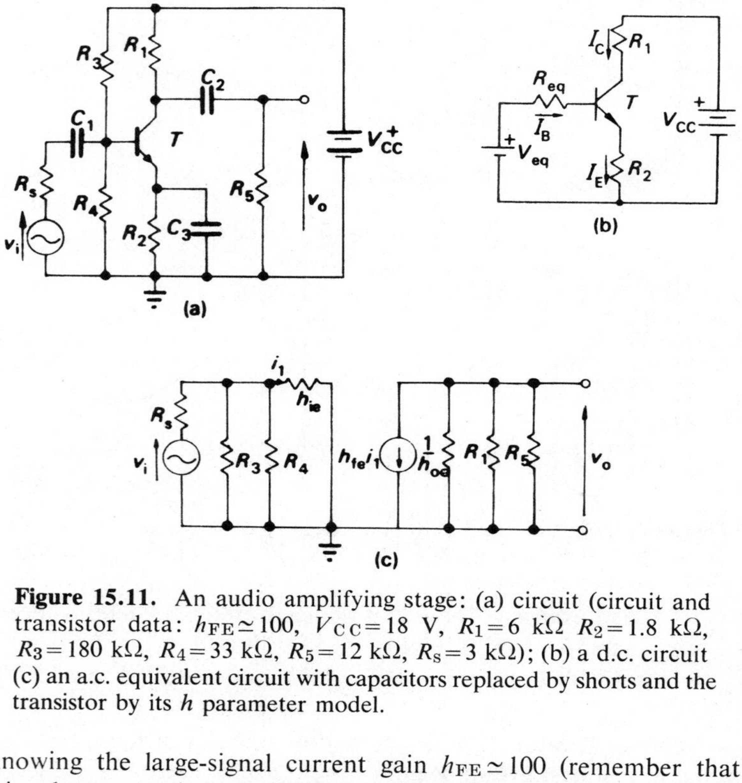

Figure 15.11. An audio amplifying stage: (a) circuit (circuit and transistor data: $h_{FE}\simeq100$, $V_{CC}=18$ V, $R_1=6$ kΩ $R_2=1.8$ kΩ, $R_3=180$ kΩ, $R_4=33$ kΩ, $R_5=12$ kΩ, $R_s=3$ kΩ); (b) a d.c. circuit (c) an a.c. equivalent circuit with capacitors replaced by shorts and the transistor by its h parameter model.

Knowing the large-signal current gain $h_{FE}\simeq100$ (remember that the small-signal current gain in the CE connection is denoted by h_{fe})and assuming $V_{BE}\simeq0.7$ V, we can find the operating point from the d.c. circuit following the approach outlined in Section 15.1. To do this we first replace the base bias circuit of R_3, R_4 and power supply V_{CC} by their Thévenin equivalent asshown in Fig. 15.11(b), where

$$R_{eq}=\frac{R_3R_4}{R_3+R_4}=28\ \text{k}\Omega,\qquad V_{eq}=V_{CC}\frac{R_4}{R_3+R_4}=2.8\ \text{V}.$$

(Notice that V_{CC} continues to serve as the collector supply since originally it had the dual function of supplying both base and collector circuits).

Assuming $V_{BE}=0.7$ V for the forward-biased base–emitter junction, we get for the base circuit of Fig. 15.11(b)

$$V_{eq}=I_B R_{eq}+V_{BE}+I_E R_2.$$

But

$$I_B=\frac{I_C}{h_{FE}}, \qquad I_E=I_C+I_B=I_C\left(1+\frac{1}{h_{FE}}\right).$$

Therefore

$$I_C=\frac{V_{eq}-V_{BE}}{(1/h_{FE})\,(R_{eq}+R_2)+R_2}=1 \text{ mA}$$

$$V_{CE}=V_{CC}-I_C(R_1+R_2)\simeq 10 \text{ V}.$$

For this operating point we get from Fig. 15.10:

$$h_{ie}=3.5 \text{ k}\Omega, \qquad h_{re}=1.3\times 10^{-4}\simeq 0,$$

$$h_{fe}=120, \qquad h_{oe}=8.5 \ \mu\text{mho}.$$

h_{re} is so small that it can be neglected.

Assuming that high enough capacitor values have been chosen so that they can be represented by short circuits in the relevant frequency range, we can draw the a.c. equivalent circuit, including the transistor h-parameter model, as in Fig. 15.11(c).

The input impedance is seen to be simply

$$R_i=\left(\frac{1}{R_3}+\frac{1}{R_4}+\frac{1}{h_{ie}}\right)^{-1}=3.1 \text{ k}\Omega.$$

R_i is mainly determined by h_{ie}, the smallest of the three terms. In the case of a CB connection the input resistance is determined by h_{ib}, which is $(h_{FE}+1)$ times smaller and it is very difficult to match it to the preceding amplifying stage output resistance, represented in Fig. 15.13(a) by R_s. This is of the order of a few kilohms at least. This is one reason why common-emitter stages are preferred.

The output resistance of our stage is

$$R_o\simeq\left(\frac{1}{R_1}+\frac{1}{R_5}+h_{oe}\right)^{-1}=3.87 \text{ k}\Omega.$$

The output voltage is

$$v_o=-i_1 h_{fe} R_o.$$

But the signal current i_1 flowing into the transistor base is

$$i_1=\frac{v_i}{R_i+R_s}\frac{R_i}{h_{ie}}.$$

Substituting i_1 in v_o we get for the amplification:

$$\frac{v_o}{v_i} = -\frac{h_{fe} R_o R_i}{(R_i + R_s) h_{ie}} \simeq -67.$$

The h parameters given by the manufacturer are typical values for the transistor type used. Actually there may be a large spread among individual transistor parameters. This spread results from minute variations in the original semiconductor substrate or in some of the processing steps used for each batch of transistors. Due to the sensitivity of the semiconductor to extremely minute contaminations and to very small deviations in processing conditions (such as the exact position in the diffusion furnace of the wafer), some such spread is inevitable. The manufacturer's data usually include the worst-case value of a parameter (such as the lowest h_{fe} or the highest C_c) beside the typical value. A given circuit design should be checked against a worst-case combination of critical parameters.

15.5 The Drift Transistor

In a uniform-base transistor the base transit time, τ_B, is governed by diffusion only and is given by (11.11):

$$\tau_B(\text{dif}) = \frac{W_B^2}{2D_h}.$$

In a planar transistor, however, there is a steep gradient in the base doping profile (Fig. 14.2). If one approximates that profile by an exponential function

(15.15a) $$N_D(x) = N_D(0) \exp\left(-\eta \frac{x}{W_B}\right),$$

where x is measured from the emitter junction, then η represents the logarithmic ratio of the impurity concentrations at both base edges:

(15.15b) $$\eta = \ln \frac{N_D(0)}{N_D(W_B)}$$

In Section 4.4 it was shown that an impurity gradient creates a built-in field, given by (4.26), which yields for our exponential gradient the constant value of

(15.16) $$E = -\frac{kT}{q} \frac{1}{N_D(x)} \frac{dN_D(x)}{dx} = \frac{kT}{q} \frac{\eta}{W_B}$$

This field helps the minority holes on their movement towards the collector junction. The hole current through the base will now contain both drift and diffusion components, the first being the more important. This is why these transistors are also called *drift transistors*, as was mentioned before.

The drift field shortens the minority carrier transit time through the base considerably. A rough estimate can be obtained as follows:

$$\tau_B(\text{drift}) \simeq \frac{W_B}{v} = \frac{W_B}{\mu_h E} = \frac{W_B^2 q}{\mu_h \eta k T}, \tag{15.17}$$

where (15.16) has been used. Remembering Einstein's relation, we obtain

$$\frac{\tau_B(\text{dif})}{\tau_B(\text{drift})} = \frac{\eta}{2}. \tag{15.18}$$

(The solution to Problem 15.16 gives a more accurate value.) Since η may be as high as 8, drift transistors have better high-frequency performance. It is also obvious that very narrow base width W_B is a must for a high-frequency transistor.

In the hybrid π model, Fig. 15.8, the emitter diffusion capacitance is proportional to τ_B. For a drift transistor, therefore, $C_{b'e}$ is also much lower than for a diffusion (uniform-base) transistor.

Another difference arises because in a drift transistor the base doping is higher than that in the collector. This reduces base-width modulation with V_{CE} and therefore increases $r_{b'c}$ and r_{ce}. In fact $r_{b'c}$ becomes so large compared to the reactance of $C_{b'c}$ that it can usually be regarded as an open circuit.

The drift-field effects disappear gradually as the operating-current level is increased towards high injection. The large number of injected minority holes draw into the base an equally large number of majority electrons to neutralize their charge. At high injection this modifies the original majority concentration gradient and the field disappears.

15.6 The CE Connection at High Frequencies, the Gain–Bandwidth Product

The complete hybrid π model enables one to calculate the transistor behavior at high frequencies, so long as the base transit time τ_B is much shorter than the signal period T. Otherwise α becomes complex as already mentioned.

The high-frequency limit for the applicability of the hybrid π model can be estimated from the requirement

$$\omega \tau_B = 2\pi \frac{\tau_B}{T} \ll 2\pi$$

or

$$\frac{\tau_B}{T} \ll 1. \tag{15.19}$$

τ_B is related to C_{dif} in the emitter by (11.10), but since in any transistor $T_B \ll T_h$ this equation is reduced to

(15.20) $$\tau_B = r_e C_{dif}\ .$$

For example, if $C_{dif} = 10$ pF at $I_E = 1$ mA we get, from (15.20), $\tau_B = 2.6 \times 10^{-10}$ s. Limiting τ_B/T to 0.05 yields $f \simeq 200$ MHz as the maximum frequency at which one can still use the hybrid π model of that transistor with some accuracy.

Let us now investigate that model further to see what information it yields about how the transistor behaves with frequency up to that point.

We shall need to use the small-signal β, which is defined as the ratio of the short-circuit current in the collector circuit to the a.c. base current. Short circuiting the collector in the hybrid π model leads to Fig. 15.12.

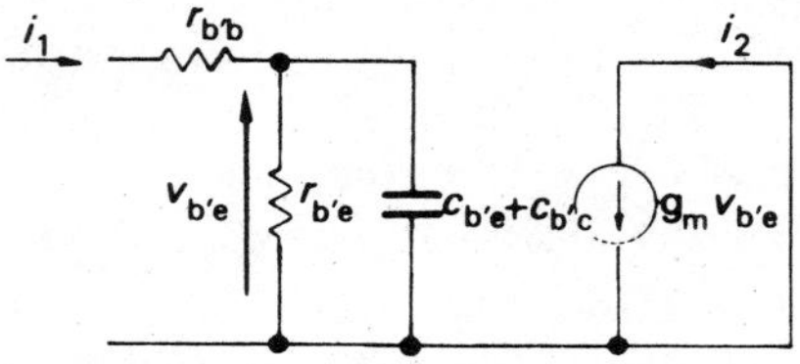

Figure 15.12. The hybrid π model with effective collector–emitter short for calculating the high-frequency β.

From the figure

$$\beta = \frac{i_2}{i_1} = \frac{g_m v_{b'e}}{i_1} = \frac{g_m r_{b'e}}{1 + j\omega r_{b'e}(C_{b'e} + C_{b'c})}\ .$$

Substituting the values of g_m, $r_{b'e}$, $C_{b'e}$, $C_{b'e}$ from Fig. 15.8(a) gives:

$$\beta = \frac{\beta_0}{1 + j\omega r_e(\beta_0 + 1)\ (C_e + C_{dif} + C_c)}\ ,$$

where $\beta_0 = h_{fe}$ is the low-frequency value of β. Remembering that $\beta_0 \gg 1$ and that $r_e C_{dif} = \tau_B$, we can write

(15.21) $$\frac{\beta}{\beta_0} = \frac{1}{1 + j\omega\beta_0(r_e C_e + r_e C_c + \tau_B)}\ .$$

Defining

(15.22) $$\omega_\beta = \frac{1}{\beta_0(r_e C_e + r_e C_c + \tau_B)}\ ,$$

we obtain

(15.23) $$\frac{\beta}{\beta_0} = \frac{1}{1 + j(\omega/\omega_\beta)}\ .$$

A graph of $|\beta/\beta_0|$ using the decibel scale (dB$=20\log_{10}|\beta/\beta_0|$) is shown in Fig. 15.13.

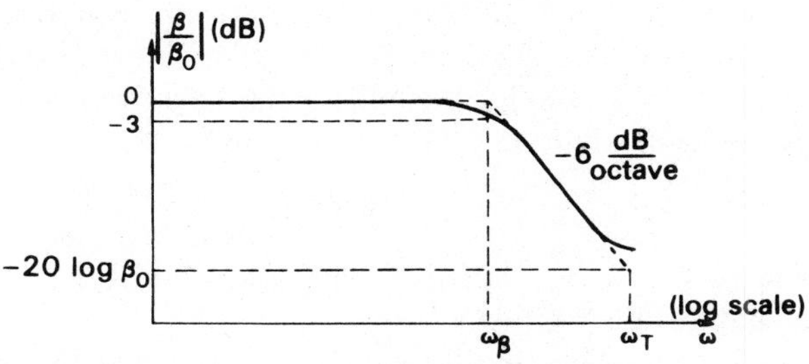

Figure 15.13. The short-circuit current gain dependence on frequency for the CE connection.

It is obvious from the figure that as long as $\omega < \omega_\beta$, one can assume $\beta \simeq \beta_0$ and constant. When $\omega = \omega_\beta$, β is reduced by 3 dB compared to its low-frequency value. For $\omega > \omega_\beta$, we can neglect unity in the denominator of (15.23) in comparison to ω/ω_β, giving

(15.24) $$\frac{\beta}{\beta_0} \simeq -j\frac{\omega_\beta}{\omega}, \qquad \omega > \omega_\beta.$$

Hence

$$20\log_{10}\left|\frac{\beta}{\beta_0}\right| = 20\,(\log_{10}\omega_\beta - \log_{10}\omega).$$

When ω changes by one octave in this frequency range, say from $\omega = \omega_1$ to $\omega = 2\omega_1$, the curve of Fig. 15.13 comes down by

$$20[(\log_{10}\omega_\beta - \log_{10}2\omega_1) - (\log_{10}\omega_\beta - \log_{10}\omega_1)] = -20\log_{10}2 \simeq -6\text{ dB/octave}.$$

This is the slope of the curve in Fig. 15.13 beyond ω_β. In order to compare and evaluate the ability of different transistors to function at high frequencies, a quality factor called the *gain–bandwidth product*, f_T, is defined for the transistor. $\omega_T = 2\pi f_T$ is the angular frequency at which $|\beta|$ equals 1 if the slope of -6 dB/octave is assumed to continue indefinitely, as shown by the dashed line in Fig. 15.13 (actually the hybrid π model no longer represents the transistor with any accuracy near ω_T and the measured slope is lower, as shown by the full line in Fig. 15.13). Putting $\omega = \omega_T$ and $|\beta| = 1$ in (15.24) gives

(15.25) $$\frac{1}{\omega_T} = \frac{1}{\beta_0\omega_\beta} = r_eC_e + r_eC_c + \tau_B = r_e(C_{b'e} + C_{b'c}).$$

Therefore $1/\omega_T$ is the sum of three time constants: the first is due to the emitter-junction depletion-layer capacitance (r_eC_e), the second to the collector-junction depletion capacitance (r_eC_c), and the third to the base transit time ($\tau_B=r_eC_{dif}$).

Since ω_T may be very high and the real transistor behavior near it differs from our model, we measure it indirectly: $|\beta|$ is measured at a convenient known frequency ω, high enough to fall on the negative-slope portion of Fig. 15.13 ($\omega_\beta<\omega<\omega_T$), where (15.24) yields

$$|\beta|\,\omega=\beta_0\omega_\beta=\omega_T. \tag{15.26}$$

From $|\beta|$ and ω, ω_T is calculated. Equation (15.26) explains why ω_T is called the gain–bandwidth product.

Equation (15.25) predicts that ω_T increases with I_C (or I_E) because r_e is inversely proportional to the current. This is indeed correct, but only up to the point of high injection, when the built-in drift field washes out and the effective base width starts to grow, as will be explained in Chapter 19.3. At that point ω_T starts to drop again.

The results of f_T measurement of a small-signal Si transistor are shown in Fig. 15.14. The measurements were performed at 30 MHz and by (15.26) $f_T=|\beta(30\text{ MHz})|\times 30$ MHz.

The dependence of f_T on V_{CE}, also shown in the figure, is explained by remembering that increase of V_{CE} reduces the collector depletion-layer capacitance C_c and also shortens the effective base width somewhat, reducing τ_B. Both effects contribute towards an increased ω_T, however: in modern transistors the first time constant, r_eC_e, is the largest, making the effects of the other two (and of V_{CE}) relatively small.

High-frequency power transistors are usually operated in the region $\omega_\beta<\omega<\omega_T$. The change of $|\beta|$ with ω can be tolerated in narrow-band amplifiers. The transistor load in these cases is a frequency-selective tuned resonant circuit. Only the narrow band around the resonant frequency is amplified and only this is of importance. $|\beta|$ can be assumed constant in such a narrow band.

Above ω_β the reactance of $C_{b'e}$ effectively shorts $r_{b'e}$ in the hybrid π model, reducing the input impedance to only $r_{b'b}$ (actually, because of the distributed nature of $r_{b'b}$ and C_e the effective $r_{b'b}$ at high frequencies is smaller than at low frequencies because part of it is shorted by the distributed capacitance). The r.f. input power is then determined by the remaining part of $r_{b'b}$. The transistor output impedance, on the other hand, is determined by the reactance of C_c which becomes smaller (at high ω) than r_{ce}. Detailed calculations for matched load conditions (so that maximum power output is obtained) show the power gain to be

$$G=\frac{\omega_T}{4\omega^2 r_{b'b}C_c}. \tag{15.27}$$

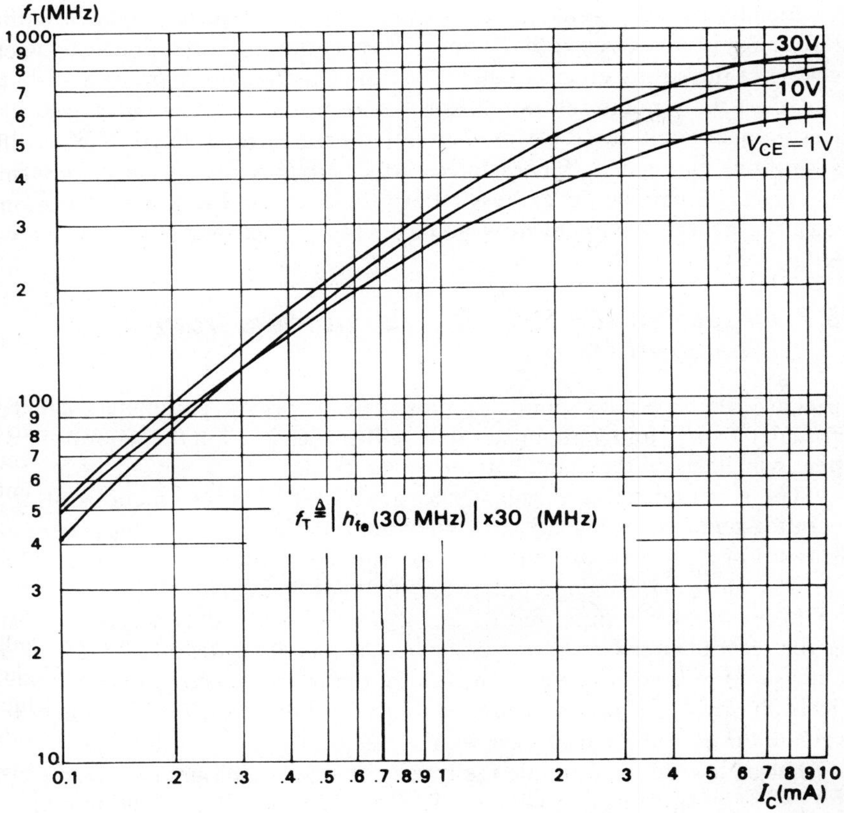

Figure 15.14. Measured dependence of f_T on operating point for the 2N3904 Si transistor.

The value of $r_{b'b}C_c$ (in picoseconds) is sometimes included in the data sheets of r.f. transistors. It is obvious how important it is to reduce both $r_{b'b}$ and C_c to the minimum possible values in such transistors.

An alternative quality factor sometimes used for comparing high-frequency transistors is the *maximum frequency for oscillation*, defined as the frequency at which G of (15.27) equals 1:

$$f_{max}(\text{osc}) \triangleq \frac{1}{4\pi}\left(\frac{\omega_T}{r_{b'b}C_c}\right)^{1/2}. \tag{15.28}$$

An oscillator is an amplifier in which part of the output power is fed back as the input, with the proper phase to build up oscillations. If the external oscillator circuit were completely lossless it could conceivably oscillate up to f_{max}. Real oscillators, of course, need $G > 1$ to operate.

Finally, it should be mentioned that use of lumped-element models in the UHF range is only a very rough approximation and is of little practical value, because of the strong effects of all the parasitic distributed components which depend on the way the semiconductor chip is mounted and connected to the measurement point. It is therefore better to describe the mounted transistor by its scattering parameters (S parameters) which are measured at specified reference planes. S parameters express ratios of incident and reflected waves and measuring them calls for microwave techniques, which will not be discussed here.

15.7 Obtaining the Hybrid π Parameters from Measured Data

Once the operating point is known, the hybrid π parameters can be calculated from y and h parameter data, either measured in the laboratory or already included in the manufacturer's data sheets.

The h parameters are usually measured at 1 kHz as functions of the operating point, as in Fig. 15.10. If they are only known at a single value of I_C and V_{CE}, one can use eqs. (15.14), and the functional dependence of r_e, r_c, h_{fe} on I_C and V_{CE} to estimate the effects of their change.

In most cases both f_T and C_c are also given in the data sheets, at least for the recommended operating point (C_c is sometimes denoted by C_{cb} if it is measured in such a way as to neutralize the transistor mount capacitance effects and by C_{ob} if it is measured with an open emitter). This is enough to evaluate the hybrid π parameters with some accuracy.

Let us take as an example the transistor whose measured h parameters and f_T are given in Fig. 15.10 and 15.14 respectively. The operating point is assumed to be at $I_C = 1$ mA, $V_{CE} = 10$ V.

$r_{b'e}$: Inspection of the hybrid π model shows that

$$r_{b'e} = r_e(1 + h_{fe}) = \frac{kT}{qI_C}(1 + h_{fe}). \tag{15.29}$$

From Fig. 15.10: $h_{fe} = \beta_0 \simeq 120$, hence $r_{b'e} \simeq 3150\Omega$.

$r_{b'b}$: The low-frequency input resistance to the hybrid π model is shown by (15.14a) to be $h_{ie} = r_{b'b} + r_{b'e}$.

$$r_{b'b} \simeq h_{ie} - r_{b'e}. \tag{15.30}$$

From Fig. 15.10 we find $h_{ie} \simeq 3500\ \Omega$, hence $r_{b'b} \simeq 350\ \Omega$. Actually, this is a very inaccurate method that may lead to absurd results because the relatively small $r_{b'b}$ is expressed as the difference between two much larger values, each known only with limited accuracy due to parameter spread. A more accurate way for obtaining $r_{b'b}$ needs knowledge of y_{ie} at a frequency

ω_1 high enough for y_{ie} to be complex. From y_{ie} definition

$$\text{(15.31)} \qquad y_{ie} = \frac{i_1}{v_1}\bigg|_{v_2=0} = \left[r_{b'b} + \frac{r_{b'e}}{1+j\omega r_{b'e}(C_{b'e}+C_{b'c})}\right]^{-1}.$$

Equation (15.31) describes a half circle in y_{ie} plane for ω varying between zero and infinity, as shown in Fig. 15.15(a). Two known points of that circle, at $y_{ie}(\omega_1) = g + jb$ and at $y_{ie}(o) = (r_{b'b} + r_{b'e})^{-1} = h_{ie}^{-1}$, enable us to locate its center 0 by the graphical technique indicated on the figure. The third point of the circle at $y_{ie}(\infty) = r^{-1}_{b'b}$ then gives us the required value.

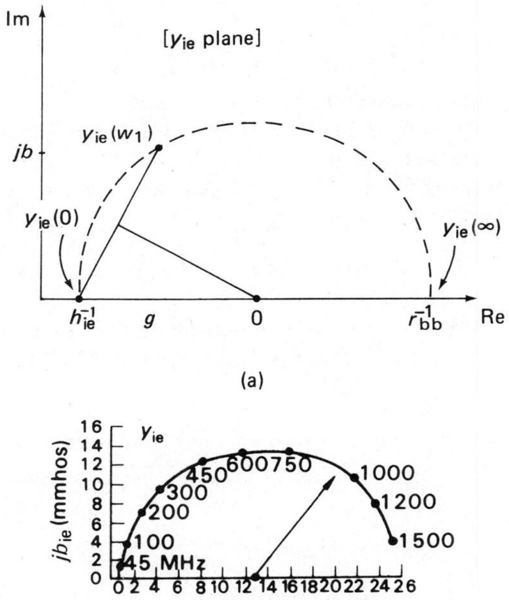

Figure 15.15. (a) Use of y_{ie} dependence on ω to obtain $r_{b'b}$; (b) the dependence of y_{ie} on f for the Motorola 2N5829 UHF transistor (measured at 2 mA, 10 V).

Such a y_{ie} curve as measured by the manufacturer, is shown in Fig. 15.15(b) (Motorola UHF transistor whose f_T is higher than 2 GHz). From it

$$y_{ie}(\omega \to \infty) = \frac{1}{r_{b'b}} = 24.6 \times 10^{-3}\,\Omega^{-1}.$$

Therefore

$$r_{b'b} \simeq 40\ \Omega.$$

If the value of $r_{b'b}\,C_c$ is given, then a knowledge of C_c gives the high-frequency value of $r_{b'b}$.

g_m: From its definition of Fig. 15.8, g_m is given by

$$g_m = \frac{\alpha_0}{r_e} \simeq \frac{1}{r_e} = \frac{qI_C}{kT}\,. \tag{15.32}$$

At 1 mA $g_m \simeq 39$ mmho.

$r_{b'c}$: From eqs. (15.14c) and Fig. 15.10 we see that approximately

$$r_{b'c} = 2r_c = \frac{r_{b'e}}{h_{re}} = \frac{r_e(1+h_{fe})}{h_{re}}\,. \tag{15.33}$$

Using $h_{re} = 1.3\times10^{-4}$ from Fig. 15.10, we get $r_{b'c} \simeq 24\,\text{M}\Omega$, which is so large that it can be regarded as an open circuit.

$C_{b'c}$: This is approximately the collector depletion-layer capacitance. For our transistor the data sheets give 2 pF at $V_{CE} = 5$ V. Assuming the collector junction, obtained by diffusion, behaves like a linear graded junction, we can use (9.53) to obtain

$$C_{b'c}(10\text{ V}) = C_{b'c}(5\text{ V}) \times \left(\frac{5}{10}\right)^{1/3} \simeq 1.6\text{ pF}.$$

$C_{b'e}$: This is the sum of the emitter-junction depletion-layer and diffusion capacitances. Using (15.25) for ω_T and remembering that $\tau_B = r_e C_{dif}$, we get

$$\frac{1}{\omega_T} = r_e(C_e + C_{dif} + C_c) = r_e(C_{b'e} + C_{b'c}).$$

Therefore

$$C_{b'e} = C_e + C_{dif} = \frac{1}{\omega_T r_e} - C_{b'c}. \tag{15.34}$$

From Fig. 15.14 we find $f_T = 305$ MHz at 1 mA, hence $c_{b'e} = 18.5$ pF. The dependence of f_T on I_C enables one to differentiate between C_e and C_{dif} since the last is proportional to I_C while the first is almost constant. At very low I_C, $C_{b'e} \simeq C_e$. Using the measured value of $f_T = 42$ MHz at $I_C = 0.1$ mA (Fig. 15.14) yields $C_e \simeq 13$ pF. Hence $C_{dif} \simeq 5.5$ pF at 1 mA.

r_{ce}: From its definition in Fig. 15.8 and (15.14c), (15.14d) r_{ce} is given by

$$r_{ce}^{-1} = \frac{h_{rb}}{r_e} = h_{oe} - \frac{h_{fe}}{r_e(1+h_{fe}) + 2r_c} = h_{oe} - \frac{h_{fe}}{h_{ie}(1+h_{re}^{-1})} \tag{15.35}$$

From Fig. 15.10, $h_{re} \simeq 1.3\times10^{-4}$, $h_{oe} = 9\times10^{-6}$ mho, $h_{fe} = 120$, $h_{ie} = 3500\,\Omega$ hence $r_{ce} \simeq 220\,\text{k}\Omega$.

Thus, all the hybrid π parameters are determined.

15.8 Thermal and Shot Noise, Transistor Noise Figure

The maximum amplification available from any active device is limited by its own noise, and the transistor is no exception. The noise output power, i.e. the random electrical fluctuations at the transistor output terminals, is not just the input noise power amplified, it is always higher. The transistor adds its own noise contribution to whatever noise that accompanies the input signal. This added noise can be expressed as an equivalent noise source at the input terminals of an otherwise noiseless transistor and obviously limits the minimum signal that can be applied there and be amplified coherently.

Let us examine the principal noise mechanisms in the amplifying devices in use today: the bipolar transistor and the junction FET. The quantity used to express the device noise contribution is termed the *noise figure* and is included in the manufacturer's data sheets of transistors intended mainly for small-signal amplification at high frequencies. This noise figure is a function of the operating conditions and frequency and we shall see how it depends on them.

There are three main noise mechanisms in the transistor. The first is known as *thermal* or *Johnson noise*. This type of noise exists in any resistive (conductive) material that is in thermal equilibrium at a temperature larger than absolute zero. Thermal noise results from the random movements of charged particles such as electrons, which keep exchanging their kinetic energy with the vibrating lattice atoms. The random charge movements appear as minute voltage and current fluctuations at the resistive element terminals, i.e. as noise. The relation between thermal noise power, temperature and resistance was calculated by Nyquist in 1928. We can reach this result by the following much simplified reasoning:

Each part of the resistive material, at temperature T, emits photons which are electromagnetic wave packets of energy $E=hf$. Being at thermal equilibrium with the surrounding parts, it also absorbs the same amount of energy on the average.

The distribution function of photons in energy, i.e., their most probable distribution, is shown by statistical thermodynamics to be given by the Bose–Einstein statistics,

$$f_{\text{BE}}(E)=\frac{1}{\exp(E/kT)-1}, \tag{15.36}$$

in much the same way as the electronic distribution function is given by the Fermi–Dirac statistics (eq. 6.40). Only those photons whose frequency falls in the frequency range of possible amplification by our amplifier are of interest to us, say up to $f=10$ GHz. The energy of such a photon, hf, is about 3000 times lower than the value of kT at 300°K. In the frequency range of interest, therefore, $E=hf \ll kT$ and $f_{\text{BE}}(E)$ is well approximated by

$$f_{\text{BE}}(E)\simeq\frac{1}{(1+E/kT)-1}=\frac{kT}{E}. \tag{15.37}$$

The wavelengths or frequencies of the various photons represent modes of oscillations that exist in the resistor. If the frequency separation between two adjacent modes is δf, then the number of modes within the frequency range Δf is

$$\text{number of modes in } \Delta f = \frac{\Delta f}{\delta f}. \tag{15.38}$$

The thermal noise energy included in the range Δf is given by the product of the energy E of the photons, their distribution in energy $f_{\mathrm{BE}}(E)$, and the number of modes in that range: that is,

$$\text{noise energy in } \Delta f = E \times \frac{kT}{E} \times \frac{\Delta f}{\delta f} = \frac{kT\Delta f}{\delta f}. \tag{15.39}$$

We can simplify matters by regarding the modes as higher harmonics of a complex noise voltage wave whose period in the time domain is τ (actually the noise is a non-analytic function, so Nyquist applied it to a transmission line whose modes he counted). From Fourier-series theory we know that the separation between the harmonics is related to τ by

$$\delta f = \frac{1}{\tau}. \tag{15.40}$$

The noise energy of (15.39) is supplied in the period τ. Therefore, the noise power in the frequency range Δf is

$$P = \frac{\text{noise energy in } \Delta f}{\tau} = kt\ \Delta f \text{ watts.} \tag{15.41}$$

This is the Nyquist equation for the Johnson or thermal noise power available from the resistor. Since P is independent of f, at least up to optical frequencies, it is termed *white noise*.

This thermal noise power can be supplied by a resistor R to a matched load (provided that load was noiseless or kept at 0° K so as not to return the same amount of power). A noisy resistor of magnitude R can therefore be represented by a noise voltage source V_{n} in series with a noiseless resistance R with values so chosen that they supply the same amount of noise power to a matched load R, i.e. the source must have a mean square value of:

$$\overline{v_{\mathrm{n}}^2} = 4kTR\ \Delta f \tag{15.42}$$

(a parallel noise current source with conductance $G = R^{-1}$ can also be used where $\overline{i_{\mathrm{n}}^2} = 4kTG\ \Delta f$).

The most significant thermal noise source in the bipolar transistor is that associated with the base spreading resistance $r_{\mathrm{b'b}}$. A noise voltage source of $4kTr_{\mathrm{b'b}}\ \Delta f$ mean square value should therefore be added to the transistor small-signal model. There are, however, additional noise sources in the bipolar transistor, as we shall see.

In the JFET, thermal noise is the main noise source. It results from the channel resistance and is accompanied by induced noise on the gate.

The second important noise mechanism is associated with non-equilibrium conditions in a junction through which a current I flows. It is termed *shot noise*, and is a direct result of the discrete nature of the current carriers and therefore of the current-carrying process. The current I should be viewed as the sum total of very many short and small current pulses, each contributed by the passage of a single electron or hole through the junction depletion layer.

This type of noise is also practically white, as can be seen if we consider the spectral density obtained by the Fourier transform of a single such pulse, whose duration is from $-\tau/2$ to $+\tau/2$, where τ is now the electron transit time across the depletion layer. The current pulse height is then q/τ and its width is τ. The time- and the frequency-domain pictures of the pulse are shown in Fig. 15.16.

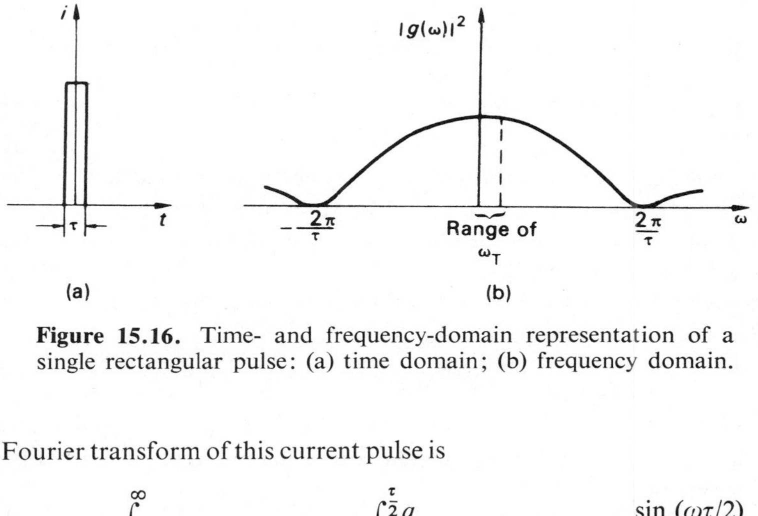

Figure 15.16. Time- and frequency-domain representation of a single rectangular pulse: (a) time domain; (b) frequency domain.

The Fourier transform of this current pulse is

$$(15.43)\quad F(f)=\int_{-\infty}^{\infty} i(t)\exp(-j\omega t)\,dt=\int_{-\frac{\tau}{2}}^{\frac{\tau}{2}}\frac{q}{\tau}\exp(-j\omega t)\,dt=q\,\frac{\sin(\omega\tau/2)}{\omega\tau/2}.$$

The spectral power density is proportional to $|F(f)|^2$. We are interested, however, only in those noise frequencies that are well below the ω_T of our transistor. Equation (15.25) gives ω_T, but in deriving it we neglected time delays as short as τ necessary to cross the depletion region. We shall consider this in Chapter 20 when we deal with microwave transistors, but essentially these time delays are added on the right-hand side of (15.25). This makes $\tau \ll 2\pi/\omega_T$, so that $\omega_T \ll 2\pi/\tau$. Our frequency range of interest is therefore limited to frequencies for which the right-hand side of (15.43) is approximately constant, as shown in Fig. 15.16(b). Let us therefore replace $F(f)$ by a constant, which is equivalent to regarding the current pulses as narrow impulses of duration approaching zero, and magnitude $(q/\tau)\times\tau=q$. To handle the spectrum of a multitude of such random impulses, random signal techniques are needed (see Refs. 21, 23). Carson's theorem, which is useful in such cases, states that if

$$I(t)=\sum_k i_k(t-t_k)$$

is the sum of the small pulses $i_k(t-t_k)$ occurring randomly at times t_k at an average rate $\bar{n}$, and if $F(f)$ is the Fourier transform of a single pulse, then the power spectral density of $I(t)$ is given by

$$S(f)=\overline{2n}\ \overline{|F(f)|^2}$$

which in our case becomes

$$S(f)=2\bar{n}q^2.$$

But if $\bar{n}$ current carriers cross the junction per unit time on the average, the d.c. component is $\bar{I}=\bar{n}q$. Therefore

$$S(f)=2q\bar{I}.$$

This is called the Schottky theorem for the shot-noise power density, though its dimensions are not those of power. Actually the integration of $S(f)$ over all frequencies gives the mean square value of the noise current. If we are interested in a limited bandwidth of Δf only, the shot-noise contribution can be represented by a current source with a mean square value of

$$\overline{i_n^2}=\int_{f_0}^{f_0+\Delta f} S(f)\,df=2q\bar{I}\,\Delta f \tag{15.44}$$

It should be noted that $\bar{I}$ is the current carried by one type of current carrier crossing the junction.

If two types of particles cross, as in a forward-biased junction, where the majority carriers contribute a current of $I_0 \exp(qV/kT)$ (due to diffusion) and the minorities contribute $-I_0$ (due to drift), the two noise contributions, which are *uncorrelated*, are additive:

$$\overline{i_n^2}=\overline{i_{n1}^2}+\overline{i_{n2}^2}=2qI_0(\exp(qV/kT)+1)=2q(I+2I_0), \tag{15.45}$$

where $I=I_0(\exp(qV/kT)-1)$.

The equivalent noise current source should be added across the relevant junction. Shot noise increases with the biasing current and in a reverse-biased junction will be proportional to the leakage current.

Shot noise is usually insignificant in a JFET because of its negligible small leakage current.

A third noise mechanism, called *flicker* or *l/f noise*, is of importance only at low frequencies, usually below 1 kHz. Its origin is not too clear, but it apparently results from carrier trapping and recombining at the crystal imperfections, mostly at the surface. In modern transistors this noise is of less importance except at very low frequencies (roughly below 1 kHz) in both bipolar and JFET.

The noise sources in the bipolar transistor can be incorporated in its small-signal model. In order to do this one may start from the Ebers–Moll equations in the active zone ($V_{EB}>0, V_{CB}<0$) and determine the particle flows crossing each junction in terms of the Ebers–Moll parameters. Thus in a PNP transitor $\alpha_F I_{ES}$ exp (qV_{EB}/kT) is a hole flow across the emitter junction that continues and also crosses the collector junction. Such a flow contributes shot noise that can be represented by a current of a mean square value given by (15.44). Adding the noise contributions of the various current components across each junction (which are uncorrelated), assuming $I_{CBO} \ll |I_C|$ (so that the source between collector and base terminals can be neglected) and remembering that the base resistance contributes thermal noise, one finds (Ref. 21) that the hybrid π model, including noise sources, looks like Fig. 15.17(a).

Here

$$\overline{v^2_{b'b}} = 4kTr_{b'b}\,\Delta f\,,$$

$$\overline{i_1^2} = 2qI_B\,\Delta f\,,$$

$$\overline{i_2^2} = 2qI_C\,\Delta f\,.$$

Obviously the transistor should be operated at a low level of bias current to reduce its noise.

The total noise contributed by the transistor is represented by its *noise figure* (*NF*), which is the ratio, in decibels, between the total noise power P_o(noise) delivered by the transistor to the load in the real case, and the noise power delivered to the load in the ideal case in which the transistor is noise free, so that the only noise originates in the input signal source internal resistance R_s, held at 290°K. This resistance at the input delivers a thermal noise power of P_i (noise) to the transistor input which appears as $G_P P_i$(noise) at the load, where G_P is the transistor power amplification. Therefore

$$NF \triangleq 10 \log \frac{P_o(\text{noise})}{G_P P_i(\text{noise})} \tag{15.46}$$

But

$$G_p = \frac{P_o(\text{signal})}{P_i(\text{signal})};$$

therefore

$$NF = 10 \log \frac{P_i(\text{signal})/P_i(\text{noise})}{P_o(\text{signal})/P_o(\text{noise})} \quad (15.47)$$

$$= 10 \log \frac{\text{input signal-to-noise ratio}}{\text{output signal-to-noise ratio}}.$$

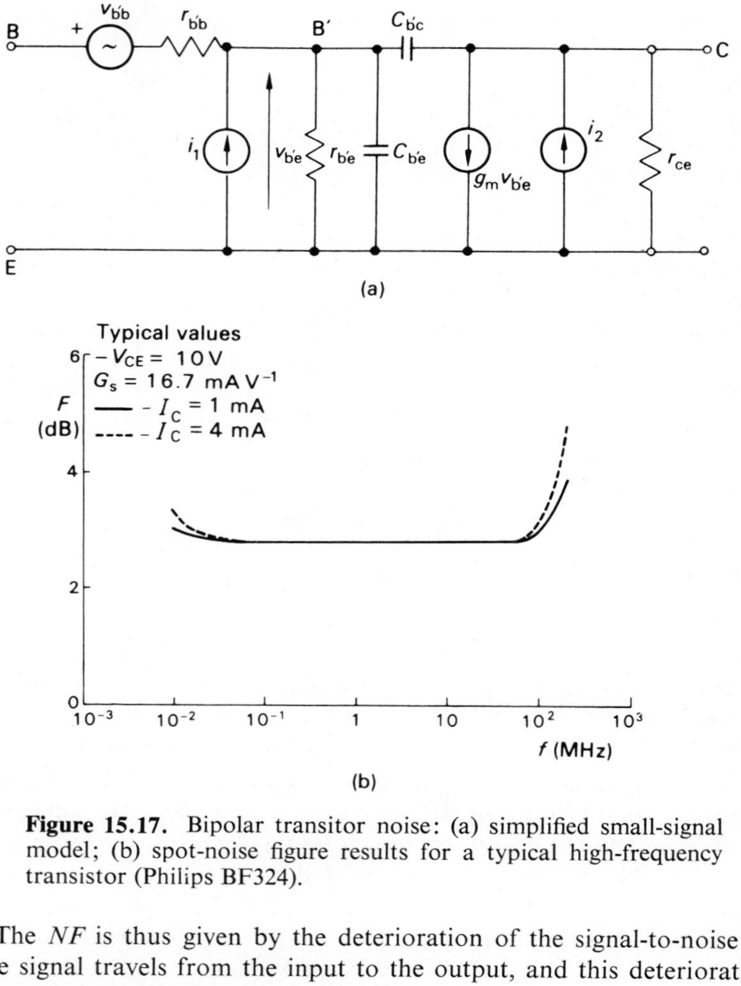

Figure 15.17. Bipolar transitor noise: (a) simplified small-signal model; (b) spot-noise figure results for a typical high-frequency transistor (Philips BF324).

The *NF* is thus given by the deterioration of the signal-to-noise ratio as the signal travels from the input to the output, and this deterioration is due to the additional noise contributed by the transistor.

The *NF* obviously depends on the amplifier frequency band, and one can talk about an average noise figure in a wide band, or, as is more common, refer to the *spot noise figure*, i.e. the value measured with a very narrow band-pass filter centered at the desired frequency *f*.

Typical results for a bipolar high-frequency transistor look like Fig. 15.17(b). the *NF* depends on the ohmic source admittance G_S connected at the input, and on the operating point. Obviously, these are chosen by the manufacturer to give the minimum *NF*. This choice cannot always be followed in practice: other considerations may dictate a compromise.

The higher *NF* in the low-frequency range is due to the l/f noise. The constant value in the middle frequency band is due to thermal and shot noise sources in the transistor model, which have a practically constant white-noise spectrum. The increase at higher frequencies is related to the reduction of the transistor power amplification there which, by (15.46), increases the *NF*. A low mid-range *NF* necessitates a high h_{FE} (so that a low base bias current is needed). A low high-frequency *NF* requires low $r_{b'b}$ and high f_T (so that thermal noise is reduced while high-frequency power amplification is increased according to (15.27).

QUESTIONS

15.1 What is the small-signal amplification of a transistor biased into the saturation region?

15.2 What are the dimensions of the various h-parameters in eqs. (15.1)? Check the dimensions in eqs. (15.14) and compare.

15.3 What does the model of Fig. 15.5 predict for i_c/i_e at infinitely high frequencies? Does it mean that transistor action continues at those frequencies?

15.4 Why does the common-base model in Fig. 15.5 not contain a diffusion capacitance associated with the collector junction?

15.5 According to (15.27) a small $r_{b'b}$ is required for high-frequency transistors. Why does one not simply increase the base doping to a value high enough to make $r_{b'b}$ negligible?

15.6 Find the current gain $(i_c/i_e) \mid_{v_2=0}$ in Fig. 15.5 as $f \rightarrow \infty$. Explain the result in terms of power amplification.

15.7 Fig. 15.7 is supposed to describe the general two-part equations in terms of the y parameters.

(a) By calculating its y parameters, prove that it does so;

(b) suggest another equivalent circuit that does the same but with two separate controlled current sources.

15.8 Suggest laboratory set ups for measuring h_{ie} and h_{re}.

15.9 Draw the equivalent small-signal circuit to the real circuit in Fig. 15.11 that will be able to represent it through a wide frequency range. What is the worst-case combination of transistor parameters from the viewpoint of (a) amplification, and (b) input impedance.

15.10 An r.f. power transistor circuit is being tested. A constant-amplitude input signal, $v_S \sin \omega t$, is fed into the base by a signal generator of very low output impedance. The test frequency is increased by steps and the output power in the load circuit is measured. Suddenly, the transistor burns out. It is replaced, the measurement repeated and around the same frequency it burns out again. Can you suggest a possible cause for this?

PROBLEMS

15.11 Calculate h_{fe} at 25°C for the transistor, whose h_{FE} dependence on I_C is shown in Fig. 14.9(b). do this for $I_C = 10\,\text{mA}$, $100\,\text{mA}$, $200\,\text{mA}$ and 1 A.

15.12 Develop an expression for the low-frequency output admittance g_0 of a *CB*-connected transistor whose input is effectively shorted. [*Hint*: use a similar approach to that leading to (14.24) and base it on the minority carriers distribution in the base for two different values of V_{CB}.]

15.13 Calculate the ratio of diffusion to depletion-layer capacitance for the emitter junction of a PNP Ge alloy junction transistor of the following parameters:

$A = 10^{-3}\,\text{cm}^2$	$D_h = 38\,\text{cm}^2\,\text{s}^{-1}$
$N_A(\text{emitter}) = 10^{20}\,\text{cm}^{-3}$	$\tau_h = 20\,\mu\text{s}$
$N_D(\text{base}) = 10^{16}\,\text{cm}^{-3}$	$\varepsilon(\text{Ge}) = 16$
$W_B = 12\,\mu\text{m}$	$I_C = 1\,\text{mA};\ 10\,\text{mA}$

Calculate the output resistance, assuming that the doping of the collector is equal to that of the emitter. What is the expected ω_a?
Do the calculation for the two values given for I_C, with $V_{CE} = -5\text{V}$.

15.14 Calculate the voltage amplification at audio frequencies, v_{out}/v_{in}, and the input resistance to the circuit of Fig. 15.11(a), using the *h* parameter obtained in the text. Do this for the following two cases: (a) $C_3 = 0$; (b) $C_3 = \infty$.

15.15 A planar NPN Si transistor has a graded base-doping profile that can be assumed to be of exponential form as in (15.15a). The acceptor concentration in the base is 2×10^{17} cm^{-3} near the emitter junction and 6×10^{15} cm^{-3} near the collector junction. Base width is 0.7 μm. Assume that minority carrier movement through the base is due to drift only, and compare the base-transit time of this transistor to that of a uniform-base transistor of similar base dimensions. Assume

$$\mu_e = 900 \text{ cm}^2 \text{ V}^{-1} \text{ s}^{-1} \text{ for both.}$$

15.16 Assuming an exponential base doping profile like (15.15a), express I_h in the base of a PNP transistor as a function of $\hat{p}_n(x)$ and show that neglecting recombination,

$$I_h = \frac{qAD_h\hat{p}_n(0)}{W_B} \frac{\eta}{1 - \exp(-\eta)}, \tag{15.48}$$

$$\hat{p}_n(x) = \frac{I_h W_B}{qAD_h\eta} \{1 - \exp[-\eta(1 - \frac{x}{W_B})]\}, \tag{15.49}$$

where

$$\hat{p}_n(0) = \bar{p}_n(\exp \frac{qV_{EB}}{kT} - 1).$$

Using these results show that the excess hole charge stored in the base when a current I_E flows is

$$\hat{Q}_s = \frac{\alpha_0 I_E W_B^2}{D_h} \frac{\eta - 1 + \exp(-\eta)}{\eta^2}. \tag{15.50}$$

Using $\hat{Q}_s$ and the approach outlined in Chapter 11, find an expression for τ_B.

15.17 What is f_T of the transistor in Problem 15.13 for $V_{CE} = -5$ V, $I_C = 10$ mA?

15.18 Express the h parameters in the CB connection by $r_{b'b}$, r_e, r_c, and α by calculating them directly from the circuit of Fig. 15.3(b), with $r_{b'b}$ added. Assume $r_c \gg r_{b'b}$.

15.19 For a certain transistor operating at

$$V_{CE} = 5 \text{ V}, \quad I_C = 0.5 \text{ mA}, \quad f = 1 \text{ kHz},$$

the following parameters were obtained:

$$h_{ie} = 5.3 \text{ k}\Omega, \qquad h_{re} = 6 \times 10^{-4}.$$

At 30 MHz y_{ie} was measured:

$$y_{ie} = (1.066 + 2.8j) \text{ mmho}, \qquad y_{re} = -3.77 \times 10^{-4} j$$

At 58 MHz it was found that $|\beta| = 5$ and $r_{b'b} C_c = 200$ ps.

Find the components of the hybrid π model of this transistor (at 5 V, 0.5 mA) and its f_T.

15.20 Show that in thermal equilibrium a junction diode gives the same shot noise as would be obtained from a resistor of a value $r_e = kT/qI_0$ from thermal reasons. (I_0 is the reverse saturation current of the diode. Neglect the small resistances of the bulk and contact regions.)

INTEGRATED CIRCUIT (IC) TECHNOLOGY 16

16.1 The Integrated Circuit Approach

Integrated Circuit (IC) technology enables one to produce a large number of complete circuits on the same Si wafer. Each circuit may contain a large number of transistors, diodes, resistors and possibly some small capacitors, all interconnected by overlying thin Al lines, ending up at a small number of Al pads to which electrical connections from the outside are made.

The whole wafer is processed as a single unit. When the metallization interconnection is completed each circuit is electrically tested, marked if bad, and not until then is the wafer cut up into individual dies, each comprising a single circuit. From here onwards each circuit needs individual (and costly) handling. Each good circuit die (rectangular chip of the original wafer) is bonded on a header, Au or Al, wires are bonded to the Al pads on the die and to the header terminals, and then the encapsulation is finished by sealing. (New, automated techniques are replacing manual bonding today.)

A typical *v*ery *l*arge *s*cale *i*ntegrated circuit (VLSI) is shown in Fig. 16.1. In order to manufacture such complex microstructures in the original Si wafer, special materials, processes and equipment have been developed by the Integrated Circuit (IC) industry.

IC technology consists of many processes, some are common to both bipolar and MOS circuits, others are not (the two are not usually designed into the same circuit). Complete processing necessitates thousands of separate steps, many of them critical. It must be done in an extremely clean environment, where humidity, temperature and sometimes light conditions are carefully controlled. Ultra pure materials and chemicals (sometimes 99.999% pure) must be used to prevent unwanted contamination.

In this chapter we shall review the most important processing steps to gain a general idea of the technology. Further details can be found in Refs. 1 & 12.

Figure 16.1. A very large scale integrated circuit microphotograph. (The NS16081 Floating Point Unit, containing about 30,000 transistors, courtesy of National Semiconductor, Israel, Ltd).

16.2 A Short Summary of the Planar Technology

Before going into details, let us review the steps needed to manufacture a bipolar IC and an MOS IC by the so-called planar technology.

A section of a bipolar IC, containing an NPN transistor and a diffused load resistor is shown in Fig. 16.2(a). They are interconnected as shown on the right.

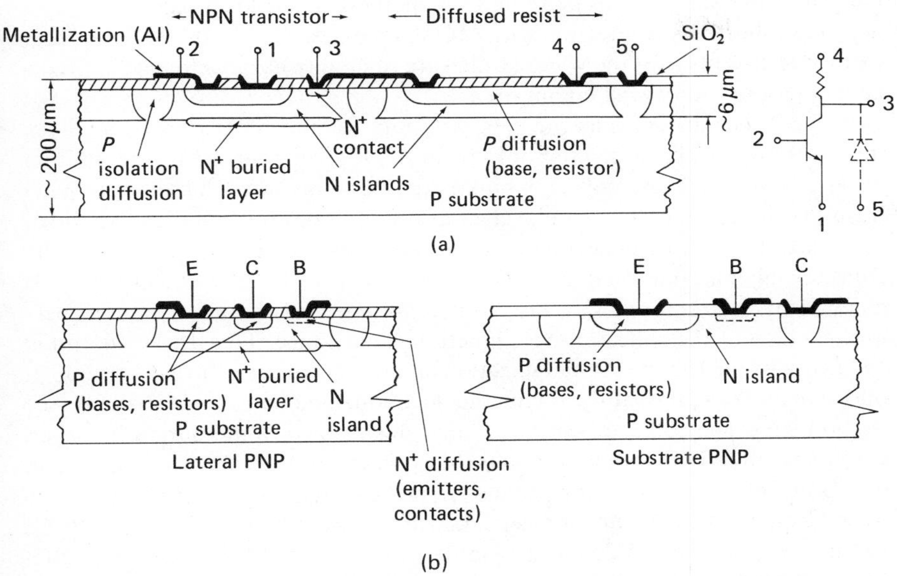

Figure 16.2. Elements of bipolar integrated circuits: (a) NPN transistor connected to a diffused load resistor; (b) compatible PNP lateral and substrate transistors (all substrate PNPs in the same circuit have the same grounded substrate collector).

Problems that must be overcome in such a circuit are:

(a) to isolate the transistor from the resistor, though both are made in the same Si substrate, and do the necessary interconnection by top lying Al film conductors only, and

(b) to reduce the N collector parasitic resistance which is due to the long and narrow path through which I_C must flow to get from the collecting junction to the collector contact on top. This resistance is represented by the dashed resistor in the figure.

The isolation between the various components in Fig. 16.2(a) is achieved by building each of them in a separate N-type 'island', sitting on a P-type substrate and surrounded by P-type walls on all sides except the top. If we take care to connect the P substrate (node 5 in the figure) to the most negative potential applied to the circuit, the junctions between the N islands and the P substrate will always be reverse biased, isolating each such island from the rest of the circuit.

A very small leakage current and parasitic capacitance are the side effects of this junction isolation method. Instead of diffusing P walls isolation can be achieved by selectively oxidizing the silicon around the transistor, thus turning it into an insulator. This can be done by a method called local oxidation, to be described shortly in connection with MOS processes. This method also reduces oxide step heights over the wafer (which are reliability hazards for the interconnections) and the overall circuit area.

The N island serves as the collector bulk for the NPN transistor. Since this collector can be contacted only from the top (in contrast to the discrete NPN transistor, whose collector bulk is the N^+ substrate which is contacted from the underside) a buried N^+ layer at the N island bottom must be added to reduce the ensuing collector parasitic series resistance to a few ohms. The collector N material itself must be of a higher resistivity (0.1–0.5 Ω cm) dictated by the required V_{CB} breakdown voltage and by the maximum permitted value of the collector–base junction capacitance. To achieve an ohmic contact between the top Al metallization and this N collector surface at node 3, one uses an N^+ region at the contacting location, as shown in Fig. 16.2(a) (see Section 8.5). The collected current I_C first flows down to the buried N^+ layer, continues laterally to the point under the contact and then vertically up into it.

Some parasitic collector resistance R_s remains and this, in combination with the collector–substrate junction capacitance, C_{es}, add their time constant R_sC_{es} to the f_T expression (15.25), reducing the gain–bandwidth product of an integrated transistor below that of a discrete one of the same dimensions.

The *integrated resistor* is a P layer that is diffused into an N island at the same time as the P bases of the transistor. This resistor is shown on the right N island in Fig. 16.2(a). The sheet resistivity ρ_s of this diffused layer is a compromise between the transistor and the resistor requirements. It is usually chosen around 150 Ω per square (see Section 5.1). The required values of the resistors are obtained by having the correct geometries for the holes in the diffusion mask. The resistor value is given by $R = \rho_s L/W$, where L/W is the length-to-width ratio of the resistor geometry. A higher ρ_s will reduce the size of the resistors but will also increase $r_{b'b}$ of the transistor and adversely influence the base drift field. High resistors, above about 30 kΩ, become very costly in area and should be avoided if possible.

The *interconnection* among the various IC components is done by thin (about 0.5 μm) aluminum (Al) lines that pass on top of a protective SiO_2 layer, that lies over the IC. The contacting is made through holes in that layer to the underlying silicon. The various components must be so placed that no two Al lines would have to cross. Actually a cross-under is possible by having one Al line stop, connect to an N^+ diffused underpass and come up again on the other side. One can also, of course, pass over a long resistor which then serves as the underpass.

Outside connections to an IC are made by thermocompression bonding of gold wire (about 25 μm in diameter) to pre-prepared Al pads over the oxide. A special machine that heats and presses the gold wire to the Al pad makes that bonding possible. Al wires are also increasingly used today, but then one must use an ultrasonic machine to get a bond. The major steps in fabricating an IC like the one shown in Fig. 16.2(a) are summarized in Fig. 16.3.

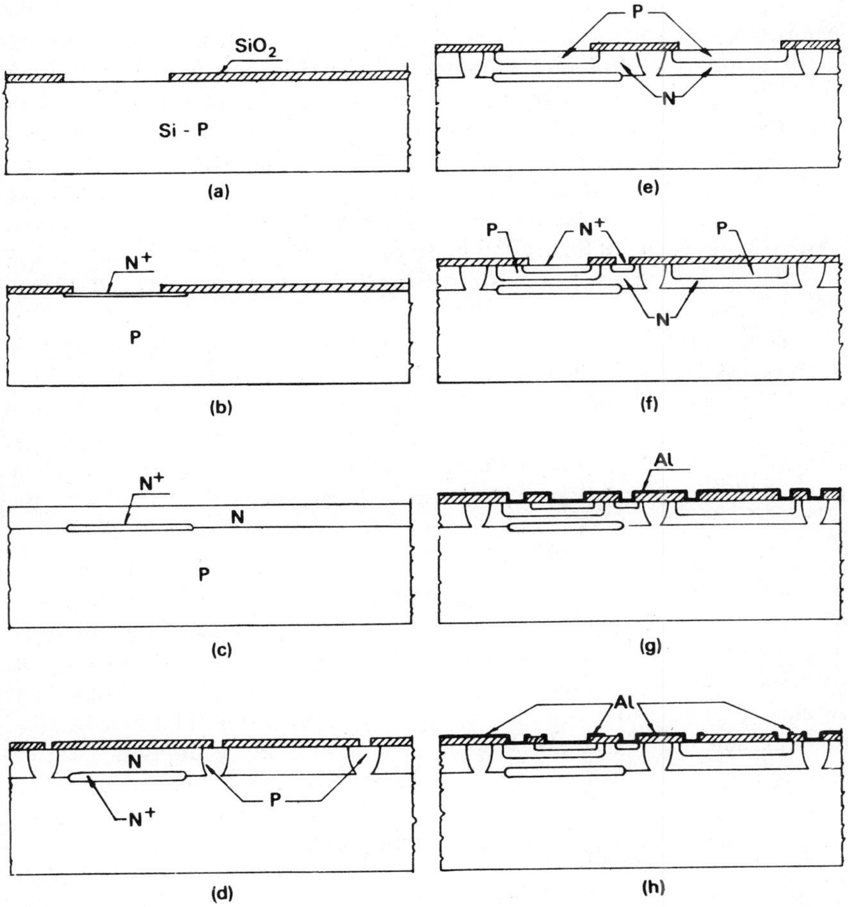

Figure 16.3. The major steps in production of a bipolar IC containing an NPN transistor and a diffused resistor.

One starts from a polished P-type Si wafer (10 cm dia. are in standard use today, but 12.5 cm are becoming available) of about 10 Ωcm resistivity and 500 μm thickness (for mechanical strength). The wafer is oxidized to form a

1 μm layer of oxide (SiO_2) over its whole surface, in which holes are engraved by a photolithographic technique to be described in Section 16.4. The shapes of the holes and their locations are determined by a pattern prepared beforehand on a special mask. The first hole engraved corresponds to the N^+ layer buried under the collector in Fig. 16.2(a). This results in Fig. 16.3(a). The wafer now undergoes a high temperature diffusion of N-type impurity, usually As or Sb. The donor atoms diffuse through the oxide holes into the bare Si surface, transforming its top layer to N^+-type as shown in Fig. 16.3(b). This N^+ region later forms the buried low-resistivity layer under the collectors of the transistors. Thousands of such regions are diffused on the same wafer at the same time. Each of them later becomes a transistor in the hundreds of identical circuits that will be made on each wafer. All traces of the oxide are now removed, and a thin, N-type layer, about 6 μm thick, of the required collector resistivity (about 0.5 Ωcm), is grown by epitaxial crystal growth technique (Section 16.5). The wafer now looks like Fig. 16.3(c), with the formerly diffused N^+, arsenic doped, layer buried under the epitaxial layer (As or Sb are chosen since their diffusion constant is very low and so the buried layer will not diffuse away during successive thermal cycles). From this epitaxial layer we will form the N islands.

A new oxide layer is again thermally grown and a second photolithographic step and mask are used, aligned with the first, to open a network of lines in the SiO_2. This network divides the surface of the epitaxial layer into regions that will be isolated from each other. A deep P-type diffusion (boron) is performed for sufficiently long to ensure that the resulting penetration is deeper than the thickness of the epitaxial layer. The newly formed P walls connect with the P-type substrate, leaving isolated N islands as shown in Fig. 16.3(d).

During the isolation diffusion a new oxide layer is grown on the surface. A third photolithographic step, using a third mask aligned with the first two, opens new holes in the oxide baring the N silicon surface in the regions intended to become P-type bases or diffused resistors. A P diffusion is performed again, shorter than the one before, to form those regions with the required sheet resistivity (around 150 Ω per square). The wafer now looks like Fig. 16.3(e). Another oxide and a fourth mask opens the holes for the N^+ emitters diffusion into selected parts of the previously diffused base areas. At the same time a part of the N collector surface is also bared so that an N^+ region will form there too and make possible an ohmic contact to that point.

The dopant used for the emitter diffusion is usually phosphorus, which can reach high concentrations in Si, as is necessary for emitters. (For UHF transistor, with very narrow bases, arsenic is preferred since its atomic size is more nearly like that of the Si and it introduces less strains into the host crystal.) The wafer now looks like Fig. 16.3(f).

Additional oxidation and a fifth photolithographic step and mask are used to open contact holes in an oxide layer that now covers the whole circuit and protects it. Holes are opened everywhere the metallization is supposed to make a contact to the silicon. Pure Al is now deposited in vacuum over the whole wafer surface, creating a film about 0.5 μm thick that adheres to the oxide very well. At this stage the wafer looks like Fig. 16.3(g). A sixth mask and photolithographic step are now applied, this time to remove the excess Al from where it is not wanted, leaving an interconnection pattern on top of the circuit oxide as shown in Fig. 16.3(h). During this stage larger Al pads are left on the periphery of each circuit, situated over thick oxide, for later bonding wires for outside connections there. Protective low-temperature glass is now chemically deposited overall in which holes are made over the bonding pads only. The wafer is now transferred to an automatic tester, each circuit is contacted by a bunch of metal needle probes and a computer performs a series of previously determined tests. Defective circuits get an ink stain. The wafer is now either scribed by diamond point or sawn apart crosswise between the circuits, thus separating it into chips or dies, each containing one circuit only. The good dies are then bonded on a header in which there are a number of metal pins. Wires of Au or Al are now bonded and connect each Al pad on the Si chip to the nearest metal pin head. The integrated circuit is now sealed, hermetically or in plastic, and passed on to the final testing stage. This testing is very elaborate, intended to check each facet of the circuit operation through a whole range of specified conditions.

Because there are several appropriate N dopants with sufficiently high solubilities in Si (As, P, Sb) but only one (boron) for P-type doping (Al has low solubility and Ga cannot be masked by SiO_2) all bipolar IC's are constructed of NPN transistors on P-type substrates. A PNP transistor that is compatible with the described technology can be made either laterally, i.e., the emitter and collector are situated side by side and current flow is lateral instead of vertical, or by using the substrate as a common collector. both configurations are shown in Fig. 16.2(b). Such a *lateral PNP transistor* can be incorporated in an NPN circuit, but the relatively wide PNP base reduces its β and f_T much below that of the NPN.

A typical MOS structure commonly used in ICs is the N channel MOS (NMOS) which uses MOS transistors of both Enhancement (E) and Depletion (D) types and an additional conducting polysilicon (poly) layer, used both for gates and as a second interconnect level. A section through such a circuit is shown in Fig. 16.4(g) with its main processing steps shown in Fig. 16.4(a) to (f).

Fabrication starts with a P substrate, doped for the required drain junction breakdown voltage (usually about 25 V). This doping would lead to a slightly negative threshold voltage V_T. To prevent spurious N channels from forming in the field region, i.e., the region between transistors, doping is increased there by boron ion implant. This makes $V_T>0$ and is called *channel stopper* implant (Fig. 16.4(a)). The transistors areas are protected from this implant by an oxide (SiO_2) and photoresist mask (to be described in Section 16.4). This mask is now removed, thin SiO_2 layer is grown by thermal oxidation and then covered by

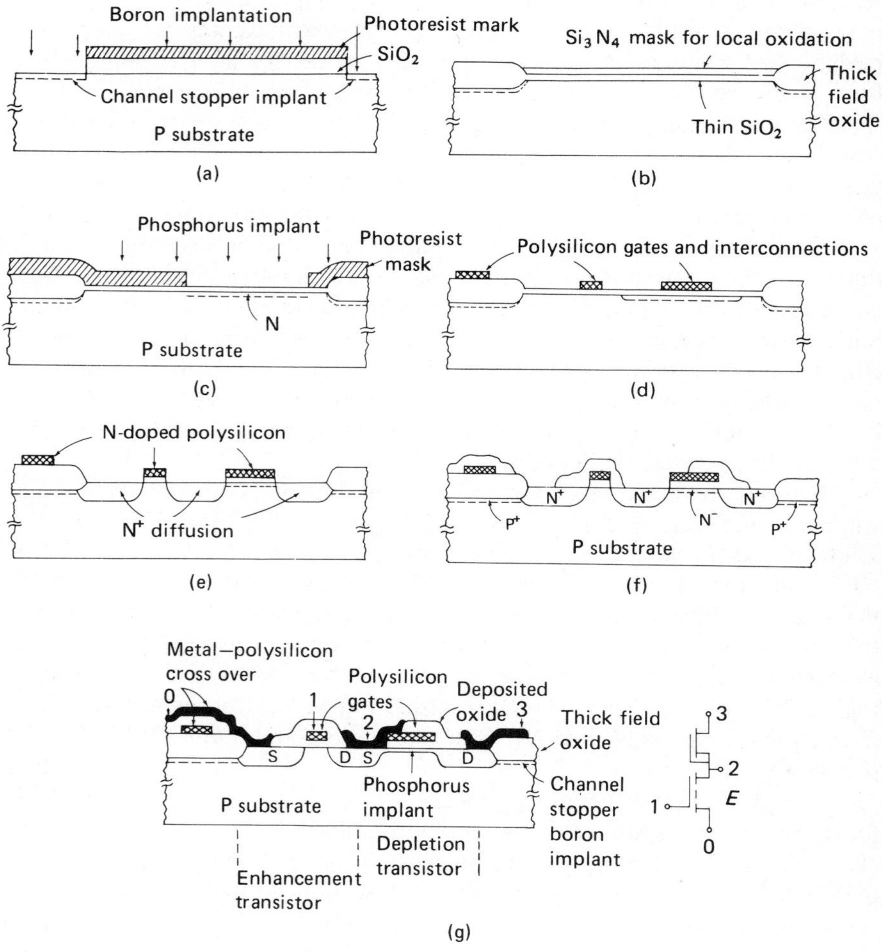

Figure 16.4. Cross section and main fabrication steps of N-channel enhancement–depletion MOS circuit: (a) channel stopper implant between the transistors; (b) building a thick field oxide by local oxidation; (c) N type implant for the depletion transistor; (d) after poly layer deposition and engraving; (e) N^+ diffusion (or implantation) to dope sources, drains and poly layer; (f) low temperature oxide (glass) deposition for top insulation; (g) the finished circuit, interconnected as on the right.

chemically deposited layer of silicon nitride (Si_3N_4). A new mask is then engraved in the nitride leaving it only over future transistor areas. A long thermal oxidation step is now performed. Since oxygen cannot diffuse through the nitride, oxidation proceeds only in the field regions. Si converted to SiO_2 more than doubles its volume and the wafer looks like Fig. 16.4(b). This step, called *local oxidation*, reduces the heights of oxide steps on the surface over which metal interconnect lines would later be evaporated, without sacrificing field oxide thickness necessary for reduced parasitic capacitance. High oxide steps may cause breaks in the thin metal lines. Next, the nitride is etched away and another photoresist mask is used to direct N-type ion implant (As or P) into the area of the future depletion transistors to convert it to N-type with an exactly controlled negative V_T (Fig. 16.4(c).

An undoped polysilicon layer is next deposited over the oxide and patterned to form transistor gates and the lower interconnect level (Fig. 16.4(d)). The thin oxide is now removed except over future channels where it is protected by the polysilicon and an N^+ source and drain diffusion is performed with the polysilicon and thin gate oxide acting as a *self-aligned* mask (Fig. 16.4(e)). This eliminates the most critical mask alignment step that would otherwise be required. The poly layer is also doped by this diffusion and its sheet resistivity drops to about $20\,\Omega/\square$. A phosphorous doped oxide (glass) layer is now deposited to insulate the poly layer from the next metal interconnect layer. Holes are etched wherever the two layers should make connection (Fig. 16.4(f)). A thin aluminum layer is now vacuum evaporated and patterned to form the upper interconnect and bonding areas (called bonding pads) for outside connections to give our circuit of Fig. 16.4(g). For mechanical protection, the whole circuit is usually covered by low temperature glass, chemically deposited over it, in which holes are engraved over the bonding pads through which the circuit will connect with the package pins. The number of pins is limited today to 64 by mechanical and electrical parasitic problems. All tests of the circuit (which might contain tens of thousands of transistors) must be done via this small number of outside leads which creates a severe testing problem.

From this short description, the following processes stand out as specially important and affecting device design:

1. Pattern generation for photomask making
2. Photolithography
3. Epitaxial growth
4. Oxidation, diffusion and ion implant processes
5. Metallization for interconnect and lead bonding
6. Circuit testing

They will now be described in more detail.

16.3 Pattern Generation and Photomask Making

Integrated circuit design ends with a layout of the complete circuit which is usually stored on a magnetic tape in digital form. The geometry of all components and interconnections is specified in terms of their coordinates on the circuit map. Since processing is done sequentially, like base diffusion before

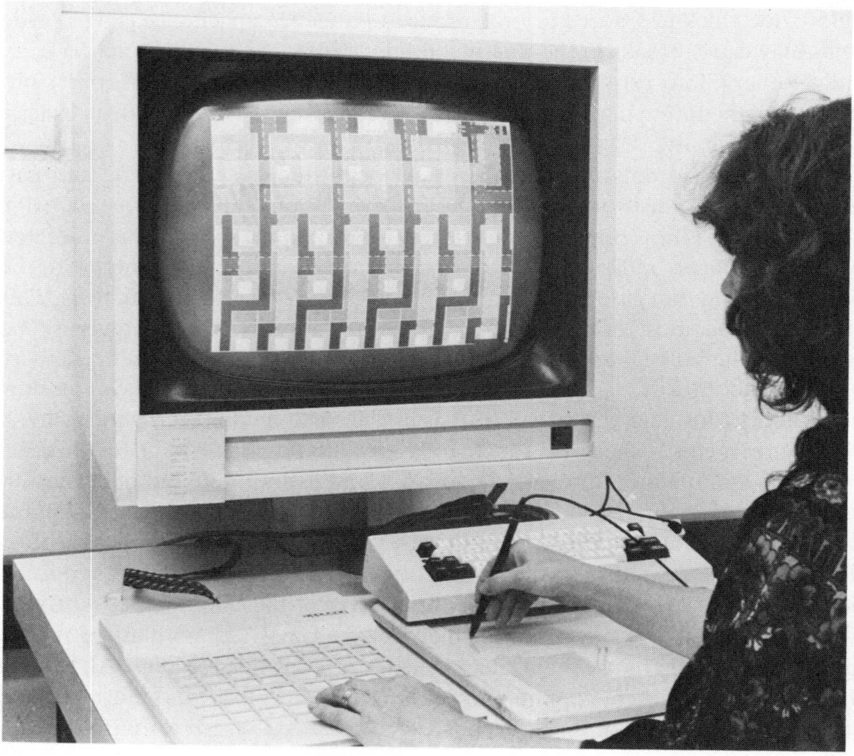

Computer-aided design of an integrated circuit mask. The Microelectronics Laboratory, Technion IIT, Haifa, Israel.

emitter diffusion, and all bases (and diffused resistors) in all the identical circuits that can be accommodated on a single wafer are diffused at the same time, it is necessary to prepare a set of working masks, one with the pattern of all bases, another with all emitters, a third with all interconnect lines and so on. Each mask must be transferred to the wafer at the proper time and must be aligned with the previous ones all over the wafer area. Most processes necessitate from 6 to 11 masks. A pattern generator is a machine used in making such a mask. It is controlled by the layout information and makes a $10\times$ actual size pattern of, say, all base areas in a single circuit, on a photoemulsion covered glass substrate. It does it by exposing the image of a laser illuminated variable shape aperture, about 100 times per minute, to form the desired pattern in the emulsion. After photodevelopment this 10× mask is put in a step and repeat camera that transfers its image reduced by a factor of 10 (to actual size) to another emulsion covered mask and steps it repeatedly many times in the *X* and *Y* directions, covering an area larger than the wafer. This is a multibarreled camera that reduces and steps all the process masks of a circuit at the same time to maintain their relative alignment. The result is a set of master masks which are usually made from glass substrates covered by thin chromium film in which the repeated pattern has been photoengraved. (Chromium masks are more durable, accurate and expensive than emulsion covered masks.) Working masks are made from the masters by contact printing and are used in the photolithographic process to be described next. When they get scratched or pin-holed, they are easily replaceable.

16.4 Photolithography

This is the art of photoengraving, i.e., transferring a pattern from the working mask to the wafer so that all its surface is protected except where etching, implantation or diffusion should take place.

Most useful dopants diffuse very slowly through silicon dioxide. An SiO_2 layer thermally grown on the wafer surface can therefore serve as a mask against high temperature diffusion provided the desired pattern can be engraved on it. The pattern is transferred from the mask to the oxide as follows: a liquid material called *photresist* (or resist for short) is thinly spread over the oxidized wafer and dried. Negative resist is an organic material that polymerizes under ultraviolet (u.v.) light ($\lambda = 0.3 \div 0.4\ \mu m$), i.e. cross links are formed between its molecules which increase its resistance to organic solvents. Positive resist is a similar material in which such links are destroyed by u.v. light. An optical alignment system (using yellow light which does not affect the resist) is used to first align the mask pattern with previous patterns already processed on the resist-covered wafer and then expose it with u.v. light. Organic solvents are now used to dissolve the unpolymerized parts of the resist leaving the rest sticking to the wafer surface. Next the oxide layer is etched through the holes in the resist, using either wet chemical etchant (diluted hydrofluoric acid) or more modern dry plasma etch (plasma—a mixture of positive and negative ions—is created by r.f. field acting on low pressure gas). The pattern is thus transferred from the mask to the oxide which can withstand diffusion temperatures. For ion implant masking the developed resist layer can be used by itself as implantation does not necessitate very high temperatures. The resolution of negative resist is two to three times its thickness due to swelling while being developed. This limits minimum pattern line widths to about 3 μm. There is less swelling in positive resist, yielding a somewhat better resolution. Interference and standing wave patterns appear in the resist when the minimum feature size on the mask is of the same order of magnitude as the u.v. wavelength, setting a limit to resolution (about 1 μm). For submicron line widths (necessary for microwave MESFETs and future high density VLSI circuits) one must go to shorter λ. Alignment systems using soft X-rays ($\lambda \simeq 0.1$ nm) or electron beam exposure, and special photoresists for them, have been and are being developed for this purpose. After the oxide is etched the remaining resist mask is stripped, either chemically or by oxygen plasma. The wafer is cleaned and is ready for diffusion. Resist is also used to obtain a pattern of metallized interconnection on the wafer: a thin metal (usually 0.5 μm of Al) is evaporated all over the wafer and a resist mask is used to etch it in the shape of the desired interconnections. Another technique, called *lift off*, uses positive resist that is first patterned on the wafer to leave a mask covering areas where metallization is not wanted. The metal film is evaporated on top of the resist which is then dissolved in a strong solvent. The dissolved resist lifts off taking with it the excess metal film. Narrower metal lines can thus be obtained.

A resist mask by itself is sufficient to block implanted ions with energies up to 100 keV from entering undesired regions of the wafer. Thick oxide can also serve as ion implant mask but implantation is frequently done through thin (e.g., gate) oxides (see Fig. 16.4(c)).

16.5 Epitaxy

Epitaxy is a high temperature process by which a single crystal semiconductor layer of controlled thickness, composition and doping, is grown on a single crystal substrate of different electrical properties. Bipolar ICs, like the one shown in Figs. 16.2 and 16.3, are always built in a thin (about 6 μm) N-type layer grown epitaxially on a supporting P-type substrate. Epitaxy is also extensively used in the GaAs technology for microwave and optoelectronic devices and makes possible the construction of heterostructures like $Al_xGa_{1-x}As$ on GaAs.

Epitaxial growth is obtained when semiconductor atoms from the vapor or liquid phase are deposited on a hot, thoroughly clean substrate. For single crystal growth an almost perfect match between lattice constants of substrate and layer is necessary, otherwise polycrystallinity results. Even if substrate and layer are of the same material, polycrystallinity would result if the substrate surface is not perfectly clean and mechanically undamaged or the temperature is not high enough.

Silicon is grown from the vapor phase on silicon or alumina substrates. Alumina (Al_2O_3) also called sapphire, is an insulator that matches the silicon lattice constant in a certain crystallographic orientation. Single crystal Si grown on it is used for making very fast Si on Sapphire (SOS) integrated circuits. Si grown on SiO_2 (which is amorphic) covered surface is polycrystalline. That is the way the poly layer is formed in Fig. 16.4. A typical epitaxial system for silicon growth is shown in Fig. 16.5.

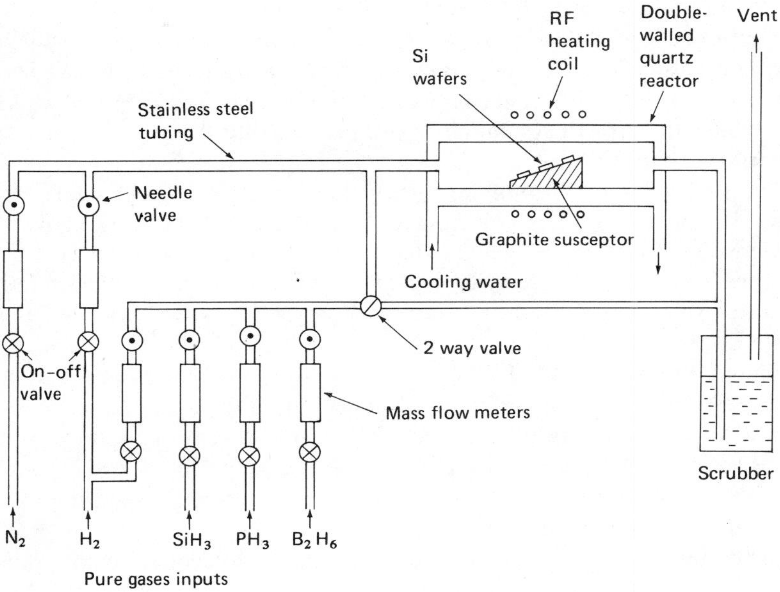

Figure 16.5. An epitaxial reactor for Si growth.

The precleaned and dried Si wafers serving as substrates are placed on a conducting graphite susceptor inside a quartz reactor in a purified hydrogen atmosphere. The susceptor is heated to about 1100°C by an induction heating generator. Silane (SiH_4) gas in controlled amount is mixed with the H_2 carrier gas and pyrolitical (heat aided) decomposition takes place with the Si atoms depositing on the substrates. Doping is achieved by mixing PH_3, AsH_3 or B_2H_6 gas with the carrier, keeping the molar ratio of dopant to Si at the desired value. The Si atoms deposited on the substrate can roll around or re-evaporate (because the high temperature gives them high kinetic energy) unless they happen to 'fall' into an 'energy well', such as happens when the atom settles at a proper lattice site. Thus a single crystal grows. Another, even more common Si growth system, uses $SiCl_4$ in hydrogen which decomposes near the hot substrate surface into

$$SiCl_4 + 2H_2 \rightleftarrows 4HCl(gas) + Si. \quad (16.1)$$

This necessitates higher temperatures, about 1150°C, which increases outdiffusion effects—diffusion from the doped substrate into the growing layer. Also the reaction (16.1) goes in both directions with different rates depending on temperatures and concentrations. There is therefore some Si substrate etching by the HCl gas which brings dopant atoms from the substrate into the growing layer. This limits the maximum resistivity of the growing layers. HCl etching, however, helps in obtaining better crystal quality in the layer.

Vapor phase growth of high quality (therefore high mobility) GaAs layers on semi-insulating GaAs substrate is used in microwave and digital GaAs device fabrication. The large difference between vapor pressures of Ga (low) and As (high) makes the growth system more complicated and the growth conditions more critical than for Si.

Films of many III-V compound semiconductors (like GaAs, GaP, InAs, $GaAs_{1-x}P_x$) and II–VI semiconductors (like ZnSe, CdTe, CdS) can be grown by the relatively new Metal–Organic (MO) Chemical Vapor Deposition (CVD) technique. To obtain GaAs, e.g., an organic compound of gallium like trimethylgallium (TMG) is pyrolized in an atmosphere of H_2, mixed with AsH_3 (to provide the arsenic).

Liquid Phase Epitaxy (LPE) is used to grow multilayers of GaAs and $Al_xGa_{1-x}As$, each with a different composition, doping and thickness, as required for heterostructure lasers. Here the substrate is brought into contact with various melts in turn, each with its own specific composition, and by careful control of temperatures and times, layers of corresponding compositions are allowed to solidify epitaxially on it.

In the last few years, a new technique called Molecular Beam Epitaxy (MBE) made it possible to construct extremely thin (down to several atomic monolayers) multilayers of homo- and heterostructures. Molecular beams of the various layer constituents are generated inside an ultra high vacuum system ($5 \times 10^{-9} \mathrm{Ncm}^{-2}$) from the elements vapor and are directed in turn towards the substrate. Very low growth rates of about 1 μm per hour are obtained. The ability to obtain step changes in the growing layer composition and doping within a few monolayers opens up new possibilities for devices based on quantum effects (Chap. 21) and heterojunctions.

16.6 Oxidation, Diffusion and Ion Implantation

(a) Silicon dioxide (SiO_2) is an excellent insulator, and also protects the Si surface against unwanted contamination (passivation). All the useful Si dopants (B, P, As, Sb) have very low diffusion constants in it, so it can be used as a mask against their diffusion. Other possible dopants, like Ga, Al or In, have high diffusion constants in SiO_2 and are therefore not used in the Si technology.

Diffusion furnaces. Note flow meters in the back that control gas flows. Wafer loading is from the front through a laminar filtered air flow region. The Microelectronics Laboratory, Technion IIT, Haifa, Israel.

An SiO_2 layer can be thermally grown on the Si wafer surface by holding it at elevated temperature in an atmosphere containing oxygen or water vapor. (A layer of about 15 Å would form even at room temperature.) When an oxide layer of thickness d grows, a silicon layer of $0.44d$ is consumed from the surface. The impurity atoms originally in the consumed layers are *redistributed*: As, Sb and P are mostly segregated from the growing oxide and pile up in the underlying Si. Boron prefers to move into the oxide and its concentration in the Si decreases.

An oxide layer can also be chemically deposited, using heat-assisted decomposition of silane (SiH_3) gas in the presence of oxygen (called the silox process). This can be done at relatively low temperatures of 250°C and above on all types of semiconductors to protect their surfaces. The resulting oxide density, however, its diffusion blocking capability and its etching resistance all increase with the deposition temperature.

During thermal oxidation, the O_2 or H_2O molecules diffuse from the furnace atmosphere, through any oxide layer already grown on the Si down to its surface, to combine with Si atoms there. This leads to a parabolic oxide growth rate (except for a short linear spell at the beginning):

$$d_{ox}^2 = Bt, \quad B = \text{a constant}; \; t = \text{time}. \qquad (16.2)$$

The oxide growth rate increases with temperature and depends on the surface crystallographic direction. It is much higher for steam than for dry O_2. A thermal oxidation system is shown in Fig. 16.6.

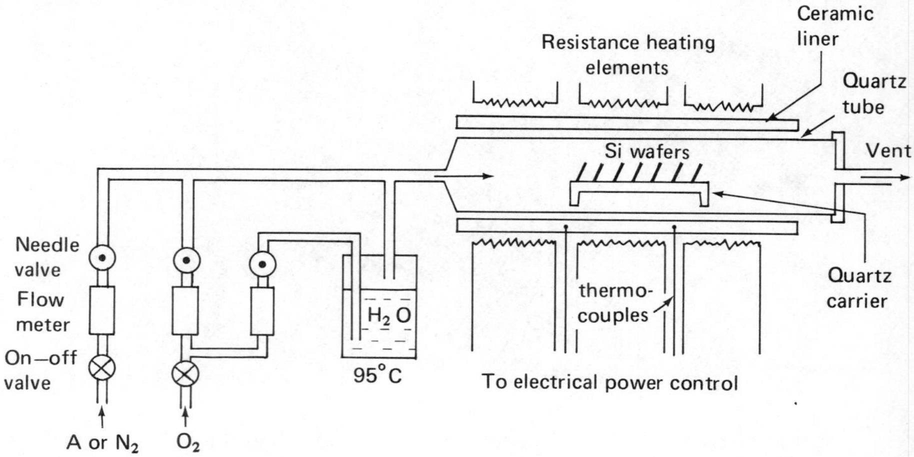

Figure 16.6. A system for thermal oxidation of silicon wafers.

The densest oxide is obtained in an atmosphere of dry O_2 mixed with N_2 or argon. For thick oxides, however, dry oxidation is too slow and a dry–wet–dry cycle is used with the oxygen bubbling through 95°C ultra-clean water to provide the water vapor for the wet spell. Special precautions must be taken when growing gate oxides for MOS circuits to prevent sodium (Na) contamination (Na^+ ions have high mobility in hot SiO_2 and their movement leads to unstable V_T) or excessive interface states charge Q_{SS} formation (which shifts V_T). For that purpose HCl is added to the gas flow and sodium-free furnace accessories are used.

(b) Diffusion is the most common technique for junction formation. When impurity atoms are allowed to diffuse at high temperature into a substrate of the opposite type, the impurity profiles obtained are solutions of the continuity (4.12) and diffusion (4.19) equations in one dimension, with the lifetime of the diffusing atoms taken as infinite. This leads to the linear diffusion equation

$$\frac{\partial N(x,t)}{\partial t} = D\frac{\partial^2 N(x,t)}{\partial x^2} \tag{16.3}$$

D = the impurity diffusion constant. (Assuming D a constant is a rough approximation as D is enhanced by high impurity concentrations. This leads to a nonlinear equation. Also, the same impurity atom may diffuse in neutral or in multi-ionized state, each with its own value of D.) Electrically active impurities are substitutional and to diffuse must avail themselves of vacancies in the crystal lattice. Since vacancy formation necessitates high energy, high diffusion temperatures must be used. Even so the diffusion constants of substitutional impurities in Si are in the 10^{-13} to 10^{-14} cm^2/s range at 1100°C. They are several orders of magnitude larger for interstitial impurities, like gold (used for shortening lifetime and minority storage effects in high-speed Si devices). Equation (16.3) can be solved analytically for a given set of boundary conditions. E.G., in an atmosphere containing unlimited supply of impurity atoms, their surfact concentration $N(0,t)$ will equal the solid solubility limit N_0 of that impurity in the semiconductor at the diffusion temperature. Deep inside the substrate (at $x \to \infty$) the boundary condition is $N(x,t) = 0$. The solution of (16.3) is then

$$N(x,t) = N_0 \operatorname{erfc}\left[\frac{x^2}{4Dt}\right]^{1/2} \tag{16.4}$$

where erfc is the tabulated complementary error function.

If, on the other hand, the available number of impurity atoms is limited to N_t and at the start of the diffusion can be assumed to constitute a δ function of area N_t at $x = 0$, then the solution of (16.3) has the Gaussian form:

$$N(x,t) = \frac{N_t}{(\pi D t)^{1/2}} \exp\left[-\frac{x^2}{4Dt}\right]. \tag{16.5}$$

Most diffusion processes are composed of two steps: first a shallow (relatively low temperature) unlimited source diffusion is performed for a short time t_1. This is called *predeposition* and the profile obtained when it ends is similar to a δ function whose area, the total number of impurity atoms that entered the Si (the integral of (16.4) on x), is

$$N_t = \int_0^{\infty} N(x,t_1)dx = 2N_0\left[\frac{D_1 t_1}{\pi}\right]^{1/2} \tag{16.6}$$

The second step, called *drive-in* diffusion, is then performed (usually at higher temperature, i.e. with $D_2 >> D_1$) for a period t_2. The final profile, using (16.5) and (16.6), will then be

$$N(x,t_2) = \frac{2N_0}{\pi}\left[\frac{D_1 t_1}{D_2 t_2}\right]^{1/2} \exp\left[-\frac{x^2}{4D_2 t_2}\right] \tag{16.7}$$

The point at which N equals the substrate background doping concentration N_B gives the junction depth. It must be remembered, however, that each successive thermal cycle causes further diffusion and junction movement. Since the diffusion constant depends on crystallographic directions, the lateral diffusion (sideways, under the oxide mask edges) will proceed at a different rate from that normal to the surface. One finds that the junction distance laterally is 60–90% of the planar junction depth. Lateral diffusion of source and drain appreciably shorten the effective channel length in MOS ICs compared to its size on the oxide mask and must be taken into account for correctly modeling the transistors (Fig. 16.4).

Numerical data for diffusion profile calculations in Si is given in Appendix 4.

Most diffusion systems are open tube and similar to the oxidation system of Fig. 16.6. The carrier gas (N_2 or A) bubbles through a liquid compound of the desired impurity, carrying its vapor into the furnace, or the carrier can be mixed with the impurity in gas form. Thus for phosphorous diffusion $POCl_3$ (liquid) or PH_3 (gas) may be used, for boron BBr_3

(liquid) or B_2H_6 (gas) and for arsenic AsH_3 (gas). Some oxygen is also introduced into the gas stream so that new oxide builds up on the Si surface during diffusion to be used for masking in the next photolithographic step.

Actual diffusion profiles may differ from calculated ones due to the already mentioned nonlinearities in the diffusion process and to its dependence on the wafer history of past diffusions, each of which contributes additional crystal defects. Therefore each manufacturer characterizes his diffusion process by experimental measurements of the resulting profile, sheet resistance and junction depth, using control wafers that undergo the same processing without masking.

(c) *Ion implantation*: in this technique, a highly focused beam of the desired impurity ions, accelerated to high energies (up to several hundred keV) is directed at the semiconductor surface. The beam is made to scan the surface, so that the ions enter the semiconductor wafer wherever it is not protected by a mask that can withstand the ions' energy. The implanted dose size is limited by the necessity to prevent excessive crystal damage to the substrate. In a subsequent heat treatment, called *annealing*, the crystal is able to heal itself of that damage and the implanted ions move into substitutional lattice positions to become electrically active. Annealing can be achieved either thermally, by heating the whole wafer to around 950°C in inert atmosphere for about 30 minutes, or by intense optical energy from a laser source that is absorbed by the semiconductor surface where the implant damage is and causes local melting and recrystallization. In *laser annealing*, there is no diffusion redistribution inside the substrate. Too high an implant dose makes the surface amorphous (noncrystalline) and the ruined lattice structure can no longer be regained by annealing. For the same reason the maximum ion energy is limited and the average implant depth is around 0.5 μm. The anneal step often doubles as drive-in diffusion step that redistributes the implanted impurities and causes them to diffuse further inside. The impurity profile after implantation normal to the surface is approximately Gaussian (provided the direction of implantation does not coincide with any major crystal axis).

(16.8) $$N(x) = \frac{N_s}{(2\pi)^{1/2}\sigma_p} \exp\left[-\frac{(x-R_p)^2}{2\sigma_p^2}\right],$$

where $N_s \left[\frac{\text{ions}}{\text{cm}_2}\right]$ is the implanted dose, R_p is called the *projected range*, which is the average implant depth; σ_p is called the *straggle*, which is the standard deviation in the depth, i.e., it measures the width of the profile. Both R_p and σ_p have the dimensions of x and depend on the ion species and energy. Numerical data for R_p and σ_p for some common Si dopants is given in Appendix 4.

Ion implantation is a much more accurate, controllable and uniform method of introducing impurities than diffusion. However, very high concentrations and deep junctions cannot be obtained. Since implantation necessitates high vacuum, very high voltages, a strong magnet and associated equipment, it is a much more expensive technique.

A completely different use of ion implant consists of bombarding selected areas of single crystal semiconducting GaAs by a high dose of protons (hydrogen ions), thereby transforming these regions into semi-insulating GaAs. The loss of conduction properties result from damage incurred by the lattice structure: large numbers of deep traps are created in which all free electrons are caught. Thermal energy (at room temperature) is not sufficient to free these electrons or generate new pairs and the mobility is also ruined. The damaged regions therefore become practical insulators and can be used to isolate devices in GaAs ICs and reduce parasitic capacitances and leakage.

16.7 Metallization and Interconnections

In the example of Fig. 16.4 two levels of interconnections were used. A lower doped polysilicon level that has a relatively high sheet resistance of about $20\,\Omega/\square$ (it can therefore be used for short conductors only where no significant current flows like MOS gates and connections) and an upper metallization layer of aluminum. (Aluminum sticks very well to oxide surface, is a good electrical and thermal conductor, makes good ohmic contacts to P and N^+ silicon and forms a Schottky diode on N.) Bipolar circuits, that are used when higher currents and power or speed is needed, and some types of MOS ICs use only a single metallization level. There are also more complex bipolar ICs with two metallized interconnection levels where a deposited glass layer insulates one from the other.

Metallization is usually performed by vacuum evaporation of aluminum (Al) alloy that contains traces of other materials to improve reliability. A thin (less than 0.5 μm) Al layer deposits all over the oxide covered wafer in which contact holes have been previously etched to the underlying Si or polysilicon. The Al sheet resistance is about $0.05\ \Omega/\square$. A photolithographic masking and etching (or lift off) step is used to remove the metal from where it is not needed and an interconnect pattern is left behind with connections to the outside bonding pads located over thicker oxide around the circuit periphery.

There are some reliability problems associated with pure aluminum. To obtain good ohmic contacts between Al and Si, the two are alloyed by passing the wafer through a short thermal cycle at about 500°C, in inert atmosphere. Some of the top Si layer then dissolves and is absorbed by pure Al, creating Al spikes that may penetrate up to 1 μm into the wafer. Such spikes may short shallow junctions. One may overcome this by evaporating Al that already contains 2% of Si.

Electromigration is another problem: high current densities in the thin Al film, especially when it is hot, cause the Al atoms to migrate in time in the direction of electron flow, creating voids and breaks in the film. Inclusion of some copper in the aluminum reduces this problem. Aluminum also corrodes easily if moisture is present, so a low temperature P-doped SiO_2 (phosphor glass) is deposited over it for protection except over the bonding pads, where the glass is removed. Breaks in the metallization may occur over steps in the oxide height, especially in very high density circuits where the smaller device sizes entail smaller contact holes and thinner Al. The local oxidation technique mentioned in Section 16.2 helps to reduce the height of such steps.

16.8 Encapsulation

A wafer prober with as many sharp probes as there are bonding pads is now used to connect and electrically test each circuit in turn. Computer controlled, it runs a series of tests on currents and voltage levels at the various circuit ports as functions of inputs at other ports, automatically marking circuits that fail.

The wafer is then scribed by a thin saw impregnated with diamond particles that cuts grooves along the circuits edges to about a third of the wafer thickness (the wafer is often thinned to less than 200 μm by back lapping, before being scribed, to reduce its thermal resistance and facilitate clean breakage). The wafer is then cleaned and stressed, so that it cracks along the grooves into separate dies, each with a single circuit on it. Since the $\langle 110 \rangle$ planes are natural cleavage planes for Si, the circuits are oriented with one side parallel to a $\langle 110 \rangle$ flat marked on the wafer circumference by its manufacturer. Each die is now bonded to the bottom of a standard IC package with the required numbers of pins (up to 64 are available, but 120 and possibly 200 are in store for the future). Thin gold or Al wires ($\sim$25 μm dia.) are now bonded between the circuit bonding pads and the package pins. Heat, pressure and inert atmosphere are needed to bond gold wires to Al pads (thermocompression bonding). A supersonic vibrating jig is needed to bond Al wire to the Al pads (supersonic bonding). The packages are then sealed in dry inert atmosphere. An hermetically sealed metal–ceramic package is used for high reliability or a cheaper plastic–epoxy package for less critical uses. The IC is now ready for final testing.

16.9 Circuit Testing

Tests performed with the wafer prober mentioned before eliminate bonding and packaging (the most costly parts of the process) of faulty circuits. The wafer prober tests for static currents and voltages and also feeds the circuit with various logic inputs aimed to activate each gate, register or memory location comparing the circuit output with what it should be. Common faults are gates stuck at zero or one, shorts, open circuits and sensitivity to some logic patterns, i.e., activation of a certain circuit part may cause an unwanted change of state in a neighboring location. A good deal of design effort is invested in developing testing algorithms for complex circuits that would give high enough probability that a circuit will operate as expected by running a limited number of tests (limited by the time allocated to the tests).

Some dynamic tests are done on packaged samples of the production run using sophisticated testing systems. These cannot be performed with a wafer prober because of the excessive probe inductance and capacitance. In such tests the circuit is made to run at its top speed (highest clock frequency) to discover any timing errors. The parasitic effects of the bonding wires and package are included. Finally the packaged circuits are 'burned in', i.e., stored at elevated temperature to hasten failure of marginally good circuits. They are tested for mechanical strength by vibration and if necessary the package is also tested for hermeticity.

QUESTIONS

16.1 Why can photoresist be used as a mask against implantation but not against diffusion?

16.2 Two successive reductions and a 1 : 1 copying step are used in a mask fabricating process. Negative photoresist is to be used. If the mask in question is for etching metal interconnect lines, will regions corresponding to the metal lines in the original full-scale mask be transparent or opaque?

16.3 An oxide mask is to be etched on the wafer surface previous to a diffusion step. There is a possibility that some dust particles may fall on the photoresist covered wafer during the photolithographic step. Taking that into account, would you prefer a positive or negative photoresist?

16.4 A quartz tube cracked in a furnace used for growing SiO_2 in an MOS process. After cooling the furnace, a technician replaced the cracked tube using his bare hands in handling it. What problems can you now expect from that furnace?

16.5 Why is the range of a boron implant longer than that of phosphorus which is longer than that of arsenic when all are implanted using the same implant energy in keV (see Fig. A4.2)?

16.6 An attempt to manufacture a dense diode array by N-type diffusion into a P-type substrate ended in failure when it was discovered that all the cathodes were internally shorted, together forming a single big diode. What flows in mask design or processing could have caused this?

16.7 Why can a perfect step junction not be grown by the epitaxial growth method?

16.8 An N-type implant into a P-type substrate was followed by an annealing step that yielded a certain sheet resistivity for the implanted layer and a certain capacitance per unit area for the resulting junction. Do you expect that these properties will remain invariant if the anneal temperature and duration were to increase and why will they change if they do?

16.9 Four different threshold voltages are needed in the same circuit in an NMOS process (a National Semiconductor process): a slightly positive V_T (soft enhancement), a more positive V_T (hard enhancement), a slightly negative V_T (soft depletion) and a more negative one (hard depletion). Suggest a way to achieve this with only two implants.

PROBLEMS

(Make use of the data available in Appendix 4.)

16.10 A 20 min., 1200°C, unlimited source arsenic diffusion is performed into a boron-doped silicon substrate of $N_{A0}=1.5\times10^{17}$ cm^{-3}. Determine the junction depth. At what distance from each side of the junction is the net donor or acceptor concentration about equal to the original substrate concentration? Make a rough drawing, on a linear scale, of net concentrations in the immediate vicinity of the junction and decide whether it can be approximated by a step junction, a linear junction or a mixture of the two.

16.11 A P-type region was formed by boron diffusion into an N-type substrate having a doping density of $N_{D0}=10^{14}$ cm^{-3}. The resulting impurity distribution on the P-side was found to be given by $N_A=10^{18}\exp[-x_2/(6\times10^{-9})]$ with x in cm.
What is the expected sheet resistance of the P-layer?

Hint: The sheet resistance can be looked upon as the parallel combination of thin P-layers, Δx thick each, in which the doping and the mobility are considered constant. Use the mobility–impurity relation of Appendix 4, and perform numerical integration or divide the P-layer into a finite number of thinner layers in each of which $N_A(\max)/N_A(\min)=2$. For each use the mobility that corresponds to the average doping.

16.12 A two-step boron diffusion is performed into N-type epitaxial layer, 6 μm thick, on an N^+ substrate. The epilayer doping is $N_{D0}=10^{15}$ cm^{-7}. The diffusion process was:

Predeposition step: $T_1=1000°C$, $t_1=10$ min

Drive-in step: $T_2=1150°C$, $t_2=$ 1 hour

Determine the expected junction depth and the boron surface concentration at the end of the drive-in step.

16.13 Determine a new drive-in step duration for Problem 16.11 so that the junction will form at a depth of 4 μm.

16.14 A bipolar transistor base is formed by a two-step boron diffusion process resulting in a Gaussian doping profile. Measurements have shown that the surface concentration of that distribution is 8×10^{17} cm^{-3}, the emitter junction depth is 1.3 μm, the collector junction depth is 2 μm, and the epitaxial layer (collector) doping was 10^{15} cm^{-3}. Obtain an expression for the base doping profile and approximate it with the function: $N_A=N_A(E)\exp[-\eta\, x/W_B]$ where $N_A(E)$ is the base doping near the emitter junction, W_B the base width, and η a constant to be determined. What built-in field do you expect inside that base?

16.15 Phosphorus ions were implanted into a P-type substrate ($N_{A0}=2\times10^{14}$ cm^{-3}) at an energy of 200 keV. The implant dose was $5.5+10^{12}$ cm^{-2}. A short anneal step that followed the implant activated 91% of the implanted ions but did not change their distribution in any significant way.

(a) Calculate the range and straggle of the implanted ions.

(b) What are the surface and the peak values of the dopant density in the implanted region?

(c) Calculate the resulting junction depth, the average doping density and (using that value and the mobility data in Appendix 4) the sheet resistivity.

16.16 Show that if a shallow boron implant into a P-type substrate of uniform doping N_{A0}, is approximated by a 'square box' profile (N_{imp}=const. for $x\leq x_{imp}$ and zero for $x>x_{imp}$), then the depletion depth x_d is given by

(16.9)
$$x_d = \left[\frac{2\varepsilon_0\varepsilon_{si}}{qN_{A0}} \mid \phi_{SB} \mid - x_{imp}^2 \frac{N_{imp}}{N_{A0}}\right]^{1/2}$$

where ϕ_{SB} is the reverse surface to bulk potential difference which must be large enough for the depletion region to extend beyond the implanted depth.

16.17 A 'square box' approximation for an implant profile (N_{imp}=const. for $x \leq x_{imp}$, $N_{imp}=0$ for $x > x_{imp}$, $N_0 = N_{imp}x_{imp}$ [cm^{-2}] is the implanted dose) is useful in estimating the expected threshold voltage, V_T, after the implant. Show that the resulting V_T is given by

(16.10)
$$V_T = V_{MS} - \frac{Q_{SS}}{C_{ox}} + (\mid \phi_S \mid + \mid \phi_B \mid) - \frac{Q_{Bulk}}{C_{ox}},$$

where
$$\phi_S = \left.\frac{E_F - E_{Fi}}{q}\right|_{x=0} \quad \text{(on the silicon surface)}$$
$$\phi_B = \left.\frac{E_F - E_{Fi}}{q}\right|_{x > x_d} \quad \text{(deep inside the silicon bulk)}$$

(ϕ_{SB} of Problem 16.16 equals $\mid \phi_s \mid + \mid \phi_B \mid$ at the point of strong inversion).

$Q_{Bulk} = -q(N_{imp}x_{imp} + N_{A0}x_d)$, N_{A0} is the original substrate doping.

x_d is the depletion depth given by (16.9) in the previous problem.

16.18 An NMOS process uses ⟨100⟩ substrates doped with $N_{A0} = 2 \times 10^{15}$ cm^{-3} and gate oxide that gives V_{FB} (flat band) $= -0.6$ V and $C_{ox} = 4.26 \times 10^{-8}$ F/cm^2. What V_T do you expect with no implantation and with a boron implant dose of $N = N_{imp} = 5 \times 10^{11}$ cm^{-2} into an average depth of $x_{imp} = 0.2$ μm?

AN INTRODUCTION TO BIPOLAR INTEGRATED CIRCUITS 17

ICs can be divided into bipolar and MOS classes. Their different technologies described in Chapter 16 preclude mixing of the two classes in the same circuit (bipolar and JFETs, however, can and are mixed). A subclassification of each class relates to the field of use: linear and digital. In this chapter we shall review the design philosophy, various approaches and commonly encountered building blocks of bipolar ICs for both linear and digital uses.

17.1 The Integrated Circuit Components – Design Philosophy

The fast development in IC, that began in the early 1960s and has grown continuously ever since, stems from several important causes:

(a) low reliability of complicated circuits built of discrete components;
(b) the need for reduction in the required operating power;
(c) physical size and weight reduction;
(d) the economics;
(e) the ability of IC approach to provide new and better solutions to systems problems.

Let us examine each of those points briefly.

Electronic systems in the transistor era became larger and more sophisticated than before. Systems like those of digital computers required a huge number of discrete components. The weakness of these systems lay in the interconnection problems: the wires, the solder joints, the plugs and receptacles, and the parasitics associated with them became the major source of failures. The reliability of a system composed of hundreds of thousands of separate components became so low that for most of the time it was under repair.

The ability to build such a large system from a relatively small number of subsystems, each of which is actually a single big IC device with a small number of outside terminals proved to be a solution to this reliability problem (each such subsystem, however, may contain half a million components with highly reliable 'built-in' interconnections).

The size and the parasitics associated with the wiring of any physically large system composed of discrete devices necessitate high operating power levels so that the charging time of parasitic capacitances will not be excessively long and so that signals of sufficient amplitude be processed in order to overcome noise pickup problems. A large amount of power must then be dissipated in the system, requiring elaborate cooling and adding to the reliability difficulties.

The very small size of the integrated circuit reduces the parasitic components and noise pickup drastically so that operating power levels inside the IC can be reduced to the microwatt range, thus reducing heat problems even though the packing density is many times higher. A previously physically large system can now be built with a small fraction of the former volume and weight. This opened the way to space age instrumentation on the one hand and to pocket calculators on the other.

Since IC process technology is not based on individual handling of each component, not even of each circuit up to its packaging stage, the price was brought down considerably. Further price savings were achieved by designing the big system around a relatively small number of cataloged integrated circuits used repeatedly. High production volumes enabled automation of the process, bringing the prices even further down. This trend continues to this day.

Finally, the IC approach opened up novel ways of solving technical problems which had hitherto been insoluble, or at least not economically soluble. New super devices that could not be made from discrete parts, like microprocessors, programmable memories or charge-coupled devices for signal processing could now be made and find increasing fields of use.

When different IC devices, made by the same technology, are compared in price and area, one finds that beyond a certain circuit area the price starts to go up very steeply. The reasons are the random faults that one cannot completely avoid, faults which appear where the original crystal wafer had a dislocation, where a dust particle landed during processing or a pair of tweezers made a scratch. These faults are randomly scattered and if one happens to occur in a critical location inside the circuit that circuit fails. When the circuit area is made larger and larger the chances are that beyond a certain limit each of the circuits on a processed wafer will contain at least one such fault and fail. The yield will then drop to zero and the price rocket up.

Considering this, the 'price' tag on an internal IC component is proportional to its area. The area of a diffused resistor increases with its numerical value, and even a small resistor takes more area than an average transistor. Capacitors require even larger areas and are completely unpractical beyond several tens of picofarads. Passive inductors cannot be achieved at all (except for an Al spiral of very low inductance). This forces the circuit designer to develop sophisticated solutions for the desired circuit functions. He must use mainly transistors and diodes, minimize the number of resistors and limit their values, and exclude all inductors and, if possible, all capacitors as well.

Very high resistance values may be obtained by an arrangement similar to a JFET channel. This is called a pinch resistor and its disadvantage lies in the difficulty of achieving accurate values.

Low resistors of a few ohms are also problematical, since they must be short and wide, therefore deviations in contact resistance values and nonuniformities over the contact area raise problems.

Diffused resistors have bad temperature coefficient (up to $+3000$ PPM $°C^{-1}$) because of mobility drop with T. It is also difficult to control the sheet resistivity of a diffused layer very accurately, so the absolute values of the resulting resistors may be way off. One should therefore design bipolar circuits so that their operation would rely on *ratios* of the resistors in the same circuit and not on their absolute values. Those ratios can be well controlled, and remain almost constant with temperature, since all the circuit is processed as a single unit and the resistors are located very close to one another (the same is true of transistor parameters, like h_{fe} and dV_{BE}/dT). Much better absolute-value accuracy and uniformity can be achieved by modern ion-implant techniques.

Integrated circuit capacitors, if used at all, are usually MOS capacitors which utilize an N^+ layer on an N island as the bottom plate (diffused at the same time as the N^+ emitters). A thin SiO_2 layer is used as dielectric and an Al metallization as the top plate. A 100 nm thick SiO_2 layer will yield a capacitance of 3.4×10^{-16} F μm^{-2}. A 100 pF capacitor therefore necessitates an area of 300,000 μm^2, many times larger than the average transistor. Obviously one should try to avoid capacitors altogether and if a large one must be used it is connected to the integrated circuit as an external discrete component.

The P-type isolation walls, separating the N islands (Chapter 16) take up a lot of area, so good designs minimize the number of those islands. A given function can usually be accomplished by a variety of circuits. The preferred one for realization as an IC should have a low number of islands.

The areas required for isolation plus an inherently more complicated technology, limit the maximum size of bipolar ICs (and therefore the number of components in them) to lower values than achievable in MOS ICs (for comparable yield). A way around the need for isolation diffusion is the Integrated

Injection Logic (I^2L) approach that will be described in Section 17.4.

There is no possibility of adjusting a component value inside the IC and so the design must be very detailed, must take into consideration the production tolerances, and requires checking by simulating the operating circuit on a computer, using a detailed and if necessary nonlinear model of each internal component. The design thus becomes very expensive, and the price of the finished IC can be kept reasonable only if very many are made and sold.

17.2 Some Basic Building Blocks of Analog Bipolar ICs

There are several basic building blocks, i.e. parts of IC, that appear again and again since they perform a certain function that is needed repeatedly. We shall go over a few examples of such building blocks and see how the design principles mentioned before are applied in them.

Two building blocks frequently used in linear circuits are the differential amplifier stage, shown in Fig. 17.1(a), (b), and the constant current sources shown in Fig. 17.1(c), (d).

The design principle leading to preference of the differential stage over the single transistor stage, commonly used in discrete circuits, is the excellent match in properties and temperature tracking between transistors T_a and T_b and resistors R_{1a} and R_{1b} if the IC is so designed that they have the same geometries, are located very near each other and arranged symmetrically with respect to any heat sources on the chip (like a power transistor).

If the circuit is assumed completely symmetrical, the collectors currents will be $(I_0/2)+i_c$ and $(I_0/2)-i_c$ where $i_c \equiv \Delta I_c$ is the a.c. component. The sum of the two currents equals I_0 of the current source. The a.c. equivalent circuit of the differential stage is shown in Fig. 17.1(b). The transistors are represented by a circuit like Fig. 15.9 in which h_{re} and h_{oe} are taken as zero for simplicity. The current source is assumed ideal with an infinite output resistance. Obviously: $i_{sl}(h_{fe}+1)+i_{s2}(h_{fe}+1)=0$ or $i_{sl}=-i_{s2}$. Also

$$v_i=(i_{s1}-i_{s2})h_{ie}=2i_{s1}h_{ie};\ v_0=(i_{s1}h_{fe}-i_{s2}h_{fe})R_1=2i_{s1}h_{fe}R_1.$$

Therefore

$$A=\frac{v_0}{v_i}=\frac{h_{fe}}{h_{ie}}R_1=\frac{h_{fe}R_1}{r_e(1+h_{fe})}\simeq\frac{R_1}{r_e}=\frac{q}{kT}\frac{I_0}{2}R_1. \tag{17.1}$$

A current source may be realized in several ways. A commonly encountered form is shown in Fig. 17.1(c). Assuming T_3 and T_4 to have the same geometries, they will carry the same collector currents, since both have the same V_{BE} (the fact that the collector of T_4 is shorted to its base and it operates as a diode does not affect the injected emitter current or the collector current either—see Problem 17.11).

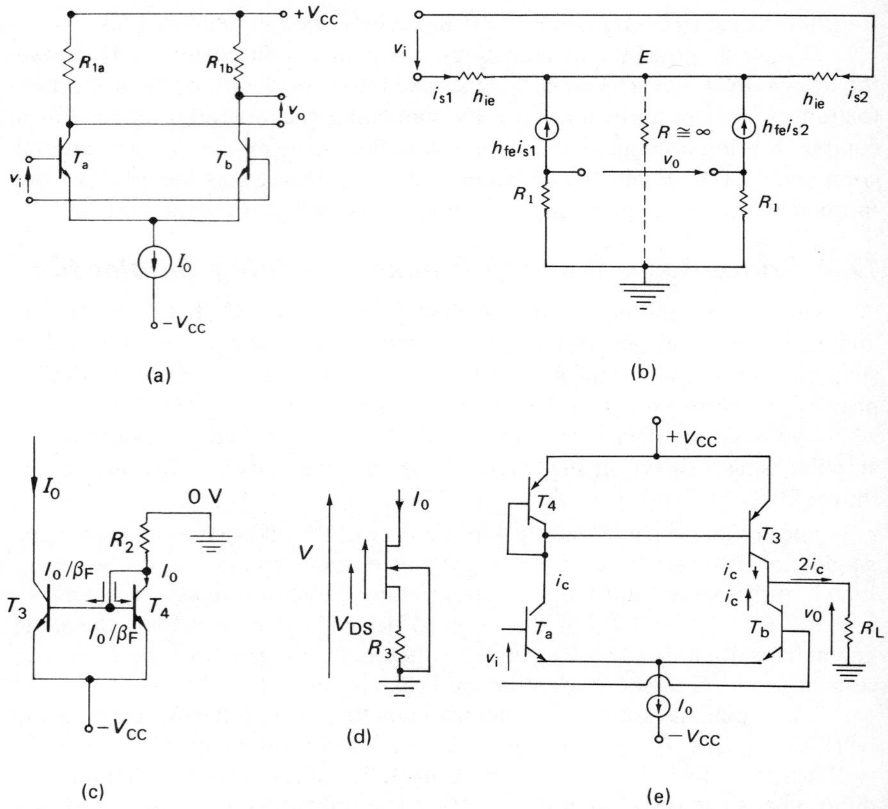

Figure 17.1. Common linear IC building blocks: (a) the differential amplifier stage (I_0 is a constant current source); (b) small signal equivalent circuit (simplified) for (a); (c) a current source requiring two transistors; (d) a current source based on depletion type JFET; (e) an active load for the differential stage.

Assuming $V_{BE} \simeq 0.7\,V$, we then have

$$I_0\left[1+\frac{2}{\beta_F}\right]R_2 = V_{CC} - V_{BE}.$$

For $V_{BE} \simeq 0.7$, $\beta_F >> 1$, this reduces to

$$I_0 = (V_{CC} - 0.7)/R_2. \tag{17.2}$$

This current is independent of the voltage at the collector of T_3 (so long as it is not saturated) and consequently T_3 acts as a current source.

The output resistance of the current source (which should be high) is h_{oe}^{-1} of T_3 (about 50 kΩ at $I_0 = 1$ mA and inversely proportional to it). The temperature dependence of I_0 stems from V_{BE} which decreases and R_2 which increases with T. For $-V_{cc} = -12$ V at $T = 300$°K one obtains approximately $\Delta I_0/I_0 \simeq -2.35\times 10^{-3}\Delta T$.

Substituting I_0 from (17.2) into (17.1), we obtain

$$A = \frac{q}{kT}\,\frac{V_{CC}-0.7}{2}\,\frac{R_1}{R_2}. \tag{17.3}$$

The amplification is therefore completely independent of any absolute value of a circuit parameter (like h_{fe} or R_1 or R_2) but is a function only of the ratio of the two resistors, a ratio that can be controlled very well through their geometries, i.e. by a proper design of the masks.

In Fig. 17.1(d) a depletion type N channel JFET (which is compatible with NPN transistor technology) is used to achieve a current source.

For the transistor to be in saturation (12.9) yields:

$$V_{DS} \geq V_{GS} - V_P = -I_0R_3 - V_P;\; V_{DS} = V - IR_3.$$

The JFET will therefore saturate for $V \geq -V_P$ (*remember*: $V_P < 0$ for N channel). As $|V_p|$ is small, this is usually fulfilled. $I_0 = -I_{DS}$ is then given by the solution of (12.10) with $V_{GS} = -I_0R_3$:

$$\frac{I_0}{G_0} = -I_0R_3\left[1-\frac{2}{3}\left(-\frac{I_0R_3}{V_P}\right)^{1/2}\right]-\frac{V_P}{3}. \tag{17.4}$$

Dividing throughout by $-I_0R_3$ this can be solved for $-\dfrac{I_0R_3}{V_P}$ yielding

$$I_0 = -\frac{V_P}{R_3}\left[5+\frac{3}{G_0R_3}+2\sqrt{4+\frac{3}{G_0R_3}}\right]. \tag{17.5}$$

Thus I_0 is determined by R_3 and G_0. If $R_3 = 0$ (a usual case) then (17.4) yields directly

$$I_0 = -\frac{G_0V_P}{3}. \tag{17.6}$$

When very high amplification is required of the differential stage then R_1 in Fig. 17.1(a) must be very large and therefore area consuming and expensive. Also it is usually necessary to have only a single-ended output between the collector of T_b and ground. The load resistors R_1 are then often replaced by an active load as shown in Fig. 17.1(e). This load is actually the same current source of Fig. 17.1(c) realized by compatible PNP transistors. Any change i_c in the collector current of T_a which is also the control current of T_4, is reflected by a similar change in the collector current of T_3 (that is why this load is also called a *current mirror*). The constant source I_0 forces a change of $-i_c$ in the current of T_b giving a total a.c. current of $2i_c$ in R_L. The amplification is still given by (17.1) with R_L replacing R_1. This is a typical approach in ICs: replace as many resistors as possible by transistors and diodes.

17.3 Some Building Blocks of Digital Bipolar ICs

Bipolar digital circuits utilize transistors that either switch between saturation and cut off or from near saturation to cut off. The last are faster as there is no need to wait out the storage time of the transistor before it can be switched off. They are, however, more complicated.

A typical building block of saturated logic networks is the NOR gate of Fig. 17.2. When four input signals, each representing either a logic '1' (binary number of value1) or a logic '0', are applied to it, its output should be a voltage corresponding to a logic '1' only if all inputs are '0'. Otherwise, its output is '0'. The binary number '1' may be represented by a positive voltage (say +5 V) and the '0' by an approximately zero voltage (like V_{CE} of a saturated NPN transistor). This is referred to as positive logic and is often used in NPN bipolar circuits where a positive voltage excursion turns a transistor on. Alternatively '1' may be represented by a negative voltage pulse, while the '0' is represented by a higher, possibly zero voltage (negative logic). This second representation is often used in P channel MOS circuits where a negative voltage pulse turns the transistor on.

The gate of Fig. 17.2(a) uses positive logic. If any one input is '1', i.e., becomes positive enough to saturate the respective transistor, then the common collectors voltage V_0 drops to approximately zero, i.e., the output is '0'. The current drawn from V_{cc} is V_{cc}/R_L. Logically it therefore performs the NOR function. (If negative logic was used it would have performed the NAND function). Only when all inputs are zero is the output positive $(+V_{CC})$, that is, '1':

$$v_0=\overline{A_1+A_2+A_3+A_4}$$

The attractiveness in such a realization lies in all the collectors being common, i.e., all the transistors are located in the same N island which serves as a common collector. A second island is needed for R_L and any additional resistor that might be needed.

A second approach to bipolar digital circuits which avoids saturation and the associated long storage times, is shown in Fig. 17.2(b). This is an *E*mitter *C*oupled *L*ogic (ECL) circuit which switches I_0 between T_5 and any one of transistors T_1 to T_4. The base of T_5 is connected to a reference voltage V_R. When

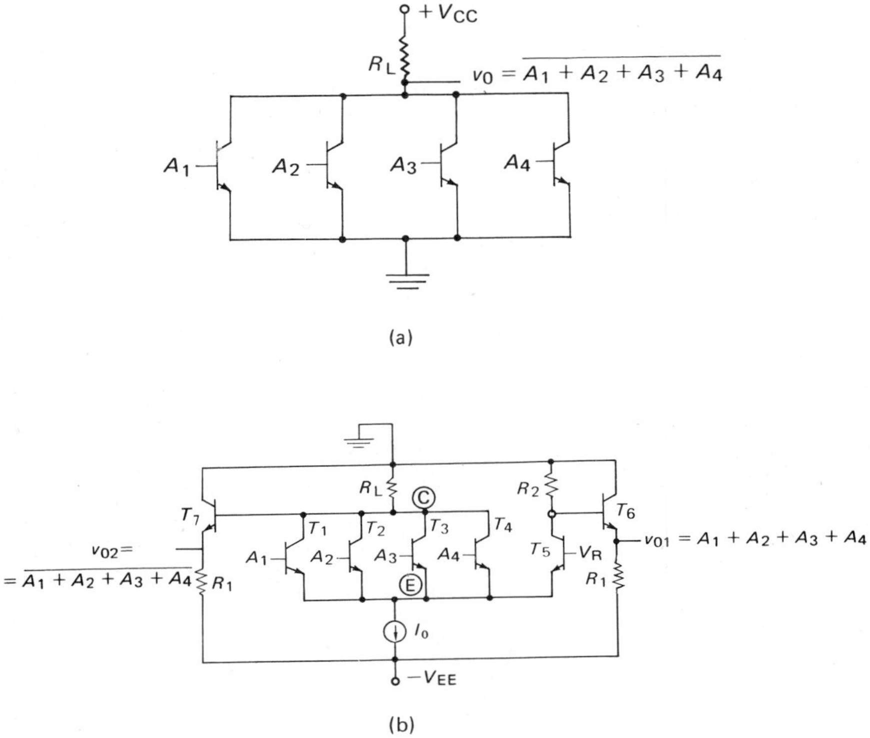

Figure 17.2. Two examples of digital bipolar ICs: (a) NOR gate realized by saturated transistors; (b) OR–NOR gate realized by emitter coupled nonsaturated transistors.

all inputs A_1 to A_4 are '0' (below V_R) then all of I_0 flows through T_5, keeping point E potential at $V_R-0.7$ V. Point C is then at $+V_{CC}$ making T_7 conduct and placing its emitter potential at $V_{CC}-0.7$ V, i.e., v_{02} is '1'. At the same time I_0 flowing through T_5 places the emitter potential of T_6 at $V_{CC}-I_0R_L-0.7$ V which is low and corresponds to logic '0', i.e., v_{01} is '0'. If any input A_i becomes more positive than V_R, I_0 will switch from T_5 to the corresponding transistor and T_5 will cut off (its emitter potential will be higher than its base). This would switch the logic states of v_{01} and v_{02}. v_{01} therefore performs the OR function and v_{02} the NOR function, and both are available from this circuit (both are usually needed). None of the transistors will be saturated if $I_0R_L<V_{EE}$. this allows the circuit to switch at very high speeds (subnanosecond delay times). The price for the higher speed is higher power dissipation since V_{CE} is higher than in saturation. Another way to obtain a nonsaturated logic is to connect a Schottky-barrier diode (SBD) in parallel with the collector–base junction as shown in Fig. 17.3(a).

The SBD is obtained by a metal to the N collector contact (at a point where the collector is not degenerated) as shown in Fig. 17.3(b). The other metal-to-Si contacts are ohmic since they are either contacts of Al to degenerate N^+ regions, as in the collector and emitter cases, or Al to P-type (base).

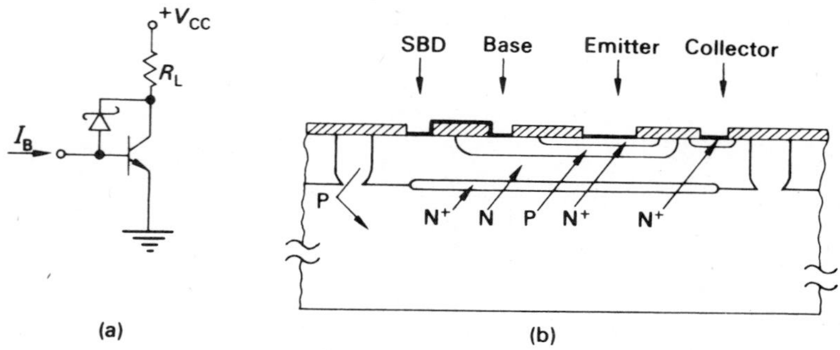

Figure 17.3 Use of Schottky-barrier diode to prevent saturation: (a) schematic; (b) IC realization.

An SBD prevents the transistor from entering deeply into saturation since it starts to conduct at about half the forward voltage necessary to start conduction in the collector–base junction. When I_B in Fig. 17.3(a) is increased, the transistor nears saturation and the collector–base junction becomes slightly forward biased. Before the transistor goes deeper into saturation the SBD starts to conduct heavily, shunting off the excess base current. In spite of its being forward biased and conducting, the SBD does not slow down the turn-off process since its storage time is practically zero (Chapter 11).

Many logic circuits require diodes. An integrated diode is usually a transistor with two of its terminals shorted together. The question as to which two is determined by the proposed use. Collector–base short and use of the emitter junction gives a low breakdown voltage (about 5 V) but also low forward voltage drop at a given current. Use of the base–collector junction gives high breakdown but higher forward drop and longer recovery time (see Problem 17.12). A circuit with many diodes, all with a common anode, is attractive for IC since it can be realized with a multiple emitter structure as shown in Fig. 17.4. Such a structure saves area and is a very common building block in diode–transistor and transistor–transistor logic (DTL and TTL).

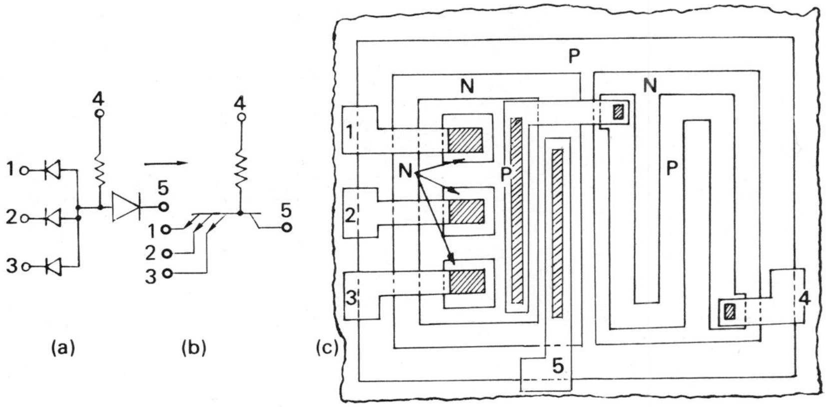

Figure 17.4. A realization of a diode array with a common anode: (a) electrical schematic; (b) an equivalent multiple emitter structure; (c) top view of the IC realization of (b). (Shading represents contact areas).

17.4 Integrated Injection Logic (I^2L)

In the struggle between the MOS and bipolar transistors for supremacy in the large-scale, integrated, digital circuit marker, the bipolars started to lose ground when the MOS technologies matured and ion implantation made possible the production of fast N-channel enhancement-depletion circuits (Chapter 12). These circuits started to replace more and more of the fast bipolars which had previously reigned supreme, but which could not be integrated on such a large scale. *Integrated injection logic* or I^2L (also known as MTL—*merged transistor logic*) is the bipolar answer to large-scale, fast and low power circuit demand. The principle of I^2L inverter with a fan-out of 2, is shown in Fig. 17.5(a). One may view it as the merging of PNP transistors T_1, T_3 and T_5 with NPN transistors T_2, T_4 and T_6. The collectors of the PNPs serve also as bases of the NPNs. The bases of the PNPs serve also as emitters of the NPNs and are all grounded. An NPN transistor may have several collectors. Instead of a collector power supply, an external base current supply V_{BB} is used.

When input A is '0' (about 0.05 V) the current of T_1 is shunted to ground and T_2, which lacks base drive, is off. The currents of T_3 and T_5 then flow into the bases of T_4 and T_6, raising their base voltages to about +0.75 V. Those transistors saturate and their collector voltages drop to about 0.05 V to act as current sinks for any currents fed into them.

When A is at +0.75 V (logic '1'), however, T_1 feeds T_2 with I_0, causing it to saturate, sinking T_3 and T_5 currents to ground and cutting off T_4 and T_6.

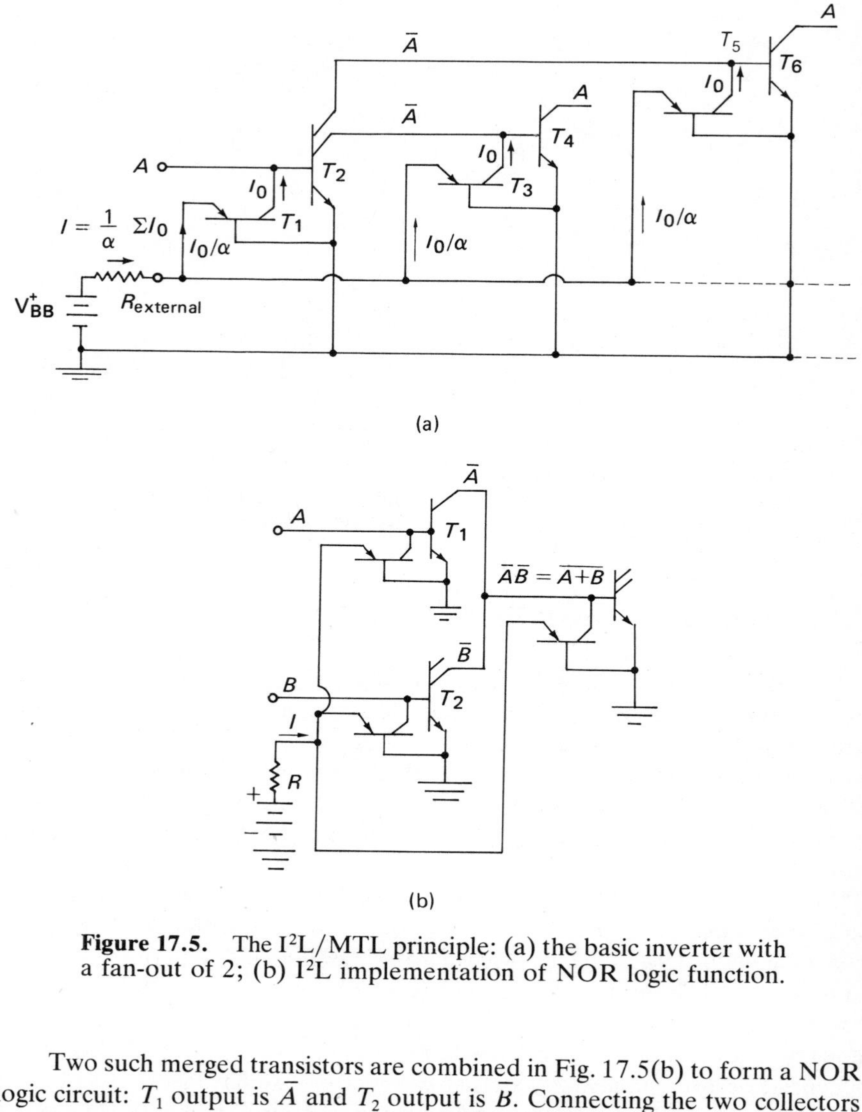

Figure 17.5. The I²L/MTL principle: (a) the basic inverter with a fan-out of 2; (b) I²L implementation of NOR logic function.

Two such merged transistors are combined in Fig. 17.5(b) to form a NOR logic circuit: T_1 output is $\bar{A}$ and T_2 output is $\bar{B}$. Connecting the two collectors together makes the combined output $\bar{A} \bullet \bar{B} = \overline{A+B}$, i.e., the NOR function.

The physical structure of the PNP and NPN transistors is different from the planar vertical form that we have met so far. In Fig. 17.6(a), a section of an I²L chip is shown in top view and in cross section through A–A′ plane. A central P diffused injector line forms the emitters of all PNP transistors which are of the *lateral* type, i.e., their emitters and collectors are located side by side and not one above the other (Chapter 16).

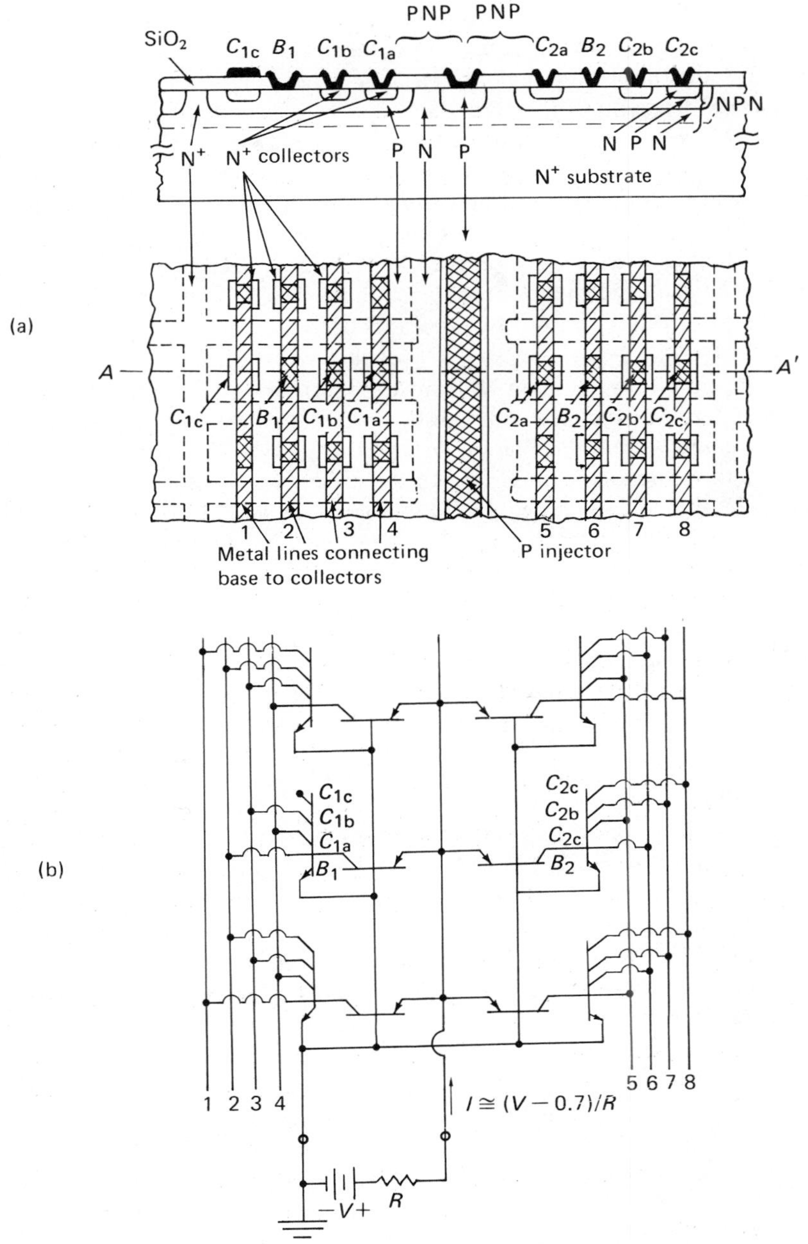

Figure 17.6. A section of an I^2L circuit: (a) top view and cross section (through plane A–A′) of an I^2L chip; (b) the circuit diagram of (a).

The NPNs, on the other hand, have a vertical structure but it is inverted: the emitter is the common grounded N^+ substrate and the collectors are the top N^+ diffused or implanted regions marked *c*. There may be several collectors to each NPN transistor (here 3). Each collector can be interconnected with another NPN base or collectors by the metal lines 1–8 that run over the chip by properly positioning the contact holes in the covering oxide. Since the substrate serves as a common ground and the P injector diffusion connects all PNP emitters and feeds the d.c. current to operate the chip from an outside, off chip, source, the metal lines serve only for logic interconnection. Very high density can thus be achieved (in normal bipolar circuits the metallized layer must also provide for ground and power lines and becomes the limiting factor in size reduction).

The circuit is built in an N^- epitaxial layer grown on an N^+ substrate. An I^2L circuit may be realized with the standard NPN technology applied to an N^+ substrate and without P isolation diffusion. But this would result in a very low value of the β 'up' of the thus inverted upward operating transistor (i.e. β_R in the Ebers–Moll model of the regular NPN transistor), and in large minority charge storage in the N region slowing down the switching speed. By the use of ion implantation for giving the impurity profiles the optimal form for upward injection, one can get higher β 'up' and faster switching at lower injected I_B currents. Further increase of β 'up' is achieved by the N^+ 'collar' around each NPN which becomes part of its emitter and enhances its upward injection efficiency. Gate delay times of 20 ns with $I_B = 100\,\mu A$ were recently reported.[16]

The advantages of the I^2L circuit over the standard bipolar IC are:

(a) No junction isolation is needed between collectors which are inherently isolated from each other in I^2L structure.
(b) Only one common N^+ emitter is necessary and that is the substrate.
(c) A structure of multiple collectors, all located in the same P base, is very easily obtainable in I^2L and is therefore preferred. Such a structure is very useful in digital circuits.
(d) No resistors are necessary, which is also the case in MOS IC.
(e) The I_B sources can be replaced with photon absorption and minority carrier generation in the N^- region. Circuits can then be made which are light activated and which do not require additional power supplies.
(f) Speed–power (or rather delay–power) products of less than 1 pJ can be obtained for a single gate. In I^2L circuits a trade off between input power and gate delay exists, so that their product is constant. For $I_B = 100\,\mu A$ and base voltage excursion of 0.7 V, the input power is 7×10^{-5} W, giving a delay of 20×10^{-9} s in a 1 pJ gate. Higher I_B will charge the circuit capacitances faster and reduce the delay at the price of increased dissipation. The possibility to operate the same circuit at faster or slower rates by outside control of I_B and the very low speed–power product are very important.

(g) Use of P substrate with N^+ buried layer for the NPN emitters and an N^- epilayer on top enables one to mix I^2L digital parts with regular NPN analog parts in the same circuit at the price of a somewhat more complicated technology.

(h) If the N^+ collars in Fig. 17.6(a) are replaced by oxide collars formed by local oxidation (Chapter 16) and the collector contacts by Schottky barrier diodes, both the capacitance and the logic swing are reduced. This results in even lower speed–power products.

All those properties, combined with an inherently simple technology (the basic I^2L circuit can be made with four masks) and high yield makes I^2L a good choice for dense VLSI circuits. Additional information about bipolar integrated circuits may be found in Refs. 11 and 13.

QUESTIONS

17.1 In many NPN bipolar ICs one frequently meets with multiple-emitter transistors. What is the attraction of these transistors to the designer?

17.2 An NPN bipolar IC uses two power supplies of +9 V and −9 V. To what voltage should the substrate be connected?

17.3 Does the impedance of a diffused resistor depend on the frequency? How do you expect it to change with f?

17.4 Why are junction capacitors not used much in integrated circuits?

17.5 What will the output of the differential amplifier in Fig. 17.1(a) be for an input that changes the base voltages of both T_1 and T_2 together by the same amount? Assume identical transistors.

17.6 How does the resistivity of the N epitaxial layer grown on the P substrate during the process of making bipolar IC affect the high-frequency properties of NPN transistors built in it?

17.7 A single-ended output is wanted from the differential stage of Fig. 17.1(a) (between T_b collector and ground). R_{1a} is therefore shorted out. What will be the effect on amplification?

17.8 We have learned that V_{BE} of the emitter–base junction goes down with temperature by about $-2\,\text{mV}\,°\text{C}^{-1}$ if I_E is kept constant. How will increase in temperature affect the constant-current source I_0 value in Fig. 17.1(b)? What will be the effect of temperature on the resistance R_2 and through it on I_0?

17.9 If one takes an NPN integrated transistor, like the one shown in Fig. 16.2, and operates it in the inverted upwards direction, as in I^2L circuits, the resulting β will be very low. Give three different reasons for this.

PROBLEMS

17.10 Assuming T_4 in Fig. 17.1(b) has one third the emitter area of T_3 and that $V_{CC}=9$ V, $R_2=6$ kΩ, calculate I_0.

17.11 Various possible connections of IC transistors as diodes are shown in Fig. 17.7. Which connection will have

(a) the highest breakdown voltage?

(b) the lowest forward voltage V_F at a given I_F? Use the Ebers–Moll equations for finding a general relationship between V_F and I_F for each connection.

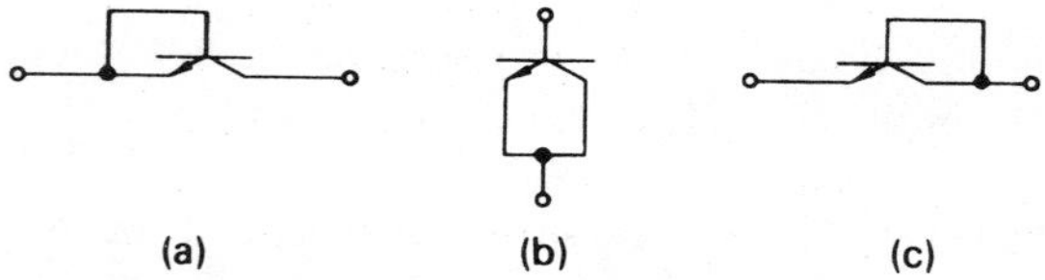

Figure 17.7. Three possible connections of integrated transistors as diodes.

17.12 Draw schematically the stored minority charge, as a function of position, at a given I_F, for each of the three diode connections shown in Fig. 17.7. Which would have the lowest reverse recoverv time?

17.13 A resistor R_E is added in series with each emitter of T_a and T_b in Fig. 17.1(a). Obtain an expression for the input resistance that the signal source v_i sees. What will be this resistance for $I_0=100\,\mu$A, $h_{fe}=150$ and $R_E=50\,\Omega$?

17.14 A lateral PNP transistor, incorporated in an NPN IC, is made in the form shown in Fig. 17.8. Assume constant doping in each region of $N_A=10^{18}$ cm^{-3}, $N_D=10^{16}$ cm^{-3} and that the hole diffusion length in the N material is 15 μm. use the dimensions in the figure to estimate α and β of that transistor. Inclusion of additional buried N^+ layer under that transistor will create a built-in reverse field that repels holes approaching from above. How will this affect the properties of this transistor?

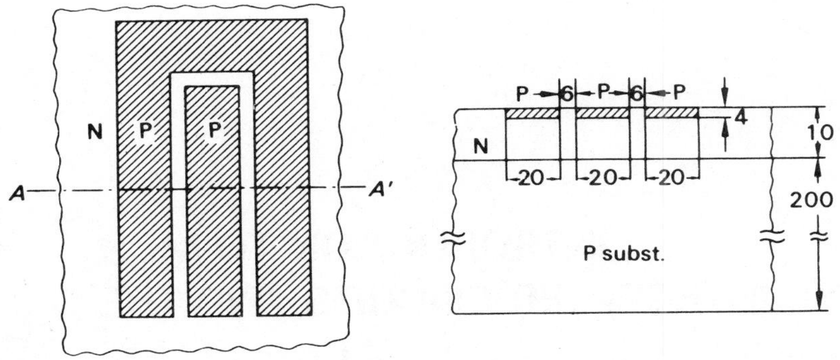

Figure 17.8. A lateral PNP built into an NPN IC. Views from above and cross section. All dimensions are in microns.

17.15 A current source that is useful for obtaining very low currents without the need for high resistors looks like Fig. 17.1(c), but with an additional resistor R_1 inserted between the emitter of T_3 and $-V_{CC}$. If the emitter junction current in the two identical transistors T_3 and T_4 is related to the junction forward voltage V_{BE} by $I = I_S \exp qV_{BE}/kT$, show that I_0 is determined by the transcendental equation

$$I_2\beta_F = I_0\left\{1 + (\beta_F + 1)\exp\left[\frac{qI_0R_1}{kT}\left(1 + \frac{1}{\beta_F}\right)\right]\right\} \tag{17.7}$$

where I_2 is the current flowing in R_2.

For $\beta_F = 100$, a forward V_{BE4} assumed constant at 0.7 V and a supply voltage of $-V_{CC} = -5$ V, obtain appropriate values for R_1 and R_2 that will yield $I_0 = 10\ \mu A$ using a total resistance $R_1 + R_2 < 3\ k\Omega$.

INTRODUCTION TO MOS INTEGRATED CIRCUITS AND THE VLSI CHALLENGE 18

Large scale integration (LSI) and very large scale integration (VLSI) digital circuits are based today almost exclusively on N channel MOS (NMOS) and Complementary MOS (CMOS) transistors (there are I^2L based VLSI circuits too).

The advantages of MOST circuits for digital use are:

(a) Logic gates can be realized and interconnected using MOS transistors only, with no area consuming resistors (Chapter 13.4). Separate polysilicon and metal layers offer the possibility of two interconnect levels—essential for complicated circuits.

(b) MOS technologies are basically simpler than bipolar ones and necessitate lower temperatures (hence lower crystal fault generation). Accurate control of surface doping, necessary for MOST, is achieved by ion implantation while bipolar processes necessitate epitaxy and diffusions, both high temperature processes with low control over the resulting resistivities.

(c) Selective ion implantation makes possible the inclusion of both enhancement and depletion transistors in NMOS logic circuits, or P and N channel in CMOS circuits, with propagation delays in the nanosecond range. This comes near the fastest bipolar circuits (the ECL) but achieved using a lot less area and power.

(d) It is possible to scale MOS transistors down to very small geometries, thereby reducing logic gate size, logic voltage swing, parasitic capacitances and operating power, so that much more logic can be packed into a given chip area. This leads to chips with huge VLSI circuits on them. Those chips are really the semiconductor devices of the eighties.

In this chapter we shall review the fundamentals of ICs based on the NMOS and CMOS families of both static and dynamic logic types. the charge coupled device (CCD) which has found use in the analog, digital and imaging fields will also be described. We shall then consider the VLSI challenge: How can one produce such a device, and what problems do they pose in technology, design, testing and economy?

18.1 Static NMOS Logic Building Blocks

The basic building block of NMOS static logic circuits is the inverter discussed in detail in Section 13.4. It contains an enhancement input transistor and a depletion load transistor (Fig. 13.11). Their different threshold voltages are achieved by surface dopant control (Chapter 12) through selective ion implant. the implantation process and the silicon gate technology used in MOS circuits are described in Chapter 16. The simple inverter of Fig. 13.11 can be used to form logic gates that perform NOR, NAND or other logic functions as shown in Fig. 18.1. When one (or more) of the input transistor in Fig. 18.1(a) is turned on by a positive input pulse representing a logic '1', current flows through the load and that input transistor and the output drops to a low voltage representing a logic '0', i.e., the NOR function is performed. In Fig. 18.1(b) the input transistors are in series so both must be on for the output to be low, i.e., a NAND operation is performed. The two circuits may be combined as in Fig. 18.1(c) to perform a more complex operation.

As in the case of bipolar ICs, the design of MOS ICs uses computer programs to simulate how the circuit will function with various inputs before masks for fabrication are made. Special programs (like SPICE, developed in the University of California at Berkeley) are used for simulation. The programs can draw from an established process file such information as the expected sheet resistance after diffusion, sideways (lateral) diffusion under the mask (which affects channel length), junction capacitance per unit area or channel mobility and use this with mask dimensions information to build an electrical model of the devices and their associated parasitics. It then uses the interconnect information to obtain the expected waveforms at the outputs. Sophisticated programs take into consideration such effects as deterioration of channel mobility under high gate fields, threshold voltage dependence on position in the channel and on reverse substrate–source voltage, channel length reduction with reverse drain voltage and short channel effects. The parameters used for such detailed simulations are obtained from a more exact device theory than we have used, coupled with measurements made on test chips. In simulating a circuit the worst conditions must be considered. Thus, if there is a production spread in some parameters or they are affected by temperature, the values that would give the worst response should be used. In a circuit like Fig. 18.1(a), v_0 representing a

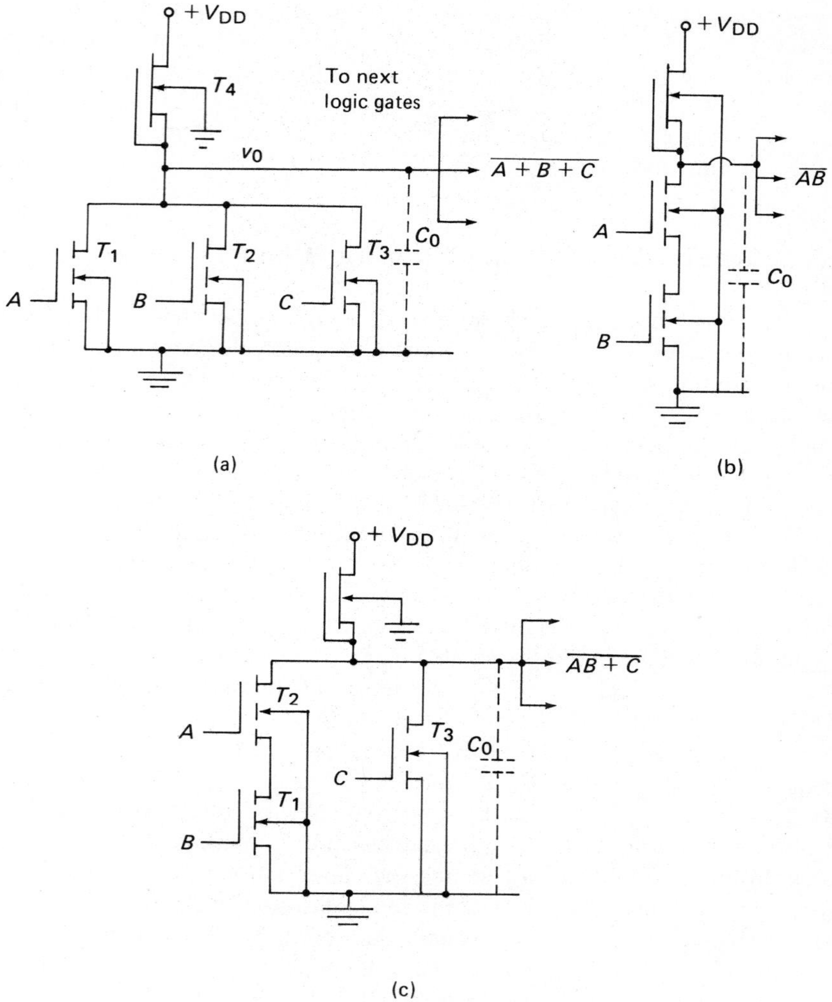

Figure 18.1. NMOS static logic building blocks: (a) a NOR gate *circuit*; (b) a NAND gate circuit; (c) a circuit for performing the $\overline{\text{AB+C}}$ operation.

logic '0' will have its highest value (worst case) when only one input transistor conducts. In the circuit of Fig. 18.1(c) the output will switch down more slowly when inputs A and B are switched to '1' then when input C is switched to '1' (unless T_1 and T_2 have twice the channel width of T_3, i.e., half its resistance).

18.2 Integrated Circuits Based on CMOS

Complementary MOS (CMOS) transistors dominate the field of low power digital circuits. Here P channel and N channel transistors are connected in pairs to give circuits in which the static current drawn from the power supply is practically zero. CMOS subdivide into two groups: bulk, which are built in single crystal substrates like in Fig. 18.2(a), and Si on sapphire (SOS) in which the transistors are built in a thin epitaxial layer grown on a single crystal alumina (Al_2O_3) which is an insulator. The parasitic drain and source capacitances and leakage currents are then vastly reduced, giving faster switching speeds at a price of a more complicated technology.

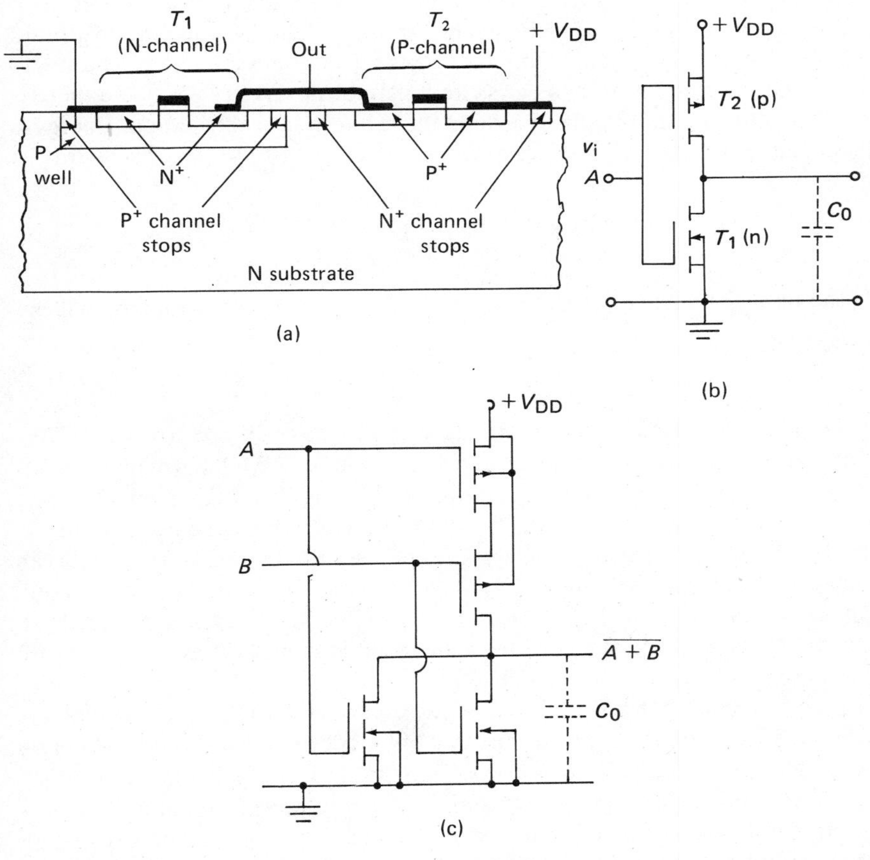

Figure 18.2. CMOS circuits: (a) a section through an inverter built on a bulk CMOS chip; (b) the inverter circuit of (a); (c) a two-input NOR gate.

To make bulk CMOS, P wells (also referred to as tubs) must first be diffused or implanted into the N substrate (Fig. 18.2(a)) in which N channel transistors like T_1 will later be built. P channel transistors like T_2 are made directly on the N substrate.

The technology was made possible by the advent of ion implantation by which threshold voltages of each transistor type can be separately and accurately controlled.

The basic CMOS inverter is shown in Fig. 18.2(b). The gates of T_1 and T_2 are connected in parallel at the input and only one power supply V_{DD} is used. It should be noticed that the source of T_1 is connected to ground while that of T_2 is connected to V_{DD}.

For a positive v_i (of the size of V_{DD}), T_1 would present a very low source–drain resistance, while T_2 would be cut off and present a very high source–drain resistance. C_0 will discharge through T_1 and v_0 will drop to ground potential. When v_i is switched to zero T_1 cuts off, T_2 conducts, and C_0 charges to $+V_{DD}$. Under static conditions v_i is either zero or positive ($+V_{DD}$) and there is no d.c. path from the supply to ground, hence no power dissipation. Energy is dissipated only when C_0 is charged from $Q = O$ to $Q = C_0V_{DD}$. This energy is:

$$E = \int V_{DD} i_c \mathrm{d}t = V_{DD} \int_{Q=O}^{C_0V_{DD}} \mathrm{d}Q = C_0 V_{DD}^2. \tag{18.1}$$

If the input is switched at a frequency $f = 1/T$, the power dissipated will be

$$P = \frac{E}{T} = C_0 V_{DD}^2 f. \tag{18.2}$$

It should be noted that this is not the case in NMOS or PMOS inverters. They dissipate static power when the input transistor is on. CMOS switching speeds can be calculated using a similar approach to the one used in Section 13.4. The fall time of v_0 depends only on T_1 while the rise time depends only on T_2 (Problem 18.9). Propagation delay times depend on V_{DD} (CMOS circuits can usually operate at a wide range of V_{DD}) and become shorter as V_{DD} is increased. Fig. 18.2(c) shows a CMOS NOR gate. Note the series connection of the P channel transistors which will increase the charging time of C_0 (the output rise time) unless channel widths are increased.

The necessity for P wells increase the area of a CMOS circuit so that less logic can be packed into a given chip area but modern technologies have nearly overcome this drawback.

The need for a single power supply, the low power demand, switching speeds in the tens of nanoseconds range and other attractive features (like high noise imunity) makes CMOS LSI circuits with polysilicon gates very popular, not only for low power uses like wrist watches and hearing aids, but also for many other logic applications.

18.3 Dynamic MOS Logic

Many MOS circuits used today are of the dynamic type. The main advantages of dynamic logic are that fewer transistors are needed per memory cell (see Section 18.4) and there is much lower power dissipation. This enables the designer to pack more components and get more computing ability out of the same chip area and for the same processing price.

The principle of dynamic logic is to turn some transistors on and off at a constant pulse rate, called the *clock rate*, and to store the digital information as a charge (or no charge) in a gate capacitance in between. The oxide is an excellent insulator and could store a charge for years if the gate were not also connected to the drain junction of a previous transistor. The junction has finite leakage current and so limits the storage time of a charge in the gate to about 2 ms. Within this time the charge must be removed or refreshed. This is done by the clock pulses that activate the refresh circuit.

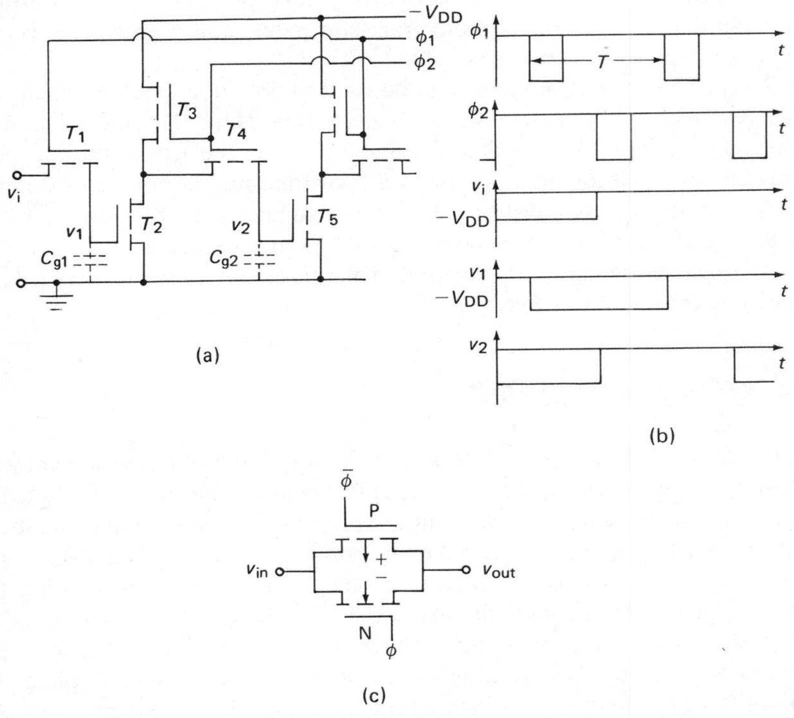

Figure 18.3. Dynamic ratio inverter principle: (a) circuit, based on enhancement PMOS; (b) timing diagram; (c) a CMOS transmission gate.

An example of a clocked enhancement PMOS inverter is shown in Fig. 18.3(a). ϕ_1 and ϕ_2 are two pulse trains supplied by the clock oscillator, displaced by $\frac{1}{2}T$ with respect to each other. ϕ_1 turns on transistor T_1 which acts as a transmission gate allowing C_{g1} to charge up to v_i potential (say $v_i = -V_{DD}$ at that moment, representing a logic '1'). At the end of ϕ_1 pulse T_1 cuts off and C_{g1} becomes isolated. T_2 cannot conduct till ϕ_2 pulse arrives and turns on both T_3 (which acts as load transistor for T_2) and T_4 which is a second transmission gate. C_{g2} can then discharge (if it was previously charged) through T_2 and T_4 and then it stores a logic '0' for the next clock period. If v_i now changes to '0' then the next ϕ_1 pulse will discharge C_{g1} and when ϕ_2 is on again T_2 will stay cut off. C_{g2} will then charge to $-V_{DD}$ (logic '1') through T_3 and T_4. We have therefore an inverter which absorbes power from the supply only during clock pulses. Note also that if v_i stays constant, the charge in C_{g1} is refreshed during the ϕ_1 pulses, and that of C_{g2} is refreshed during the ϕ_2 pulses. As power is used during clock pulses only, dynamic circuits require less power than static ones.

Based on this principle, clocked dynamic gates performing NOR, NAND or other logic functions can be constructed with ϕ_1 pulses activating transmission gates that give access to input transistor gates, and with ϕ_2 pulses that activate the load transistors.

A pair of CMOS transistors can be used to obtain an analog switch or a transmission gate if connected as in Fig. 18.3(c). Here the clock ϕ and its complement $\bar{\phi}$ must be applied simultaneously to the gates, turning both transistors on or off together. To avoid forward biasing the source or drain to substrate diode, the N substrate should be connected to the most positive voltage and the P to the most negative voltage in the circuit.

As we shall see in the next section, dynamic circuit approach makes large semiconductor memories feasible.

18.4 MOS Memory Cells

Computers or microprocessors require various kinds of fast semiconductor memories. Such a memory contains repetitive cells organized in a rectangular matrix form with each cell having an address: its row and column numbers. Each cell can store a single bit of binary information, i.e., when 'read' its output voltage can have two values corresponding to '1' or '0'. Surrounding the memory matrix there are logic circuits on the chip whose function is to decode a binary address when it arrives and connect the cell at that address to the input amplifier for 'writing' new data into it, or to the output sensing amplifier for 'reading' it. Large memories use a lot of chip area and it becomes very important to minimize the individual cell area. Bipolar memories are faster than MOS ones but need a more complicated technology and more area, hence they contain fewer cells. There are memories which can only be read (Read Only

Memory or ROM), others that can be programmed by the user (PROM), and still others that can be both read and written into during operation (known as Random Access Memories or RAMs). In this section we shall describe some static and dynamic MOS RAM cells which are the building blocks of such memories.

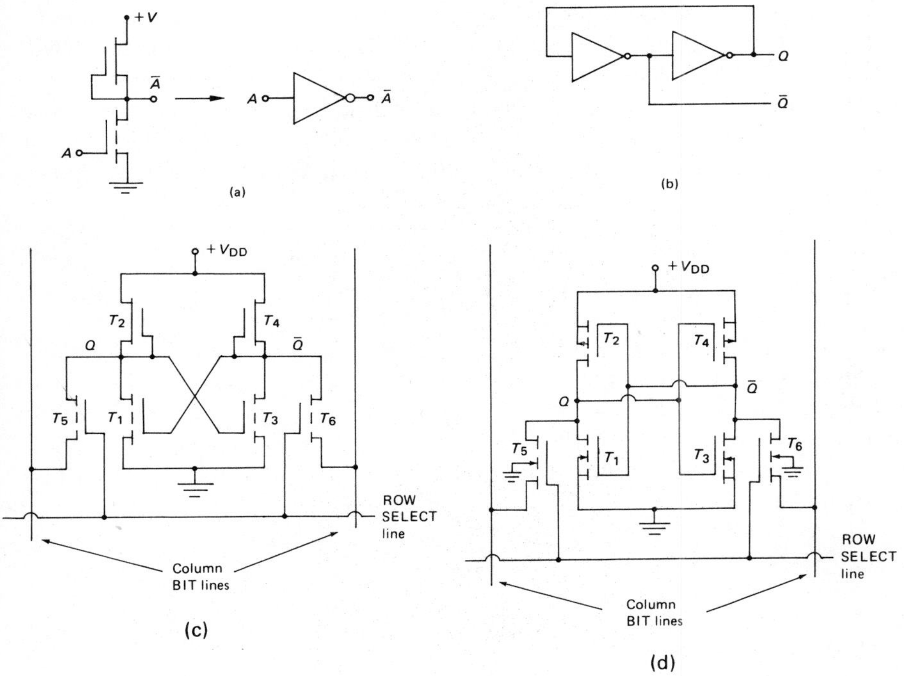

Figure 18.4. Static memory cells: (a) standard symbol for an inverter; (b) two inverters interconnected as a latch, or memory cell; (c) a 6-transistor cell based on NMOS enhancement–depletion transistors; (d) a 6-transistor cell based on CMOS technology.

Figure 18.4 shows two types of 6-transistor static memory cells, one based on NMOS, the other on CMOS technology. Each cell contains two inverters, the standard symbol of which is shown in Fig. 18.4(a), with the output of one serving as the input to the other. This is called a latch. Such a circuit can be in one of two stable states: $Q =$ '0' or $Q =$ '1'. Two possible realizations are given in Fig. 18.4(c), (d) in which transistors T_1, T_2 constitute one inverter T_3, T_4 the other. The circuit will latch into one of its stable states by establishing the proper potentials for Q and $\bar{Q}$ on the column 'BIT' lines and then activating the 'ROW SELECT' line. This turns on T_5 and T_6 connecting these potentials to the inverters input–output points. This is the WRITE operation. Because inverters do not switch instantaneously (Section 13.4), writing takes a certain time. To READ, the addressed cell bit lines are connected to a sense amplifier and its row line is selected and raised in potential. T_5 and T_6 are turned on, thus connecting Q and $\bar{Q}$ to the sense amplifier and through it to the memory output. READING takes also a certain time.

A cell of 6 transistors is relatively large. the associated capacitances require that an appreciable fraction of a microsecond be used for READ and WRITE operations. Such cells are usually used in small memories of up to 4096 (i.e., 2^{12}) cells (known as 4K memories). Larger memories use the dynamic approach requiring fewer transisors. Dynamic memory cells with 4, 3, 2 and a single transistor have been developed and used. A three transistor cell is shown in Fig. 18.5(a).

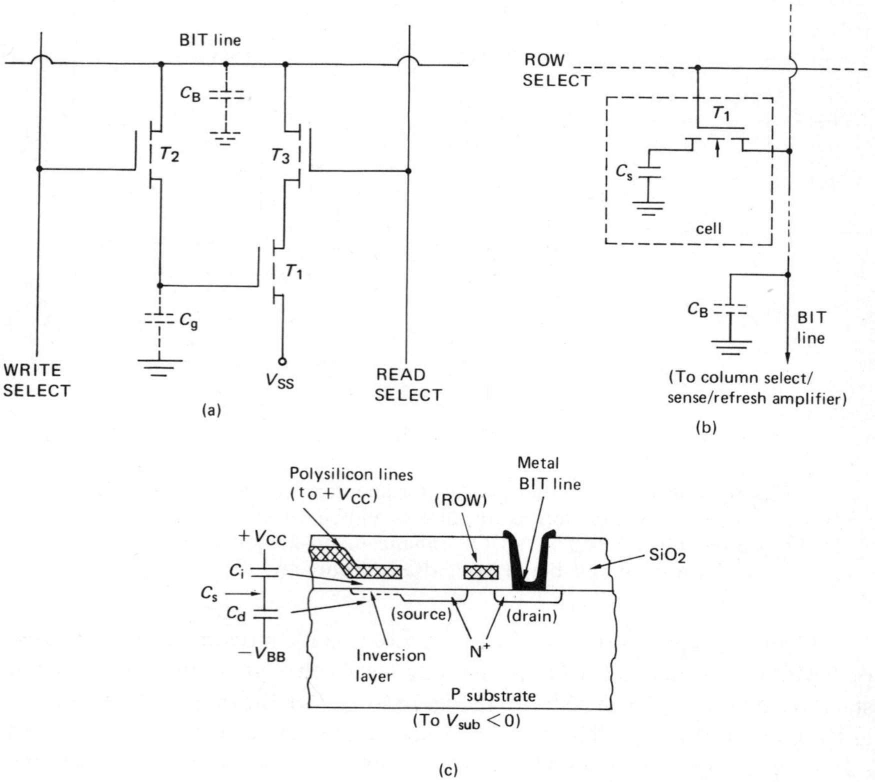

Figure 18.5. Dynamic memory cells: (a) a 3-transistor cell; (b) a 1-transistor—1-capacitor cell; (c) cross section of the 1-transistor cell.

The bit information is stored as charge ('1') or no charge ('0'), in the gate capacitor C_g of transistor T_1 and controls its conduction state. Transistors T_2 and T_3 are switches used for writing into the cell or for reading its stored data. To WRITE, the addressed BIT line is brought to the proper potential corresponding to the data and the WRITE SELECT line is pulsed to turn T_2 on so the data is transferred into C_g. To READ, the BIT line capacitance C_B is first precharged to the '1' potential and then the READ SELECT line is pulsed to turn on T_3. If the data stored is '1', C_B will discharge through T_3 and T_1, if '0' is stored it will stay charged. The BIT line will therefore attain a potential corresponding to the complement of the stored data. A refresh operation must be performed every 2 ms at least and consists of a READ cycle followed by inversion and a WRITE cycle. Note that READ is a nondestructive operation in this cell.

Though a 3-transistor cell is smaller and uses less power than the static cells, it is still relatively big and a 1-transistor/1-capacitor dynamic cell is now commonly used in the big 16K and 64K memories built on a single VLSI chip. This cell is shown in Fig. 18.5(b). The data is stored as charge in the storage capacitor C_S. For READING the BIT line is precharged to a voltage V_{B0} and when the ROW line is addressed (selected) by being pulsed positive, C_S is connected in parallel with the BIT line capacitance C_B. The charge in C_S redistributes between the two capacitors. Suppose C_S voltage was V_S, and C_B voltage was V_{B0} prior to ROW SELECT, then their common voltage after selection will be

$$V_{B1} = \frac{C_S V_S + C_B V_{B0}}{C_S + C_B}. \tag{18.3}$$

The change in the BIT line potential will be

$$\Delta V = V_{B1} - V_{B0} = \frac{C_S(V_S - V_{B0})}{C_S + C_B}. \tag{18.4}$$

C_B might be 5÷10 times larger than C_S (which is about 0.1 pF). This makes ΔV a fraction of a volt which is enough to activate a regenerative sense amplifier. The READ operation is destructive but the output is made to appear immediately across the BIT line, now acting in its refresh role, and the information is rewritten into the cell by recharging C_S to its previous voltage. Each cell must be Read/Refreshed every 2 ms at least. To WRITE, the column amplifier first brings its respective BIT line to the desired state ($+V_S$ or zero), then by selecting the ROW T_1 turns on, charging or discharging C_S.

The cell structure is shown in Fig. 18.5(c). The storage capacitance C_S is composed of two parts: the inversion layer (on the silicon surface) to the polysilicon electrode capacitance C_i and the depletion capacitance C_d between the same inversion layer and substrate. To WRITE, the metal BIT line and the polysilicon ROW line are pulsed positive, the N^+ source becomes connected to the drain and attains its potential V. C_i is then charged to $V_{CC} - V$ and C_d to $V - V_{sub}$ with V_{sub} being the negative substrate voltage. When the ROW voltage is returned to zero, the channel connecting source and drain disappears and the charge remains stored in C_S till the cell is accessed again for the Read/Refresh cycle.

Yet further saving in cell area can be achieved by eliminating the implanted N^+ source region and the lateral distance between the two polysilicon electrodes by letting them overlap (with oxide in between). C_S then becomes a sort of charge-coupled capacitor (Chapter 12) into which charge is injected from the drain region via the channel created by the ROW (gate) voltage.

Dynamic memories, however, require more sophisticated control signals then static ones and time must be allocated to the refresh operation. When small RAMs are needed therefore, static cells are frequently used.

18.5 The Charge-coupled Device (CCD) as an IC

Figure 12.14 showed that a charge packet can be stored for a limited time in an MOS capacitor. Many such capacitors can be arranged side by side and very near each other and the original charge packet can then be transferred from one capacitor to its neighbor, step by step, with a rate determined by the clock frequency.

Such an integrated device, also containing an input diode and gate for injecting a controlled charge and a sensor at the output to detect the arriving charge, and a clock circuitry to provide multiphase pulses for the charge transfer, constitutes a CCD type of an LSI circuit.

The principle of the CCD is illustrated by the three-phase N channel device, a portion of which is shown in Fig. 18.6. When φ_1 is pulsed highly positive, at $t=0$, the P substrate is deeply depleted under all the capacitor electrodes connected to φ_1 and each capacitor can store up to a certain maximum charge in it (Q in (12.31)). This charge Q is shown stored under electrode 1a while 1b stores zero charge in this case. The other phases are maintained at a voltage slightly higher than the threshold level V_T to keep surface traps constantly charged (otherwise they charge and discharge during the charge packet passage and distort its shape). Looking at the timing diagram we see that at t_1 phase φ_2 becomes positive while φ_1 starts to decrease. A deep potential well is formed under all φ_2 electrodes while those under the φ_1 electrodes become shallower.

If the distance between adjacent electrodes is less than the depletion layer (which extends sideways as well as downwards) the stored charge will flow into the newly formed deeper wells, i.e., towards the right, and be stored under electrode 2a. At t_2 all the charges have already been transferred under the φ_2

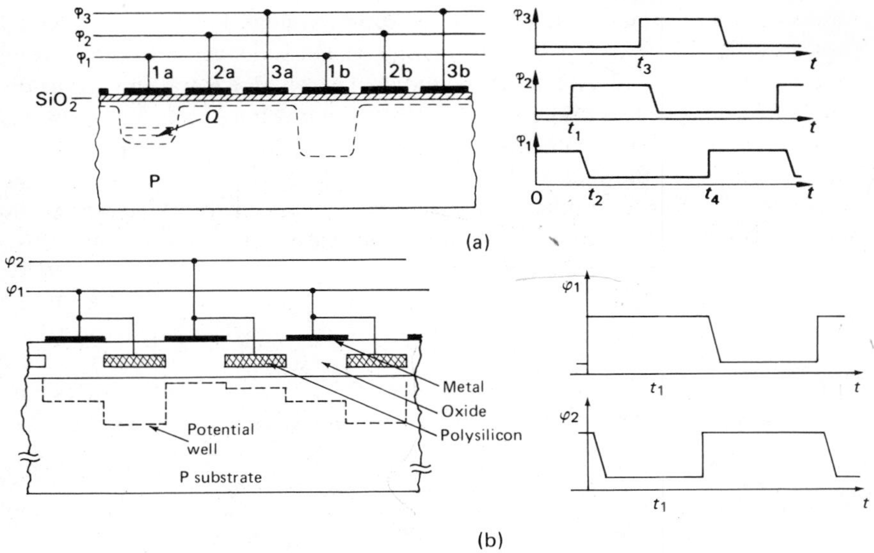

Figure 18.6. Two types of surface CCDs with their phase timing diagrams: (a) a three-phase CCD with potential wells shown for $t=0$; (b) a two-phase CCD with potential wells shown for $t=t_1$.

electrodes. At t_3 phase φ_3 comes on, transferring the charge, again towards the right, and so on. A two-phase device can also be built and the direction of the charge travel can be uniquely determined by having two electrodes connected to each phase as shown in Fig. 18.6(b). The two electrodes have different gate oxide thickness under them, i.e. different C_{ox} and different V_T. The same pulse voltage will create potential wells of different depth under each as shown, this will insure that the charge will be stored in the deeper well and the step in potential due to the difference in oxide thickness under neighboring electrodes will prevent it from moving backwards during the next transfer.

One simple method of injecting a charge into a CCD is shown in Fig. 18.7(a). The potential of the input diode S (with respect to the substrate) is varied with the signal which we want to sample. The gate G nearest to it is kept at constant potential and the electrode next to it, D, is the first storage electrode of the CCD and connected to phase φ_1. The combination of S, G and D constitute an MOS transistor structure that has a drain voltage equal to the silicon surface potential under D only during the φ_1 pulse, as shown. The charge stored under D is approximately a linear function of the input diode potential, i.e., of the signal voltage, provided the signal is small.

One way of detecting the charge that arrives at the CCD end is shown in Fig. 18.7(b). Behind the last electrode E there is a diffused region D_1 that is electrically connected to the gate of the MOS transistor T. This is the output transistor and its drain is connected to the supply voltage V_{DD} through the load resistance R_L. When E is pulsed the charge packet is delivered to the floating diffused region D_1 and changes its potential. This change is transmitted to the gate of T, which changes its drain current and output voltage accordingly. D_1 can be operated as a charge integrator and accumulate the arriving charges for a specified time. At the end of this time electrode G is pulsed on and all the accumulated charge is dumped into D_2 and V_{DD}. A less sensitive detector would omit T altogether and use the current flowing into V_{DD} as the output.

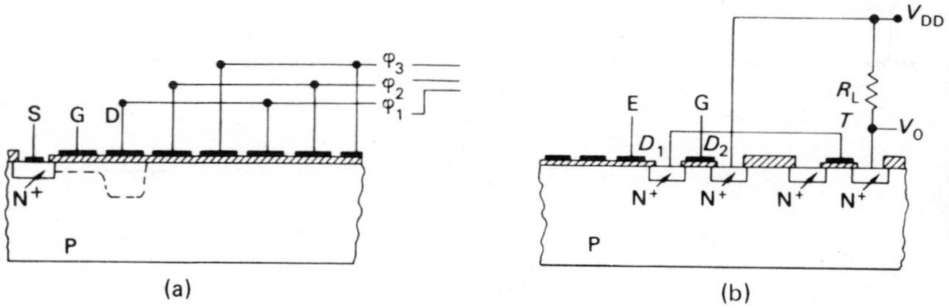

Figure 18.7. (a) A CCD input diode; (b) a CCD output detector.

Both examples of Fig. 18.6 are of surface CCD, i.e., the minimum of the potential well is located on the silicon surface (the Si–SiO_2 interface) and that is where the charge packets are stored and transferred. The interface is rich in surface states and electron traps. The surface mobility is also lower than in the bulk. This adversely affects transfer efficiency and speed. By implanting a thin ($\sim 2\,\mu m$) surface layer with N-type dopant (opposite to that of the substrate) the bottom of the potential well is shifted into the substrate bulk. This is called a *buried channel CCD*. Figure 18.8 shows the energy levels as functions of depth under the interface.

At zero gate voltage there is some depletion on both sides of the N region due to contact potentials between N to metal and N to P regions (Fig. 18.8(b)). When the metal gate is pulsed positive with respect to the substrate (which is identical with the substrate being pulsed negative) the depletion layer on the PN junction side of the N region extends to meet with the depletion region at the interface to give a potential minimum (the most positive point) that is located away from the interface (Fig. 18.8(b)). Note that the built-in field at a PN junction makes the N side more positive (lower in the energy band picture) than the P side, even without external voltage. The charge packets are now located at the potential minimum inside the bulk, where there is higher mobility, longer lifetime and no surface states. Charge transfer becomes faster and higher clock rates can be used. A penalty is paid, however, since the maximum charge that can be stored is smaller.

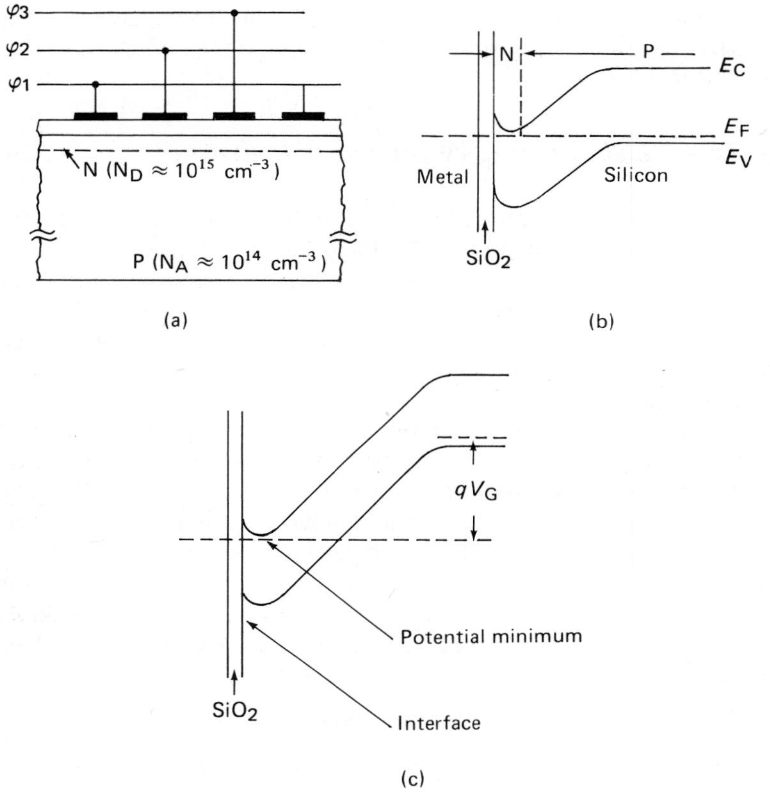

Figure 18.8. Buried channel CCD and energy band diagram: (a) cross section; (b) energy band diagram at zero gate voltage; (c) energy band diagram at positive gate voltage.

For transferred charges that are analog samples of a signal, taken at successive times, the output will be the same sampled signal delayed in time by the product of the number of cells in the CCD and the clock period. CCDs can thus be used as delay lines, as shift registers and for signal processing in various ways. Furthermore, a CCD may be combined with a light-imaging device. A matrix of buried channel capacitors with polysilicon gate electrodes is used as the imaging area. The P substrate under the capacitors is thinned down to 8 μm and when illuminated from the rear, the optically generated electrons diffuse easily into the potential wells formed by the storage capacitors and are stored there. The charge that accumulates is proportional to the light at each point and to the integration time (which can be made long if the device is cooled). After the integration period the accumulated charges are transferred in a prearranged order by CCD shift registers from the storage capacitors to the output, there to be reconstructed by a computer into a picture. Such devices have found much use in astronomy. Further information on CCDs and their applications may be found in Ref. 15.

18.6 The VLSI Circuit, What Does It Entail?

The requirements of modern electronic systems call for ever larger circuits. The ability to accommodate nearly 10,000 and more gates (about 50,000 transistors) on a single chip is what made possible the microprocessor revolution which we witness today. If a circuit is large enough, it contains all the subunits with which it needs to communicate during operation (like clocks, ROM and RAM memories, analog to digital converters, etc.), and requires less outside connections, thus becoming more reliable and economic.

There are, however, constraints on the maximum chip size and the number of components that can be 'crammed' into it. Wafer size is limited by the crystal growers ability to maintain uniform properties across it and by the IC manufacturer's ability to process big wafers without inducing excess warpage and crystal damage that bug large wafers at high processing temperatures. the maximum chip (single circuit) size is limited by yield which is related to the density of faults, original and process induced. Chip area is therefore tightly linked with processing complexity, cleverness and manufacturing skill. For VLSI circuit production at reasonable yield one should be able to:

1. Scale down device feature size and power demand.
2. Develop masking techniques that can handle the smallest feature.
3. Use processing techniques that minimize fault generation and maintain the best uniformity across the big wafers (like replacing wet acid etch and diffusion by dry plasma etch and ion implantation).
4. Develop process simulation programs that give the process engineer an exact enough idea of things, like expected dopant concentrations or junction locations, that become difficult to measure accurately because of the smaller and shallower device structures.
5. Develop the use of computer controlled processing equipment to remove variations due to human limitations.
6. Develop accurate models and simulation tools for the minimum size devices that take into account second and third order effects (which can be ignored in large devices).
7. Develop software tools to help in economic design of such huge circuits, verify their logic behavior and facilitate their testing to a given confidence level.

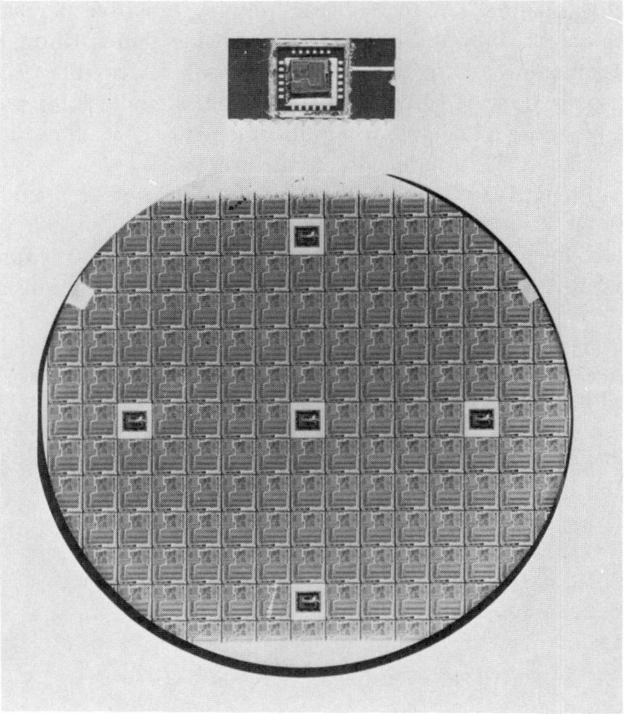

The VLSI circuit shown in Fig. 16.1 before wafer dicing (top) and when diced and encapsulated in a dual in-line package (bottom). Courtesy of National Semiconductors (Israel).

Most of these subjects extend beyond the scope of this book. Each one merits a book by itself. We shall only touch briefly those points that are more relevant to devices. For further information on VLSI see Refs. 25 & 41.

18.7 Scaling Down Devices and VLSI Chip Design

The drive to reduce device dimensions (and area) led to the development of scaling theories for the MOS and the bipolar transistors. We shall only describe the first as at present MOS predominates in the VLSI field.

The basic idea underlying present scaling theory is to keep the electric field strength invariant with size reduction. Shorter distances will then translate into shorter transit times and lower voltages. Vertical as well as horizontal distances must be scaled down. Thus source and drain junction depths should be proportionately shallower as otherwise sideways diffusion would encroach too much on the effective channel length. Substrate doping must be increased so that depletion regions are also scaled down (otherwide punch through between source and drain or interaction between neighboring devices may occur). Oxide thickness must also be scaled down to maintain the gate field at the reduced gate voltage. The height of oxide steps on the surface must also be reduced as they may cause breaks in the thinner interconnect lines.

If channel length (L), width (W), gate oxide thickness (t_{ox}), voltages (V_{GS}, V_{DS}, V_{sub}) are all scaled down by a factor K ($K>1$) while the substrate doping (N_A), is scaled down by the same factor, then the rest of the parameters will behave as follows (equation numbers refer to the original equations in previous chapters):

(12.17)
$$C'_{ox} = \frac{\varepsilon_0 \varepsilon_{ox}}{(t_{ox}/K)} = KC_{ox}$$

(7.12)
$$\phi'_F = E_F - E_{Fi} = -kT \ \ln \frac{(KN_A)}{n_i}$$

(8.22a)
$$d'_{dep} \simeq \left[\frac{2\varepsilon_{si}\varepsilon_0 (V_t/K)}{q(KN_A)}\right]^{1/2} = \frac{d_{dep}}{K} \quad (\text{for } V_t >> V_B)$$

(12.19)
$$Q'_B = -q(KN_A)\ (d_{dep}/K) \simeq Q_B$$

(12.29)
$$V'_T = V_{MS} + \frac{2\phi_F}{q} - \frac{Q_{ox}}{(KC_{ox})} - \frac{Q_B}{(KC_{ox})} \simeq \frac{V_T}{K}$$

(The last is justified if the first two terms can be neglected with respect to the last two or if V_{sub} between source and substrate, which determines Q_B, is scaled by a slightly different factor to compensate.)

(12.22)
$$I'_{DS} = \frac{\mu(KC_{ox})\ (W/K)}{(L/K)} [(V_{GS}/K - V_T/K)\ (V_{DS}/K) - \tfrac{1}{2}(V_{DS}/K)^2] = \frac{I_{DS}}{K}$$

(12.25)
$$I'_{DS}(\text{sat}) = \frac{\mu(KC_{ox})\ (W/K)}{2(L/K)} (V_{GS}/K - V_T/K)^2 = \frac{I_{DS}(\text{sat})}{K}$$

(12.26)
$$g'_m = \frac{\partial(I_{DS}/K)}{\partial(V_{GS}/K)} = g_m$$

(12.27)
$$C'_{gs} = \tfrac{2}{3}(L/K)\ (W/K)\ (KC_{ox}) = \frac{C_{gs}}{K}$$

(12.28) $$T'_{\min} = \frac{(C_{gs}/K)}{g_m} = \frac{T_{\min}}{K} \quad \text{(device delay time)}$$

Based on these relations, the following circuit properties are expected to scale as follows:

Device area (A) $\rightarrow \dfrac{1}{K^2}$

Power dissipation (IV) $\rightarrow \dfrac{1}{K^2}$

Power–delay product ($IVT'_{\min}$) $\rightarrow \dfrac{1}{K^3}$

Power dissipation per unit area $\left[\dfrac{IV}{A}\right] \rightarrow 1.$

Considerable gains in area and power–delay product (an important figure of merit in digital circuits) are therefore expected from down scaling. In real life, however, reducing size beyond a certain point increases the importance of secondary effects like the short channel effect on V_T (Chapter 12) and also a narrow (small w) channel effect. Such effects must now be included in the device model used for simulation. Another secondary effect that becomes important stems from our definition of V_T as the gate voltage for *strong* inversion. There is weak inversion already at $V_{GS} < V_T$ and therefore some subthreshold conduction which must be considered. Interconnect lines and contact holes to the devices become also proportionately smaller which increases their associated resistances and voltage drops. A lot of effort is therefore directed at improving models to correctly simulate VLSI circuit operation so that it can be designed with confidence. VLSI chip design usually progresses from the top: first the functional specifications are defined and logic block diagram drawn by logic design specialists. They then proceed to detailed logic design and verification via logic simulation. Usually complete cells previously designed and stored in a computer library are used in the design. Such a cell might be a simple gate, a memory cell or a complete shift register or ROM. In the detailed design of a cell the designer uses the various transistor structures at his disposal. He must have as his input all the relevant electrical parameters, each with its range of possible values that may vary across a processed wafer, each with its temperature dependence. Such a list includes the following data:

Transistor Data

Threshold voltage for each transistor type and for field oxide (between transistors).

Gain constant (k in (13.11)) for each type, per unit channel width.

Substrate–source reverse voltage effect (body effect) on threshold gate, junction and field oxide breakdown voltages.

Capacitance Data per Unit Area

Gate to source and gate to drain overlap capacitance.

Capacitance of bottom area of diffused or implanted junctions (at zero voltage).

Capacitance of side walls of junctions (per unit length at zero voltage). This might be different from the bottom area capacitance due to dopant density dependence on depth.

Polysilicon over gate oxide capacitance.

Polysilicon over field oxide capacitance.

Aluminum line to substrate capacitance.

Sheet Resistance Data

Of diffused or implanted and annealed areas.

Of polysilicon lines.

Of aluminum lines.

Contact hole resistance per unit area.

This data is supplied by the device specialists and is based on calculations, simulations and experimental device measurements on devices built using the particular company mask design rules and processing technology. The mask design rules give minimum allowed distances, e.g., between edge of contact hole to edge of diffused source or drain region, separation between neighboring polysilicon lines or minimum line width. Those rules depend on the particular processes and equipment used. The device specialist is thus the link between the materials and equipment people and the circuit designer.

Extensive treatment of VLSI design methods can be found in Ref. [43].

18.8 Problem Areas in the VLSI Technology

Processing Problems

Present day VLSI devices may have an area of 80 mm^2 and contain hundreds of thousands of transistors. Chennel lengths of 2 μm, junction depth of 0.3 μm, gate oxide thickness of 400 nm, 2 μm wide polysilicon lines and 3 μm wide aluminum lines were already reported (Ref. 40). To achieve reasonable yield at such dimensions, special processing approaches are being investigated. Some of them are:

1. Use of a single mask to cover a whole wafer for photolithography is no longer feasible since thermal processing distorts the wafer so that perfect alignment at two widely separate points does not mean that points in

between are aligned within the required tolerance. Wafer stepper machines that reduce a single circuit mask directly onto a photoresist covered wafer and then step across the wafer correcting the alignment as they go have entered use. Also electron beams controlled by a computer fed with the mask information can be used to directly 'write' on the photoresist covered wafer. The technique is too slow and expensive at present and is used mainly to generate masks.

2. The thin gate oxide is prone to pin holes and low breakdown fields. Dry oxidation needs high temperatures and is relatively long. Oxide properties have been found to improve somewhat if chlorine is added during oxidation. Temperatures and times of oxidations are reduced if it is performed at increased pressure.

3. The small sizes used means that very little side etching and undercutting of photoresist masks on the wafer can be tolerated. This rules out all the isotropic etching techniques (like wet acid or plasma etch). New techniques that give anisotropic (directed) etch are being developed, like reactive ion etch, sputtering and ion milling. They all use energetic ions hurled at the unwanted region to etch it at a single direction only. Those techniques are still not perfect and very slow.

4. The need for heavily doped source and drain ($N_D > 10^{20}$ cm^{-3}) coupled with shallow junction ($x_j < 0.5\,\mu$m) pose a problem. The donor atom best fitting the Si crystal is arsenic which is both toxic and has high vapor pressure. Implantation seems the best solution but takes too long for the high concentrations needed. Implant machines with high beam current (in the mA range) are needed but the increased ionic space charge makes beam focusing and scanning very difficult. Also wafer heating problems arise.

5. The interconnect methods for VLSI chips constitute another problem area. In bipolar circuits metallization constraints are usually the limiting factor controlling the maximum device density. In MOS circuits, polysilicon has a high sheet resistance ($\sim 20\,\Omega/\square$) and aluminum, when alloyed for ohmic contacts, absorbs silicon and forms spikes that enter the silicon for some distance and may short a shallow junction. Al is also severely limited in the post deposition temperatures that it can withstand. Therefore refractory metals with very high melting temperatures (like molybdenum, titanium, tantalum or tungsten) and their highly conductive silicides (compounds formed with silicon) are being tried. This opens the way to two and more metallization layers with a good insulating oxide deposited in between. Both capacitors and Schottky barrier diodes can then be incorporated. there are, however, many questions regarding such materials and their reliability that are still unanswered.

6. A problem related to the very small size of VLSI devices arises in dynamic type circuits or CCDs. Traces of radio active elements usually present in device encapsulation materials result in some α particle (proton) emission which generate electron–hole pairs in the silicon. The charge generated can be collected into a biased MOS gate capacitance and change its voltage enough to cause an error. New or cleaner encapsulation materials must therefore be used.

7. A different aspect of VLSI in which a lot of research effort is being invested is circuit design, design aids, design verification and circuit testability. The circuit complexity that existing technologies can deliver already exceed the designers capability to utilize in the optimum way. Groups of designers usually tackle each assignment, each working on one part of it with computer programs as their chief aids. As the same logic functions, or algorithms can be obtained in different ways, design approaches are sought that would give the best economic solution subject to the constraints of the technology used. The problem is also attacked in reverse: which logic schemes and algorithms are best fitted to be implemented by the existing technology. Techniques like redundancy (excess circuit parts that can be switched in to replace defective sections) or circuits that can be interconnected in different ways to best fit a problem, using internally built switches that can be controlled from the outside or by the circuit built-in software, are being investigated by computer science theorists.

8. The question of testing each part of the circuit must be faced at the design stage. It should be possible to separate the circuit into small functional units that can be communicated with and tested without feedback through other parts. Sometimes special circuit blocks are added just to facilitate testing.

As VLSI uses multiply and invade every area of human activity, exerting a profound impact on most, the efforts to improve technology and design will surely continue to increase throughout the next decade.

QUESTIONS

18.1 Draw the schematic of a logic circuit based on NMOS that performs the logic function of $(A+B)C$.

18.2 What logic function does the circuit of Fig. 18.1(a) perform if negative logic is used (i.e., if zero volts corresponds to '1' and positive voltage to '0'?

18.3 How would the substrate–source voltage present in a transmission gates like transistor T_1 or T_4 of Fig. 18.3(a) affect their operation as 'switches'?

18.4 How would increased temperature affect the operation of a dynamic MOS circuit?

18.5 Many MOS logic circuits operate with their substrate connected to a small negative bias voltage. How does this affect switching speeds? Current levels? Power consumption?

18.6 When testing a dynamic memory based on cells like Fig. 18.5(a), it was found that one cell is stuck at $Q = $ '0'. When $Q = $ '1' is written into it, this information is retained for about 100 μs and it then switches back to $Q = $ '0' by itself. Discuss possible faults that could cause this.

18.7 Can a two phase CCD like in Fig. 18.6(b) be built with the same oxide thickness under both electrodes? With different oxide thickness but with electrodes made of polysilicon?

18.8 A logic MOS circuit is scaled down by a factor K. Name at least two quantities that prevent the current I_{DS} from being scaled exactly by K.

PROBLEMS

18.9 Show that the output time response, $v_0(t)$, of the CMOS inverter of Fig. 18.2(b), when its input switches from $+V_{DD}$ to 0, is given by

(18.5) $$t = \frac{c_0 v_0}{k_P(V_{DD}) + V_{TP})^2} \text{ for } v_0 \leq -V_{TP}$$

(18.6) $$t = \frac{c_0}{k_P(V_{DD} + V_{TP})}\left[-\frac{V_{TP}}{V_{DD} + V_{TP}} + \tfrac{1}{2}\ \ln \frac{V_{DD} + 2V_{TP} + v_0}{V_{DD} - v_0}\right]$$

for $-V_{TP} \leq v_0 < V_{DD}$,

where $V_{TP} < 0$ is the threshold of the p channel transistor T_2 and $k_P = C_{ox}\mu_h W/2L$ is its gain factor.

Calculate the rise time to $v_0 = 0.9\ V_{DD}$ for $V_{TP} = -2.2$ V, $V_{DD} = 10$ V, $k_P = 50\mu A/V^2$, $C_0 = 5$pF. *Hint*: first investigate the voltage range for which T_2 is in its linear (triode) region and when it is in saturation.

18.10 Show that the output resistance of the CMOS inverter of Fig. 18.2(b) under static conditions is $[2k_N(V_{DD}-V_{TN})]^{-1}$ when the input is V_{DD} and $[2k_P(V_{DD}+V_{TP})]^{-1}$when the input is zero. V_{TP} and k_P are defined as in Problem 18.9, and k_N and V_{TN} are corresponding values for the n channel transistor. These resistances determine the amount of current that can be drawn or sunk if the inverter is loaded by a static load (like a bipolar logic circuit) without too much deterioration in the high and low values of the inverter output voltage.

18.11 Use eq. (12.31) to show that the surface potential V_S can be expressed in terms of $V'_G = V_G - V_{FB}$ and the stored electronic charge Q in a CDD as

$$V_S = V'_G + \frac{Q}{C_{ox}} + V_A - \left[2V_A\left\{V'_G + \frac{Q}{C_{ox}}\right\} + V_A^2\right]^{1/2} \tag{18.7}$$

where $V_A = \dfrac{qN_A\varepsilon_0\varepsilon_{si}}{C_{ox}^2}$.

Calculate V_S for $V'_G = 15\,V$ and $Q=0$ for an oxide thickness of $0.1\,\mu m$ and $N_A = 10^{15}\,cm^{-3}$. Find the maximum charge that can be stored under these conditions.

18.12 The BIT line capacitance C_B in a one transistor cell dynamic memory is 1.9 pF. The storage capacitor voltage for storing '1' and '0' are 5 V and 0 V respectively, and the BIT line precharge voltage is $V_{B0} = 2.1$ V. If the sense amplifier requires a minimum of 250 mV potential change for a reliable detection of '1' or '0', what value of C_S is needed?

18.13 A two-phase CCD like in Fig. 18.6(b) is built on a ⟨100⟩ P-type substrate with $N_{A0} = 10^{16}\,[cm^{-3}]$, $Q_{SS} = 10^{10}q\,[cm^{-2}]$. The polysilicon gate is doped with $N_D = 10^{18}\,cm^{-3}$ and has gate oxide 50 nm thick, while the Al gate is over 100 nm thick oxide. For a phase voltage pulse of 8 V find:

(a) the potential step on the silicon surface forming the well depth,
(b) the maximum charge that can be stored,
(c) the minimum charge that can be detected if there is a surface leakage current (caused by surface generation) of $1[nA/cm^2]$ and the clock frequency is 2 MHz.

POWER SEMICONDUCTOR DEVICES 19

High power device design implies high current and high voltage capabilities combined with the ability to operate at relatively high temperatures and conduct dissipated power in the form of heat to outside the device with a minimum of thermal resistance. Most power devices are made of silicon because of its high thermal conductivity and 1.1 eV energy gap that enable them to operate at up to a junction temperature of 200°C. Those devices include the thyristor, the bipolar and power MOS and the static induction transistor, all of which will be described in this chapter. Power devices for microwave frequencies are usually made of GaAs which, with a thermal conductivity only a third that of Si, has a much higher mobility and larger band gap that enable it to operate at higher frequencies and temperatures. They are described in Chapter 20.

19.1 General Considerations

The thyristors are switching devices used mainly in the control field. The main current can be switched on when desired and in some types also off but not controlled in between. In the other devices the output current can be continuously controlled by base current or gate voltage and they can therefore be used for either switching or linear power amplification.

When a device is used as a power switch, its important properties are:

(a) Its ability to carry large currents with a uniform current density over a large device area.

(b) While the device conducts its nominal current, its 'ON' resistance (or voltage drop) should be as low as possible to reduce heat dissipation.

(c) While the device is in the 'OFF' state, its voltage blocking capability should be as high as possible.

(d) The switching speed, or maximum switching frequency should be high. This means low capacitances and minimum minority storage effects.
(e) The device should be able to avoid unwanted switching to 'ON' when the main voltage is suddenly applied. Again, this means small parasitic capacitances.

For linear power applications one must add:

(f) The device forward β (or g_m) should be constant and independent of the signal amplitude which is necessary to avoid excessive distortion in large signal operation.

We shall refer to those requirements as each device is described. A general conclusion, however, may be reached even now: there is a conflict between high voltage blocking capability which requires a thick region of low doping density on at least one side of the junction (Section 9.5) and low 'R_{ON}' which requires the opposite. The result is a design compromise: higher voltage capability entails lower current and vice versa (for devices of the same active area and heat dissipation capabilities).

If the low doped region has an area A, doping density N_D^- and an undepleted thickness t when in the 'ON' state, then R_{ON} will be determined mainly by

$$R_{ON} = \frac{\rho t}{A} = \frac{t}{q\mu_e N_D^- A}. \tag{19.1}$$

The breakdown voltage BV will be obtained by substituting (9.47) into (9.46):

$$BV = \frac{\varepsilon\varepsilon_0}{2qN_D^- b^2} \ln^2 \left[\frac{qN_D^- b}{\varepsilon\varepsilon_0 a} + 1\right] \quad \text{with } a,\ b, \text{ given in Section 9.5.} \tag{19.2}$$

Specifying R_{ON} and BV enables one to get a good estimate of t and N_D^-.

A severe problem faced by manufacturers of high-current large-area devices is to maintain uniform doping throughout a low doped, large area N-type wafer which constitutes the starting material or power devices. Normal crystal-growing and doping techniques give about $\pm 15\%$ fluctuations around the wanted resistivity in low-doped wafers. The measured resistivity fluctuate widely when one moves radially or lengthwise on the crystal by even such small steps as 0.1 mm. Such fluctuations lead to weak spots in the device area where premature avalanche and hot spots may form.

This problem has now been solved. A high degree of homogeneity in phosphorus doping of the original Si crystal can now be achieved by irradiating a dislocation-free single-crystal silicon of a very high resistivity ($>1500\ \Omega$ cm) made by float zone technique, by thermal neutrons from a nuclear reactor.

The neutron flux transmutes Si atoms first into a Si isotope with a short (2.6 h) half-life which then decays into phosphorus. Very large diameter can thus be uniformly doped to the required resistivity, depending on the desired blocking voltage. An additional annealing step is also required to remove any crystal damage caused by the irradiation. Resistivity fluctuation of about $\pm 1\%$ can be obtained even at very low doping levels, making such Si an excellent starting material for large-area power devices. Blocking voltages of up to 5 kV with forward voltage drops around 1.6 V at 1 kA or currents of 15 kA (though not in the same device) were reported. Let us now examine each power device separately.

19.2 The Thyristor Family: The Silicon Controlled Rectifier (SCR) and the Triac

The thyristor is one of the most important semiconductor devices today in the industrial or power electronics field. It is used in high-power controlled recitifiers, d.c. to a.c. inverters or in frequency converters. It is an essential element in control of electrical motor speed, electrical furnace heat, lighting and many other uses.

The thyristor is a general name referring to a family of devices operating on similar principles. We shall describe two of the more important ones: the silicon-controlled rectifier and the triac.

The current–voltage characteristics and circuit symbol of an SCR are shown in Fig. 19.1. This is a special type of diode which, in order to start conduction, must have not only a positive anode–cathode voltage V but also a high enough positive pulse applied to a third electrode called the gate G.

When a positive voltage, smaller than some maximum V_{DSM} (D refers to forward direction, S to surge, M to maximum) is applied between anode A and cathode K, the SCR passes only a leakage current, smaller than some specified value. However, if a pulse of a certain minimum voltage and current (see Fig. 19.5) is applied as a trigger I_G between gate and cathode, the SCR switches to conduction even if V_{AK} is just a few volts positive. The device also switches to conduction if its forward voltage exceeds a value called the *break-over voltage* V_{BO} (at V_{BO} the leakage current reaches the value of I_L called the *latching current*). Once conduction starts, the voltage across the SCR drops to a low value, V_T, of about 1.5 V, and the current rises to a value I_T limited by the external circuit only.

After turn-on the gate loses control of the anode–cathode current and turn-off can be achieved only by reducing the anode current below a minimum value called the *holding current* I_H (Fig. 19.1(b)) for a certain minimum time. This is in contrast with the transistor, where the base (or gate in FET) exercises continuous control over the collector current.

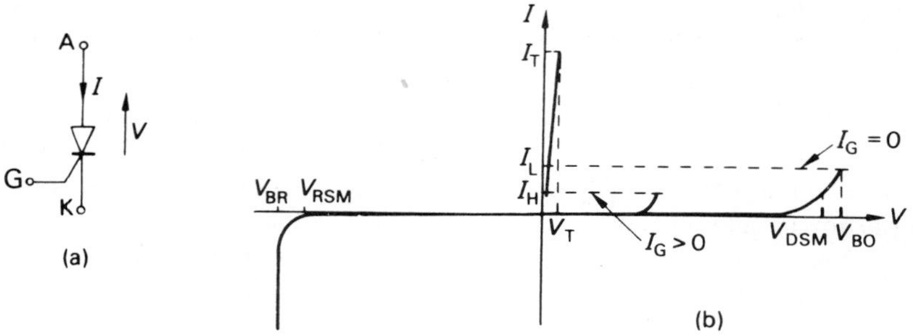

Figure 19.1. The silicon-controlled rectifier: (a) circuit symbol; (b) I–V characteristic.

When the anode is negative with respect to the cathode the SCR blocks conduction as long as the maximum reverse voltage is below its breakdown value of V_{BR}. In use the maximum reverse surge value, V_{RSM}, should not be exceeded.

The physical explanation for SCR operation is as follows. The device is a four-layer structure with three junctions between them, J_1, J_2 and J_3, as shown in cross section in Fig. 19.2(a), which shows a circular SCR. Schematically, it can be represented as in Fig. 19.2(b). To understand its operation let us divide this structure into two three-layer substructures as in Fig. 19.2(c). These structures can be visualized as two interconnected transistors, T_1 (NPN) and T_2 (PNP) as shown in Fig. 19.2(d).

Application of a positive voltage between anode and cathode will not result in conduction because junction J_2 will be under reverse bias and blocking. But comparing Fig. 19.2(c) and (d) shows that J_2 is the collector–base junction in both equivalent transistors and reverse voltage across it is normal to transistor operation in the active region.

Current can therefore flow in T_1 if a base current is supplied, i.e. if a current pulse is fed into the gate G which serves as the base of T_1. The resulting collector current of T_1 serves as a base drive for T_2, which also starts conducting then. The collector current of T_2 serves as additional base drive for T_1 and takes over when the original gate trigger pulse ends. This constitutes a positive feedback loop, and the two transistors very quickly become heavily saturated and the device turns on. In saturation the J_2 junction becomes forward biased (like any other collector junction of a saturated bipolar transistor) so that all three junctions J_1, J_2 and J_3 are forward biased. The total forward voltage drop V_T of the device consists of the algebraic sum of these voltages plus the ohmic voltage drop in the bulk parts of the SCR. However, J_1 and J_3 contribute a voltage of opposite sign to that contributed by J_2, resulting in a total V_T of between 1 to 2 V depending on the current.

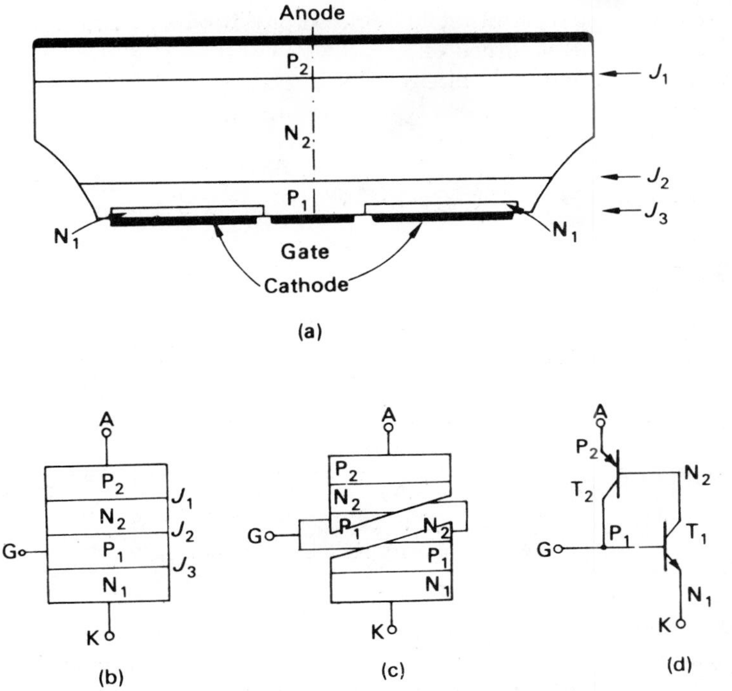

Figure 19.2. Cross section of an SCR and its two-transistor model: (a) cross section of a circular SCR; (b) describing the SCR schematically; (c) division of the device into two three-layer substructures; (d) the two-transistor model of the SCR.

At forward voltages higher than V_{BO}, the increased leakage current switches the device on even without gate triggering. When the anode–cathode voltage is negative, both J_1 and J_3 are reverse biased, and since they are also the emitter–base junctions of the two-transistor model the device remains cut off. If the reverse voltage exceeds the breakdown voltage V_{BR}, avalanche will start and the device, operating under high voltage and current conditions, will usually be destroyed. In actual use the reverse voltage should not exceed V_{RSM} in the surge case or even a lower value, V_{RRM} (reverse repetitive maximum), if the reverse voltage is repetitive but of short duration.

When the device conducts in the forward direction its current divides between the collectors of T_1 and T_2. If this current I_T falls below the holding current I_H, then the two transistors come out of saturation and regain their amplifying properties. Any further current reduction is immediately amplified by the positive-feedback loop (reduction of one collector current reduces base drive of the second—which reduces collector current of the second—

which reduces base drive of the first and so on). Both transistors are quickly cut off and the SCR is turned off.

A more quantitative picture of SCR operation can be obtained with the help of Fig. 19.3 which shows a typical impurity profile of an SCR.

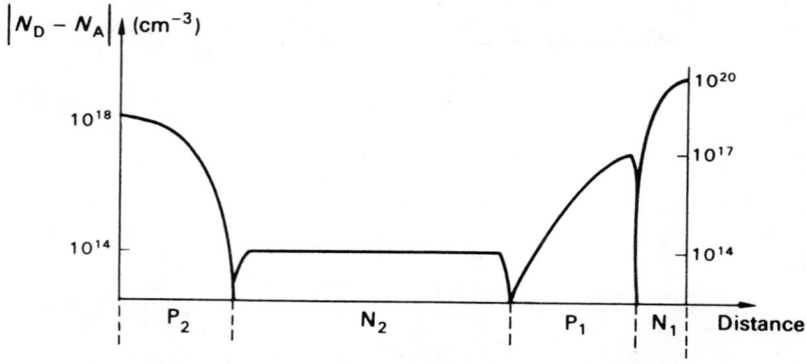

Figure 19.3. Impurity profile of a typical SCR.

The interesting thing about this figure is the relatively large width of the equivalent transistor bases, especially the $P_2N_2P_1$ one. The P_2 and N_1 regions have high impurity concentrations, as befits their role of emitters in the two-transistor model. P_1 and N_2 have lower doping, as base regions should.

The very low-doped base N_2 of the $P_2N_2P_1$ transistor may extend through 100 μm or more depending on the required value of the blocking voltage. Both base widths are longer than the minority carrier diffusion length in them.

From Chapter 14 we know that α_F for the transistor is given by (14.11). If the collector voltage is below avalanche value ($M=1$), this equation gives

$$\alpha_F = \gamma b \delta.$$

δ is low only at very low currents and quickly grows with the current to 1. If the emitter doping is appreciably higher than in the base (which is the case for Fig. 19.3 for both equivalent transistors), then $\gamma \simeq 1$. The transport factor b is given by

$$b = \frac{1}{\cosh (W_B/L)}, \tag{14.15}$$

where L is the minority diffusion length.

Since here W_B is of the same order of magnitude as L, b is low and so too is α_F at very low currents. Increase of the current, however, by applying a gate pulse, raises δ to 1 and detailed analysis shows that b grows too; α_F therefore increases with the current.

To see how this change in α_F switches the SCR on, let us denote the currents in the various parts of the two-transistor model as marked in Fig. 19.4.

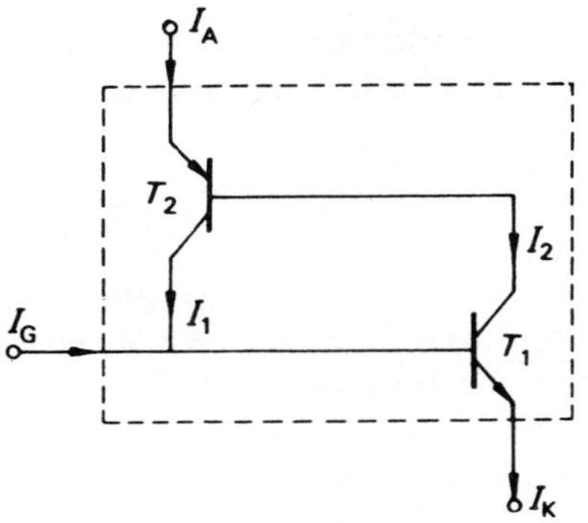

Figure 19.4. The currents in the various parts of the two-transistor model of the SCR.

From eqs. (14.8) we know that with reverse bias on the collector junction

$$-I_C = \alpha_F I_E + I_{CBO}.$$

(I_E and I_C were defined there as positive when flowing into a PNP transistor or out of an NPN one.)

We can therefore write for the T_2 transistor in Fig. 19.4,

$$I_1 = \alpha_{F_2} I_A + I_{CBO_2}, \qquad I_2 = I_A - I_1 = (1-\alpha_{F_2})I_A - I_{CBO_2}$$

And for T_1:

$$I_2 = \alpha_{F_1} I_K + I_{CBO_1}.$$

Eliminating I_2 in the last two equations and substituting $I_K = I_A + I_G$ (Kirchhoff's current law must hold for the whole SCR enclosed in the dashed box in Fig. 19.4) gives

$$I_A = \frac{\alpha_{F_1} I_G + I_{CBO_1} + I_{CBO_2}}{1-(\alpha_{F_1}+\alpha_{F_2})}. \tag{19.3}$$

On the other hand, if only current changes are considered, we get:

$$dI_K = dI_A + dI_G.$$

But

$$\alpha_2 = \frac{\partial I_1}{\partial I_A}, \qquad \alpha_1 = \frac{\partial I_2}{\partial I_K}.$$

Remembering that $I_A = I_1 + I_2$ in Fig. 19.4, we get:

$$dI_A = dI_1 + dI_2 = \alpha_2\, dI_A + \alpha_1\, dI_K = \alpha_2\, dI_A + \alpha_1(dI_A + dI_G)$$

or

(19.4)
$$\frac{dI_A}{dI_G}=\frac{\alpha_1}{1-(\alpha_1+\alpha_2)}.$$

The SCR will switch into conduction when I_A is no longer controlled by it. This will happen when either of the following two conditions is fulfilled:

(19.5)
$$\alpha_{F_1}+\alpha_{F_2}=1$$

(19.6)
$$\alpha_1+\alpha_2=1 \quad \text{or} \quad \beta_1\beta_2=1.$$

Equation (15.3) showed that as long as α_F grows with I_E we shall have $\alpha>\alpha_F$ so that condition (19.6) will be satisfied first and cause conduction if gate triggering is used. At forward break-over, with $I_G=0$, it is condition (19.5) that is fulfilled and the break-over voltage is determined by it. At V_{BO} the depletion layer extends deeply into the low-doped N_2 region, to a depth d which is a function of V_{BO} and the doping in N_2. The effective base width of the $P_2N_2P_1$ transistor will be reduced from W_{N_2} to $W_{N_2}-d$. The α_{F_2} of this PNP transistor, labelled T_2 in Fig. 19.4, will therefore grow. Since the depletion layer does not extend much into the higher-doped P_1 region the α_{F_1} of the NPN transistor T_1 remains low and one may say that forward break-over occurs when $\alpha_{F_2}\simeq 1$. Using (14.11) this requires that

(19.7)
$$\alpha_F=\gamma\delta bM=1$$

or

(19.8)
$$\gamma\delta\frac{1}{\cosh[(W_{N2}-d)/L_h]}\frac{1}{1-(V_{BO}/BV)^m}=1,$$

where (14.15) was used for b and (9.44) for M.

But since the emitter P_2 doping is high, $\gamma\simeq 1$ and also $\delta\simeq 1$ near switching. We therefore get from (19.8):

(19.9)
$$V_{BO}=BV\left(1-\frac{1}{\cosh\left[(W_{N_2}-d)/L_h\right]}\right)^{1/m},$$

where BV is the theoretical breakdown voltage of the N_2 region. For low-doped N region $m\simeq 6$. Equation (19.9) may be used to relate W_{N2} and the required V_{BO} for a given doping level for purposes of device design.

Another problem that must be considered in the design is the prevention of unwanted or premature 'on' switching. This may happen because of electrical noise in the gate circuit, or by sudden application of a high forward voltage across the SCR. This forward voltage V_D causes a high capacitive current $C(dV_D/dt)$, flowing to charge the J_2 depletion-layer capacitance. This current acts as a gate trigger current and may be sufficient to switch the device on. This puts a limitation on the maximum permitted value of dV_D/dt. In order to increase this value, the manufacturer reduces the gate sensitivity by adding a resistance between gate and cathode that shunts some of the capacitive current. The resistance need not be external. A common method is to extend the cathode metallization over part of the periphery of the P_1 region (gate) in Fig. 19.2(a) and use the high lateral sheet resistance of that region as a sort of lateral, built-in resistor. Another possibility is to mask the N_1 diffusion at many points on the cathode surface, letting the P_1 region extend to the surface there. Cathode metallization extending over these points makes them act as emitter shunts and improve the dV_D/dt rating and the turn off time.

Another limitation of the SCR, specified by the manufacturer, is the maximum rate at which the anode current may be increased just after the device is triggered on. The reason for this dI_T/dt limitation is the non-uniform distribution of I_T across the device area just after the gate pulse. Most of the current is concentrated very near the gate contact and some finite time must pass before the carriers in the P_1 region which are due to I_G diffuse all across it, starting conduction everywhere (one must remember that modern thyristors are very high current devices and their diameter may be 50 mm or more).

To obtain maximum permitted rate of growth for I_T a special interdigitated involute form may be given to the gate and cathode contacts, which assures that every location on the cathode surface is no further from the gate contact than some specified distance. The circular SCR pellet in Fig. 19.2(a) has a special contour in its circumference, designed to prevent premature surface avalanche breakdown from starting on the surface. The transition from the dielectric constant of the Si (11.8) to that of air (1) makes the surface vulnerable to high-field breakdown where the depletion layer comes out. By giving a special contour the length along the surface over which the depletion-layer voltage (i.e., the blocking voltage) drops is increased, reducing the maximum field. Otherwise, the measured maximum blocking voltage of the device will be lower than the expected value.

SCR turn-off time, t_{off}, signifies the ability of the device to withstand re-application of a forward voltage t_{off} seconds after the anode current goes below I_H, at which point the device is supposed to switch off. Due to the excess stored charge left over from the conduction period the device may turn on spontaneously if forward voltage is reapplied too quickly. To reduce t_{off} this execss charge must be caused to disappear very quickly. One way to do it is to shorten lifetime by the use of gold diffusion, thus increasing the number of recombination centers. Another way is to apply a negative voltage pulse to the gate, sweeping out the charge (gate-assisted turn off).

The design requirements for low forward voltage drop during conduction are high values of equivalent transistor α (to reduce the saturation voltage). This conflicts with fast turn-off times, necessitating low values of α, so the transistors will not go deep into saturation. Considerable ingenuity is needed to achieve both. Some of the ratings of a modern fast turn-off industrial type SCR, number BTW33-1200RM, made by N. V. Philips Gloeilampenfabrieken are as follows:

Non-repetitive forward and reverse surge voltages ($t < 10$ ms) V_{DSM}; V_{RSM}	1200 V
Repetitive peak voltage (duty cycle <0.1) V_{DRM}; V_{RRM}	1200 V
Continuous blocking voltage V_D	800 V
D.C. current I_T	110 A
Non-repetitive peak on state current I_{TSM}	1500 A
Rate of rise of on state current after triggering	$dI_T/dt < 100$ A μs^{-1}
Rate of rise of off state voltage that will not trigger the device at $T_j = 125°C$	$dV_D/dt < 200$ V μs^{-1}
On state voltage drop at $I_T = 200$ A, $T_j = 25°C$	$V_T < 3$ V
Holding current at $T_j = 25°C$	$I_H < 200$ mA
Leakage current at 1000 V, $T_j = 125°C$	$I_{DM} < 15$ mA

Two of the characteristic curves published by Philips for this thyristor are shown in Fig. 19.5. In Fig. 19.5(a) the gate characteristics are given for various device temperatures. The hatched area is that of uncertain triggering and it becomes smaller at higher temperatures. There are limitations on the maximum gate voltage (10 V) the maximum gate current (1.8 A) and the maximum power into the gate (5 W). In Fig. 19.5(b) the turn-off time t_q is given as function of the rate of application of the reapplied forward voltage V_D.

(a) The Triac

The triac is used for current switching in a.c. circuits. It is, in fact two SCRs connected in reverse parallel, as can be seen from the cross section of Fig. 19.6.

The triac has three terminals, called the first main terminal (MT_1), the second main terminal (MT_2), and the gate (G).

The triac can conduct in both directions. The main current and the triggering current paths in each of the two possible conduction directions are shown in Fig. 19.7. This device has a short-circuited emitter structure, where the N emitters are shorted to their neighboring P regions by the overlying metallizations. The voltage across those junctions is therefore zero. The gate metallization extends over two regions also—N_4 and P_2. If a pulse is applied to the gate in Fig. 19.7(a), positive with respect to MT_1, while MT_2 is also positive with respect to it, electrons will be injected from N_3 into P_2. They will be collected by N_2 and turn-on will progress (as in the SCR case) by the right-hand side of the device in Fig. 19.7(a). If a negative pulse is applied to the gate (with respect to MT_1) it is the N_4 region that will inject electrons into P_2 and so also cause triggering. In a similar fashion the triac may be triggered to conduct in the opposite direction as in Fig. 19.7(b), where the left-hand part of the device operates.

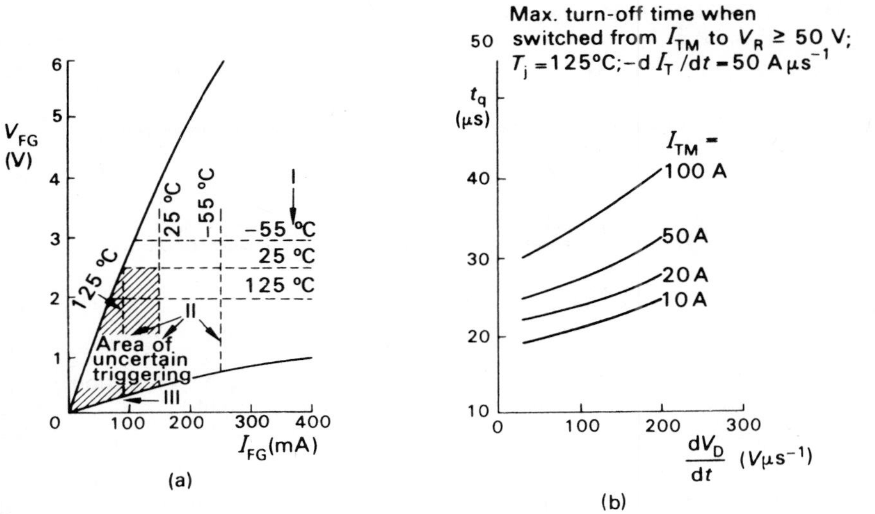

Figure 19.5. Some characteristics of the Philips BTW33 fast turn off thyristor: (a) gate characteristics; (b) turn-off characteristics.
I = minimum gate voltage that will trigger all devices at $T_j = \rightarrow$
II = minimum gate current that will trigger all devices at $T_j = \rightarrow$
III = maximum gate voltage that will not trigger any device at T_j = 125°C.

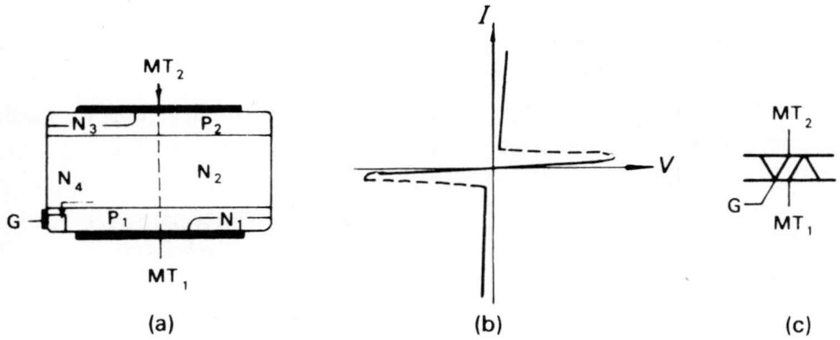

Figure 19.6. The triac: (a) cross section of the basic triac structure; (b) I–V characteristics with no gate triggering; (c) circuit symbol.

The triac can thus pass an a.c. current if triggered twice in each period. To turn it off the MT_1–MT_2 voltage should stay around zero for some minimum time, meaning that there is a maximum value of dV/dt that can be tolerated around $V=0$ (or a maximum sinusoidal wave frequency) so that the triac will not re-trigger itself.

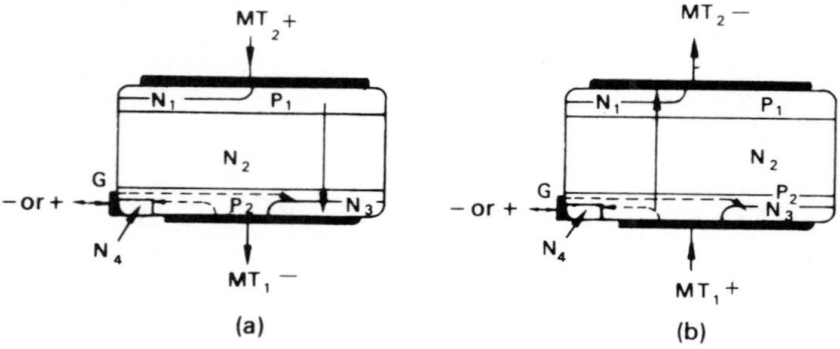

Figure 19.7. Current paths in the triac in both conduction directions: —— main current; ------ triggering current.

As in the SCR, the currents and temperatures have upper limits. At the maximum temperatures (usually 125°C) the leakage currents are high and the danger of unwanted triggering is at its highest. The thyristors are therefore mounted on heat sinks and have low junction-to-case thermal resistance.

19.3 The Bipolar Power Transistor

A bipolar power transistor should have all the properties enumerated by (a)–(f) in Section 19.1. This implies a doping profile like in Fig. 14.2, where the collector junction depletion region extends through a low doped epitaxial layer (for high breakdown voltages and low junction capacitance) while the bulk of the collector is highly doped to reduce its series resistance. For large current capacity one must operate at high injection levels where $\beta_F \equiv h_{FE}$ is already dropping (Fig. 14.9(b)). One also requires large emitter area and the ability to maintain uniform current density in it to prevent local overheating and damage.

At high I_E, $r_e = kT/qI_E$ is very low and the input resistance h_{ie}, given by (15.14(b)), consists mainly of $r_{b'b}$—the base spreading resistance. To reduce the input power necessary to drive the transistor, $r_{b'b}$ should be kept to the minimum (about 10 Ω) by increasing the base doping as much as possible, especially in those parts of the base not under the emitter, where it does not affect the injection efficiency (γ of eq. (14.12)). The cross section of such a structure is shown in Fig. 19.8(a).

Some additional effects that must be taken into account at high injection levels besides base conductivity modulation that affects γ (Section 14.4) are:

(a) Current crowding that occurs at the emitter periphery. This effect is illustrated in Fig. 19.8(b): base current, flowing from the base contact towards the emitter junction, creates a lateral voltage drop along the base, V, and causes the forward bias on that junction to go down with distance from the base contact. Because injection depends exponentially on bias, only the emitter periphery, on the side of the base contact, will inject.

To reduce this effect, the ratio of emitter periphery (facing the base contacts) to area should be increased. The interdigitated structure of Fig. 19.8(a) serves this purpose very well.

(b) Base widening, also known as Kirk effect. Let us assume an NPN transistor with N_D^- doping density in the collector depletion region. With a collector voltage of a few volts, the field in that region is already sufficient to accelerate the minority electrons leaving the base to their saturation velocity v_s. For a current density J_c this implies that a negative charge density of $Q = -J_c/v_s$ exists in the collector-base depletion region. This charge adds to the negatively ionized acceptor charge $-qN_A$ on the base side of the junction and subtracts from the positively ionized donor charge $+qN_D$ on the collector side. If J_c is high and N_D low, this would move the plane of the junction (determined by a zero net charge) into the collector, effectively widening the base, increasing the base transit time τ_B and thereby reducing h_{FE} and f_T.

(c) Swamping of the built-in drift field in diffused base transistors (Section 15.5). As the bulk of the base stays electrically neutral, minority charge injected through the emitter junction causes an equal majority charge to enter via the base contact (the diffusion capacitance is being charged). If the injected excess minority and majority densities are comparable or higher than the original base doping density, the original majority carrier distribution (determined by the graded doping in the base and responsible for the base built-in field) will be swamped. At high currents this transistor would therefore start to behave like one with a uniformly doped base. Detailed analysis of conduction at high injection levels show that the effective diffusion constant of minority carriers in the base is then doubled with the base transit time given by (11.11) like for a uniform base.

(d) The maximum switching frequency of a bipolar transistor is relatively low, about 200 kHz, because its storage time is long due to the large excess minority charge accumulated during forward conduction. To shorten storage times gold doping of the collector region may be used with a penalty of increased leakage and reduced breakdown voltage.

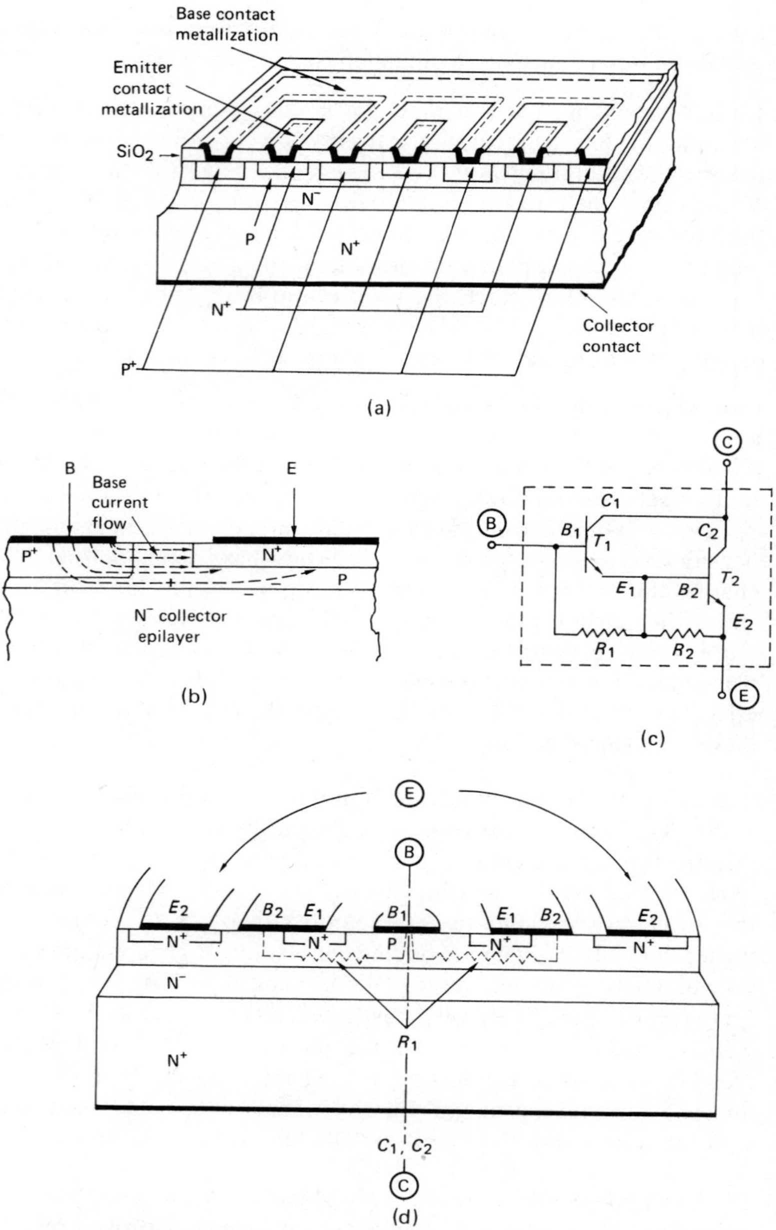

Figure 19.8. The bipolar power transistor: (a) typical cross section; (b) illustrating the current crowding effect; (c) Darlington connection of two transistors; (d) an integrated Darlington device (as made by RCA).

(e) If a power transistor is allowed to reach high currents in the high-voltage avalanche zone of Fig. 14.15(b) and allowed to stay there for some time, the *second breakdown* phenomenon may occur as shown in that figure. By 'second breakdown' we refer to a destructive process that may occur even though the current and voltage separately are still below the maximum ratings.

Secondary breakdown results from hot-spot formation in the semiconductor because of nonuniform current density distribution and a positive feedback effect. Accidental crystal faults, doping fluctuation or other nonuniformities originated by processing may cause this current nonuniformity which would result in nonuniform dissipation and temperatures. Because increased temperature affects V_{BE} (which is reduced by about $-2\,\text{mV}/°\text{C}$, see Section 9.4), β_F (which increases – Section 14.4) and collector leakage current (which increases exponentially), the current density at the hotter location would increase further, the vicinity would get even hotter and *thermal runaway* develops. Within a few microseconds local melting may occur with irreparable damage. This is evident in the characteristics by a sudden collector voltage drop followed by a sharp current increase.

Some manufacturers supply an $I_C - V_{CE}$ map which divides the active region into *safe operating areas* or SOAR. The transistor is safe from secondary breakdown if its stay in that area is shorter than some specified time. Such a typical map is shown in Fig. 19.9(b). For example, transistor 2N3719 can tolerate $I_C = 10$ A at $V_{CE} = 30$ V for only 5 μs but may tolerate 1 A at the same V_{CE} for 500 μs and 0.1 A indefinitely.

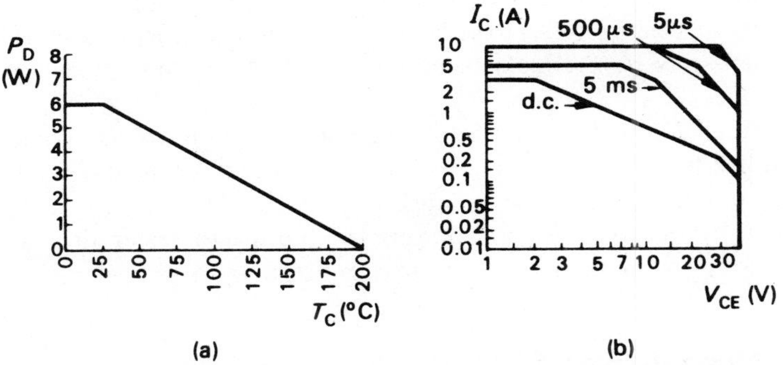

Figure 19.9. Power specifications for a typical Si transistor (Motorola 2N3719): (a) allowed dissipation derating curve versus case temperature; (b) safe operating area map.

The permitted transistor power dissipation is usually specified for a case temperature of 25°C. At higher case temperatures a derating curve, like in Fig. 19.9(a), is used to ensure that T_j will not exceed 200°C (one may obtain θ_{jc} from it).

(f) Thermal runaway may occur even in small transistors if there is an appreciable heating due to current. It is likely to happen in large area transistors or when one tries to connect several transistors in parallel to increase the current output. To combat the positive thermal runaway feedback one may use a local negative feedback mechanism by connecting a small resistance in series with each emitter of the parallel connected transistors. An increased I_E would result in increased voltage drop in the base-emitter circuit and reduced V_{BE} across the junction that negates the original increase. This technique is also used in large area transistors with multiple emitter stripes. By thin film deposition small film resistors may be deposited on the surface of the Si chip in series with each emitter stripe. Current uniformity can thus be achieved but only at the cost of increased losses.

(g) The design for high currents leads to devices with low h_{FE}. To increase current amplification, two transistors can be connected as in Fig. 19.8(c) in what is known as the *Darlington pair.* Neglecting the resistors for the moment, h_{FE} of the pair equals the product of the h_{FE}'s and may reach several thousands. The resistors are needed for thermal stabilization: at the high operating temperatures of power transistors the leakage currents are significant. R_1 (about 10 kΩ) reduces I_{CEO1} from the high value corresponding to open base towards the much lower value corresponding to shorted base-emitter (Section 14.5). R_2 (about 150 Ω) provides an external path for this leakage current that would otherwise enter the base of T_2, increasing its conduction and heat dissipation. Because the collectors are connected together, the pair can be integrated into a single device with the substrate serving as a common collector. Figure 19.8(d) shows one approach (RCA) to such integration, in which R_1 is 'built-in' and the transistors have circular symmetry. Both NPN and PNP pairs can be made.

A Darlington device has higher saturation voltage than a single transistor, since V_{CB2} equals V_{CE1} which can be near zero (when T_1 saturates) but can never change its polarity as needed for saturating T_2. The device has also longer turn-off times and faster drop of β with frequency compared to a single transistor.

19.4 The Vertical MOS Power Transistor

The MOS power transistor is a newcomer to the power field that is likely to become the leading figure in it.

To increase drain current capabilities of a normal MOS transistor one must increase the channel width, W, and reduce its length, L, (eq. (12.25)). Short channel length, however, reduces the drain breakdown voltage which becomes limited by drain to source punch-through. Very wide gates create problems such as gate electrode resistance which, together with its distributed capacitance, may turn it into an RC transmission line of an appreciable electrical length and drain contact problems at the high current involved.

Those problems are avoided in the vertical double diffused MOS structure shown in Fig. 19.10. Construction starts from an N^+ Si wafer on which an N^- epitaxial layer is grown. Two consecutive diffusions, P and N, are then made using the mask patterns outlines in Fig. 19.10(a) and (b). Both P and N dopant atoms diffuse laterally as well as vertically. The difference in lateral diffusion distances between the two dopant types determines the channel length L ($L<1\,\mu m$) which can be very accurately controlled, much as a diffused base width is controlled in the bipolar technology. Notice also that the thick SiO_2 mask in Fig. 19.10(a) and (b) is the same and there is no critical alignment step in between. The gate is a layer of highly doped polysilicon, insulated by SiO_2 all around and contacted from the periphery. A top metallized layer contacts all the N sources, shorting them at the same time to the P regions (that in a normal MOST would correspond to the substrate) as in Fig. 19.10(c). The gate may be made very wide by patterning it in special shapes like the hexagonal form shown in Fig. 19.10(d). The electron current flow starts from the source central contact, crosses the N channel (formed on the P surface by the gate) horizontally and then continues vertically towards the drain contact as indicated in Fig. 19.10(c).

Another approach to power MOST is to selectively etch V grooves through the surface of an emitter and base of an NPN bipolar structure as shown in Fig. 19.10(e). Selective etching in V groove form is possible on ⟨100⟩ Si surface since in this crystal direction the Si is etched faster than in the ⟨111⟩ directions that form the sides of the groove. Drain breakdown however limits VMOS to operation below 200 V.

Like in the other power devices, the power MOS design entails a compromise in doping density and thickness requirements of the N^- layer between high voltage and high current design demands.

The special features of the power MOST are:

1. The combination of very small channel length, L, and very large channel width, W, makes possible devices with continuous currents in the tens of ampers range.

2. Since the P region which is later inverted by the gate potential to form the channel, is made by diffusion, its doping density is much higher than that of the N^- epitaxial layer, so that drain depletion region does not extend into the channel or modulate its length (Section 12.4) and drain breakdown voltage is determined by the N^- layer. Voltages of 500 V and more can be achieved.

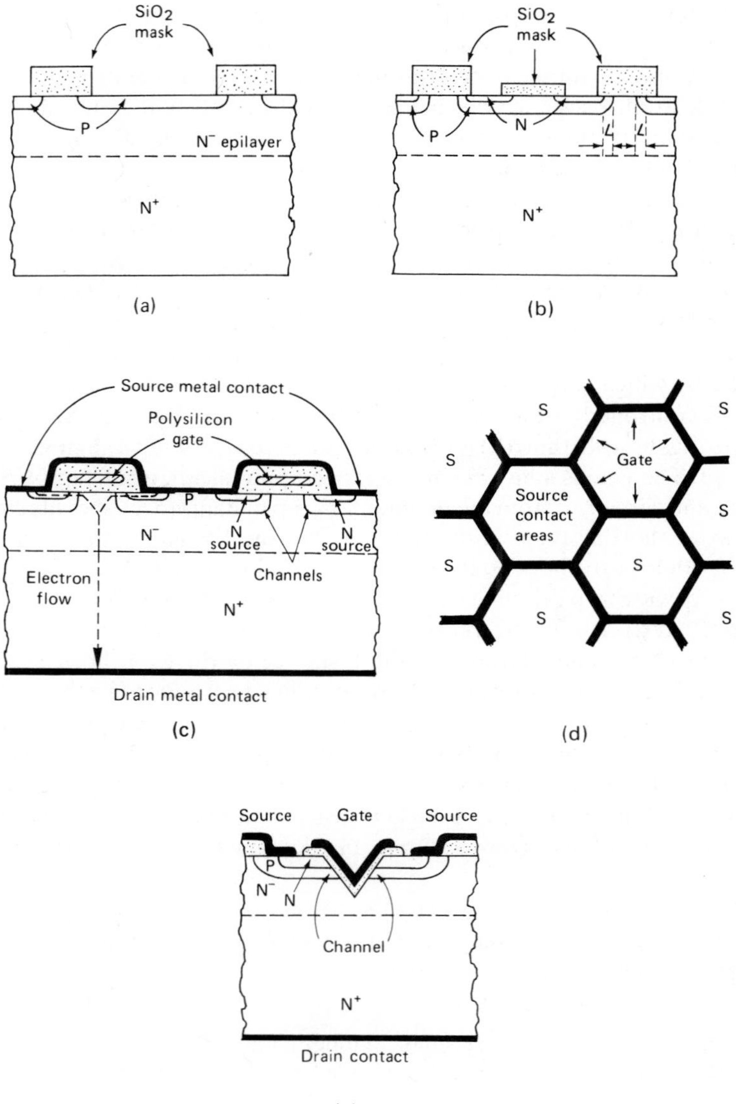

Figure 19.10. The vertical power MOSFET: (a) an SiO_2 mask for diffusing the P regions; (b) an additional mask for diffusing the N source regions which do not necessitate critical alignment with the first; (c) cross section of the finished device. (d) top view of an hexagonal gate shape (the HEXFET power MOST made by International Rectifier has this shape); (e) the VMOS structure for power MOST.

3. Since there is almost no channel length modulation, the $I_{DS}-V_{DS}$ characteristics are practically horizontal and the output resistance is very high in the saturation region.

4. The parasitic drain junction capacitance is relatively small, in spite of the large drain area.

5. g_m is constant, and independent of V_{GS}, in contrast to the normal MOS where it is proportional to $V_{GS}-V_T$ (eq. (12.26)). The reason being that I_{DS} is the product of the free channel charge times its velocity. In normal MOS the charge is proportional to $V_{GS}-V_T$ and the velocity, μE, is also proportional to it since the average field along the channel in current saturation is $E=(V_{GS}-V_T)/L$ (Fig. 12.11). This makes I_{DS} proportional to $(V_{GS}-V_T)^2$ in normal surface MOS. In the vertical power MOS, L is so short that when $V_{GS}-V_T>1V$, E already exceeds the point at which electron velocity saturation occurs so that the channel charge velocity becomes constant and I_{DS} becomes proportional to $V_{GS}-V_T$ only, which makes $g_m=\partial I_{DS}/\partial V_{GS}=$constant. This results in very linear characteristics, well adapted to linear power amplification.

6. The gate leakage current is negligible because of the SiO_2 isolation. The input impedance is governed by gate capacitance alone (which may reach a few thousand pF for high current, large area, devices).

7. The device operates as an MOS transistor only if V_{DS} has the proper polarity (drain positive for N channel). If V_{DS} polarity is reversed, the N drain region and the P region connected to the source form a forward conducting diode that shorts the device. This built-in diode may be used to advantage in some applications.

8. Since the power MOS like any MOS device is based on majority carrier conduction, it does not suffer from minority storage effects. The maximum switching frequencies are determined by the capacitances and may be as high as 1 MHz for currents of several ampers. This is an order of magnitude higher than for bipolar transistors of comparable current and voltage ratings.

9. The power MOS is not prone to hot point formation that may destroy a bipolar device through current crowding and secondary breakdown (Section 19.3). This is because any nonuniformity in current density in a large area power MOS, which increases the temperature of a certain part of it, causes thereby a reduction of the N region mobility and increase of its resistance to current flow. This acts as a negative feedback mechanism to restore current uniformity. This feature makes it possible to increase the device area or connect several devices in parallel without adding small series resistances to equalize current distribution as is necessary in the bipolar case (which increases losses and heat dissipation).

10. Finally the fact that the MOS is voltage and not current controlled and its input loads the previous stage by only a very small capacitive current, simplifies circuit design considerably compared to the bipolar case. On the other hand, the current capability of the bipolar is about four times higher for comparable areas and forward voltage drops.

The vertical power MOS is therefore a very promising new device which is already available in several forms and will undoubtedly play a major role in the power electronics field. Further information on power MOS devices can be found in Ref. 27.

19.5 The Static Induction Transistor (SIT)

The static induction transistor, which has been invented in Japan, is a large area multi-channel JFET intended for high power applications at the HF and VHF bands (such as RF heating). Its cross section is shown in Fig. 19.11(a). It consists of many very thin ($\simeq 4\,\mu$m) P^+ diffused gate stripes, interdigitated with parallel similarly thin and much shallower ($\simeq 0.5\,\mu$m) N^+ source stripes, with very small spacing ($\simeq 4\,\mu$m) in between. All the sources are connected together by a top metallized layer. The longer gate stripes extend underneath and beyond the source contact and are connected together at the front and back of Fig. 19.11(a).

The device operation and characteristics are explained as follows. Even at zero external gate-source voltage, the P^+N-depletion layer at the built-in voltage V_B extends deep enough to reach the edges of the N^+ sources as shown in Fig. 19.11(c) for $V_{GS}=0$, $V_{DS}=0$. The reason being the very low doping level (about $10^{14}\,\text{cm}^{-3}$) of the N^- epitaxially grown layer. If V_{DS} is now made positive, current can flow through the still open channels and a resistive like characteristic marked I of Fig. 19.11(b) is obtained. If a negative voltage V_{GS_2} is applied to the gate, large enough for the depletion layer to extend and close the gap under the sources but with V_{DS} still kept at zero, then Fig. 19.11(d) is obtained. Notice that there is a field component at the source bottom that repels electrons back into the source. This results in I_{DS} remaining zero even if V_{DS} is slightly positive. If V_{DS} is made more positive, like at $V_{DS}=V_{DS_1}$ of Fig. 19.11(b), the depletion layer width must increase towards the drain. The new field lines formed between the P^+ gate and N^- drain increase the gate charge and redistribute is so that the field lines emanating from the gate and terminating on or near the source change their direction and become more parallel or even downward oriented with respect to the surface. There is a field component now that draws electrons out of the source and pulls them towards the drain as shown in Fig. 19.11(e). This results in characteristic II of Fig. 19.11(b) which resemble those of a vacuum triode. We see that a highly positive drain induces virtual channels under the

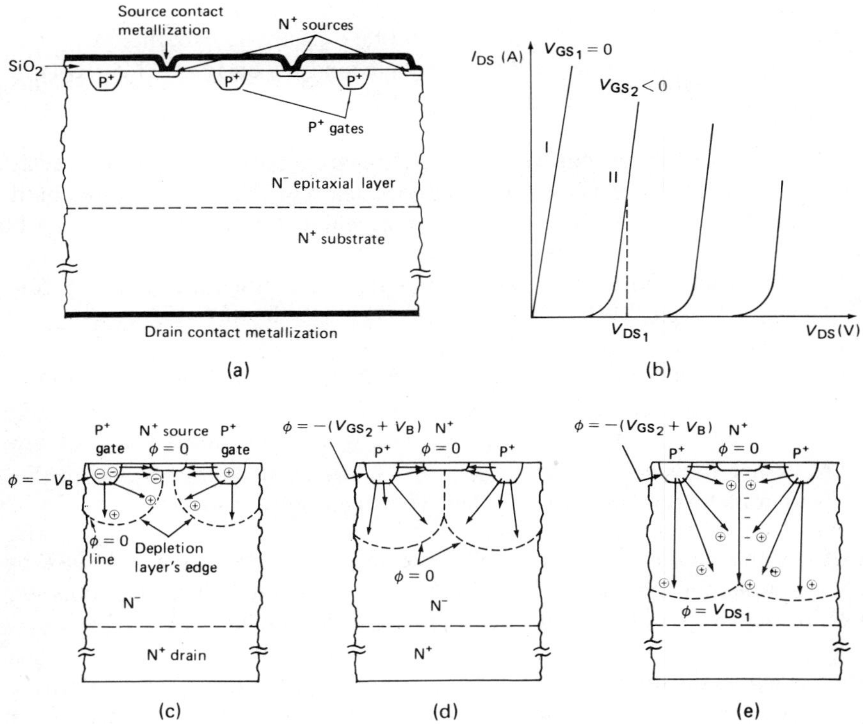

Figure 19.11. The Static Induction Transistor (SIT): (a) cross section (all the gates are connected together at the front and back); (b) the drain output characteristics; (c) depletion layers, equi-potential surface and field lines for $V_{GS}=0$; $V_{DS}=0$ (with source potential taken as zero); (d) same as (c) but with $V_{GS}=V_{GS2}<0$; $V_{DS}=0$; (e) same as (c) but with $V_{GS}=V_{GS2}<0$; $V_{DS}>0$.

sources through which current flows, hence the name. For a drain voltage of about 40 V and N^- layer thickness of 20 μm the average field strength in the channel is already high enough for the electrons to move at their saturation velocities leading to short transit times. The gate and drain capacitances are also low, (considering the device area and current capabilities) due to the N^- region. Devices with maximum frequencies of oscillations (Section 15.6) of 700 MHz or more can be made. Several devices can be connected in parallel in the same package to increase power output and several hundred watts were obtained at 100 MHz.

Further information on SIT can be found in Ref. 28.

QUESTIONS

19.1 What will happen if a negative voltage is applied to the gate of a strongly conducting SCR? Base your analysis on internal currents in the two-transistor model of the SCR.

19.2 It was suggested that by applying a negative pulse to the SCR gate at the moment that its main current goes below I_H, the turn-off time could be shortened. What is the reasoning behind that claim?

19.3 At which temperature should the maximum forward blocking voltage be tested? Why?

19.4 Explain why it is region N_2 in the SCR that determines the maximum forward and reverse blocking voltages.

19.5 What prevents us from connecting many small bipolar transistors in parallel to obtain an equivalent very high power device?

19.6 Can one control the threshold voltage of a vertical power MOST by implanting the channel region? Can one manufacture the transistor using implantation with no following diffusion?

19.7 Why is the drain characteristics of a vertical MOST much more horizontal than those of the normal lateral structure? What does it imply in terms of the electrical parameters of the transistor?

PROBLEMS

19.8 An SCR is connected in a rectifying circuit similar to the one shown in Fig. 9.14(a). It gets a positive gate pulse which is delayed by an angle ωt_1 with respect to the anode–cathode voltage. Assume an ohmic load.

(a) Draw in schematic form the dependence of the SCR current and voltage on time with respect to the transformer secondary voltage.
(b) Find an expression for the d.c. current in the load R_L.
(c) Find an expression for the effective (rms) current in the load.
(d) Assuming the forward voltage drop across the conducting SCR is constant and equal to V_T, find an expression for the increase in junction temperature with respect to the mounting base. The thermal impedance between junction and base is given and so is the maximum instantaneous value of the SCR current.

19.9 The base spreading resistance, $r_{b'b}$, limits the effective width of an emitter strip, W_E in Fig. 19.12. Show that the contribution to $r_{b'b}$ of the active base region ($0 \leq y \leq W_E$) is given by

$$r_{b'b} = \frac{V_B}{I_B} = \frac{\rho_B W_E}{12 L_E W_B} \tag{19.10}$$

where $V_B = \frac{2}{W_E} \int_0^{W_E/2} V(y)dy$ is the average lateral voltage drop in the active base between $y=0$ and $y=W_E/2$, I_B is the total base current in the two base contact stripes, ρ_B is the base resistivity (in Ωcm). L_E is the emitter stripe length and W_B the base thickness. Assume that the lateral component of $I_B/2$ from each base contact reduces linearly with y because of reverse base injection and recombination.

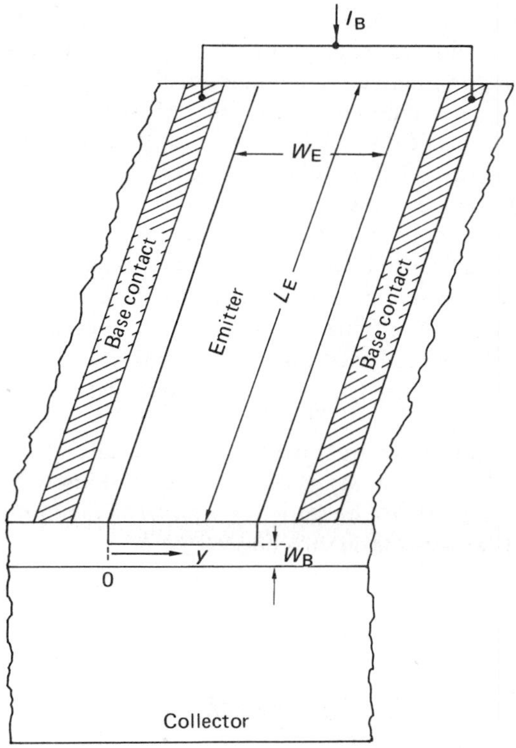

Figure 19.12 Cross-section of emitter stripe for Problem 19.9.

MICROWAVE SEMICONDUCTOR DEVICES 20

The microwave frequency range, i.e. from 1 GHz (10^9 Hz) up to 100 GHz and further, is becoming more and more important in present-day communication systems. The first active semiconductor devices, especially intended for microwave use, appeared about 15 years ago. More advanced such devices are gaining control of this field in the low power (up to a few watts) part of it. The high-power microwave field is still dominated by vacuum tubes. The requirements for high power and high frequency, as we shall see, are contradictory in many respects of semiconductor-device design.

Some of the devices to be described, transistors and variable-capacitance diodes, we have already met. Their operation may be extended into the microwave range by modifying the design or by operating the device in a novel way. Other devices based on different physical principles will also be described. These are the transferred-electron and avalanche-transit-time devices.

Complete quantitative treatment of this specialized field is beyond the scope of this book and, in many cases, requires solid knowledge in microwave engineering. We shall therefore settle for a partially qualitative description of some aspects of microwave circuits and of the devices.

20.1 Microwave Bipolar Transistors

Equations (15.25) for f_T and (15.27) for the maximum high-frequency gain are the starting point for answering the question: what modifications should be made to the bipolar transistor to enhance its ability to operate at high frequencies? The equations are repeated below for convenience:

$$\frac{1}{\omega_T} = r_e C_e + r_e C_c + \tau_B \tag{15.25}$$

$$G = \frac{1}{4\omega^2} \frac{\omega_T}{r_{b'b} C_c}. \tag{15.27}$$

From (15.27) it is obvious that ω_T should be maximized while $r_{b'b}$ and C_c should be minimized. ω_T^{-1} is seen to be the sum of three time constants. Additional time constants that were neglected previously must be considered in the microwave range. They are summarized in Fig. 20.1 which shows the transistor when operated as an amplifier (in the active zone) in the common-emitter connection.

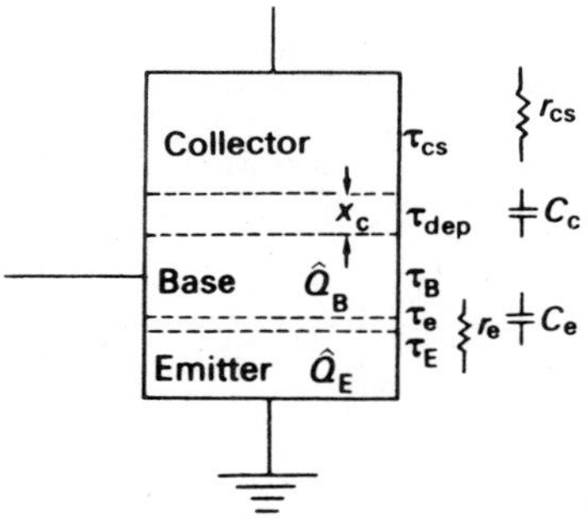

Figure 20.1 Time constants and signal delays in the bipolar transistor.

Starting from the top we see that the collector bulk resistance, r_{cs}, lies in the path of the charging current of C_c. Before, only r_e was considered. We must therefore add $r_{cs}C_c$ to r_eC_c. This gives rise to time delay τ_{cs}. Another time delay is caused by the collector depletion layer, whose width is X_c. There is a high field in it and the collected minority carriers move through that layer with their scattering limited velocity v_s. Remembering that the voltage across it contains both d.c. and a.c. components, and that the total current through it contains both conduction and displacement components, it is possible to calculate the delay time that this depletion layer adds and one obtains:

$$\tau_{dep} = \frac{X_c}{2\, v_s}. \tag{20.1}$$

An additional delay time is associated with minority charge storage in the emitter, $\hat{Q}_E$, that resides there when the transistor operates in the active region (see Fig. 14.8(b)). Minority storage in the base, $\hat{Q}_B$, resulted in the emitter diffusion capacitance and in a time delay of

$$\tau_B = \frac{\hat{Q}_B}{J_C} = \frac{C_{dif}}{r_e}. \tag{11.7}$$

In Chapters 11 and 14 the much smaller $\hat{Q}_E$ was neglected in comparison to $\hat{Q}_B$. Here, however, the base is so narrow and $\hat{Q}_B$ so small that the effect of $\hat{Q}_E$ in increasing the diffusion capacitance must be added. This results in additional delay of

$$\tau_E = \frac{\hat{Q}_E}{J_C} = \frac{\hat{Q}_E}{h_{FE} J_B}. \tag{20.2}$$

The emitter in NPN microwave transistors is also very shallow, its thickness being W_E, and the stored charge in it has the same triangular shape as in a narrow diode:

$$\hat{Q}_E = \frac{q\hat{p}_{nE}(0) W_E}{2}.$$

Due to the narrowness of the base (about 0.15 μm) there is practically no recombination in it and base current consists only of holes injected back into the emitter:

$$J_B = -qD_{hE} \left. \frac{\partial \hat{p}_{nE}(x)}{\partial x} \right|_{x=0} = \frac{qD_{hE}\hat{p}_{nE}(0)}{W_E} = \frac{2D_{hE}\hat{Q}_E}{W_E^2}.$$

Substituting J_B into (20.2) gives

$$\tau_E = \frac{W_E^2}{2D_{hE} h_{FE}}. \tag{20.3}$$

It should be remembered (Problem 15.16) that $\hat{Q}_B$ itself is much reduced because of the built-in drift field which is intentionally strong in the base of a microwave transistor. If the exact base and emitter impurity profiles and the degradation of D_{eB} with high doping are taken into account one may write

$$\tau_B = \frac{W_B^2}{kD_{eB}}, \tag{20.4}$$

with $k \simeq 3$ ($k = 2$ in a uniform-base transistor).

The resulting ω_T^{-1} is given by the sum of all these time delay constants:

$$\frac{1}{\omega_T} = r_e C_e + (r_e + r_{cs}) C_c + \frac{W_B^2}{kD_{eB}} + \frac{X_c}{2v_s} + \frac{W_E^2}{2D_{hE} h_{FE}}. \tag{20.5}$$

Increase of f_T requires that each of the terms in (20.5) be minimized.

Present-day diffusion, and especially implantation techniques, makes possible transistors with ultra-shallow emitters of $W_E \simeq 0.15$ μm. They are usually As doped (arsenic fits better than phosphorus in the Si lattice and creates less strains). To keep D_{hE} high, the emitter doping should not be increased to the maximum solubility limit.

To keep r_e small, the transistor is operated at as high a current as thermal considerations allow.

Minimization of the junction capacitances C_e and C_c requires that very small geometries be used. This is contradictory to current and power requirements and there is a trade off between frequency and power. To minimize C_c, the collector junction must be located in a high-resistivity epitaxial layer. But to reduce r_{cs} this layer must be thin enough to be fully depleted at the operating collector–base voltage, right down to the substrate which is again highly doped.

Finally, bases as narrow as 0.1 μm are used, with a steep impurity gradient to increase the built-in field and reduce the transit time. In order not to reduce D_{eB}, the base doping cannot be too high, and because of the base thinness, $r_{b'b}$ then becomes too large. This reduces the high-frequency gain as can be seen from (15.27). Another detrimental effect of high base-sheet resistivity is *current crowding* at the emitter periphery mentioned in Section 19.3. In order to reduce $r_{b'b}$ the base is divided into intrinsic and extrinsic regions. The first are the active base regions and are very thin and low doped. The second, intended to carry the base current from the contact, are thicker and have higher doping. The emitter crowding effect is reduced by increasing the emitter periphery-to-area ratio. The emitter is frequently interdigitated (Fig. 19.8), with long, thin, parallel fingers, alternating with similarly long parallel base contacts.

Finally it should be mentioned that a different metallization system must be used here, as pure Al micro-alloys with Si. In thin shallow junctions this would result in emitter–collector short circuits.

20.2 The GaAs MESFET

As a semiconductor, GaAs is more attractive for microwave devices than Si is, for several reasons:

(a) The electron mobility in GaAs is several times higher than in Si, shortening transit times and increasing the high-frequency capability.

(b) GaAs can withstand higher working temperatures due to its larger band gap. This is particularly important in the very small geometry power devices used in microwaves that must dissipate a lot of heat.

(c) Because of its large E_g, low power GaAs amplifying devices that operate at room temperature have very low thermal generation and leakage currents which contributes towards lower noise figure (Section 15.8).

(d) Single crystal semi-insulating (SI) GaAs substrates are available (Section 2.4) on which a transistor can be built without the relatively large (for microwaves) parasitic capacitances that bug devices and the surface metallization interconnections to them if a conducting substrate is used.

GaAs technology has been developing fast recently but is still behind that of Si. Complicated bipolar structures are difficult to make with good repeatable parameters. Also low hole mobility and absence of a naturally grown oxide with good properties rule out bipolar and even MOS type devices. A GaAs majority carrier device, however, similar in principle to the JFET, has a simpler structure and can be realized with a relatively simple technology.

The GaAs *Me*tal *S*emiconductor *F*ield *E*ffect *T*ransistor (MESFET) is the most important microwave device today and has the highest f_T yet achieved in a transistor. It can also be integrated to obtain ultra fast digital circuits (see Chapter 21). The MESFET is shown in Fig. 20.2(a).

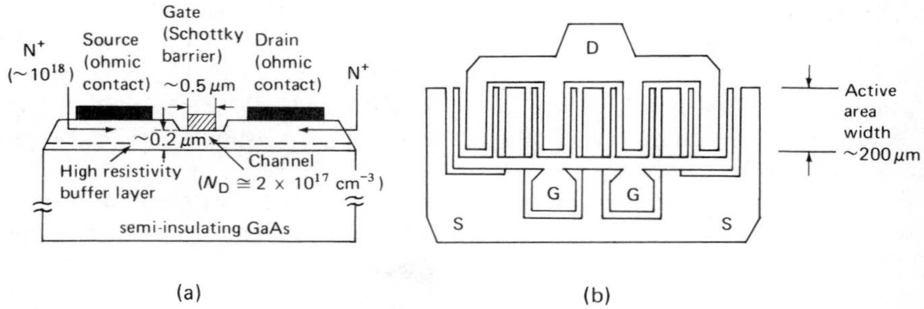

Figure 20.2. GaAs MESFETs for microwave use: (a) a section through a low-noise low-power MESFET; (b) top view of a high-power MESFET.

It differs from the lower-frequency Si JFET in the following respects. The channel region is a very thin (about 0.2) μm for 13 GHz operation) epitaxial N-type GaAs grown on chromium-doped semi-insulating GaAs substrate. The gate is not a PN junction but a Schottky-barrier metal contact (1 μm gate length is needed for operation at 13 GHz, 0.5 μm can be achieved). At a channel doping of about $2\times10^{17}\ \text{cm}^{-3}$, the very thin channel under the gate is only partially depleted by the Schottky barrier built-in voltage. When a positive drain-source voltage is applied, current will flow yielding characteristics that are very similar to those of the JFET (Fig. 12.4). Negative V_{GS} will further deplete the channel, reducing I_{DS} till the device cuts off when V_{GS} reaches the pinch-off voltage. A slightly positive V_{GS} (less than about 0.8 V at which the Schottky gate starts forward conduction) will cause I_{DS} to increase. The carrier transit time through a channel of length L is approximately $\tau = L/v_s$ (carriers move at the saturation velocity v_s throughout most of the channel since it is so short that most of it is pinched off and has high lateral field in it). In GaAs, v_s for electrons is about 2×10^7 cm s^{-1}, compared to 0.8×10^7 cm s^{-1} in Si. The device cut-off frequency f_T will be

$$f_T = \frac{1}{2\pi\tau} = \frac{v_s}{2\pi L}. \tag{20.6}$$

A channel length of 1 μm would thus result in a device whose f_T is about 35 GHz.

For use as a low-noise small-signal microwave amplifier, a structure like in Fig. 20.2(a) is used, in which the active layer is etched a little before the Schottky gate metal is applied (Al may be used). The recessed gate structure, together with an N^+ implant into the source and drain areas, reduce the source and drain parasitic series resistance and simplifies the job of making good ohmic contacts to them. Reduced resistances contribute lower noise (eq. (15.42)) and result in devices with noise figure of less than 2 db at 12 GHz and higher g_m (see Problem 20.8). For power amplification at microwave frequencies high currents are needed which means very wide gates. A structure like that of Fig. 20.2(b) is used which is, in fact, many small MESFETs connected in parallel. The maximum gate width of each is limited for it not to act like a transmission line and introduce excessive phase difference between the gate voltages at its two extremes. Paralleling makes possible total gate widths of several millimeters and there is no danger of nonuniform current distribution, hot spot formation and thermal runaway as in the bipolar case. Any local increase in current density and temperature tends to decrease electron mobility. The resistance of the hotter section increases and the current is reduced back again. The gate metal lines in Fig. 20.2(b) must cross over the source metallization and a deposited SiO_2 layer is used as insulation. Note also that the conductive N layer is etched away everywhere but in the rectangle that represents the device active area. The large metal pads to which outside contacts are made, are laid over the semi-insulating substrate and so add little capacitance.

A long rectangular shape is chosen for the active area, rather than a square, since the larger circumference to area ratio reduces thermal resistance by reducing the density of the dissipated heat flow sideways and down through the substrate to the heatsink.

The reduction in size of present day MESFETs to submicron channel lengths which are within an order of magnitude of distances between collisions that an electron undergoes in GaAs, can possibly change the nature of its movement to ballistic type. An electron may be accelerated by V_{DS} and leave the channel before it has a chance of getting scattered. Its velocity will overshoot the value expected from mobility considerations (that gave us Fig. 6.11 of v vs. E) in the first picosecond, or so of field application. The transit time is then expected to be extremely short. Since the mean time between polar optical phonon emission events (which are the main scattering events in GaAs) is $\tau \simeq 0.3$ ps. A relatively low field of $E = 10^4$ V/cm will result in a distance L travelled after $t = 0.5$ ps of:

$$L = \frac{qE}{2m_e^*} t^2 \simeq 0.3\,\mu\text{m} \quad (m_e^* = 0.07\, m_0),$$

which is a sizeable fraction of a 0.5 μm gate device. For such a device f_T is expected to be higher than the value given by (20.6). Further information regarding MESFETs can be found in Refs. 17 & 18.

20.3 Varactors and Step Recovery Diodes and Their Uses

The change in capacitance with voltage that we have encountered in junction diodes (Section 9.6) can be used for microwave small-signal amplification or for frequency multiplication.

The principle of *parametric amplification* used to achieve this is demonstrated in Fig. 20.3. A signal v_s, whose frequency is f_s, is applied across our variable capacitance diode, or varactor, together with an internally generated voltage v_i whose frequency is f_i. The sum of the two voltages $v_s + v_i$ is also shown in Fig. 20.3(a), for the case where the two have the same amplitude. Obviously, $v_s + v_i$ crosses the zero voltage line at a frequency of $f_p = f_i + f_s$, since

$$v_s + v_i = A \sin \omega_s t - A \sin \omega_i t = 2A \cos\left(\frac{\omega_s + \omega_i}{2} t\right) \sin\left(\frac{\omega_s - \omega_i}{2} t\right)$$

$$= 2A \cos\left(\frac{\omega_p}{2} t\right) \sin\left(\frac{\omega_s - \omega_i}{2} t\right).$$

If a large-amplitude square-wave voltage v_p, called the *pump voltage*, is also applied across the varactor with a frequency of f_p, its capacitance C changes periodically as shown in the figure. Each time the varactor capacitance is decreased (figuratively speaking, the parallel plates of the depletion-layer capacitance are pulled apart) the pump source is doing work and putting energy into the capacitor circuit. Each time the varactor capacitance is increased energy is taken out of it. But if all capacitance increases are synchronized to occur when $v_s + v_i = 0$, i.e. when the varactor is empty of charge, there is no force between the capacitor plates and the energy taken out of it is therefore zero. There would then be a net energy flow of ΔE_i from the pump source into the varactor each time the capacitance is reduced. This energy is transferred into the resonant circuit of the signal, of which the varactor is a part. This energy input is shown as E in the figure. Actually only the pump voltage is generated locally and applied across the varactor, which is a part of three resonant circuits, as shown in Fig. 20.3(b). The circuits are tuned to f_s, f_i and f_p and only currents at those respective frequencies can flow in each of them. The voltage v_i automatically forms as the varactor is pumped with a frequency f_p. The input impedance which the signal source sees can then be shown to have a negative real part, signifying that more energy comes out of the varactor at a frequency of f_s than goes in. The device, therefore, amplifies.

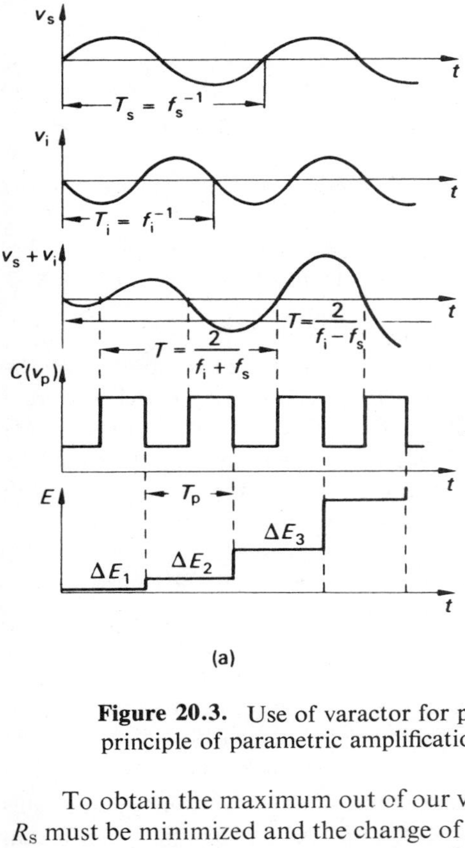

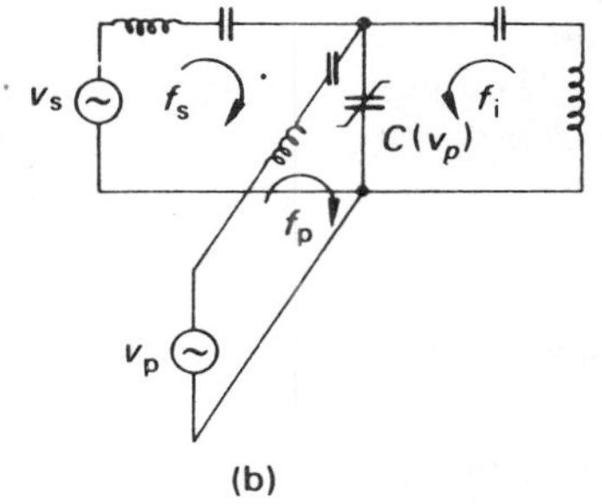

Figure 20.3. Use of varactor for parametric amplification: (a) the principle of parametric amplification; (b) the basic circuit.

To obtain the maximum out of our varactor, its parasitic series resistance R_s must be minimized and the change of C with V should be high. A figure of merit may be defined for a varactor, called the cut-off frequency, f_c, which is specified at a given reverse bias voltage V_R:

$$f_c = \frac{1}{2R_s(V_R)C_j(V_R)}. \tag{20.7}$$

R_s is composed of the ohmic resistance of the non-depleted parts of the P and N regions and the two metal contacts. A P^+NN^+ structure is often used where

N is an epitaxial layer grown on an N^+ substrate. The P^+ region is then obtained by diffusion.

The capacitance–voltage relations are given by (9.52) and (9.53) for the step and graded junction respectively.

Varactors are also used for *frequency multiplication* or *harmonic power generation* in the microwave range. A voltage whose amplitude is large enough to swing the varactor from near breakdown (where the capacitance is a minimum) to forward conduction (where the capacitance is practically infinite) is applied to the varactor at a frequency f_1. The varactor is a part of a resonant circuit tuned to nf_1, where n is an integer which may be as high as 8 but is usually 2 or 3. The large change in the capacitance, i.e. the extreme circuit nonlinearity, results in efficient generation of harmonics of which only the nth can cause current flow in the appropriately tuned resonant circuit. An output at nf_1 is thus obtained, though at a much reduced power level. Two or three such multipliers can be connected in tandem, giving a high-frequency multiplication ratio.

The output frequency stability of a multiplier is directly related to the input frequency stability, which may be crystal controlled, thus giving a very frequency-stable output.

Both Si and GaAs varactors are in use.

A stronger capacitance nonlinearity than that of the PN varactor can be obtained from a P^+IN^+ structure called a *step recovery diode* (SRD). Here a relatively small reverse voltage is sufficient to deplete the whole intrinsic (or almost intrinsic) region and the capacitance is then very small. When the applied voltage is in the forward direction the I region is swamped with electrons and holes, its forward resistance becomes very low and is shunted by a practically infinite capacitance. The change from forward conduction to the low-capacitance state is very sudden and is related to the diode charge storage and reverse recovery (Chapter 11). Figure 20.4 shows the voltage and current in an SRD. The diode conducts first in the forward and then in the reverse directions till the excess stored charge is removed from the I region. When the excess carrier concentrations at the boundaries of the I region have fallen to zero, the applied voltage is already high in the reverse direction and the depletion layer propagates very quickly throughout the whole I region. The current drops to zero and the capacitance jumps to the low reverse value. This change occurs within less than a nanosecond, thereby making the SRD an efficient harmonic generator.

20.4 The Impatt Device

The impatt, or *imp*act *a*valanche *t*ransit *t*ime device, is used for power generation at microwave frequencies.

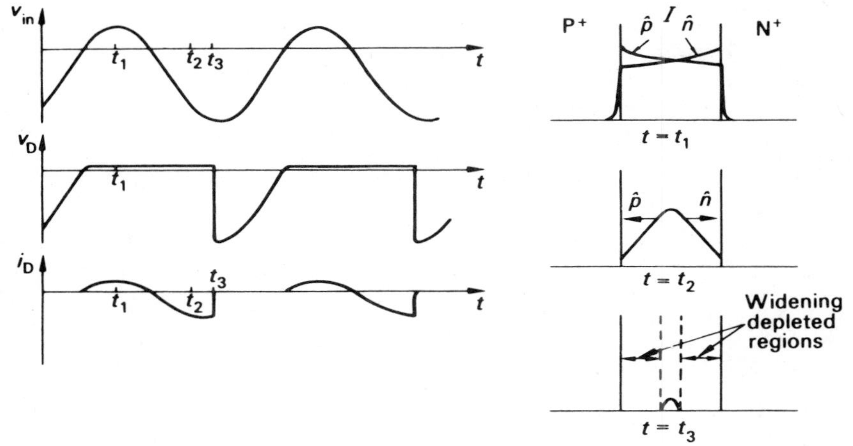

Figure 20.4. Input voltage v_{in}; diode voltage v_D; diode current i_D and carrier concentrations in the intrinsic region of an SRD at various times.

PN diodes of different impurity profiles may be used as impatt devices but the operation is best explained by referring to the structure proposed by W. T. Read and named after him.

The doping profile of the Read diode is shown in Fig. 20.5(a). When a reverse voltage is applied to it the field in the various regions looks like in Fig. 20.5(b) (which is directly obtained by applying Poisson's equation). E_a represents the field at which avalanche multiplication starts. E_s is the field at which carrier velocity saturates (about 20 kV cm^{-1} in Si).

Let us examine what happens if the device is biased with a d.c. voltage V_R, causing a field equal to E_a, and on top of that an a.c. voltage component is added. The a.c. voltage is a result of oscillations of a resonant circuit across which the diode is connected. The total voltage is as shown in Fig. 20.5(c). At t_0 avalanche starts in the narrow P region. A charge of electrons and holes then starts to grow, continuing to do so until t_1, at which time the avalanche-generated charge reaches its maximum value. The holes drift to the left and leave the avalanche zone. The electrons drift to the right and have a long way to go before they reach the P$^+$ region. Since the avalanche starts from a very low leakage current and the charge grows by repeated multiplication, most of it is generated just before t_1. At that moment E_{max} drops below E_a and multiplication stops. The already created charge packet of electrons continues to drift through the long I region, called the drift zone, with an almost constant saturation velocity v_s, since the field throughout that zone is higher than E_s.

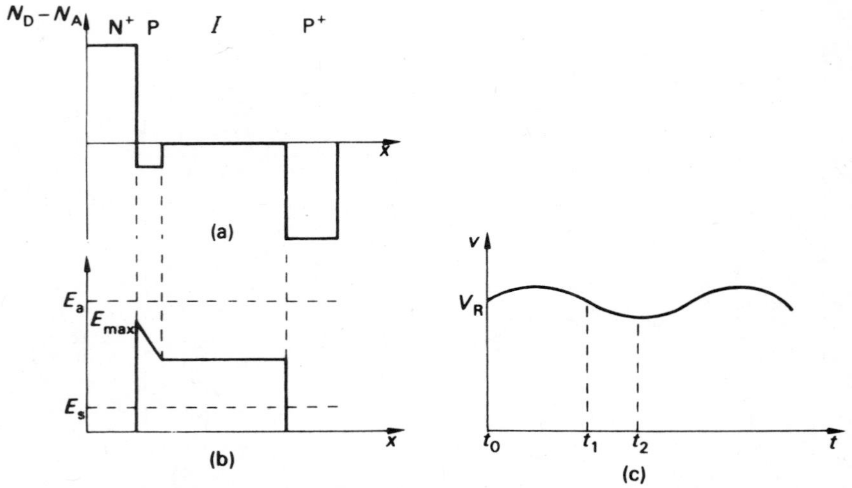

Figure 20.5 The Read diode: (a) the doping profile; (b) the field along the device when biased in reverse (at $t=t_2$), E_a—field at which avalanche starts, E_s—field at which carrier velocity saturates; (c) voltage across the device.

After a delay of $\tau = L_d/v_s$ (L_d = length of drift zone), the charge packet reaches the P^+ region and the conduction or real component of the device current reaches a maximum (the total current contains also a capacitive or imaginary component, caused by charge movement in the drift zone). The drift zone length is related to the frequency of the resonant circuit (cavity in microwave parlance) so that the conduction component maximizes when the voltage is at its minimum (t_2 in the figure). The impedance presented by the device to the cavity at that frequency has a negative real part. In other words: if the a.c. current component maximizes when the a.c. voltage minimizes they are in antiphase, and the impatt acts as a generator for that a.c. energy. Power is then delivered from the impatt to the cavity and any load connected to it. Oscillations build up to a steady-state amplitude as shown in Fig. 20.5(c). At this amplitude the losses of the device and cavity together (which grow with amplitude and are represented by a positive resistance) are just balanced by the negative resistance (as in any other oscillator).

Most impatt diodes have a simpler structure, such as P^+NN^+ or N^+PP^+ in which the high-field zone is less well defined. This results in a lower efficiency. The Read structure, however, is rather complicated to make, especially in GaAs.

Calculation of the impatt device input impedance depends on the impurity profile and on knowledge of the ionization coefficients for holes and electrons and their dependence on the field. Efficiencies as high as 30% were achieved in GaAs devices. Output power as high as 10 W (CW) at 10 GHz was also obtained. This is higher than any other semiconductor device can deliver today at this frequency.

20.5 The Gunn or Transferred-Electron Device (TED)

In Chapter 6 the special shape of the energy bands in GaAs was discussed and shown in Fig. 6.10(c). It was mentioned that conduction-band electrons can transfer from the central, lowest energy minimum to the slightly higher other minima in the conduction band if their energy is increased by an external electric field. The radius of curvature and therefore the effective mass (eq. 6.27) are much lower while the mobility is much higher (eq. 3.8) in that lowest minimum (called the central valley since it occurs at $k = <0,0,0>$) than in the higher minima (called the satellite or higher valleys). By transferring to these satellite valleys the electrons lose their high mobility and consequently the drift velocity and current drop. But this current reduction is effected by an increase in the electric field, so this will result in the I–V characteristic going through a negative-resistance region. This effect was predicted by Ridley and Watkins in 1961 and its basic theory developed by Hilsum in 1962, but no high quality GaAs was available then to verify it experimentally. In 1963 J. B. Gunn, working on noise problems in GaAs, discovered accidentally that microwave power was generated by his device under certain biasing conditions. This so-called *Gunn effect* was soon traced to the electron-transfer theory developed before. Devices based on it are called either Gunn diodes or transferred-electron devices (TED).

Basically the device is not even a diode. It is a piece of N GaAs with N^+ regions for contact. It is shown in Fig. 20.6 with the I–V characteristic. We shall now develop an approximate model and theory for this device and point out some of its properties.

The effective mass of the electron when it occupies a state in the lower central valley of the conduction band (Fig. 6.10(c)) is $m_l^\star = 0.07\, m_0$. There are six upper valleys in the $k <100>$ directions but they happen to be near the edge of the first Brillouin zone and only half of each such valley contributes states to the first zone. The effective mass of the electron in an upper valley state is $m_u^\star = 1.2\, m_0$. Assuming a parabolic energy–momentum relationship, so that the density of available states in each valley can be expressed by an equation similar to (6.37), we obtain

$$S \triangleq \frac{\text{available states in all upper valleys}}{\text{available states in lower central valley}} = \frac{6}{2}\left(\frac{m_u^\star}{m_l^\star}\right)^{3/2} \simeq 210. \tag{20.8}$$

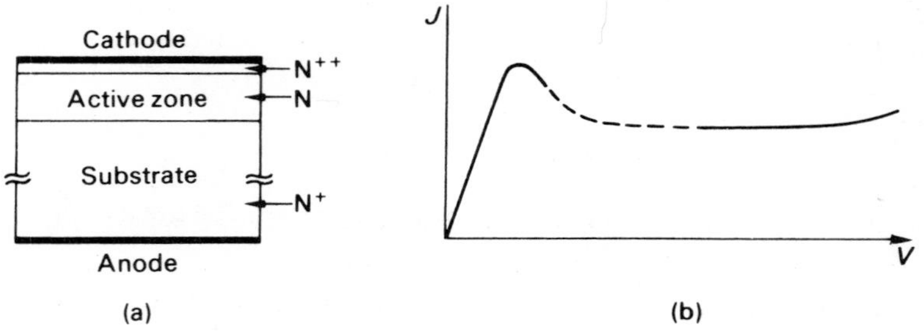

Figure 20.6. The Gunn device: (a) cross section; (b) *I–V* characteristic (dashed region represents the unstable, negative-resistance part where oscillations start).

Because there are many more available states in the upper valleys most electrons, if given the energy, would transfer into them. To find how many there actually are in each valley at a lattice temperature of T_0, we proceed as follows:

We call the unknown density of electrons in the lower valley n_l and in all upper valleys n_u. Their mobilities are respectively μ_l (high, about 8000 cm^2 V^{-1} s^{-1} because of the low $m_l^\star$) and μ_u (low, about 100 cm^2 V^{-1} s^{-1}, because of the high $m_u^\star$).

When an electric field F is applied, the average drift velocity is

$$v_{av} = \frac{n_l\mu_l + n_u\mu_u}{n_l + n_u} F \simeq \frac{n_l\mu_l}{n_l + n_u} F = \frac{\mu_l}{1 + n_u/n_l} F. \tag{20.9}$$

since $\mu_l >> \mu_u$.

But from eq. (6.42) we know that the population ratio of any two allowed energy levels differing by ΔE is

$$\frac{n_u}{n_l} = S \exp\left(-\frac{\Delta E}{kT_e}\right), \tag{20.10}$$

where S is the densities of state ratio of (20.8).

The energy difference between lower and upper valleys in GaAs is $\Delta E = 0.36$ eV. The temperature T_e of the electrons (which measures their kinetic energy) is higher than that of the lattice, T_0. This is because the field F accelerates the electrons and increases their kinetic energy beyond what they would have if they were in thermal equilibrium with the lattice.

If the field drops to zero suddenly those energetic, or hot, electrons will relax back and lose their excess energy by colliding with the lattice. If the energy relaxation time is denoted by τ_e (about 10^{-12} s), one can equate the excess energy of the hot electron with that supplied by the electric field during τ_e seconds:

$$\frac{3}{2} k(T_e - T_0) = qFv_{av}\tau_e. \tag{20.11}$$

where the left-hand side is the excess kinetic energy by (2.3).
Substituting v_{av} from (20.9) and n_u/n_l from (20.10) into (20.11) and rearranging, we obtain

$$T_e = T_0 + \frac{2q\tau_e\mu_l}{3k} F^2 \left[1 + S \exp\left(-\frac{\Delta E}{kT_e}\right)\right]^{-1}. \tag{20.12}$$

This is a transcendental equation for T_e. One can compute T_e as a function of F for a given value of T_0.

By substituting (17.10) into (17.9) the velocity can be written as

$$v_{av} = \mu_l F \left[1 + S \exp\left(-\frac{\Delta E}{kT_e}\right)\right]^{-1}. \tag{20.13}$$

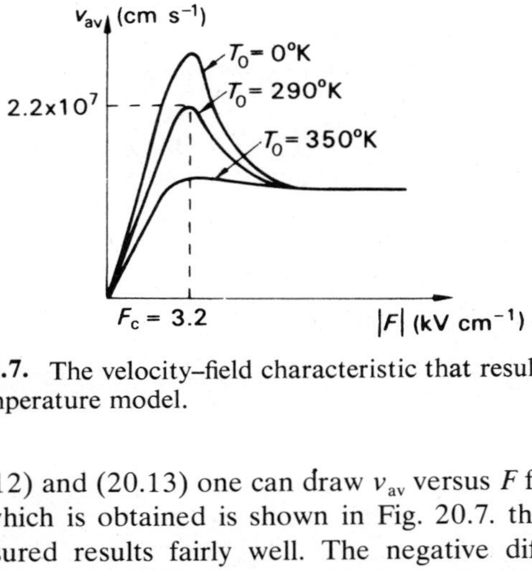

Figure 20.7. The velocity–field characteristic that results from the single-temperature model.

Using both (20.12) and (20.13) one can draw v_{av} versus F for a given T_0. The general shape which is obtained is shown in Fig. 20.7. this model approximates the measured results fairly well. The negative differential mobility region is obvious, and becomes more pronounced as the lattice temperature is lowered. This is known as the single-temperature model (electrons in both lower and upper valleys are assigned the same temperature T_e). It is possible, however, to develop more sophisticated models that would fit the experimental results even better.

We see that negative resistance in GaAs appears when the field increases beyond a critical value of about 3.2 kV cm^{-1} at 290°K. The carrier velocity then reaches a maximumof about 2×10^7 cm s^{-1}.

Let us examine what happens to any small charge Q inside the device when the differential mobility becomes negative (we shall now revert to denoting the electric field by $\mathbf{E}$). From Maxwell's equations we know that

$$\operatorname{div} \mathbf{D} = Q \tag{20.14}$$

where $\mathbf{D} = \varepsilon\varepsilon_0 \mathbf{E}$ is the displacement vector and Q the net charge density.

For a field in the x-direction only (20.14) has the form

$$\frac{\partial E}{\partial x} = \frac{Q}{\varepsilon\varepsilon_0}. \tag{20.15}$$

Let us multiply both sides of (20.15) by $\partial J/\partial E$, where J is the current density:

$$\frac{\partial J}{\partial E}\frac{\mathrm{d}E}{\mathrm{d}x} = \frac{\partial J}{\partial E}\frac{Q}{\varepsilon\varepsilon_0}$$

or

$$\frac{\partial J}{\partial x} = \frac{\partial J}{\partial E}\frac{Q}{\varepsilon\varepsilon_0}. \tag{20.16}$$

But $J = qN_\mathrm{D}v$: therefore,

$$\frac{\partial J}{\partial E} = qN_\mathrm{D}\frac{\partial v}{\partial E} = qN_\mathrm{D}\mu_\mathrm{d},$$

where μ_d is the differential mobility $\partial v/\partial E$ and N_D is the doping density. Substituting this in (20.16), we obtain

$$\frac{\partial J}{\partial x} = \frac{qN_\mathrm{D}\mu_\mathrm{d}Q}{\varepsilon\varepsilon_0}. \tag{20.17}$$

But the charge continuity equation states that

$$\frac{\partial Q}{\partial t} = -\frac{\partial J}{\partial x}; \tag{20.18}$$

therefore

$$\frac{\partial Q}{\partial t} = -\frac{qN_\mathrm{D}\mu_\mathrm{d}}{\varepsilon\varepsilon_0}Q. \tag{20.19}$$

The solution of this is

$$Q = Q_0 \exp\left(-\frac{qN_\mathrm{D}\mu_\mathrm{d}}{\varepsilon\varepsilon_0}t\right). \tag{20.20}$$

As long as the differential mobility μ_d is positive, any charge fluctuation Q_0 decays exponentially with a relaxation time of

$$\tau = \frac{\varepsilon\varepsilon_0}{qN_\mathrm{D}\mu_\mathrm{d}} = \frac{\varepsilon\varepsilon_0}{\sigma};$$

this is well known. The value of τ for GaAs doped with $N_D = 5 \times 10^{15}$ cm^{-3} at low fields ($\mu_d \simeq 8000$ cm^2 V^{-1} s^{-1}: $\varepsilon = 12.5$) is about 1.7×10^{-13} s, which is extremely short. The charge fluctuation decays practically immediately.

If, however, μ_d is negative (about -2000 cm^2 V^{-1} s^{-1} for GaAs at fields above 3.5 kV cm^{-1} at 290°K according to Fig. 20.7) the original fluctuation will grow instead of decay and do it almost as fast.

The situation along the N-type GaAs semiconductor bar at two moments during the charge-growth phase can be visualized as in Fig. 20.8.

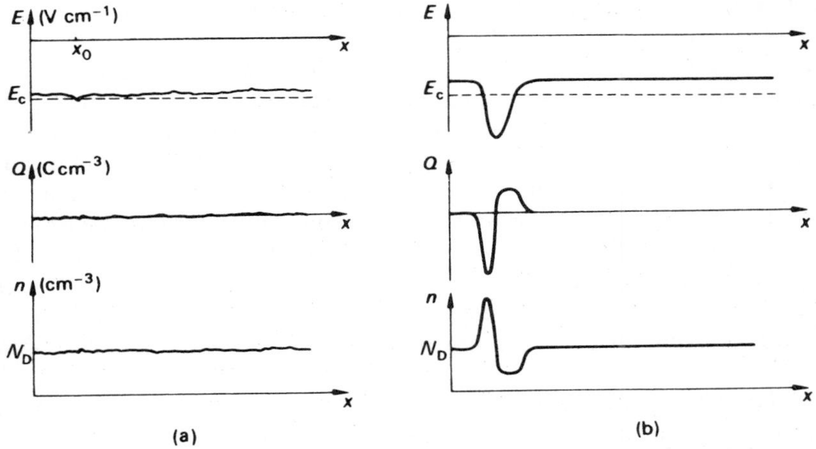

Figure 20.8. The formation of a dipole domain: (a) at time t_0 when the field just exceeds E_c at x_0; (b) at $t_0 + \Delta t$, when the domain has already formed.

At $t = t_0$ the voltage across the bar is increased and somewhere along it, at point $x = x_0$ (where the doping is slightly lower), the field E exceeds the critical field E_c. The electrons which drift along the bar towards the right (because of the field) will now have lower velocity at x_0 than everywhere else, since the field is higher than E_c there. Electrons on the left of x_0 will therefore overtake those at x_0, while those on the right of x_0 will move faster onwards, leaving behind them some uncompensated positive donor charge. The situation very shortly afterwards is as shown in Fig. 20.8(b): a pulse of negative electronic charge has accumulated and moves relatively slowly towards the right. This pulse is preceded by a positive uncompensated donor charge pulse where electrons are lacking. A dipole has thus formed. Because of Poisson's equation,

$$\frac{\partial E}{\partial x} = \frac{Q}{\varepsilon \varepsilon_0}.$$

$E(x)$ must have a negative slope where $Q<0$ and a positive slope where $Q>0$. This means that the field must now look as in Fig. 20.8(b): a high-field zone, called a *domain*, is associated with the dipole. The domain takes up a lot of voltage (the area under it) reducing the field everywhere else below E_c. Domain growth stops when the field in the domain and the field outside it result in the same drift velocity, which is related to the instantaneous voltage. The domain then drifts with this velocity (about 10^7 cm s^{-1}) until it reaches the anode electrode on the right. At that moment there is a current pulse in the outside circuit, the domain disappears into the electrode and the voltage across the device starts to rise again until a new domain forms.

The frequency at which the domains arrive depends on the length of the device and on the frequency tuning of the cavity of which the device is a part. If that cavity (i.e. resonant structure) is tuned correctly and has a high Q (low loss), sinusoidal oscillations build up in it. The frequency of the oscillations depends on the domain transition time, i.e. on the device length, but it can be tuned through a limited bandwidth by changing the cavity resonant frequency. This can be done either mechanically, by changing the cavity dimensions, or electronically by a varactor whose controllable reactive admittance adds to that of the Gunn diode.

Due to the small size of the TED only a few volts are necessary for its operation, in contrast with the impatt diode that requires much higher voltage to start the avalanche.

TEDs are used today in all microwave systems in which their power capability (up to nearly a watt of CW power at 10 GHz) is sufficient. The power is limited by thermal considerations and if operated under pulsed conditions much higher peak powers can be obtained. TEDs may also be designed and operated in such a way that the domain cannot grow much. This mode is called LSA – limited space-charge accumulation – and it promises, at least in the laboratory, that higher powers and efficiencies can be achieved.

Finally, it should be mentioned that InP also has the right energy-band structure for transferred electron effects and an intensive research effort is going on at various places with the aim of perfecting it.

QUESTIONS

20.1 Measurements of base transition time τ_B in planar bipolar transistors show that it is not reduced as much as the built-in drift field would suggest. Try to find the reason for this by referring to the base impurity profile of Fig. 14.2(b).

20.2 Operation of a high-frequency bipolar transistor at high current levels shows that it behaves as if its effective base width has grown with the current. Can you find a physical explanation for this?
[*Hint:* Consider the total charge in the base–collector depletion layer at high currents, remembering that the carriers cannot move faster than their finite saturation velocity.]

20.3 Why should a PNN^+ diode, in which the avalanche zone is wide, have less efficiency in impatt operation than a diode with the Read structure where avalanche is limited to a narrow, well defined, zone?

20.4 Why should the single-temperature model for the TED as developed in Section 20.5 results in a velocity–field characteristic that has constant mobility at high fields?

20.5 Figure 20.7 shows that the negative differential mobility disappears at high temperatures. Can you give a qualitative physical explanation to this?

PROBLEMS

20.6 Show that the change in series resistance in a linear graded PN junction varactor, when the reverse voltage changes from zero to $-V$, is given by

$$\Delta R_S = \frac{1}{Aqg}\left(\frac{1}{\mu_e}+\frac{1}{\mu_h}\right)\ln\left(1+\frac{V}{V_B}\right),$$

where
g is the slope of the doping profile (cm^{-4}),
A is the area,
V_B is the built-in voltage of the linear graded junction and is given by

$$V_B = \frac{2kT}{q}\ln\frac{qd(0)}{n_i},$$

$d(0)$ is the depletion-layer thickness for zero voltage.

20.7 An $N^+P\pi P^+$ impatt diode is given with the following doping levels and region widths:

N^+ region – $N_{D1} = 10^{20}\ cm^{-3}$;	$W_1 = 2\ \mu m$
P region – $N_{A2} = 10^{16}\ cm^{-3}$;	$W_2 = 2\ \mu m$
π region – $N_{A3} = 10^{14}\ cm^{-3}$;	$W_3 = 5\ \mu m$
P^+ region – $N_{A4} = 10^{18}\ cm^{-3}$;	$W_4 = 100\ \mu m$.

Calculate the d.c. voltage required to start avalanche and oscillations. Assume a breakdown field of $350\,kV\ cm^{-1}$.

20.8 Use the FET equivalent circuit (Fig. 13.8) to show that any residual parasitic resistance R_S that appears in series with the source of a MESFET will reduce its effective transconductance from g_{m0} to $g_m = g_{m0}/(1 + R_S g_{m0})$.

20.9 Calculate the necessary thickness of the active, N-doped layer ($N_D = 1.5 \times 10^{17}$ cm^{-3}) on semi-insulating GaAs for a MESFET with a pinch-off voltage of -2 V. Note that surface states pin the Fermi level $\frac{2}{3}E_g$ below E_c at the metal–GaAs interface under the gate.

20.10 GaAs surface covered with its native oxide has many surface states that pin the Fermi level at about the middle of the gap. It can be shown that gate–drain avalanche voltage is maximized (important for maximizing output power) if the gate is recessed into the active layer (Fig. 20.2) by an amount equal to the depletion region caused by this pinning. Calculate the necessary notch depth for a layer doped with $N_D = 10^{17}$ cm^{-3}.

20.11 The lateral field in the channel of a MESFET in saturation is usually high enough for the electrons to drift with their scattering limited saturation velocity v_s. Show that expression (12.6) for G_0 should then be modified and I_{DSS} expression becomes

$$I_{DSS} = \tfrac{1}{3} G_0 V_p = \tfrac{2}{3} WqaN_D v_s$$

where a is the undepleted active layer thickness at $V_{GS} = 0$. Calculate a for $N_D = 10^{17}$ cm^{-3} and $I_{DSS} = 250$ mA/mm of gate width. Assume $v_s = 1.1 \times 10^7$ cm/s.

DEVICES OF THE FUTURE 21

Among modern technologies, the semiconductor device field is one of the fastest developing areas. New materials, innovative processes and equipment, novel device structures and better modelling and simulation are announced almost daily in the technical communication media. Many of the budding new ideas and experimental devices would probably perish in the harsh climate of semiconductor industry, facing such hardships as yield, reliability, repeatability, price and technological competitors. Some would survive and develop into pillars of future electronics. It is our purpose to describe here some of the most interesting and promising new technologies and devices that have already been shown to work in research laboratories, are on the verge of being produced commercially and are expected to have a very strong impact on the field. These are:

1. integrated digital and linear GaAs circuits
2. heterojunction transistors
3. modulation doped devices
4. the Josephson junction devices
5. the permeable base transistor
6. integrated optoelectronic devices
7. future technologies of silicon-based devices

Some references are given for each subject at the respective section.

21.1 Ultra Fast GaAs Digital and Linear ICs

GaAs ICs are not really in the future. They are already being made at near LSI complexity level though in small quantities. The attraction of such devices lies in their ultra fast switching speeds (for digital) or ultrahigh frequency response (for linear), coupled with low power demands.

These properties stem from the following:

1. Micron and submicron Schottky gate technology have already been developed for microwave MESFETs (Chapter 20) with far fewer processing steps than for Si ICs and less demanding mask alignment requirements.
2. The higher electron mobility in GaAs (about six times that of Si) and saturation velocity (double that of Si) yield correspondingly shorter transit times.
3. The availability of single crystal semi-insulating (SI) GaAs substrates (Section 2.4) in which the active components of the IC can be directly made, reduces parasitic capacitances and leakages associated with these components and their interconnections.
4. The higher E_g of GaAs reduces thermal generation and noise and makes it possible to operate the circuits at lower voltage levels with reduced power demands.

There are competing views as to the best technology for GaAs ICs. The most promising approach uses localized N-type implants into selected areas of a lightly Cr doped SI substrate, through an SiO_2 or Si_3N_4 layer that is first deposited on its surface. This oxide or nitride serves as a cap that prevents arsenic atoms from escaping the substrate surface in subsequent thermal cycles (because of the high As vapour pressure). Annealing at 850°C activates about 80% of the implanted atoms (Si, Se or S), i.e., they substitute for Ga atoms in the lattice and become donors. The implanted areas become N^-, N or N^+ (depending on the implanted species and dose) with good mobility (up to 6000 cm²/vs at low fields). The energy at which the implant is performed controls the thickness of the resulting N regions (usually less than 0.5 μm). An Au–Ge metal layer is used for making low resistance ohmic contact to N^+ regions, Mo–Au is used for making Schottky diodes when deposited on N-regions and a high conductivity Ti–Pt–Au layer can be used for interconnections. Each metal layer is patterned and isolated from the others by deposited dielectric layers except where contacts are desired. The field areas (between circuit components) are subjected to selective proton bombardment that wrecks the crystal structure and vastly increases the resistance of those regions. This reduces leakage currents and parasitic interaction effects that may otherwise occur between two neighboring components (voltage and field applied to one component may affect the depletion layer of the other that may be only 3 μm away).

Figure 21.1(a) shows a cross section through transistor, Schottky diode, resistor and capacitor of a possible circuit. Note that ohmic contacts are made over highly doped N^+ regions into which two N implants were made. The thick (about 0.5 μm) SiO_2 layer is the one also used to cap the substrate for annealing.

The figure shows recessed Schottky gates which necessitate some etching of the GaAs before metal deposition to obtain both the desired MESFET current I_{DSS} at $V_{GS}=0$ (which depends on N layer thickness and resistivity) and low drain and source parasitic series resistance.

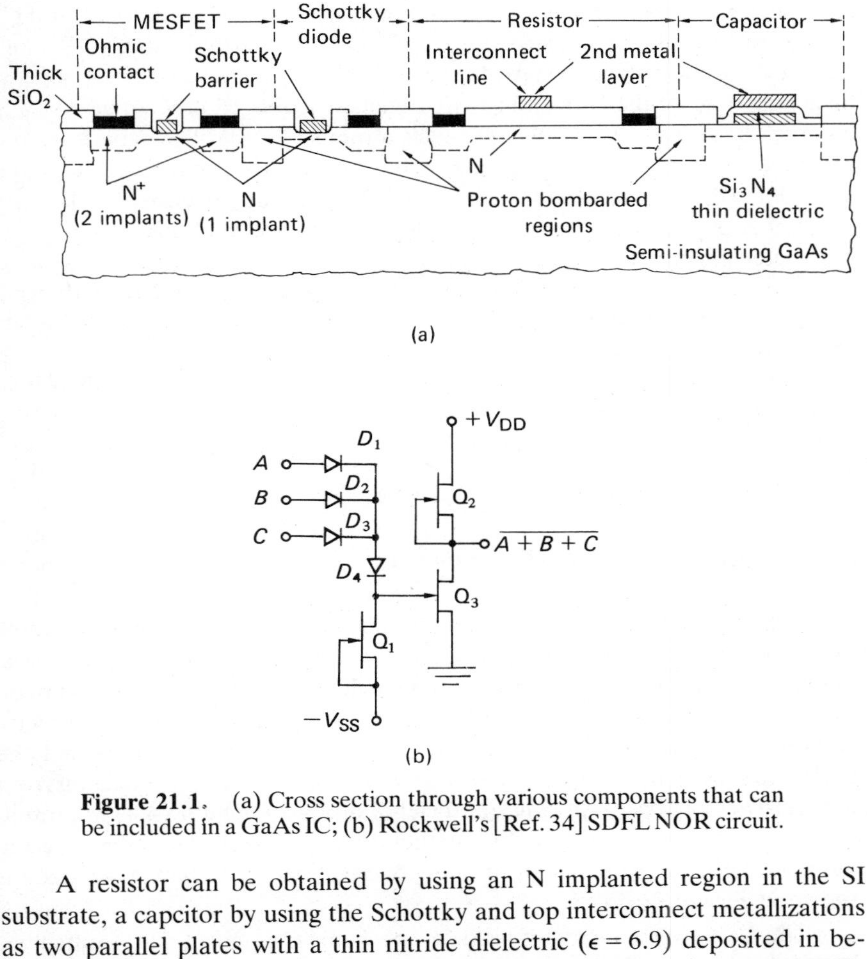

Figure 21.1. (a) Cross section through various components that can be included in a GaAs IC; (b) Rockwell's [Ref. 34] SDFL NOR circuit.

A resistor can be obtained by using an N implanted region in the SI substrate, a capcitor by using the Schottky and top interconnect metallizations as two parallel plates with a thin nitride dielectric ($\epsilon = 6.9$) deposited in between. The implants are usually tailored to give depletion type MESFETs (enhancement type can also be obtained but as yet not with well controlled V'_{TS}). From the transistors and Schottky diodes one can build all kinds of logic circuits. The fact that Schottky barrier height on GaAs is approximately $\frac{2}{3}E_g \simeq 0.9$ V (Section 8.5) means that no appreciable forward conduction will take place in the gates up to about +0.8 V. The MESFET pinch-off voltage is about −1.2 V which makes it possible to use supply voltages around ±2 V.

Figure 21.1(b) shows Rockwell's *S*chottky *D*iode *F*ET *L*ogic (SDFL) NOR circuit (Refs. 34, 35) based on depletion MESFETs. There are two types of diodes: D_1, D_2, D_3 are used for switching, and D_4 for d.c. level shifting. When all inputs are zero, the gate potential of Q_3 is below pinch-off, Q_3 is off and the output is high. If even one input is high, Q_3 gate potential becomes positive (but less than 0.8 V), Q_3 conducts and the output drops very close to zero. Q_1 and Q_2 are connected as current sources of I_{DSS}. The circuit performs the NOR function. The small voltage swings during switching increases switching speeds. Switching times in the 100 ps range are obtained at about 1 mW per gate power dissipation (giving power–delay products around 10^{-13} J). The capacitors and resistors are used in analog or combined analog–digital circuits. Integrated amplifiers with bandwidth of several GHz have already been realized.

Some problems still to be solved or perfected are to obtain better device parameter uniformity over large wafer areas, achieve repeatable circuits based on enhancement MESFETs (for even lower power consumption) with good control of threshold voltages and get better ohmic contacts with lower contact resistance.

GaAs LSI circuits will probably dominate the field of picoseconds switching at femto-Joule power–delay products and gigahertz amplification till better material or technology comes along. Further information can be found in Refs. 34–36.

21.2 Heterojunction Transistors

In Section 8.6, we have seen that the energy levels at a heterojunction show different barriers to electrons and holes. This can be used to obtain a special bipolar transistor with a wide gap emitter. Such a transistor had been suggested by H. Kroemer a long time ago with the following reasoning: Under forward emitter-base bias, only the wider gap emitter would inject carriers and the increased barrier in the reverse direction would prevent reverse injection from the narrower gap base. An emitter efficiency of $\gamma = 1$ (Section 14.4) will result, irrespective of base doping, which can therefore be increased to reduce $r_{b'b}$ and improve the high frequency properties. A cross section of such a structure is shown in Fig. 21.2(a).

The N^+ GaAs substrate is used for mechanical support and to contact an epitaxially grown wider gap N^- AlGaAs that serves as emitter. On top of that another narrower gap GaAs layer is grown to serve as P base and N collector (doping is achieved by implants). A deep p^+ implant is used to contact the P base. The energy band diagram for the transistor when biased in the active region is shown in Fig. 21.2(b). The emitter–base barrier for holes in the valence band is higher than that for electrons in the conduction band, therefore only electrons will be injected even though the base has higher doping than the

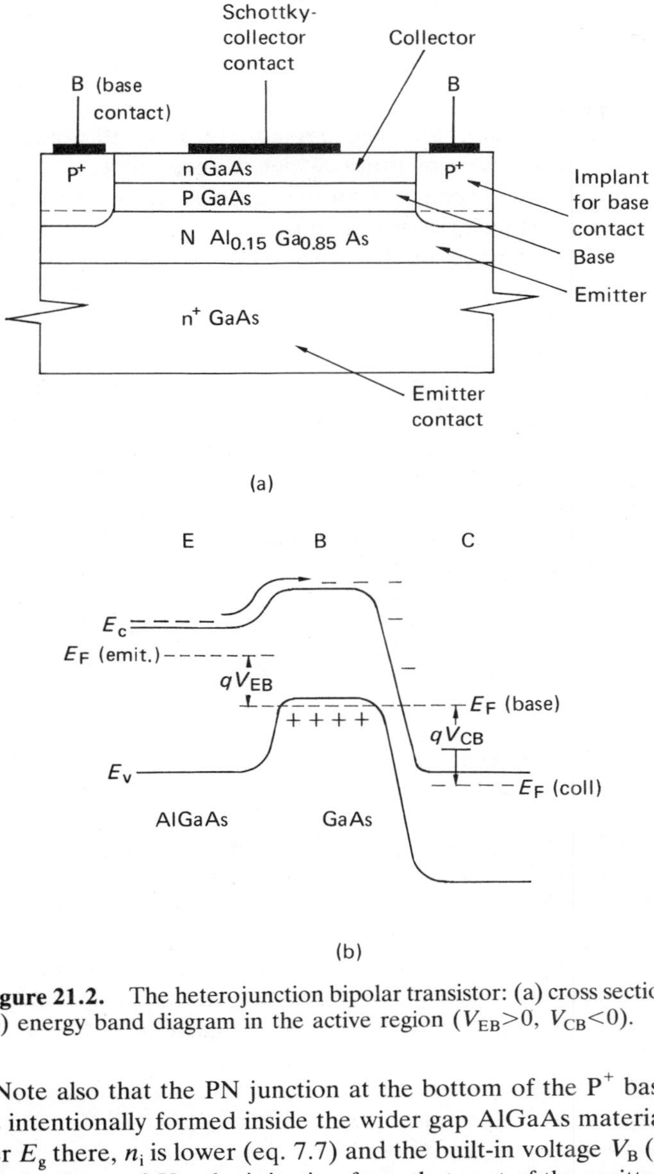

Figure 21.2. The heterojunction bipolar transistor: (a) cross section; (b) energy band diagram in the active region ($V_{EB}>0$, $V_{CB}<0$).

emitter. Note also that the PN junction at the bottom of the P^+ base contact region, is intentionally formed inside the wider gap AlGaAs material. Due to the higher E_g there, n_i is lower (eq. 7.7) and the built-in voltage V_B (eq. 8.6) is higher. Under forward V_{BE} the injection from that part of the emitter junction would be reduced by a factor of $\exp(-q\Delta V_B/kT)$ compared to the rest of that junction area (eq. (8.26)). This is highly desirable since electrons injected there will never reach the collector but recombine in the base anyway and thus reduce the base transport factor b (Section 14.4). This is now eliminated with an

additional bonus of reduced emitter-base junction and diffusion capacitances. The expected $\alpha = \gamma b$ should therefore approach 1 with a resulting very high β. The reduced capacitances and $r_{b'b}$ should give better high frequency performance (Section 20.1).
The base-collector junction can also be replaced by a Schottky barrier junction which have practically zero minority carrier storage (Section 9.7). This will greatly benefit switching speeds in saturated logic circuits since in saturated homojunction transistors it is the stored minority charge in the collector that is associated with long storage and switching times (Section 14.5). The inverted bipolar structure of Fig. 21.2(a) can be made a part of a digital IC designed with all transistors having a common emitter. A somewhat more complicated structure built on top of semi-insulating GaAs and contacted from the top surface by localized deep implants can be used to obtain the more conventional IC structure with emitters on top. Direct ohmic metal to AlGaAs contacts, however, are still a problem and at present such layers are contacted via a GaAs layer of the same type doping.

Heterojunction phototransistors (Section 14.5), which do not necessitate a base contact have already been made with βs exceeding 1000. However, the compromises necessary to contact the base reduce the β of three terminal heterojunction transistors at present to about 100. The wide gap emitter transistor must still prove its better high frequency properties and to do that the AlGaAs–GaAs technology must be further perfected. Additional information may be found in Refs. 29–31.

21.3 Modulation-doped Structures

Molecular beam epitaxy (Chapter 16) made it possible to form ultra thin layers (from a fraction of a micron down to a few atomic monolayers) one on top of the other. This opened up new device possibilities, some of which have already been tested. Thin layers of wide band gap, N doped material (AlGaAs) alternating with narrow band gap, undoped material (GaAs) were made. The changes in E_g appear as steps in the conduction and valence bands, like those shown in Fig. 21.3(a). Electrons donated by donors in the AlGaAs diffuse and drop into the energy wells formed by the narrower gap GaAs. Thus separation is achieved between the electrons and their donors. If an electric field is applied, perpendicular to the figure plane, the electrons, drift will be limited to the undoped GaAs layers which have a high mobility due to absence of impurity scattering (Section 3.2). Order of magnitude higher mobility at low temperatures (where impurity scattering predominates) have been achieved though at room temperature (where lattice scattering predominates) the mobility is only improved by about 75% at electric fields of 2 kV/cm (the mobility decreases with increasing field due to phonon emission by the accelerating carriers).

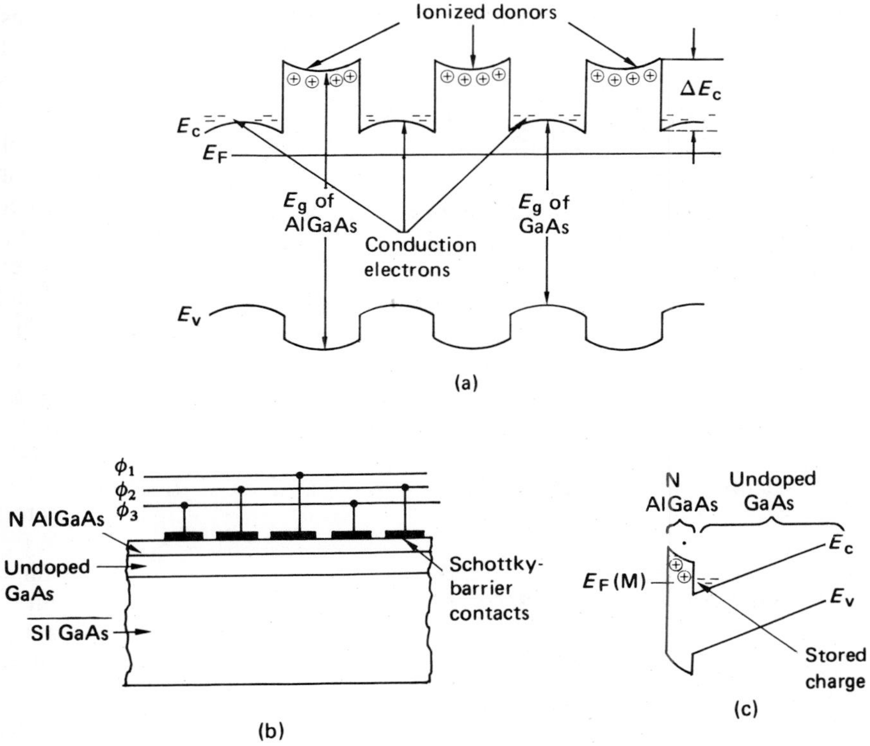

Figure 21.3. Modulation doping: (a) energy band of modulation doped multilayered heterostructure (Ref. 32); (b) the principle of modulation doped CCD (Ref. 33); (c) energy band diagram of (b) with a positive pulse on the Schottky gate.

An undoped layer of GaAs that is modulation doped by a second layer of N–AlGaAs is used in Fig. 21.3(b) to obtain a charge coupled device (Chapter 18) in which the electronic charge is stored and transported in the undoped layer where the higher mobility (up to $8000\,\text{cm}^2/\text{Vs}$ at 300°K) makes it possible to operate at higher clock frequencies. ΔE_c prevents the transported stored charge from reaching the surface, as can be seen in Fig. 12.3(c). The same type of structure can also be used to make modulation doped MESFETs with higher values of g_m due to the enhanced mobility.

Another interesting possibility of modulation doping is to increase the negative differential mobility effect (Section 20.4). By making the GaAs layers thin enough, quantization effects appear in the energy wells of Fig. 21.3(a). The quantization is for the component of momentum normal to the well walls which become discrete and separate from each other. Momentum components parallel to the walls are not quantized since the well dimension in these directions is large. The parabolic energy–momentum relation of eq. (6.33(a)) now becomes

$$E = E_c + \frac{\hbar^2}{2m}\left[k_x^2 + k_y^2 + \left(\frac{n\pi}{L_z}\right)^2\right] \tag{21.1}$$

where L_z is the well width.

The overall effect is a reduction of the total number of conduction band states which is specially pronounced near the bottom of the band where the energies are lowest. The ratio S of upper to lower valley states in GaAs (eq. 20.8) is expected to increase which in turn will increase the negative differential mobility effect. Moreover, accelerated electrons whose energy is increased by more than ΔE_c will spill over into the larger E_g material. Because of the lower mobility there, negative differential mobility effect would result just from that. The quantization effects are also expected to reduce the temperature sensitivity of injection lasers. Modulation doping, therefore, is a powerful new tool indeed in the scientist's hand. Further information can be found in Refs. 30, 32, 33.

21.4 The Josephson Junction Device

Josephson tunnel junction devices combine switching delays of a few tens of picoseconds with power dissipation of a few microwatts per gate. They are based on thin film technology and can be large-scale integrated which makes them extremely attractive for the logic field and also for mixing and detection in the microwave millimeter wavelength range.

The junction is composed of two superconducting lead (Pb) based alloy electrodes, separated by a very thin oxide layer that forms a tunnel barrier as shown in Fig. 21.4(a):

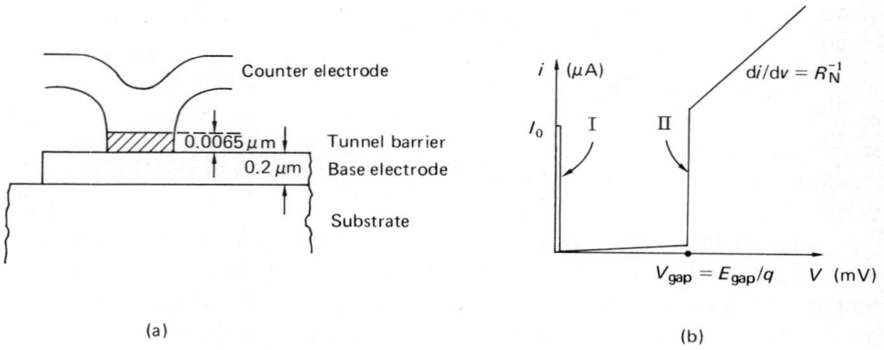

Figure 21.4. The Josephson junction device: (a) basic structure; (b) I-V characteristics.

At liquid helium (4.2°K) operating temperatures the electrodes are in a superconducting state, i.e., phonon–electron interaction causes the electrons near the Fermi energy level to form pairs with resulting zero electrical resistance. Such electron pairs can tunnel freely across the oxide tunnel barrier with zero voltage drop and this gives branch I of the characteristics in Fig. 21.4(b). The energy E_{gap} needed to break an electron pair is known as the superconducting gap energy ($E_{gap} = 2.8$ meV for lead alloys used at IBM laboratories). Pair breakup energy can come from thermal or optical sources and also from current flow through the device that exceeds a value I_0 given by

$$I_0 = \frac{\pi V_{gap}}{4R_N} \text{ at } T = 0°\text{K}, \tag{21.2}$$

where $V_{ga-} = E_{gap}/q$, and R_N is the device resistance in the normal state. I_0 is therefore proportional to device area which must be carefully controlled.

When pair breakup occurs, device operation shifts to branch II of the characteristics. For logic uses, a bias current $I_B < I_0$ is made to flow through the device, resulting with a zero voltage across it (logic 'zero'). For switching to logic 'one', a signal current I_s is also passed through the device where $I_B + I_s > I_0$. This causes a voltage jump across the device to approximately $V_{gap} = E_{gap}/q$ with a delay of a few picoseconds. Special circuits that perform logically like inverters and AND gates have been developed. They also achieve input–output isolation since this two-terminal device has no such inherent isolation.

Memory effect is achieved by storing data as circulating currents in superconducting loops. What such a loop actually stores is quantized units of magnetic flux and it can do it indefinitely, much like an ideal capacitor that stores an electric charge. Inclusion of Josephson junctions in the loop that can be switched in and out of the superconducting state enables one to read and write in the loop.

Josephson devices have also been used for microwave mixing and detection, roles which necessitate strongly nonlinear devices with minimum capacitance, storage effects or ohmic losses. The strong nonlinearity at V_{gap} has been used for this purpose for frequencies in the millimeter wavelength range.

Josephson device technology must yet overcome problems like reliability, uniformity, efficient refrigeration and other problems in order to prove its technical and economic superiority before it is adopted for inclusion in systems outside the laboratory. Further information on Josephson devices can be found in Ref. 38.

21.5 The Permeable Base Transistor (PBT)

This is a GaAs microwave device which can be integrated. The principle behind it is similar to that of the MESFET. A cross section is shown in Fig.

21.5(a). Schottky barrier diodes are formed by tungsten grid fingers of submicron dimensions embedded in GaAs. The Schottky barrier height of about 0.8 V creates a depletion layer that extends throughout the grid openings so that no emitter–collector current flows with base voltage below some predetermined value V_T (which depends on the grid openings). Both enhancement ($V_T>0$) and depletion type ($V_T<0$) transistors can be built therefore, connected as shown in Fig. 21.5(b). This would operate as an inverter, similar to the circuit used with NMOS.

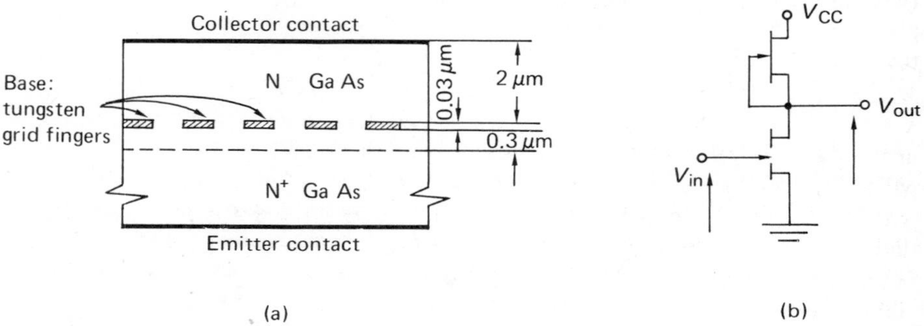

Figure 21.5. The permeable base transistor: (a) cross section (grid fingers are connected together at the back to form the base contact); (b) a possible integrated inverter based on enhancement–depletion PBT.

Transit times through the device are extremely short since electron velocity between base stripes is in the low field (high mobility) range when $V_{CE}<0.1$ V, reaches a maximum of 2.5×10^7 cm/s at $V_{CE}=0.25$ V due to velocity overshoot effects and then decreases monotonically to 1.65×10^7 cm/s at $V_{CE}=1.5$ V. It is this high velocity and small input capacitance (2.3 fF for an experimental PBT) that give this device its high switching speed (simulation predicts 2 ps and measurements on experimental device with 0.16 μm grid spacing, $V_T=0.132$ V and $V_{CC}=0.8$ V gave a switching delay time of 4.3 ps; see Ref. 37).

21.6 Integrated Optoelectronic Devices

Since the heterostructure injection laser (Section 10.8) and fiber optics (Section 10.9) were invented, it was realized that an optical communication link, like the one shown in Fig. 10.12, would have a much higher transmission rate capacity (in bits per second) if (a) the laser would operate at the wavelength for which the fibers have minimum loss ($\lambda=1.55$ μm), and (b) the laser could be integrated with a detector and/or transistors for electronic signal processing.

Such a system can be used as a repeater in long distance optical communication or the transistors can be used to multiplex several input data channels into the same transmitting laser and demultiplex them at the other end following the detector. Such systems are seriously limited at present by the excessive parasitic capacitances, inductances and losses introduced by the interconnections between the units which are physically much larger than the laser, the detector or the transistors. Research efforts which have already shown successes are therefore in progress to obtain a reliable low-threshold laser made of $In_{1-x}Ga_xAs_yP_{1-y}$ (with $y \simeq 2.2x$) or InGaAs, both on InP substrates. These lase at wavelengths above $1\,\mu m$. Also integration of a PIN detector diode with a MESFET type transistor on InP substrate has been achieved.

Though AlGaAs/GaAs heterostructure lasers operate around $\lambda = 0.85\,\mu m$, their technology is much more developed and threshold currents around 10 mA can already be obtained at room temperature. Furthermore, MESFET technology on semi-insulating GaAs (Section 20.2) can be combined with AlGaAs heterostructure laser to obtain an integrated repeater including detector, amplifier and laser (Ref. 42). It is therefore just a question of time before such integrated optoelectronic devices will become available commercially.

21.7 Future Silicon Technologies and Devices.

Silicon will probably continue to dominate the semiconductor field in the foreseeable future. It is worthwhile therefore to look at new developments and trends in the use of this material.

Polycrystalline and Amorphous Silicon:

The high price and energy investment necessary to produce single crystal Si hinders advances in direct solar to electrical energy conversion. To reduce solar cell price, cheaper Si is needed. Since solar cells (Section 10.5) always operate with forward junction voltage, high grade single crystal is not required. In fact what is needed is Si with long enough diffusion length, $L = \sqrt{(D\tau)}$ (eg. (4.23)) for the optically generated carriers to reach the junction depletion layer before recombining. This means lifetime τ and diffusion constant D (proportional to mobility, eq. (4.10) that are not too low. Polycrystalline Si in which the crystallites are long and parallel is a good candidate. Solar cells with their junction built normal to the long grain boundaries direction in such a material do not require of the carriers to cross many such boundaries and 12% efficiencies were already obtained (similar to single crystal cells of a few years back).

An even cheaper approach is to use very thin amorphous Si layer which can be deposited on some cheap conducting substrate. Amorphous (non-crystalline) Si was found to have a much higher absorption coefficient than single crystal Si, so that a layer about 1 μm thick is sufficient to absorb most of the photons of the solar spectrum. It has also larger band gap which is better suited to the solar spectrum.

The main drawbacks of amorphous Si are its very high density of localized states that result in very short lifetimes (Section 9.4) and its low mobility. It was discovered, however, that amorphous Si produced in hydrogen plasma atmosphere absorbs a lot of hydrogen atoms which vastly reduces the density of the troublesome states, sufficient for carriers generated within 0.5 μm or so from a Schottky or pn junction to reach it. Cells with areas of 0.8 cm^2 and 8.5% efficiencies were already reported.

Semi-Insulating (SI) Silicon

One serious drawback of MOS ICs in Si is the parasitic capacitance to the substrate of all devices and interconnections. Increasing field oxide thickness reduces interconnect capacitance but creates larger oxide steps on the surface which is contradictory to the technological requirements for dense, very shallow circuits, as used in VLSI. CMOS circuits have also an area penalty since N (P) islands must be made in the P (N) substrate in which the P (N) channel transistors are located. The island must be larger than the transistor so more area is required. These drawbacks will disappear if SI silicon substrates similar to SI GaAs were available for such circuits. A step in that direction has been achieved (Ref. 39) by using high resistivity Si substrate ($\sim$1.5 kΩcm) which are first neutron irradiated to increase their resistivity to about 1 MΩcm. The irradiation transmutes about 10^{14} cm^{-3} Si atoms to phosphorus which, however, remain inactive in the damaged crystal. Selective implantation is now used to introduce N and P dopants to the required surface areas. A ruby laser ($\lambda = 0.694$ μm) is used to anneal just those implanted areas (Chapter 16) which are then expected to heal the damage and regain their normal semiconducting properties. The bulk of the substrate remains SI if process temperatures do not exceed 600°C. Carrier mobilities in such circuits are still too low ($\mu_e \simeq 300$ cm^2/Vs, $\mu_h \simeq 100$ cm^2/Vs) for the technique to become commercial. (Note that silicon on sapphire has similar objectives and suffers from similar difficulties).

Very Large to Ultra Large Integrated Circuits

Future ULSI circuits will use high density submicron components. For that, new photolithographic techniques using shorter wavelengths, new equipment and new photoresist materials are being developed. Two approaches—electron beam that writes directly on the resist covered wafer, and X-ray lithography—are still competing. Larger wafers with diameters of 12.5 cm and more will give more ULSI circuits per wafer but also present wafer warpage problems that occur under the high temperature processing and affect the critical alignment requirements. Other approaches intend to increase circuit complexity by going three dimensional. A polycrystalline Si layer can be deposited, implanted and patterned over a single crystal substrate in which circuits have already been made and covered by deposited oxide. Laser annealing that causes local melting and recrystallization of the top polysilicon increases its grain size and mobility and makes the annealed parts into relatively good conductors. Other parts of the polysilicon can serve as resistors. Oxide deposition and metallization are then added on top of the poly layer so that three layer structures are obtained.

An altogether different aspect of ULSI is the role of software in their operation. Ultra large area digital circuits can use redundancy to replace a defective subunit of the circuit by a working one. The replacement can be done by programming the circuit from the outside or by built-in programs. Also, since complex logic operations can be performed in many alternative ways, a ULSI circuit should be able to interconnect itself (by internal device switching) in the most efficient way for a given job. ULSI design for testability is another very difficult aspect whose weight in circuit design consideration will become more and more important in the future.

One can therefore prophesy with high level of certainty that the next decade of the semiconductor device era will be no less innovative and exciting than the last decade, if not more so.

REFERENCES AND FURTHER READING

1. S. P. Keller (ed): *Handbook on Semiconductors, vol. 3, Materials Properties and Preparation,* North Holland, Amsterdam (1980).
2. H. F. Wolf: *Silicon Semiconductor Data,* Pergamon Press, Oxford (1969).
3. M. A. Omar: *Elementary Solid State Physics,* Addison-Wesley, Reading, Mass. (1975).
4. W. R. Runyan: *Semiconductor Measurements and Instrumentation,* McGraw-Hill, New York (1975).
5. F. F. Y. Wang: *Introduction to Solid State Electronics,* North-Holland, Amsterdam (1980).
6. J. P. McKelvey: *Solid State Semiconductor Physics,* Harper and Row, New York (1966).
7. H. Kressel (ed): *Semiconductor Devices for Optical Communication, 2nd Edn., Topics in Applied Physics, vol.* **39**, Springer Verlag, Berlin (1982).
8. M. J. Howes and D. V. Morgan (eds.): *Optical Fibre Communications,* Wiley, Chichester (1980).
9. RCA Staff: *Optoelectronics Handbook,* RCA Corporation, Harrison, N.J., (1974).
10. R. S. C. Cobbold: *Theory and Applications of FETs,* Wiley, New York (1970).
11. C. A. Holt: *Electronic Circuits, Digital and Analog,* Wiley, New York (1979).
12. R. A. Colclaser: *Microelectronics, Processing and Device Design,* Wiley, New York (1980).
13. A. B. Glaser and G. E. Subak-Sharpe: *Integrated Circuit Engineering,* Addison-Wesley, Reading, Mass. (1977).
14. American Microsystems, Inc.: *MOS Integrated Circuits,* Van Nostrand, New York (1972).

15. J. D. E. Beynon and D. R. Lamb: *Charge Coupled Devices and Their Applications,* McGraw-Hill, London (1980).
16. J. M. Herman and S. A. Evans, *IEEE J. Solid State Circuits,* **SC–12** (2), Special issue on I^2L (April 1977).
17. M. J. Howes and D. V. Morgan, (eds.): *Microwave Devices,* Wiley, London (1976).
18. *IEEE Trans. on Elec. Dev.,* **ED–27** (6), Special issue on Power, Logic and Special Dev. in III–V Compounds (1980); and **ED–28** (2), Special issue on Advances in Monolithic Microwave III–V Dev. and Circuits (Feb. 1981).
19. H. F. Wolf: *Semiconductors,* Wiley, New York (1971).
20. Bell Laboratories: *Quick Reference Manual for Semiconductor Engineers.*
21. R. D. Thornton, *et al. Characteristics and Limitations of Transistors,* SEEC, vol. 4, Wiley, New York (1966).
22. E. Merzbacher: *Quantum Mechanics,* Wiley, New York (1961).
23. R. King: *Electrical Noise,* Chapman and Hall, London (1966).
24. M. G. Panish and A. Y. Cho: *Molecular Beam Epitaxy, IEEE Spectrum* **17** (4), (1980).
25. D. F. Barbe (ed): *VLSI Fundamentals and Applications,* Springer Verlag, Berlin (1980).
26. D. Frohman Bentchkowsky: *FAMOS* – a new semiconductor charge storage device, *Solid State Electron*, **17**, p. 517 (1974).
27. *IEEE Trans. on Elec. Dev.,* **ED–27** (2), Special issue on Power MOS Devices, (1980).
28. M. Kotani *et al:* Characteristics of high power and high breakdown voltage static induction transistor, *IEEE Trans. on Elec. Dev.,* **ED–29** (2) (1982).
29. H. Kroemer: Heterostructures for everything, device principles of the 1980's?, *Proc. 12th Conf. on Solid State Dev.,* Tokyo (1980).
30. K. Hess *et al*: Negative differential resistance through real space electron transfer, *Appl. Phys. Lett.*, **35** (1979).
31. W. V. McLevige *et al*: GaAs/AlGaAs heterojunction bipolar transistors for IC applications, *IEEE Elec. Dev. Lett.*, **EDL–3** (2) (1982).
32. W. Kopp *et al*: A new $Al_{0.3}Ga_{0.7}As$/GaAs modulation doped FET, *IEEE Elec. Dev. Lett.*, **EDL–3** (5) (1982).
33. R. A. Milano *et al*: Modulation doped AlGaAs/GaAs heterostructure CCD's, *IEEE Elec. Dev. Lett.*, **EDL–3**, (8) (1982).
34. R. Zucca *et al*: GaAs digital IC technology, *IEEE Trans. on Elec. Dev.*, **ED–27** (6) (1980).
35. B. M. Welch *et al*: LSI processing technology for planar GaAs ICs, *ibid.*
36. *IEEE Trans. on Elec. Dev.*, **ED–29** (7) Special issue on GaAs ICs (1982).

37. C. O. Bozler and G. D. Alley: Fabrication and simulation of PBT, *IEEE Trans. on Elec. Dev.*, **ED–27** (6) (1980).
38. *IEEE Trans. on Elec. Dev.*, **ED–27** (10), Special issue on Josephson junction devices (1980).
39. V.Q. Ho and T. Sugano: Fabrication of Si MOSFETs using neutron-irradiated Si as SI substrates, *IEEE Trans. on Elec. Dev.*, **ED–29** (4) (1982).
40. H. S. Fu *et al*: HQMOS—A high performance NMOS technology, *Hewlett-Packard J.* (1982).
41. *IEEE Trans. on Elec. Dev.*, **ED–27** (8), Special issue on very large scale integration (1980).
42. N. Bar-Chaim *et al*: Integrated optoelectronics, *IEEE Spectrum* **19** (5) (1982).
43. C. Mead and L. Conway, *Introduction to VLSI systems*, Addison-Wesley, Reading, Mass. (1980).
44. R. S. Muller and T. I. Kamins: *Device Electronics for ICs*, Wiley, New York (1977).

TWO-PORT REPRESENTATIONS APPENDIX 1

In order to pass from one type of two-port representation to another one should distinguish between two cases:

(a) The connection, i.e. common terminal, is left unchanged. For example, it is common base and one just changes from, say, h_b parameters representation to y_b.
(b) The common terminal is changed too, as for example when the change is from common base to common emitter and it is required to express e.g. the new h_e or y_e parameters in terms of the known y_b ones.

The first case is simple. To relate two families of parameters with the same common terminal we just change the roles of the dependent and independent variables.

Let us demonstrate it by going from h to y parameters. In h-parameter representation (eqs. 15.1):

(A1.1a) $$v_1 = h_{11} i_1 + h_{12} v_2$$

(A1.1b) $$i_2 = h_{21} i_1 + h_{22} v_2.$$

To describe the same two ports by y parameters we should consider v_1 and v_2 the independent variables and i_1, i_2 the dependent ones and rearrange (1.1) accordingly:

(A1.2a) $$i_1 = \frac{1}{h_{11}} v_1 - \frac{h_{12}}{h_{11}} v_2 = y_{11} v_1 + y_{12} v_2$$

(A1.2b) $$i_2 = \frac{h_{21}}{h_{11}} v_1 + \left(h_{22} - \frac{h_{21} h_{12}}{h_{11}}\right) v_2 = y_{21} v_1 + y_{22} v_2.$$

Equations (A1.2) give the desired relations between the ys and the hs for any common terminal e, b or c.

To find the transfer relations for case (b) we proceed in three steps:

(1) Transfer to y-parameter description with the same common terminal;
(2) Transfer to y-parameter description for the new common terminal;
(3) Transfer from the y to the required parameter description, both with the same new common terminal.

Let us demonstrate it by obtaining the relations between known h_b parameters and desired y_e ones. Step (1), h_b to y_b, was done in the previous example.

Step (2) is achieved by three stages, as shown in Fig. A1.1:

(a) Open the short between the old common terminal (base) to the reference terminal (ground).
(b) Write down the y-parameter matrix with none of the device terminals connected to the reference terminal (the so called indefinite matrix).
(c) Short circuit the new common terminal (emitter) to the reference terminal.

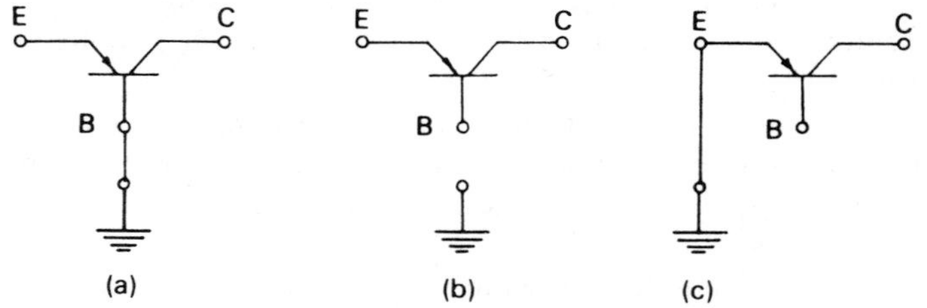

Figure A1.1. Steps in transferring from common-base to common-emitter connection: (a) common-base connection; (b) indefinite connection; (c) common-emitter connection.

Changing from (a) to (b) in Fig. A1.1 means that instead of the previous two independent variables (the emitter node E and the collector node C voltages measured with respect to the reference terminal) we now have three variables (the base node B voltage too). But the third node equation is not independent of the other two, since Kirchhoff's current law states that the sum of the currents flowing into nodes C, B, and E must be zero. It can be easily shown that this condition is fulfilled if the indefinite y matrix, that describes the circuit in Fig. A1.1(b), is obtained by adding a column and a row to the definite y matrix describing A1.1(a) in such a way that the sum of terms in each row and column in the indefinite matrix is zero.

For our case (in brackets: the node to which the relevant row or column belongs):

$$
\begin{array}{cc} & \begin{array}{cc}(E) & (C)\end{array} \\ \begin{array}{c}(E)\\(C)\end{array} & \begin{bmatrix} y_{11b} & y_{12b} \\ y_{21b} & y_{22b} \end{bmatrix} \end{array}
\rightarrow
\begin{array}{c|ccc|} & (E) & (C) & (B) \\ (E) & y_{11b} & y_{12b} & -(y_{11b}+y_{12b}) \\ (C) & y_{21b} & y_{22b} & -(y_{21b}+y_{22b}) \\ (B) & -(y_{11b}+y_{21b}) & -(y_{12b}+y_{22b}) & \sum_{j,k=1}^{2} y_{jkb} \end{array}.
$$

Connecting the emitter terminal to the reference node is equivalent to changing the emitter node voltage to zero. In the indefinite 3×3 matrix this would mean the elimination of the emitter row and column (the first row and column in this case). The remainder is the definite matrix for the common-emitter case in which the various y_e parameters are stated in terms of the original y_b parameters:

$$
\begin{array}{c|ccc|} & (E) & (C) & (B) \\ (E) & y_{11b} & y_{12b} & -(y_{11b}+y_{12b}) \\ (C) & y_{21b} & y_{22b} & -(y_{21b}+y_{22b}) \\ (B) & -(y_{11b}+y_{21b}) & -(y_{12b}+y_{22b}) & \sum_{j,k=1} y_{jkb} \end{array} \rightarrow
$$

$$
\begin{array}{c|cc|} & (C) & (B) \\ (C) & y_{22b} & -(y_{21b}+y_{22b}) \\ (B) & -(y_{12b}+y_{22b}) & \sum_{j,k=1}^{2} y_{jkb} \end{array}.
$$

In common-emitter connection one usually numbers the base node as 1 and the collector as 2 (so that position BB in our final matrix becomes y_{11} and so on). One therefore obtains

(A1.3a) $$y_{11e} = y(\mathrm{B,B}) = \sum_{j,k=1} y_{jkb} = y_{11b} + y_{12b} + y_{21b} + y_{22b},$$

(A1.3b) $$y_{12e} = y(\mathrm{B,C}) = -(y_{12b} + y_{22b}),$$

(A1.3c) $$y_{21e} = y(\mathrm{C,B}) = -(y_{21b} + y_{22b}),$$

(A1.3d) $$y_{22e} = y(\mathrm{C,C}) = y_{22b}.$$

These equations were used in Chapter 15. From the y_e parameters one can obtain any other set of parameters for the CE connection as outlined in the beginning.

THERMIONIC EMISSION, CATHODES AND VACUUM TUBES

APPENDIX 2

Vacuum tubes fulfilled the job of amplifying in electronic circuits up to the middle of this century. Since then the tube has been mostly replaced by the transistor, but is still of importance in all those fields where the transistor cannot operate or successfully compete.

The severe drawbacks of the tube are size, cost, the need to heat the cathode, limited lifetime and the impossibility of integration, i.e. of building very complex systems as can be done with transistors.

We continue to use tubes today either in old instruments or in applications where the transistor functions badly or not at all. Examples in which this is the case include applications necessitating high power at high frequency, systems operating at high voltage, hard radiation environment and, of course, display devices such as television screens and oscilloscopes (it should be mentioned, however, that flat TV screens of solid state or liquid crystal design are being developed and will probably start to replace cathode ray tubes (CRT) within a few years).

We shall give here a short review of ordinary diode and amplifying vacuum tubes, their characteristics and small-signal models and then go on to describe the CRT and photomultiplier tubes.

A2.1 Thermionic Emission

All the vacuum tubes for amplification, rectification, photo detection, X-ray production and cathode-ray uses are based on electronic emission from the cathode material into the evacuated space around it (or also into gas-filled tubes which contain some gas at low pressure). The motion of these electrons is then controlled by electric or magnetic fields.

In order to get electronic emission from the cathode metal we must increase the average energy of its higher-energy electrons, i.e. the Fermi energy, by a quantity called the work function E_W of that material.

This additional energy can be supplied by various methods. If it is done by heating the material we speak of *thermionic emission*. If a very high field is applied at the material surface we may get *field emission*. Bombarding the cathode with high-energy electrons may cause *secondary emission* and if the bombardment is by photons we get *photoelectric emission*. In this appendix we shall discuss only thermionic emission and the proper materials to be used as cathodes.

To obtain an expression for the electron current density, emitted by a unit area of a hot cathode kept at temperature T°K, we start from eq. (7.1), which gives the density of electrons in the material with energies between E and $E+dE$ (E is measured from the bottom of the conduction band and E_F is somewhere in the conduction band):

$$\text{(A2.1)} \qquad dn(E)=\frac{4\pi(2m)^{3/2}E^{1/2}}{h^3}\left[1+\exp\left(\frac{E-E_F}{kT}\right)\right]^{-1}dE.$$

The energy of the electron above the bottom of the conduction band is kinetic and related to its absolute velocity v by

$$\text{(A2.2)} \qquad E=\tfrac{1}{2}mv^2=\tfrac{1}{2}m(v_x^2+v_y^2+v_z^2).$$

Therefore

$$dE=mv\,dv.$$

Substituting into (A2.1) gives

$$\text{(A2.3)} \qquad dn(E)=\frac{8\pi m^3}{h^3}\left[1+\exp\left(\frac{E-E_F}{kT}\right)\right]^{-1}v^2\,dv.$$

This is the total number of electrons per unit volume with speed between v and $v+dv$, independent of direction.

To obtain only the fraction with a specific direction one must multiply $dn(E)$ by $dv_x dv_y dv_z/(4\pi v^2\,dv)$:

$$\text{(A2.4)} \qquad dn_1(E)=\frac{2m^3}{h^3}\left[1+\exp\left(\frac{E-E_F}{kT}\right)\right]^{-1}dv_x dv_y dv_z.$$

Choosing x so that it is perpendicular to the cathode surface, all those electrons moving in the $+x$ direction and whose distance from the surface is less than v_x will hit it during one unit of time, as shown in Fig. A2.1. Taking a unit surface area, the volume containing those electrons is $1\times v_x$. Since $dn_1(E)$ is per unit volume, it should be multiplied by $1\times v_x$ to give $dn_2(E)=v_x\,dn_1(E)$.

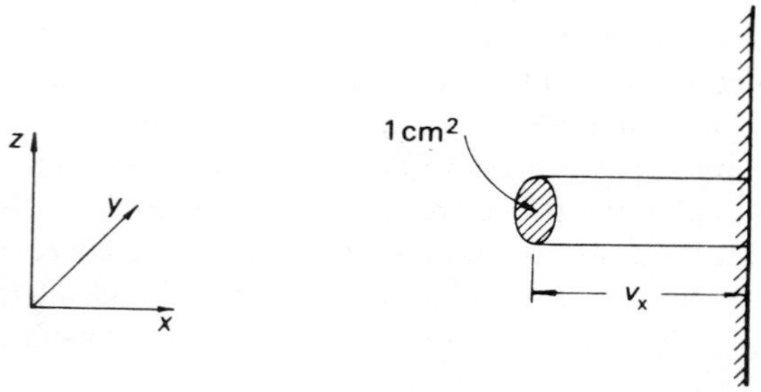

Figure A2.1. The cathode volume from which electrons can be emitted in a unit time.

To obtain the sum total of those emitted we must sum on all v_y and v_z (since the emission is independent of those velocities) and consider only those electrons whose x velocity component v_x is above a minimum value v_{x0}, set by the work function:

$$\frac{1}{2}mv_{x0}^2 = E_F + E_W. \tag{A2.5}$$

The emitted current density is therefore

$$J = q\int\int\int \mathrm{d}n_2(E) \tag{A2.6}$$

$$= \frac{2qm^3}{h^3}\int_{v_x=+v_{x0}}^{+\infty}\int_{v_y=-\infty}^{+\infty}\int_{v_z=-\infty}^{+\infty}\left[1+\exp\frac{E-E_F}{kT}\right]^{-1} v_x\,\mathrm{d}v_x\,\mathrm{d}v_y\,\mathrm{d}v_z.$$

The energy E can be expressed by v according to (A2.2). Since only high-energy electrons can be expected to overcome the work-function barrier we can assume $\exp[(E-E_F)/kT] \gg 1$, giving:

$$J = \frac{2qm^3}{h^3}\exp\left(\frac{E_F}{kT}\right)\left[\int_{v_{x0}}^{\infty} v_x \exp\left(-\frac{mv_x^2}{2kT}\right)\mathrm{d}v_x\right]\left[\int_{-\infty}^{\infty}\exp\left(-\frac{mv_y^2}{2kT}\right)\mathrm{d}v_y\right] \tag{A2.7}$$

$$\times\left[\int_{-\infty}^{\infty}\exp\left(-\frac{mv_z^2}{2kT}\right)\mathrm{d}v_z\right].$$

The solution to the definite integrals in v_y and v_z can be found from tables to be of the form

$$\int_{-\infty}^{\infty} \exp(-x^2)\, dx = \sqrt{\pi}.$$

In our case each of these integrals therefore yields $\sqrt{(2\pi kT/m)}$. The integral in v_x can be easily solved (by substituting $v_x^2 = t$) and gives

$$\int_{v_{x0}}^{+\infty} v_x \exp\left(-\frac{mv_x^2}{2kT}\right) dv_x = \frac{kT}{m} \exp\left(-\frac{E_F + E_W}{kT}\right).$$

J will therefore be:

$$J = \frac{4\pi mq(kT)^2}{h^3} \exp\left(-\frac{E_W}{kT}\right) = A_0 T^2 \exp\left(-\frac{E_W}{kT}\right), \tag{A2.8}$$

where

$$A_0 = \frac{4\pi mqk^2}{h^3} = 1.2 \times 10^6 \text{ A m}^{-2}\ {}^\circ\text{K}^{-2}.$$

This is known as the *Richardson–Dushman equation.* We see that the thermionic emitted current depends exponentially on the work function of the cathode material and its temperature dependence comes also mainly through the $1/T$ factor in the exponent.

Experiment shows that work function and temperature indeed have the expected effect but the numerical value of A_0 varies from material to material and depends on surface treatment. This is probably because cathode materials are polycrystalline with uneven surfaces. Locations near a grain boundary have slightly different properties than in the bulk and they may depend on the local crystal orientation.

The practical value of a material as a cathode lies not only in its emission properties but, also in its mechanical strength and durability at the high working temperatures.

Tungsten (W), which has $E_W = 4.52$ eV and can be operated at 2500°K, is used where very high voltages are present, as in X-ray diodes. It can withstand positive-ion bombardment (always present in high voltage tubes) for a long time.

The tungsten work function can be reduced to 2.6 eV if it is coated with a monoatomic layer of thorium (Th). The contact potential between the thorium and tungsten causes the first to be more positive, accelerating the electron towards the outside. The so-called thoriated tungsten cathodes have therefore much enhanced emission. Other practical cathodes, the so-called oxide coated cathodes, utilize thermionic emission from degenerate semiconducting material. A mixture of barium and strontium oxides (BaO + SrO) thinly coated over a nickel body (for strength and good conductivity) gives cathodes with a work function of 1 eV having excellent emission. They can be operated up to 1100°K only, and cannot withstand heavy positive-ion bombardment. Such cathodes are used in tubes with anode voltages of less than 1000 V.

A2.2 The Vacuum Diode

This is a two-electrode device, although it has one or two additional terminals for heäting. The electrodes are (a) the cathode, made of material with a low work function, which is electrically heated to sufficiently high temperatures for it to emit a flow of electrons (see Appendix 2 for the thermionic emission), and (b) the anode, which collects those electrons when a positive voltage is applied between it and the cathode. Both electrodes are enclosed in vacuum. They may have a cylindrical structure, with the cathode in the center and the coaxial anode surrounding it, or a planar structure, in which the electrodes form two parallel planes with a distance d between them. This last structure, used in high-frequency tubes, lends itself to somewhat simpler mathematical treatment and we shall refer to this.

Not all the electrons emitted from the cathode per unit time (as determined by the Richardson–Dushman equation (A2.8) reach the anode. Some of them are turned back to the cathode by the negative space charge of their fellow electrons. To obtain the V–I characteristic it is necessary to obtain the potential distribution in the presence of this space charge. When no space charge is present the potential distribution between cathode ($x = 0$) and anode ($x = d$) is a simple straight line, as shown by the dashed line in Fig. A2.2. The presence of the space charge creates a reverse field near the cathode and the potential distribution has the general shape shown by the solid line in the figure. The point $x = x_a$, where the potential is at its minimum, is called a *virtual cathode*.

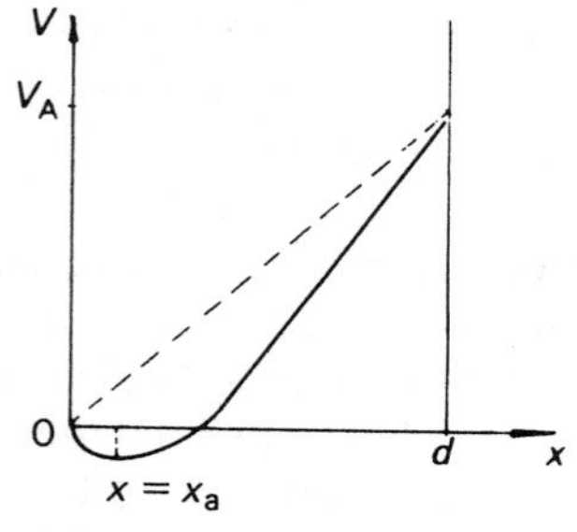

Figure A2.2. The potential distribution in a planar diode: ----- with no space charge present; —— with the effect of the electronic space charge.

Under static conditions of a constant cathode temperature and constant anode–cathode voltage V_A, the amount of space charge is also constant (statistically). The net number of electrons entering the space-charge cloud per unit time from the cathode equals the number of those leaving towards the anode. Poisson's equation for this planar, one-dimensional case (neglecting any edge effects) is:

(A2.9)
$$\frac{d^2V}{dx^2} = -\frac{\rho}{\varepsilon_0} = \frac{J}{\varepsilon_0 v}$$

where $\rho = J/v$ is the density of electronic charge, moving at a velocity $v(x)$ and resulting in a current density J (independent of x and flowing in the $-x$ direction).

The velocity is related to the potential-energy $qV(x)$ lost by the electron in travelling from $x=0$ to x:

$$\frac{m_0 v^2}{2} = qV(x).$$

(We are assuming nonrelativistic velocities.)

Substituting v into (A2.9) gives

(A2.10)
$$\frac{d^2V}{dx^2} = \frac{J}{\varepsilon_0 \sqrt{(2q/m_0)V}} = \frac{K}{\sqrt{V}},$$

where K contains all the factors independent of x.

Multiplying both sides of (A2.10) by $2dV/dx$ makes it possible to write it in the form:

$$\frac{d}{dx}\left(\frac{dV}{dx}\right)^2 = 4K\frac{d}{dx}(V^{1/2}).$$

Integrating both sides and taking the square root gives

(A2.11)
$$\frac{dV}{dx} = 2\sqrt{K}\,V^{1/4} - E_0,$$

where E_0 is an integration constant and represents the field at the cathode where $V=0$. To simplify the following expressions, let us neglect this small field, and then the integration of (A.2.11) gives

$$\frac{4}{3}V^{3/4} = 2(\sqrt{K})x.$$

Substituting the value of K from (A2.10) and separating J out gives

(A2.12)
$$J = \frac{4\varepsilon_0}{9}\sqrt{\left(\frac{2q}{m_0}\right)}\frac{V^{3/2}}{x^2}.$$

(The position of the virtual cathode cannot be found from this equation since E_0 was neglected.)

At the anode $V = V_A$ and $x = d$. Substituting this and the numerical values of the physical constants in (A2.12) gives

$$J = 2.34 \frac{V_A^{3/2}}{d^2} \ \mu A \ m^{-2}. \tag{A2.13}$$

This is known as the *Langmuir–Childs law* or the *three-halves law*. A cylindrical diode yields a similar three-halves law but with a different coefficient. This law is characteristic of tubes in which the current is space-charge limited.

Our results hold for positive V_A only. When $V_A < 0$ electrons are repelled by the anode and the space-charge cloud grows, increasing the negative field at the cathode surface and forcing the return to the cathode of more and more of those electrons emitted with slower velocities, until the number returning equals the number being emitted.

The current density of (A2.13) is smaller than the emitted thermionic current density (A.2.8), which is the upper limit of the anodic current when V_A is very high. In such a case all the emitted electrons are swept immediately towards the anode and no virtual cathode forms. This situation exists in very high-voltage diodes, such as those intended for X-ray production (the electrons, accelerated through very high voltage, hit the anode with tremendous energy causing X-rays to be radiated from its surface). The cathode in such cases is made of tungsten, which is strong enough to withstand the positive-ion bombardment that results from the absence of the virtual cathode. These ions are the result of collisions of the fast electrons with the residual air molecules still present in the evacuated tube. These positive ions bombard the negative cathode unless a virtual cathode is in the way to stop and neutralize them. High-efficiency oxide-coated cathodes cannot withstand such bombardment for long without being ruined.

Since the vacuum diode conducts with a positive anode voltage and cuts off when it is negative, it has a rectifying characteristic like the PN junction diode. The forward voltage drop, however, is much higher in the tube and the current density is much lower. This leads to a much higher dissipation loss in the vacuum diode.

A2.3 The Vacuum Triode, Amplification

The triode has three electrodes and is the simplest active device in the tube family.

The conventional triode is cylindrical with a circular or oval anode. A cross section of such a triode and its circuit symbol are shown in Fig. A2.3. A cylindrical cathode K is in the center. It is electrically heated by a thin filament, with terminals H_1, H_2 which are usually insulated from the cathode.

The high temperature (1100°K or more) to which the cathode is heated gives the thermionically emitted electrons high enough kinetic energies to form the space-charge cloud around it. The cathode is surrounded by a grid which is a thin wire net or helix that forms the second electrode. The cylindrical anode that surrounds both is the third one. Since the grid is near the cathode, the potential difference e_C between them, which is usually negative, governs the number of electrons that manage to continue towards the positive anode. e_C therefore has strong control over the anode current i_B, stronger than that of the anode–cathode voltage e_B. It is in the space between control grid and anode that d.c. energy from the power supply is converted to a.c. power at the signal frequency. So long as the grid is negative, practically no electrons hit it and its current is negligible. The electrons pass between the grid wires to continue towards the anode. We shall consider the negative e_C case only.

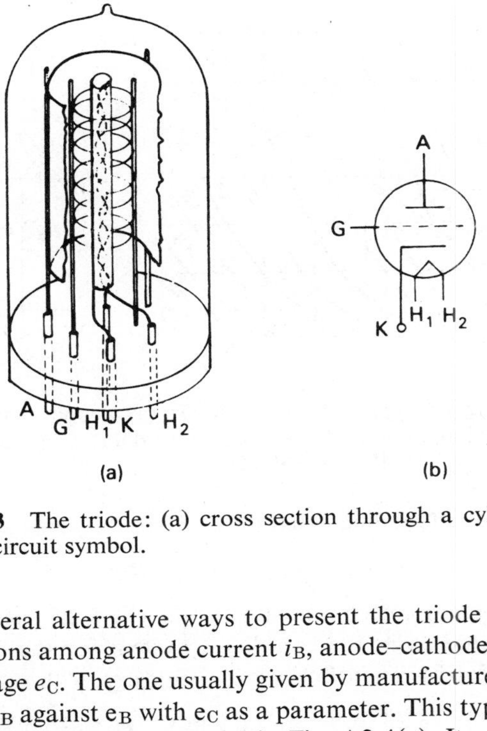

Figure A2.3 The triode: (a) cross section through a cylindrical triode; (b) circuit symbol.

There are several alternative ways to present the triode characteristics, i.e., the interrelations among anode current i_B, anode–cathode voltage e_B and grid–cathode voltage e_C. The one usually given by manufacturers is the anode characteristics of i_B against e_B with e_C as a parameter. This type of characteristic for the 12AU7 triode is presented in Fig. A2.4(a). It can be seen that although e_B is positive, i_B may be made negligible by making e_C sufficiently negative. The triode then acts as an open switch. On the other hand it is impossible to pass a high anodic current without a very appreciable voltage drop across the tube. Obviously, it cannot simulate very well a short-circuit or closed-switch condition. Tubes are therefore completely excluded today from digital circuit work. They can, however, be used for analog amplification.

To analyze the triode operation as small-signal amplifier and obtain an idea of its gain–bandwidth product, we refer to the typical audio-amplifying stage of Fig. A2.4(b). This stage is similar to the one shown in Fig. 13.3 with a JFET, although the values of the components are different. Capacitors C_1, C_2, C_3 are chosen as before, so that they present an effective short circuit in the frequency range of interest. The d.c. component I_B, in the total anode current i_B, must flow through R_K, thus causing the cathode to attain a positive potential, $I_B R_K$, with respect to ground. The grid, carrying no d.c. current, is at ground potential because of R_G. The d.c. component of e_C will therefore be

(A2.14) $$E_c = -I_B R_K.$$

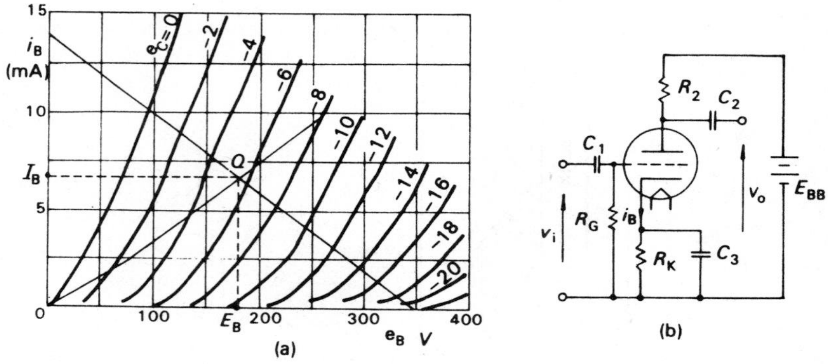

Figure A2.4. Typical triode 12AU7: (a) anode characteristics; (b) typical audio-amplifier stage (circuit data: $E_{BB}=350$ V, $R_2=25$ kΩ, $R_G=0.5$ MΩ, $R_K=800$ Ω).

This and the static load-line equation

(A2.15) $$E_{BB} = e_B + i_B(R_K + R_L)$$

determines the quiescent or operating point Q of the triode. Both bias and load lines are entered in the coordinate system for the component values given in Fig. A2.4(b). Their intersection yields Q, with coordinates.

$$l_B \simeq 180 \text{ V}, \quad i_B \simeq 6.8 \text{ mA}, \quad e_C \simeq -5.5 \text{ V}.$$

The characteristics can be approximated by a set of straight, parallel equidistant lines for small-signal modelling in the vicinity of Q. The triode can then be replaced by a small-signal model with constant coefficients in the same way as was done in Chapter 13, leading to the model of Fig. 13.7(a).

Towards that aim the triode parameters are defined as:

$$\text{Anode resistance} \qquad r_b \triangleq \left.\frac{\partial e_b}{\partial i_b}\right|_{e_C=\text{const}}$$

$$\text{Amplification factor} \qquad \mu \triangleq \left.\frac{\partial e_b}{\partial e_c}\right|_{i_B=\text{const}}$$

$$\text{Transconductance} \qquad g_m \triangleq \left.\frac{\partial i_b}{\partial e_c}\right|_{e_B=\text{const}}$$

From our characteristics, in the vicinity of Q, we get

$$r_b \simeq 7.7\ \text{k}\Omega, \quad \mu \simeq 20, \quad g_m \simeq 2600\ \mu\text{mho}.$$

The dynamic load line is determined by R_L only, as C_3 shorts R_K. The small-signal equivalent circuit of the complete stage will look like in Fig. A2.5(a) for the middle-frequency range (since the grid draws no current and the interelectrode capacitances are small enough to be neglected, the input impedance to the triode in this frequency range depends on R_G only.

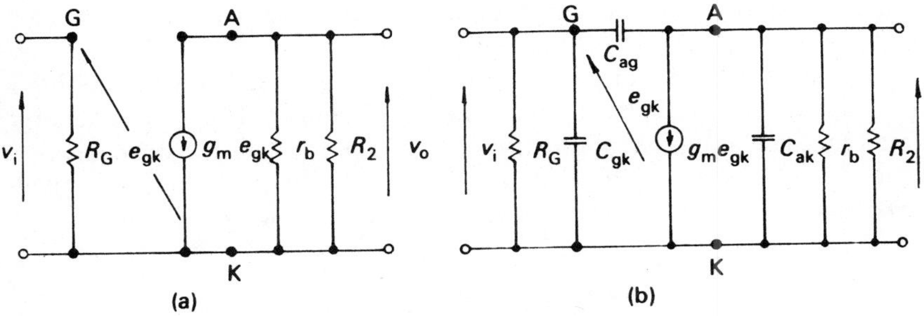

Figure A2.5 The small-signal equivalent circuit of Fig. A3.3(b): (a) for the middle-frequency range; (b) for the high-frequency range.

The voltage amplification expected from this circuit is

$$A_0 = \frac{v_o}{v_i} = -\frac{g_m}{1/R_L + 1/r_b} \simeq -15. \qquad \text{(A2.16)}$$

(The minus sign indicates phase reversal.)

At higher frequencies one cannot neglect the interelectrode capacitances c_{ga}, c_{gk} and c_{ak}. These are supplied by the manufacturers and are of the order of magnitude of 1 pF.

The equivalent circuit with the capacitances included is shown in Fig. A2.5(b). The dynamic load impedance is no longer R_L in parallel with r_b but the parallel connection of this and c_{ak}. Substituting it in (A2.16) and rearranging gives:

$$A=\frac{A_0}{1+j\omega c_{ak}R_L r_b/(R_L+r_b)}, \tag{A2.17}$$

where A_0 is the middle-frequency amplification of (A2.16). The half power frequency at which $A=A_0/\sqrt{2}$ is

$$\frac{1}{\omega_1}=c_{ak}\frac{r_b R_L}{r_b+R_L}. \tag{A2.18}$$

$\omega_1/2\pi$ represents the bandwidth in which the amplification is constant within 3 dB. The gain–bandwidth product will be

$$G\times BW=A_0\frac{\omega_1}{2\pi}=\frac{1}{2\pi}\frac{g_m}{c_{ak}}. \tag{A2.19}$$

The ratio g_m/c_{ak} is therefore a figure of merit and a criterion for comparing the operation of various triodes as high-frequency amplifiers. (Our triode model is limited to frequencies for which the period f^{-1} is short compared to the anode–cathode electron transit time: otherwise the parameters are complex.)

A severe limitation in triode operation at high frequencies is the high-input capacitance presented by it to the signal source. This can be demonstrated by calculating the input admittance to the triode using the equivalent circuit of Fig. A2.5(b). At high frequencies the load R_L is usually the impedance of a loaded tuned circuit at resonance and is low enough to satisfy

$$R_L \ll \frac{1}{\omega c_{ga}} \quad \text{and} \quad R_L \ll r_b.$$

Assuming these conditions one gets from Fig. A2.5(b)

$$Y_{in}=\frac{1}{R_G}+j\omega\,[c_{gk}+c_{ga}\,(1+g_m R_L)], \tag{A2.20}$$

i.e., instead of having an input capacitance of $c_{gk}+c_{ga}$ the second term is multiplied by the amplification $g_m R_L$. This is called the *Miller effect*. It is also present in a transistor because of the collector–junction capacitance (compare Fig. A2.5(b) to the hybrid π model).

The result of the Miller effect is to load the preceding amplifying stage by this input capacitance, which adds to that stage c_{ak}, thus appreciably reducing its half-power frequency ω_1. This drawback, plus the search for higher amplification, brought about the development of multigrid tubes like the tetrode and pentode in which an additional screen grid prevents this effect.

A2.4 The Cathode Ray and the Photomultiplier Tubes

Two specialized vacuum tubes, which have as yet no transistor equivalent, are the cathode ray tube (CRT) and the photomultiplier (PM) tube.

The CRT utilizes the ability of shaped electric (or magnetic) fields to focus and bend the trajectories of free electrons, thermally emitted from the cathode. The electrons are first shaped into the form of a circular beam by having them pass through a control grid with a single circular aperture in its center, as shown in Fig. A2.6(a). They are then accelerated towards a much

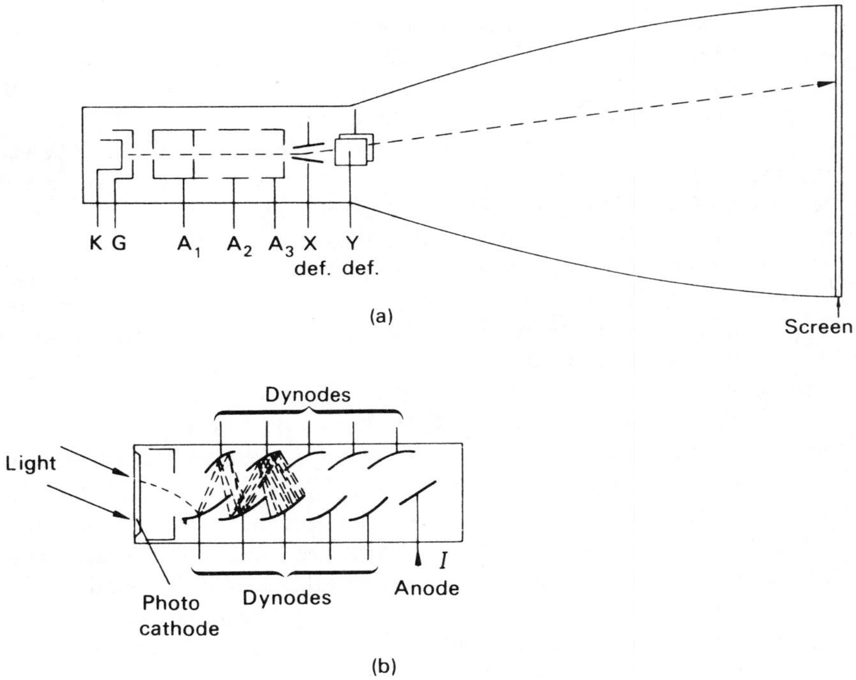

Figure A2.6. Special tube types: (a) the cathode ray tube; (b) the photomultiplier tube.

more positive anode of a special shape that creates a curved electric field which focuses the beam to a narrow spot on the distant glass face of the tube called the screen. The anode is actually divided into three separate parts with the middle kept at a lower potential. This results in an electrostatic lens or focusing system. Behind the lens the beam passes through a deflection system, which may be either electrostatic, as shown in Fig. A2.6(a), or electromagnetic. The parallel-plate capacitor type deflection system can deflect the beam in both X and Y directions as dictated by the instantaneous values of the voltages between the deflection plates at the moment the electron passes through. The beam can thus be made to focus on any point of the screen surface. The screen is coated internally by one of many possible phosphors, which are materials that have both fluorescent and phosphorescent properties, i.e., they emit light when irradiated by high energy electrons and for a short time afterwards. Each phosphor has its own particular color and light-persistence properties.

The CRTs form the heart of the cathode ray oscilloscopes and, of course, the televisions sets. In oscilloscopes electrostatic deflection is used, since it enables one to get to much higher frequencies. The maximum deflection angle, however, is small, necessitating long tubes for even small screens. For the big screen TV picture tubes electromagnetic deflection coils must be used. and they are mounted outside, on the tube neck, and make possible a full deflection angle of 110° (i.e. $\pm 55°$ from the beam axis).

The photomultiplier or PM tube is based on secondary emission. This tube, shown in Fig. A2.6(b), has an unheated semitransparent cathode made of material with a low work function coated on the inside of the glass. Photons of a wavelength shorter than some minimum value have high enough energy to cause photoelectric emission of electrons from the cathode when they are absorbed (cathodes of different spectral sensitivities are available).

The emitted electrons are accelerated towards a nearby electrode, kept at a positive potential, which is called the first dynode. It is made of a material that emits 3–6 secondary electrons for every primary electron hitting it. A second dynode, which has a higher potential than the first, is situated so that it attracts those secondary electrons which are accelerated towards it and upon hitting it cause further multiplication of the current. Eleven dynodes or more may be used in a single PM tube, giving amplifications of up to 10^9. The dynodes have curved surfaces which shape the field in between them so that the secondary electrons will move from one dynode to the next with a transition time that is more or less the same for all. Different structures are possible, and sometimes additional focusing electrodes are added inside the tube. Behind the final dynode is the anode, which is the most positive electrode and collects all the electrons.

Well stabilized power supply of up to several thousand volts is needed for use with the PM tube, which then provides a very sensitive and fast radiation detector. In such tubes one must endeavor to reduce the number of thermally emitted electrons (resulting in a dark current) by as much as possible since they constitute noise which becomes troublesome as the multiplication ratio is increased.

A2.5 The Vacuum Tube in the Transistor Era

Triodes are used today mostly in high-power transmitter circuits, where r.f. power in the kilowatt range is needed. The ability of the transistor to handle power falls off quickly with the frequency. Its small size is a drawback when large amounts of dissipated power, in the form of heat, must be removed. Its sensitivity to temperature is another obstacle, that and the fact that the heat is generated in the most sensitive location – the collector junction. In tubes the power is dissipated mainly in the anode, where the kinetic energy acquired by the electrons is transformed into heat. The anode is the outside electrode. It may be made large, with air-cooling fins or even with a water-cooling system. Tubes can thus be made for many kilowatts of output power. Another limitation of the transistor is the necessity to operate at a relatively low collector voltage, usually below a hundred volts. This limits the r.f. voltage amplitude, and to achieve high power one must operate at very high currents. This involves on the one hand large areas with the associated high capacitances, and on the other hand poses severe circuit and components problems to avoid high internal losses. Vacuum tubes that can operate in the kilovolt range reduce this problem.

Finally there is a fundamental limit to transistor speed, and this is the scattering-limited carrier velocity in the semiconductor. Frequency and size are therefore reciprocally related (see e.g., eq. 20.6). In the vacuum tube, on the other hand, the carrier transition time may be made smaller by either decreasing size or increasing voltage. Modern high-frequency triodes have parallel planar structure in which the effective cathode–grid–anode distances are in the tens of microns range, and operate at voltages of a thousand volts or so. Under these circumstances carrier transition time is very low. Such tubes are not made of glass, but of titanium and ceramic materials that can withstand very high operating temperatures.

Tubes are therefore still used, but in specialized fields only. The main ones are high-power r.f., microwave high-power generation (by magnetrons), high-voltage and X-ray production, display (CRT), and high-sensitivity radiation detectors (PM tube).

PHYSICAL CONSTANTS AND IMPORTANT PARAMETERS OF SEMICONDUCTOR MATERIALS APPENDIX 3

A3.1 Important Physical Constants

Electronic charge	$q = 1.6 \times 10^{-19}$ C
Electronic rest mass	$m_0 = 9.11 \times 10^{-31}$ kg.
Avogadro's number	$N = 6.02 \times 10^{26}$ kg^{-1}
Boltzmann's constant	$k = 1.38 \times 10^{-23}$ J °K^{-1} $= 8.617 \times 10^{-5}$ eV°K^{-1}
Thermal voltage (300°K)	$kT/q = 0.026$ V
Planck's constant	$h = 6.63 \times 10^{-34}$ J s
Permittivity of free space	$\varepsilon_0 = 8.85 \times 10^{-12}$ F m^{-1}
Permeability of free space	$\mu_0 = 4\pi \times 10^{-7}$ H m^{-1}
Velocity of light	$c = 2.998 \times 10^{8}$ m s^{-1}

A3.2 Properties of Some Common Semiconductors and SiO_2 at 300°K

Property	Si	Ge	GaAs	InSb	GaP	SiO_2
Atomic (molecular) weight	28.09	72.60	144.6	236.6	100.7	
Atomic density (cm^{-3})	5×10^{22}	4.4×10^{22}	2.21×10^{22}	2.9×10^{22}	4.94×10^{22}	
Lattice const. (nm)	0.543	0.566	0.565	0.648	0.545	
Density ($g\,cm^{-2}$)	2.33	5.32	5.32	5.79	4.13	~2.2†
Melting point (°C)	1415	937	1238	525	1470	~1600
Energy gap (eV)	1.12	0.67	1.424	0.18	2.26	8
Gap type*	Ind.	Ind.	D	D	Ind.	
Effective density of states						
N_c (cm^{-3})	2.8×10^{19}	1.04×10^{19}	4.7×10^{17}	—	1.7×10^{19}	
N_v (cm^{-3})	1.04×10^{19}	6.0×10^{18}	7.0×10^{18}	—	2.25×10^{19}	
n_i (cm^{-3})	1.4×10^{10}	2.4×10^{13}	2×10^{6}	$\sim 10^{16}$	8	
Dielectric constant ε	11.8	16	13.1	15.9	10.2	~3.85†
μ_e($cm^2\,V^{-1}\,s^{-1}$)	1350	3900	8500	8×10^4	300	
μ_h($cm^2\,V^{-1}\,s^{-1}$)	480	1900	450	1250	150	

* Ind – indirect, D – direct.

† Depends on the oxidation or deposition process.

See Refs. 1, 2, 19 or 20 for additional data.

SILICON PROCESSING DATA
APPENDIX 4

The data in this Appendix has been compiled from many sources and is presented in a simple form, suitable for basic calculation of the diffusion and ion implantation processes, using the most common dopants As, P (donors) and B (acceptor).

A4.1 Solid Solubilities

The solid solubility is the maximum concentration that a specific dopant species can reach in the silicon crystal without seggregating and forming clusters of the dopant in the host crystal. Solubility is a function of temperature but in the range of 1000 – 1200°C it is approximately constant:

Dopant	*Solid solubility* [atoms/cm^3]
As	1.5×10^{21}
P	10^{21}
B	5×10^{20}

Only about one-third of the dopant atoms at these maximum concentrations attain a substitutional position in the silicon crystal lattice and are electrically active.

A4.2 Diffusion constants and process

The diffusion constants depend exponentially on the diffusion temperature according to

$$D = D_0 \exp\left(-\frac{a}{T}\right). \quad \text{(A4.1)}$$

This equation is approximate and neglects nonlinear effects due to high concentration values or dependence on the charged state of the diffusing ion. Values of D_o and a for the common dopants are:

Dopant	D_0 [cm²/s]	a [°K]
As	17.7	4.7×10^4
P	4.7×10^{-3}	3.06×10^4
B	2.62	4.15×10^4

The complementary error function (16.4) and the Gaussian function (16.5) are drawn in Fig. A4.1, normalized to the surface concentration for each case:

$$F_1 = \frac{N(x,t)}{N_0} = \text{erfc}\,(z)$$

$$F_2 = \frac{N(x,t)}{N_t/(\pi D t)^{1/2}} = \exp\,(-z^2)$$

where $z = x/2\sqrt{(Dt)}$.

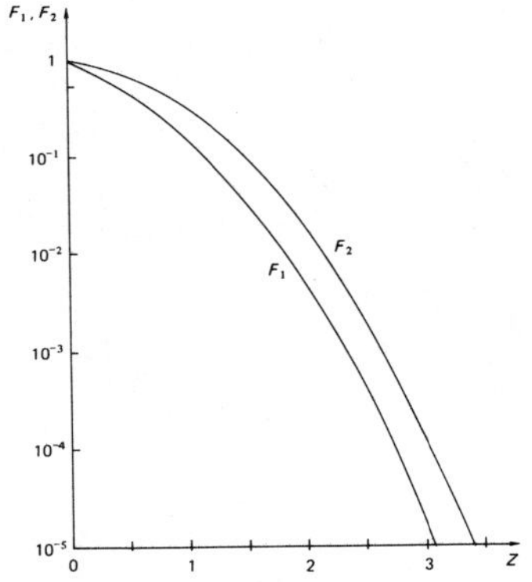

Figure A4.1 The $F_1 = \text{erfc}(z)$ and $F_2 = \exp(-z^2)$ functions.

A4.3 The Ion Implantation Process

The projected range R_p and the straggle, σ_p, of implanted ions (see eq. 16.8) for the common dopants are given in Fig. A4.2 as function of the implant energy.

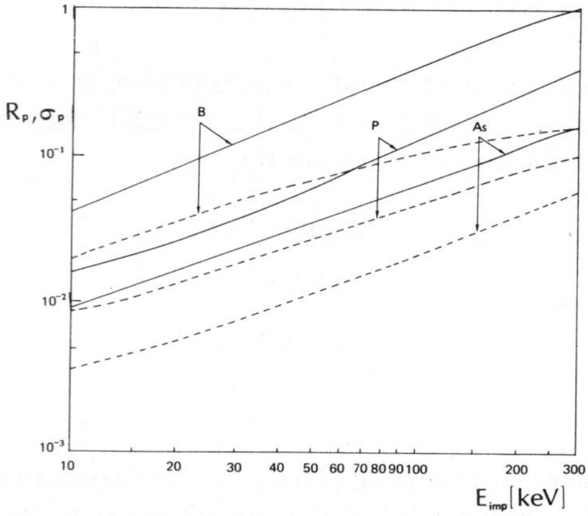

Figure A4.2 Projected range R_p (——) and straggle σ_p (----) as functions of implant energy E_{imp} for boron, phosphorus and arsenic.

A4.4 Mobility Dependence on Impurity Concentration

The reduction of mobility with increased impurity content N[cm^{-3}] in doped silicon at 300°K can be approximated by the empirical relation (Ref. 44):

$$\mu_e = 1350 \left[1 - \frac{0.933N^{0.91}}{N^{0.91} + 3.75 \times 10^{15}}\right] \text{ [cm}^2\text{/Vs]} \tag{A4.2}$$

$$\mu_h = 480 \left[1 - \frac{0.9N^{0.76}}{N^{0.76} + 5.85 \times 10^{12}}\right] \text{ [cm}^2\text{/Vs]} \tag{A4.3}$$

INDEX